DICTIONARY OF ORGANIC COMPOUNDS

First Supplement

DICTIONARY OF ORGANIC COMPOUNDS

The constitution and physical, chemical and other properties of the principal carbon compounds and their derivatives, together with relevant literature references

FOURTH EDITION

FIRST SUPPLEMENT

incorporating new material published in and before 1964

NEW YORK
OXFORD UNIVERSITY PRESS
1965

Fourth Edition of the
Dictionary of Organic Compounds
in five volumes published 1965
This first supplement to the Fourth Edition
published simultaneously

Printed in Great Britain

PREFACE TO FIRST SUPPLEMENT

The exponential expansion in scientific activity referred to in the preface to the main work makes it impossible to produce a work the size of the *Dictionary* which is up to date at the time of publication. New knowledge will require that a few entries will need to be amended before the ink is dry and in addition to this, new compounds are constantly being described. Some of these are isolated from natural products, others are produced in the laboratory. Many are of fundamental importance.

In order to keep the *Dictionary* up to date and to make the properties of these new compounds readily available to readers it is intended to publish regular annual supplements to the *Dictionary* of which this is the first.

This *First Supplement* appearing with the main work, contains new material published in the chemical literature up to the end of 1964. There are two types of entry. Those which supplement entries in the main work are marked with an asterisk (★). Entries not marked in this way deal with compounds that do not appear in the main work. In the same way, a *cross-reference* with an asterisk refers to the main work, but an unmarked cross-reference refers to an entry in the *Supplement* (even if the entry itself is supplementary to the main work).

It is intended to produce four similar supplements. The fifth *Supplement* will be a cumulative edition containing both new material collected during that year and that brought forward from the previous four supplements.

The present supplement also includes corrections to errors found in the main work after it had gone to press.

A

$\Delta^{7,13}$-Abietadienoic Acid. *See* Abietic Acid.

$\Delta^{8,12}$-Abietadienoic Acid

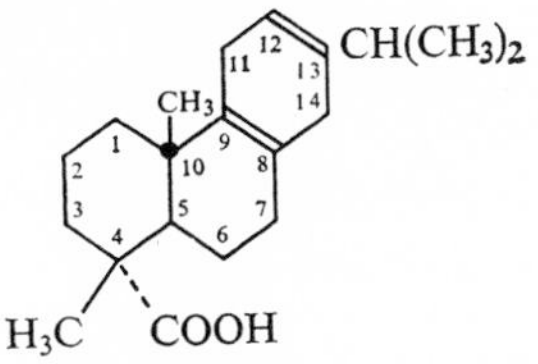

$C_{20}H_{30}O_2$ MW 302

(+)-.

Cryst. from EtOH.Aq. M.p. 160·5–162°. $[\alpha]_D$ +55°.

Dibutylamine salt: needles from Me_2CO. M.p. 117·5–120·5°.

(±)-.

Dibutylamine salt: cryst. from Me_2CO. M.p. 126–7°.

Burgstahler, Worden, *J. Am. Chem. Soc.*, 1964, **86**, 96.

$\Delta^{8,13}$-Abietadienoic Acid. *See* Palustric Acid.

$\Delta^{12,14}$-Abietadienoic Acid. *See* Levopimaric Acid.

Abietic Acid★ (*$\Delta^{7,13}$-Abietadienoic Acid*)

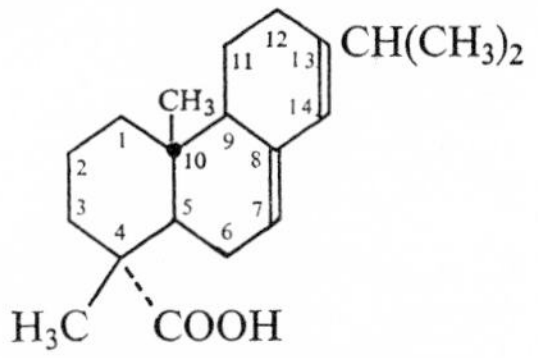

Alternative numbering

(±)-.

Cryst. from EtOH.Aq. M.p. 148–150°. Light absorption: $\lambda_{max.}$ 235 (ε, 19,500), 241·5 (22,000), 250 mμ (14,300).

Di-isopentylammonium salt: cryst. from Me_2CO–EtOH. M.p. 138–41°.

Burgstahler, Worden, *J. Am. Chem. Soc.*, 1964, **86**, 96.

Synthesis:

Wenkert *et al.*, *J. Am. Chem. Soc.*, 1964, **86**, 2038.

See also:

Harris, Sanderson, *Organic Syntheses*, Coll. Vol. **4**, 1.

Abminthic. *See* Dithiazanine.★

Abscisin II

$C_{15}H_{20}O_4$ MW 264

Abscission-accelerating substance from young cotton fruit. Cryst. from $CHCl_3$–light petroleum. M.p. 160–1° with sublimation at 120°. Light absorption: $\lambda_{max.}$ 252 mμ (ε 25,200).

Ohkuma *et al.*, *Science*, 1963, **142**, 1592.

Acacic Acid (3 : 16 : 21-*Trihydroxyolean*-12-*en*-28-*oic Acid*)

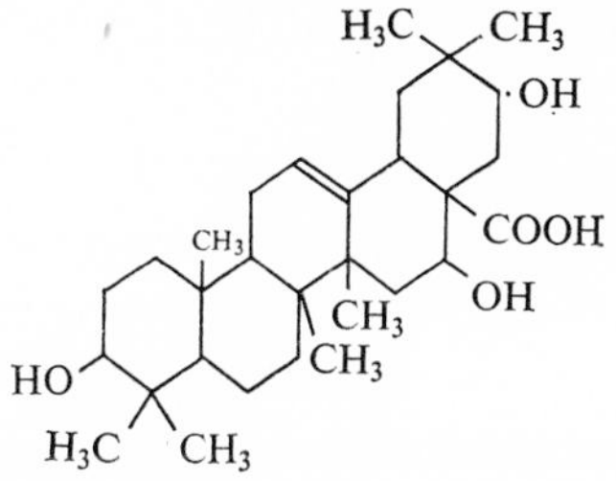

$C_{30}H_{48}O_5$ MW 488

Sapogenin from *Acacia* and *Albizzia* spp. M.p. 268–72°.

Di-Ac lactone: $C_{34}H_{52}O_6$. MW 556. M.p. 235–6°.

Farooq, Varshney, Naim, *Arch. Pharm.*, 1961, **294**, 133; 1962, **295**, 12.

Varshney, Shamsuddin, *Tetrahedron Letters*, 1964, 2055.

Acalamid. *See* Phenaglycodol.★

Acalo. *See* Phenaglycodol.★

Acenocoumarin. *See* Nicoumalone.★

2-Acetamido-1β-(L-β-aspartamido)-1 : 2-dideoxy-D-glucose

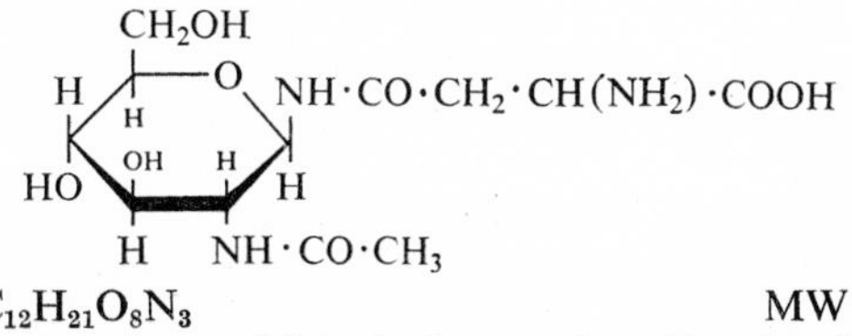

$C_{12}H_{21}O_8N_3$ MW 335

Present in partial hydrolysate of ovalbumin glycopeptide. Needles from EtOH. M.p. 255–8° decomp. $[\alpha]_D^{22}$ 23·6° (c, 1 in H_2O). Plates from EtOH.Aq. of hydrate. M.p. 215–22° decomp. $[\alpha]_D^{24}$ 23·2° (c, 1·5 in H_2O).

Marks, Marshall, Neuberger, *Biochem. J.*, 1963, **87**, 274.

Tsukamoto, Yamamoto, Miyashita, *Biochem. Biophys. Research Commun.*, 1964, **15**, 151.

***p*-Acetamidobenzaldehyde.★**

Thiosemicarbazone:★ Berculon A, Neustab, Seroden, Thioparamizone.

See also:

Domagk *et al.*, *Naturwiss.*, 1946, **33**, 315.
Behnisch, Mietzsch, Schmidt, *Angew. Chem.*, 1948, **60**, 113.
Chubrier, Cattelain, *Bull. soc. chim.*, 1950, 52.
Das, Mukherjee, *J. Am. Chem. Soc.*, 1953, **75**, 1241.

3-Acetamido-2-butanone

$CH_3{\cdot}CH(NH{\cdot}CO{\cdot}CH_3){\cdot}CO{\cdot}CH_3$

$C_6H_{11}O_2N$ MW 129

B.p. 102–6°/2 mm. n_D^{25} 1·4560.

Wiley, Borum, *Organic Syntheses*, 1953, **33**, 1; Coll. Vol. **4**, 5.

***N*$^\alpha$-[2-(2-Acetamido-3-*O*-D-glucosyl)-D-propionyl-L-alanyl-D-γ-glutamyl]-L-lysyl-D-alanyl-D-alanine**

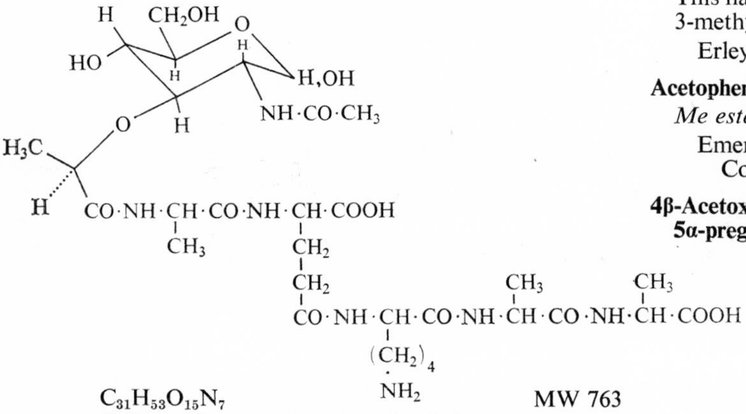

$C_{31}H_{53}O_{15}N_7$ MW 763

Cell wall precursor in *Staphylococcus aureus*. Colourless amorph. solid. M.p. 148–50° decomp. $[\alpha]_D^{25}$ 14° (c, 0·9 in H_2O).

Lanzilotti, Benz, Goldman, *J. Am. Chem. Soc.*, 1964, **86**, 1880.

***S*-(1-Acetamido-4-hydroxyphenyl)cysteine**

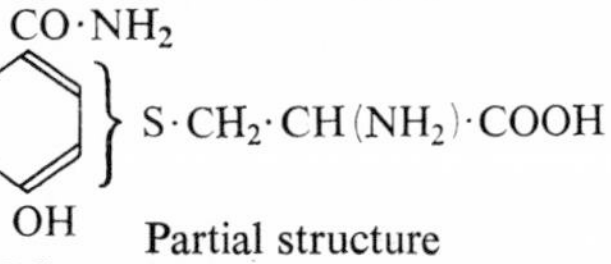

Partial structure

$C_{11}H_{14}O_4N_2S$ MW 207

Urinary metabolite of acet-*o*-toluidide★ (acetophenetidine). Colourless needles from H_2O. M.p. 187–8°.

Jagenburg, Toczko, *Biochem. J.*, 1964, **92**, 639.

4-Acetamidophenol★ (*Amadil, Apamide, Calpol, Eneril, Febrilix, Lyteca, Nobedon, Panadol, Tabalgin, Tempra, Tralgon, Tylenol*).

Benzoyl: needles from EtOH. M.p. 171°.

5-Acetonyl-2 : 3-dichloro-8-hydroxy-7-methyl-1 : 4-naphthoquinone. *See* Mollisin.★

3-Acetonylglutaric Acid

$CH_3{\cdot}CO{\cdot}CH_2$
$HOOC{\cdot}CH_2{\cdot}CH{\cdot}CH_2{\cdot}COOH$

$C_8H_{12}O_5$ MW 188

Oil.

Di-Me ester: $C_{10}H_{16}O_5$. MW 216. B.p. 100–1°/0·4 mm. n_D^{20} 1·4467.

Di-Et ester: $C_{12}H_{20}O_5$. MW 244. B.p. 113–15°/1 mm. n_D^{20} 1·4465.

Lukeš, Paleček, *Coll. Czech. Chem. Commun.*, 1964, **29**, 1073.

3-(α-Acetonyl-*p*-nitrobenzyl)-4-hydroxycoumarin. *See* Nicoumalone.★

Acetophenetidine.★ *See* Acet-*o*-toluidide.★

Acetophenone-*o*-carboxylic Acid.★

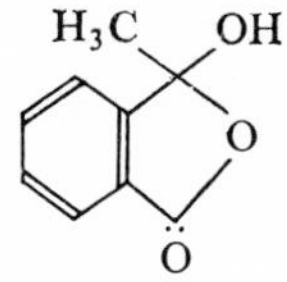

This has been shown to have the structure 3-hydroxy-3-methylphthalide.

Erley *et al.*, *Chemistry and Industry*, 1964, 1915.

Acetophenone-*p*-carboxylic Acid.★

Me ester:

Emerson, Deebel, *Organic Syntheses*, 1952, **32**, 81; Coll. Vol. **4**, 579.

4β-Acetoxy-3α-benzoylmethylamino-20α-dimethylamino-5α-pregnane. *See* Pachysandrine A.

17α-Acetoxy-6-chloro-6-dehydroprogesterone. *See* Chloromadinone acetate.

3-β-Acetoxy-5 : 10-seco-$\Delta^{1(10)}$-cholesten-5-one

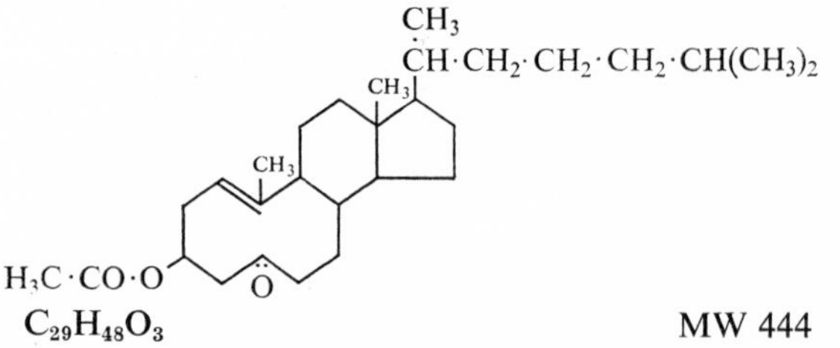

$C_{29}H_{48}O_3$ MW 444

Cis-.

M.p. 138°. $[\alpha]_D$ +31° (c, 1·61 in $CHCl_3$).

Oxime: m.p. 158–9°.

Trans-.

M.p. 136°. $[\alpha]_D$ +3° (c, 3·03 in $CHCl_3$). Hydrol → 3β-hydroxy comp. M.p. 158°.

Oxime: m.p. 141–2°.

Mihailović *et al.*, *Tetrahedron Letters*, 1964, 1867.

4-Acetoxy-8 : 9-epoxy-7-[2,4-hexadiynylidene]-1 : 6-dioxaspiro[4,4]non-2-ene

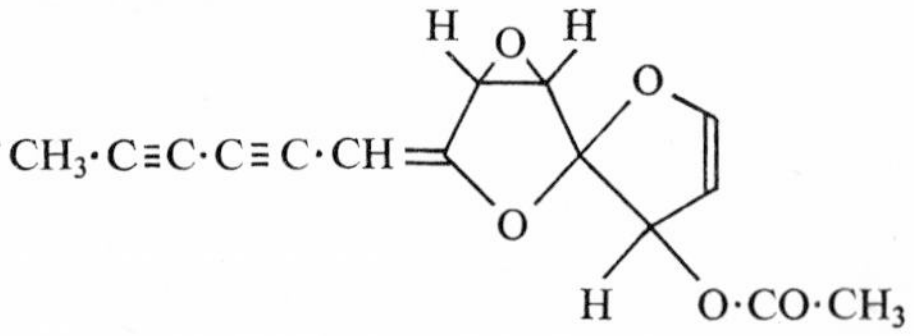

$C_{15}H_{12}O_5$ MW 272

Constituent of *Chrysanthemum leucanthemum* L. Cryst. from Et$_2$O–light petroleum. M.p. 153·5°. $[\alpha]_{546}{}^{20}$ −78° (c, 0·88 in Et$_2$O) $\lambda_{max.}$ 292 (ε, 15,500), 277 (18,900), 263·5 (13,400), 251 (7200), 222·5 mμ (3200).

Bohlmann, Bornowski, Arndt, *Ann.*, 1963, **668**, 51.

10-[3-{4-(2-Acetoxyethyl)piperazin-1-yl}propyl]-2-chloro-phenothiazine. *See* Thiopropazate.★

3β-Acetoxy-22-hydroxyhopane. *See under* 3β : 22-Di-hydroxyhopane.

1-Acetoxymethyl-2-propyl-4-quinolone

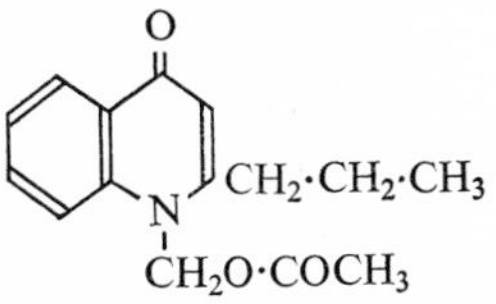

C$_{15}$H$_{17}$O$_3$N   MW 259

Alkaloid from *Boronia ternata* Endl. (Rutaceae) Prisms from C$_6$H$_6$–light petroleum. M.p. 112°. Light absorption: $\lambda_{max.}$ 208 (ε, 18,200), 236 (28,200), 314 (15,500), and 328 mμ (17,400). Hyd. → 2-propyl-4-quinolone, m.p. 166–8°. (*B,HCl*: m.p. 214–16°.)

Duffield, Jefferies, *Austral. J. Chem.*, 1963, **16**, 292.

2-Acetoxypropyltrimethylammonium chloride. *See* Methacholine chloride.★

Acetylalthiomycin

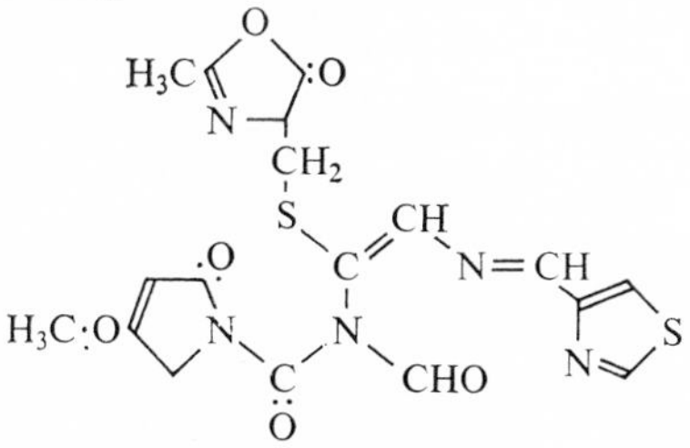

Tentative structure

C$_{18}$H$_{19}$O$_6$N$_5$S$_2$ MW 465

Degradation product from Althiomycin. Two forms: (i) pale yellow plates from CH$_2$Cl$_2$. M.p. 183–6° decomp. (ii) Soft white needles from EtOH. M.p. 187–9°.

Cram *et al.*, *J. Am. Chem. Soc.*, 1963, **85**, 1430.

3β-Acetylamino-20α-dimethylamino-5α-pregnan-18-ol. *See* Malouphylline.★

3β-Acetylamino-5α-conanine. *See* Malouphyllamine.★

N-(p-Acetylaminophenyl)rhodanine

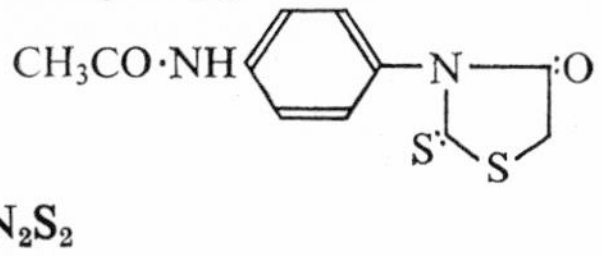

C$_{11}$H$_{10}$O$_2$N$_2$S$_2$ MW 266

M.p. >240° decomp.

Strube, *Organic Syntheses*, 1959, **39**, 1; Coll. Vol. **4**, 6.

9-Acetylanthracene. *See* Anthryl methyl Ketone.

1-Acetylaspidoalbidine

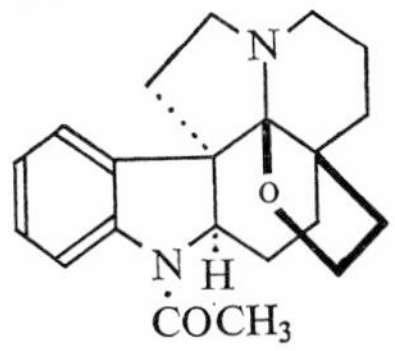

C$_{21}$H$_{26}$O$_2$N$_2$ MW 338

Alkaloid from *Vallesia dichotoma* Ruiz et Pav. M.p. 173–4°. $[\alpha]_D$ +46° (CHCl$_3$). Light absorption: $\lambda_{max.}$ 212 (log ε, 4·43) 253 mμ (4·17).

Brown, Budzikiewicz, Djerassi, *Tetrahedron Letters*, 1963, 1731.

α-Acetyl-δ-chloro-γ-valerolactone

$$Cl \cdot CH_2 \cdot CH \cdot CH_2 \cdot CH \cdot CO \cdot CH_3$$
$$O \!-\!\!-\!\!-\! CO$$

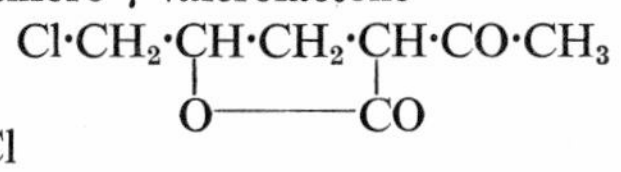

C$_7$H$_9$O$_3$Cl   MW 176·5

B.p. 164–8°/11 mm. 151–6°/8 mm. $n_D{}^{25}$ 1·4820.

Traube, Lehman, *Ber.*, 1901, **34**, 1980.
Zuidema, van Tamelen, Van Zyl, *Organic Syntheses*, 1951, **31**, 1; Coll. Vol. **4**, 10.

2-Acetylcyclohexane-1 : 3-dione

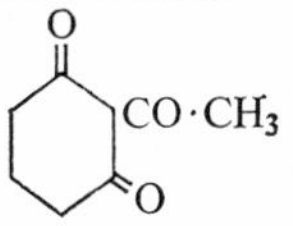

C$_8$H$_{10}$O$_3$ MW 154

M.p. 29–32°. B.p. 63–8°/0·1 mm, 126–7°/22 mm. *Cu salt*: blue needles from CHCl$_3$. M.p. 263–5° decomp. (rapid heating).

Smith, *J. Chem. Soc.*, 1953, 803.
Merényi, Nilsson, *Acta Chem. Scand.*, 1964, **17**, 1801.

1-Acetylcyclohexanol

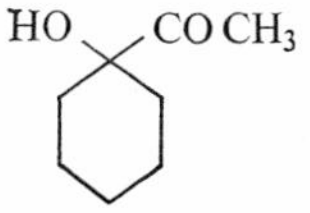

C$_8$H$_{14}$O$_2$ MW 142

B.p. 92–4°/15 mm. $n_D{}^{25}$ 1·4670. D$_4{}^{25}$ 1·0248.

Stacey, Mikulee, *Organic Syntheses*, 1955, **35**, 1; Coll. Vol. **4**, 13.

2-Acetylcyclopentane-1 : 3-dione

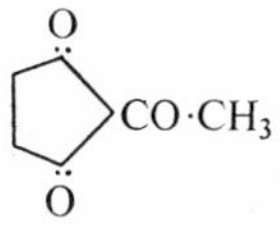

C$_7$H$_8$O$_3$ MW 140

Cryst. from light petroleum. M.p. 73–4°. Sublimes. Light absorption: $\lambda_{max.}$ 220 (ε, 11,800) and 265 mμ (7040). pK$_a$ 3·5.

Sieglitz, Horn, *Chem. Ber.*, 1951, **84**, 607.
Merényi, Nilsson, *Acta Chem. Scand.*, 1964, **17**, 1801.
Vandewalle, *Bull. soc. chim. belg.*, 1964, **73**, 628.

2-Acetylcyclopent-4-ene-1 : 3-dione

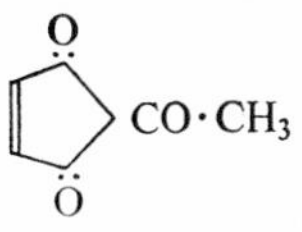

C$_7$H$_6$O$_3$ MW 138

Pale yellow cryst. from light petroleum. M.p. 83–4°. Light absorption: $\lambda_{max.}$ 223 (ε, 14,000), 259 (13,800), and 317 mμ (820).

Nilsson, *Acta Chem. Scand.*, 1964, **18**, 441.

Acetylcyclopropane.★
See also:

Cannon, Ellis, Leal, *Organic Syntheses*, Coll. Vol. **4**, 597.

2-Acetyl-2-decarboxamidotetracycline

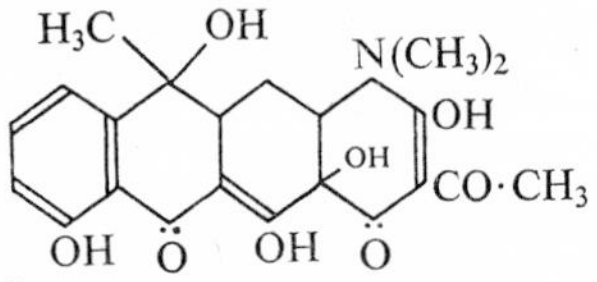

$C_{23}H_{25}O_8N$ MW 443

Metabolite of *Streptomyces psammoticus*. Hydrate. Yellow cryst. M.p. 178–85° decomp. $[\alpha]_D$ $-125°$ (c, 1 in 0·5*N*-HCl–MeOH). Light absorption: $\lambda_{max.}$ 276 ($E^{1\%}_{1\ cm.}$ 312) and 359 mμ (300) in 0·01*N*-HCl. $\lambda_{max.}$ 270 (388) and 382 mμ (367) in 0·01*N*-NaOH.

Lancini, Sensi, *Experientia*, 1964, **20**, 83.

3-*O*-Acetyl-2 : 6-dideoxy-D-*lyxo*hexopyranose. *See* Chromose D.

4-*O*-Acetyl-2 : 6-dideoxy-3-*C*-methyl-L-*arabo*pyranose. *See* Chromose B.

3-Acetyl-2 : 2-dimethylcyclobutaneacetic Acid★ (*Pinonic acid*).

The form, m.p. 68°, has been shown to have the *cis* configuration, and the oily isomers *trans.*

Harispe, Mea, Horeau, *Bull. soc. chim.*, 1964, 1035.

3-Acetyl-2 : 2-dimethylcyclobutane-1-carboxylic Acid★ (*Pinononic acid*).

Cis-.
The form, m.p. 131°, reported in the main work. $[\alpha]_D$ +73·7° (c, 4 in $CHCl_3$).
Trans-.
M.p. 75°. $[\alpha]_D$ −79° (c, 3 in C_6H_6), −82·8° (c, 2·5 in Et_2O).

Harispe, Mea, Horeau, *Bull. soc. chim.*, 1964, 1035.

1-Acetyl-17-hydroxyaspidoalbidine

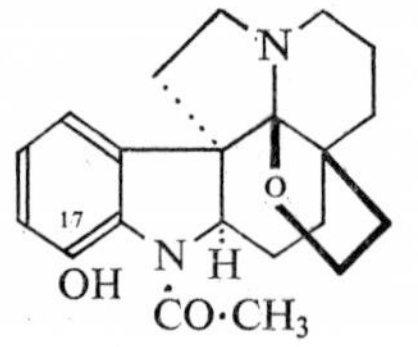

$C_{21}H_{26}O_3N_2$ MW 354

Alkaloid from *Vallesia dichotoma* Ruiz et Pav. Amorph. Light absorption: $\lambda_{max.}$ 219 (log ε, 4·45), 257 (3·94), 290 mμ (3·59).
O-*Me ether*: m.p. 237–9° decomp. $[\alpha]_D$ +6° ($CHCl_3$).

Brown, Budzikiewicz, Djerassi, *Tetrahedron Letters*, 1963, 1731.

5-Acetylimino-4-methyl-2-sulphamoyl-1 : 3 : 4-thiadiazoline. *See* Methazolamide.★

Acetyl-β-methylcholine chloride. *See* Methacholine chloride.★

***N*-Acetylneuraminic Acid.★**
Synthesis:

Rinderknecht, Rebane, *Experientia*, 1963, **19**, 342.

3-(2-Acetyl-1-*p*-nitrophenylethyl)-4-hydroxycoumarin. *See* Nicoumalone.★

3-(2-Acetyl-1-phenylethyl)-4-hydroxycoumarin (*Coumadin, Warfarin*)

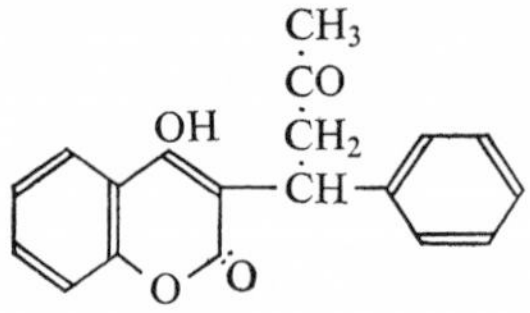

$C_{19}H_{16}O_4$ MW 308

Rodenticide. Cryst. from EtOH. M.p. 161°.
Na salt: Marevan.
Ac: m.p. 117–18°.
Oxime: m.p. 182–3°.
2 : 4-*Dinitrophenylhydrazone*: m.p. 215–16°.

Stahmann, Ikawa, Link, U.S.P. 2,427,578 (*Chem. Abstracts*, 1948, **42**, 603).
Schroeder, Link, U.S.P. 2,765,321 (*Chem. Abstracts*, 1957, **51**, 5356).
Link, U.S.P. 2,777,859 (*Chem. Abstracts*, 1957, **51**, 9078).

3-(3′-Acetylpropionyl)furan. *See* Ipomeanine.★

Acetylquinol.★
See also:

Amin Shah, *Organic Syntheses*, Coll. Vol. **4**, 836.

3-Acetylstrophadogenin. *See under* Strophadogenin.★

Acetylsulphisoxazole. *See under* Sulphisoxazole.★

Acetylxanthorrhoein

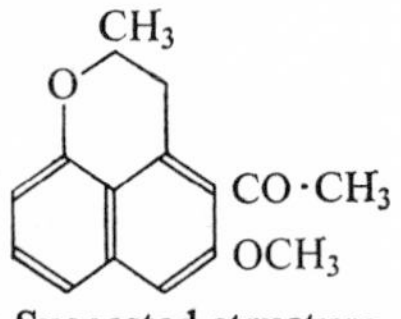

Suggested structure

$C_{16}H_{16}O_3$ MW 256

Constituent of *Xanthorrhoea preissi.* M.p. 124–5°. $[\alpha]_D^{20}$ 127° (c, 0·13 in $CHCl_3$).

Birch, Salahud-Din, Smith, *Tetrahedron Letters*, 1964, 1623.

Acolen. *See* Dehydrocholic Acid.★

Aconitine.★
See also:

Weisner *et al.*, *Coll. Czech. Chem. Commun.*, 1963, **28**, 2462.

Acraldehyde.★
Di-Et acetal:
See also:

Van Allen, *Organic Syntheses*, 1952, **32**, 5; Coll. Vol. **4**, 21.

Acrylic Acid Dibromide. *See* 2 : 3-Dibromopropionic Acid.★

Actidione★ (*Cycloheximide*)

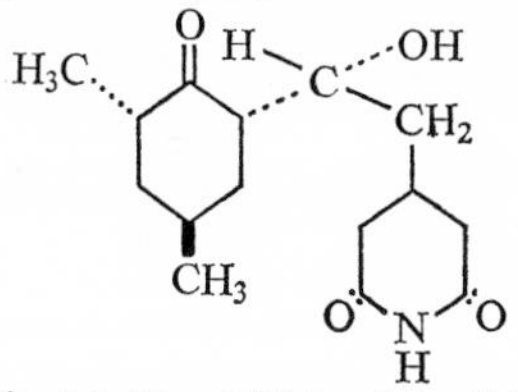

(R) (−)-.
M.p. 144–5°. $[\alpha]_D^{25}$ −33° (c, 1 in $CHCl_3$).
(±)-.
M.p. 139–40°.
Absolute configuration:
Starkovsky, Johnson, *Tetrahedron Letters*, 1964, 919.
Total synthesis:
Johnson *et al.*, *J. Am. Chem. Soc.*, 1964, **86**, 116.

Actinidine

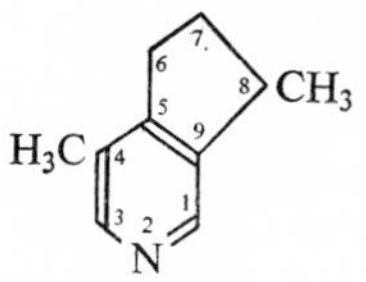

$C_{10}H_{13}N$ MW 147
(−)-.
Constituent of the leaves and gall of *Actinidia polygama*. Oil. B.p. 100–3°/9 mm. $[\alpha]_D^{11}$ −7·2° (c, 17·54 in $CHCl_3$).
Picrate: m. p. 143°.
(±)-.
B.p. 100–3°/12 mm. M.p. 142–3°.
Picrate: fine needles from Et_2O. M.p. 139–40°.
Sakan *et al.*, *Bull. Chem. Soc. Japan*, 1959, **32**, 315, 1155.
Djerassi *et al.*, *Chemistry and Industry*, 1961, 210.

Actinomycin C_1 (D).★
Syntheses:
Brockmann, Manegold, *Naturwiss.*, 1964, **51**, 382.
Brockmann, Lackner, *Naturwiss.*, 1964, **51**, 384, 435.

Actinomycin C_2.★
Synthesis:
Brockmann, Lackner, *Tetrahedron Letters*, 1964, 3517.

Actinomycin C_3.★
Synthesis:
Brockmann, Lackner, *Naturwiss.*, 1964, 407.
Cryst. structure:
Backmann, Müller, *Nature*, 1964, **201**, 261.

Actinomycin (Ser–Val–Pro–Sar–Meval)

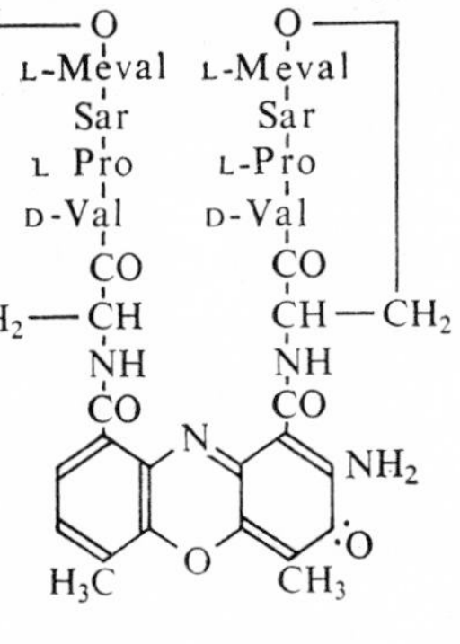

$C_{60}H_{82}O_{16}N_{12}$ MW 1226

Synthetic actinomycin. Red cryst. from AcOEt–C_6H_{12}. M.p. 269–73° decomp. $[\alpha]_D^{21}$ −435° (c, 0·25 in MeOH). Light absorption: $\lambda_{max.}$ 450 mμ (ε, 24,950).
Brockmann, Lackner, *Tetrahedron Letters*, 1964, 3523.

Actinophenol. *See* Actiphenol.

Actiphenol★ (*Actinophenol*).
Metabolite of *Streptomyces noursei*. M.p. 201–3°. Light absorption: $\lambda_{max.}$ 216 (log ε, 4·40), 260 (4·08), and 342 mμ (3·80).
Rao, Cullen, *J. Am. Chem. Soc.*, 1960, **82**, 1127.
Vondráček, Vaněk, *Chemistry and Industry*, 1964, 1686.

Adamantane★ (*Tricyclo*[3,3,1,$1^{3,7}$]*decane*).
Present in various petroleums.
Stetter, *Angew. Chem.*, 1954, **66**, 217; 1962, **74**, 361.
Fort, Schleyer, *Chem. Rev.*, 1964, **64**, 277.

Adenine 9β-D-arabinofuranoside (9β-D-*Arabinofuranosyladenine*)

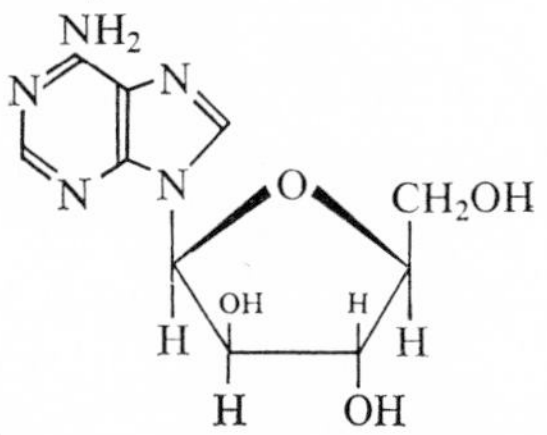

$C_{10}H_{13}O_4N_5$ MW 267
Cryst. + $5H_2O$. M.p. 257°. $[\alpha]_D^{27}$ −5° (c, 0·25 in H_2O).
Lee *et al.*, *J. Am. Chem. Soc.*, 1960, **82**, 2648.
Reist *et al.*, *J. Org. Chem.*, 1962, **27**, 3274.

Adeninedeoxyriboside (2′-*Deoxyadenosine*, 9-[2′-*deoxyribofuranosyl*]*adenine*)

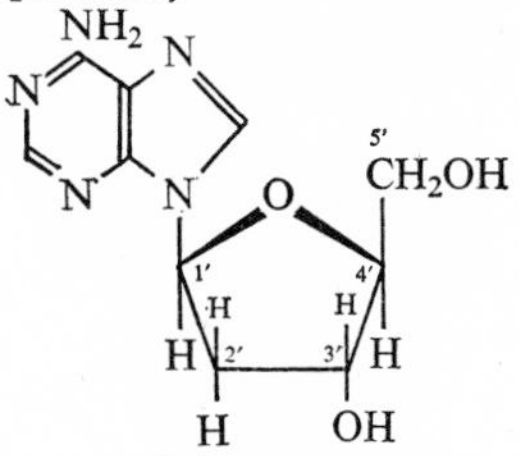

β-Anomer

$C_{10}H_{13}O_3N_5$ MW 251
β-D-Ribofuranosyl-.
Universal nucleosidic component of deoxyribonucleic acids. Cryst. from H_2O. M.p. 187–90°. $[\alpha]_D^{20}$ −25·6° (c, 0·31 in H_2O). Light absorption: λ_{max} 260 mμ, $\lambda_{min.}$ 226 mμ.
3′-*Ac*: colourless prisms from EtOH. M.p. 216–17°.
5′-*Ac*: colourless needles. M.p. 140–1°.
3′ : 5′-*Di-Ac*: needles from AcOEt–light petroleum. M.p. 151–2°.
α-D-Ribofuranosyl-.
Cryst. from H_2O. M.p. 209–11°. $[\alpha]_D^{20}$ 71° (c, 0·54 in H_2O). Light absorption: $\lambda_{max.}$ 259 mμ, $\lambda_{min.}$ 227 mμ.
Andersen, Dekker, Todd, *J. Chem. Soc.*, 1952, 2721.
Andersen *et al.*, *J. Chem. Soc.*, 1954, 1882.

Hayes, Michelson, Todd, *J. Chem. Soc.*, 1955, 808.
Anderson, Goodman, Baker, *J. Am. Chem. Soc.*, 1958, **80**, 6453; 1959, **81**, 3967.
Ness, Fletcher, *J. Am. Chem. Soc.*, 1959, **81**, 4752.
Pedersen, Fletcher, *J. Am. Chem. Soc.*, 1960, **82**, 5210.
Kurzmann, Varghn, *Chem. Ber.*, 1963, **96**, 2327.

Infra red spectrum:
Angell, *J. Chem. Soc.*, 1961, 504.

Adenosine.★
2′-O-*Me*: present in the ribonucleic acid from various plant, animal, and bacterial sources.
Smith, Dunn, *Biochim. Biophys. Acta*, 1959, **31**, 573.
Hall, *Biochim. Biophys. Acta*, 1963, **68**, 278; *Biochem. Biophys. Research. Commun.*, 1963, **12**, 429.

Adenosine 5′-diphosphate glucose

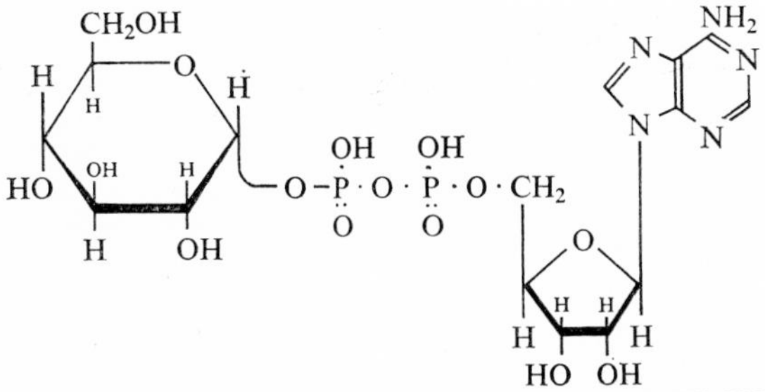

$C_{17}H_{25}O_{15}N_5P_2$ MW 589
Nucleotide present in ripening cereal grains. Synthesised by the general method of Roseman *et al.*, *J. Am. Chem. Soc.*, 1961, **83**, 659.
Recondo, (Dankert), Leloir, *Biochem. Biophys. Research Commun.*, 1961, **6**, 85; 1963, **12**, 204.
Murata *et al.*, *Arch. Biochem. Biophys.*, 1964, **106**, 371.

Adenosine 5′-triphosphate.★
γ-^{32}P.
Verheyden, Wehrli, Moffatt, *J. Am. Chem. Soc.*, 1964, **86**, 1253.

***S*-Adenosylhomocysteine.★**
See also:
Johnson, Shaw, Wagner, *Biochim. Biophys. Acta*, 1963, **72**, 107.

Adenylosuccinic Acid.★
L-(Aspartic acid)-.
$[\alpha]_D$ $-7{\cdot}5°$ (c, 1 in H_2O. pH 7), $-32°$ (pH 1), $-11°$ (pH 12).
Synth. D-(Aspartic acid)-.
$[\alpha]_D$ $-80°$ (c, 1 in H_2O. pH 7), $-46°$ (pH 1), $-81°$ (pH 12).
Ballio, Barcellona, di Vittorio, *Arch. Biochem. Biophys.*, 1963, **101**, 311.

Adhulupone

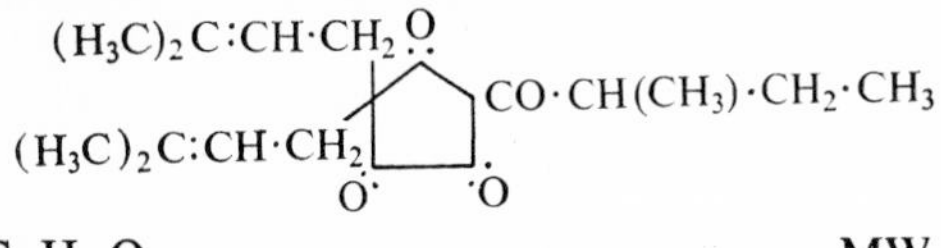

$C_{20}H_{28}O_4$ MW 332
Minor constituent of hops (*Humulus lupulus* L.). Oil. B.p. 130°/7 × 10^{-3} mm. With 1 : 2-diaminobenzene → quinoxaline, m.p. 95°.
Spetsig, Steninger, *J. Inst. Brewing*, 1960, **65**, 413.
Brown, Burton, Stevens, *J. Chem. Soc.*, 1964, 4774.

Adiantone (19α-*Norhopanone*)

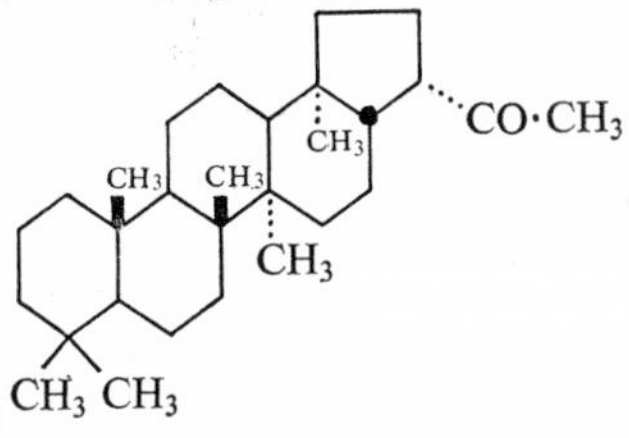

$C_{29}H_{48}O$ MW 412
Constituent of fern *Adiantum capillus veneris* L. M.p. 222–4° (218°). $[\alpha]_D$ +83°.
Baddeley, Halsall, Jones, *J. Chem. Soc.*, 1961, 3891.
Berti *et al.*, *Tetrahedron Letters*, 1963, 1283.

Adiantoxide

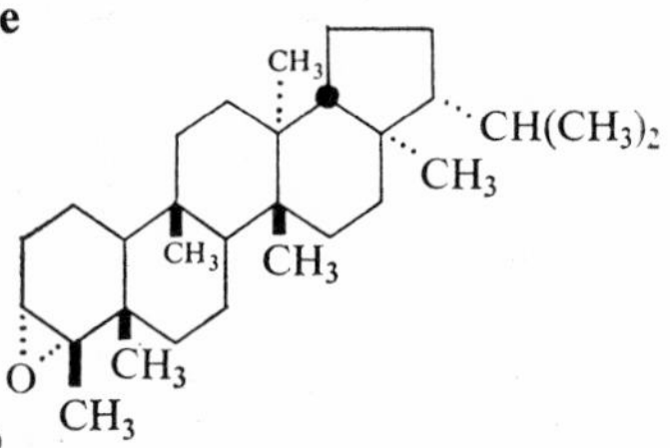

$C_{30}H_{50}O$ MW 426
Constituent of the fern *Adiantum capillus veneris* L. M.p. 229–31°. $[\alpha]_D^{30}$ 46·8°.
Berti, Bottari, Marsili, *Il Farmaco (Parvia) Ed. Sci.*, 1963, **18**, 441; *Tetrahedron Letters*, 1964, 1.

***N*: *N*′-Adipyl*bis*-(3-amino-2 : 4 : 6-tri-iodobenzoic acid).**
See under 3-Amino-2 : 4 : 6-tri-iodobenzoic Acid.★

Adlumine★

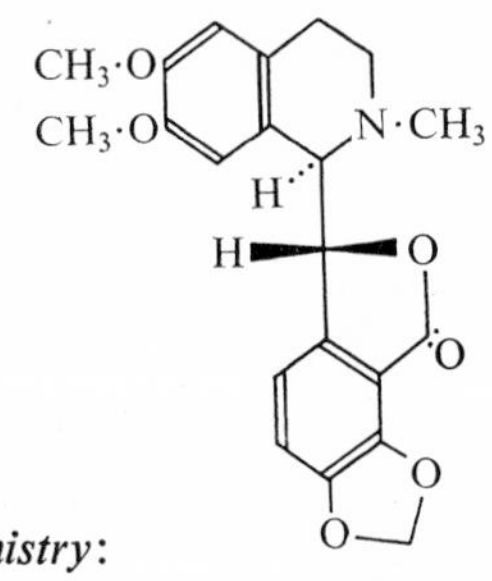

Stereochemistry:
Safe, Moir, *Can. J. Chem.*, 1964, **42**, 160.

Adonitoxin (*Adonitoxigenin*-3-O-β-L-*rhamnopyranoside*, 19-*oxogitoxigenin*-3-O-β-L-*rhamnopyranoside*)

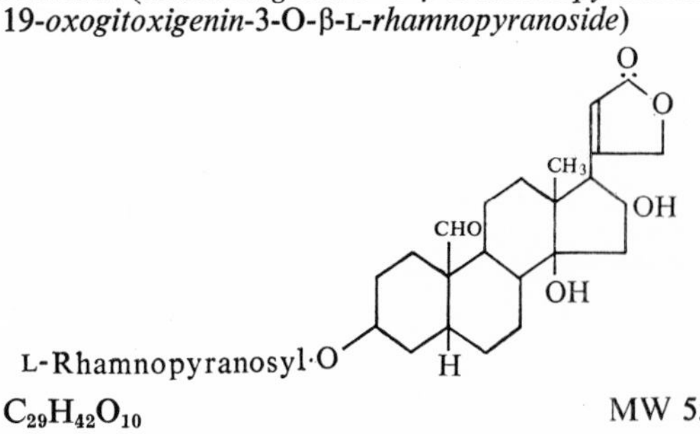

$C_{29}H_{42}O_{10}$ MW 550

Present in the aerial parts of *Adonis vernalis* L.
3-O-*Ac*: $C_{31}H_{44}O_{11}$. MW 592. Adonitoxigenin 3-*O*-acetyl-L-rhamnopyranoside. Present in *A. vernalis* L. Cryst. from MeOH.Aq. M.p. 213–19° decomp. $[\alpha]_D^{23}$ −19·9° (MeOH).
Oxime: m.p. 262–5°.

Rosenmund, Reichstein, *Pharm. Acta Helv.*, 1942, **17**, 1176.
Katz, Reichstein, *Pharm. Acta Helv.*, 1947, **22**, 437.
Tschesche, Petersen, *Chem. Ber.*, 1953, **86**, 574.
Čekan, Pitra, *Chemistry and Industry*, 1960, 497; *Coll. Czech. Chem. Commun.*, 1961, **26**, 1551.

Adrenoglomerulotropin. *See* 1 : 2 : 3 : 4-Tetrahydro-6-methoxy-1-methyl-2-carboline.

Aegiceradiol

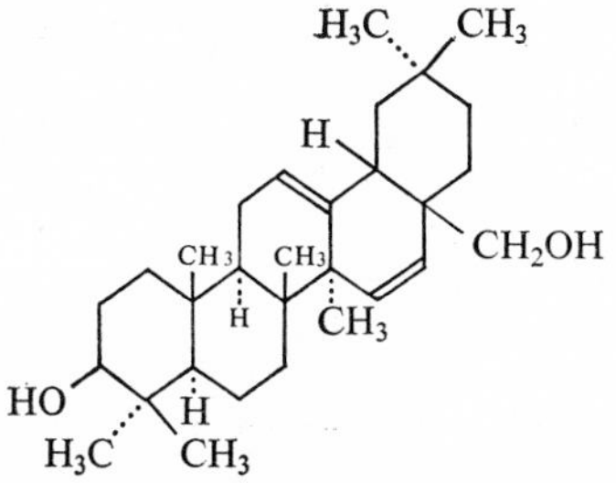

$C_{30}H_{48}O_2$ MW 440
Constituent of *Aegiceras majus* Gaertn. Prisms from Me_2CO. M.p. 236–8°. $[\alpha]_D^{33}$ +40·3° (c, 0·62 in $CHCl_3$).
Di-Ac: needles from $CHCl_3$–MeOH. M.p. 214–15°. $[\alpha]_D^{33}$ +52·7° (c, 0·87 in $CHCl_3$).
3-*Mono-Ac*: needles from MeOH. M.p. 203–4°. $[\alpha]_D^{36}$ +44·1° (c, 0·34 in $CHCl_3$).
Di-benzoyl: needles from C_6H_6–EtOH. M.p. 217°. $[\alpha]_D$ 45·5 (c, 0·9 in $CHCl_3$).

Rao, Bose, *Tetrahedron*, 1962, **18**, 461.

Aegicerin (13β : 28-*Epoxy*-3β-*hydroxy*-16-*oxo*-18β-*oleanane*)

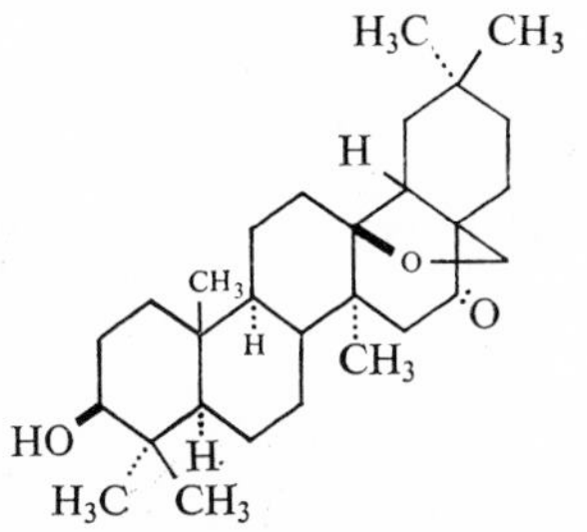

$C_{30}H_{48}O_3$ MW 456
Constituent of the bark of *Aegiceras majus* Gaertn. Microcryst. needles. M.p. 254–6°. $[\alpha]_D^{28}$ −23·6° (c, 0·87 in $CHCl_3$).
Ac: colourless flakes from $CHCl_3$–MeOH. M.p. 273–5°. $[\alpha]_D^{30}$ −17·7° (c, 1·07 in $CHCl_3$).
Oxime: needles from EtOH.Aq. M.p. 244–6°. $[\alpha]_D^{26}$ −6·9° (c, 0·73 in $CHCl_3$). *Di-Ac*: m.p. 210–11°.

Rao, Bose, *Tetrahedron*, 1962, **18**, 461.
Rao, *Chemistry and Industry*, 1963, 1523; *Tetrahedron*, 1964, **20**, 973.

Aeruginosin A (2-*Amino*-6-*carboxy*-10-*methylphenazinium betaine*)

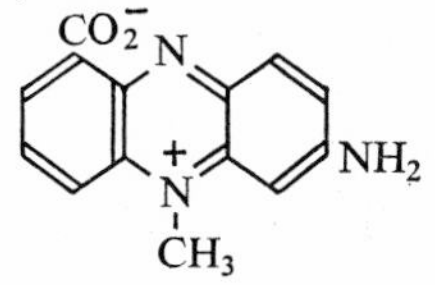

$C_{14}H_{11}O_2N_3$ MW 253
Pigment from *Pseudomonas aeruginosa*. Decomps. on heating. Sol. H_2O. Insol. in non-polar solvents. Gives red-purple fluorescence in ultra-violet light.

Holliman, *Chemistry and Industry*, 1957, 1668; *S. African Ind. Chem.*, 1961, **15**, 233.

Aeruginosin B (2-*Amino*-6-*carboxy*-10-*methyl*-8-*sulphophenazinium betaine*)

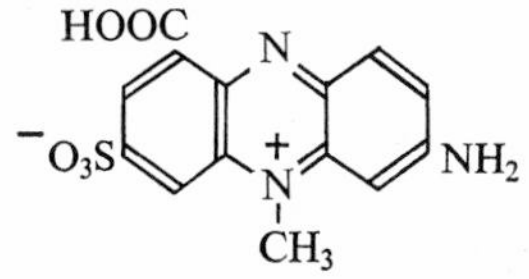

$C_{14}H_{11}O_5N_3S$ MW 333
Pigment from *Pseudomonas aeruginosa*. Decomps. on heating. Sol. in H_2O but insol. in polar solvents.

Holliman, *Chemistry and Industry*, 1957, 1668.
Herbert, Holliman, *Proc. Chem. Soc.*, 1964, 19.

Aescigenin. *See* Escigenin.

Aescin. *See* Escin.

Afalon®. *See* *N*-(3 : 4-Dichlorophenyl)-*N'*-methoxy-*N'*-methylurea.

Affinin.★

2-*Trans*-6-*trans*-8-*trans*-.
M.p. 91–2°. B.p. 145°/0·25 mm.
Maleic anhydride add. comp.: m.p. 175°.
2-*Trans*-6-*cis*-8-*cis*-.
B.p. 120–5°/10^{-3} mm. n_D^{21} 1·5090. $\lambda_{max.}$ 228 mμ (ε, 24,300).

Crombie, Krasinski, Manzoor-i-Khuda, *J. Chem. Soc.*, 1963, 4970.

Affinine

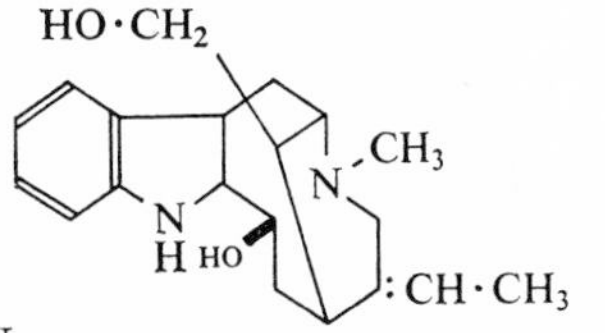

$C_{20}H_{24}O_2N_2$ MW 324
Alkaloid from *Peschiera affinis* (Muell. Arg) Miers. Cryst. from MeOH–AcOEt. M.p. 265° decomp. Light absorption: $\lambda_{max.}$ 238, 318 mμ (log ε, 4·18, 4·35).
O-*Ac*: cryst. as solvate from Me_2CO. M.p. 95–115°.
B,HCl: cryst. from MeOH–AcOEt. M.p. 267–9° decomp. $[\alpha]_D^{20}$ −105·4° (c, 0·5 in MeOH).

Weisbach *et al.*, *J. Pharm. Sci.*, 1963, **52**, 350.
Cava *et al.*, *Chemistry and Industry*, 1964, 1193.

Affinisine (*Deshydroxymethylvoachalotinol*, N_α-*Methyldesoxysarpagine*)

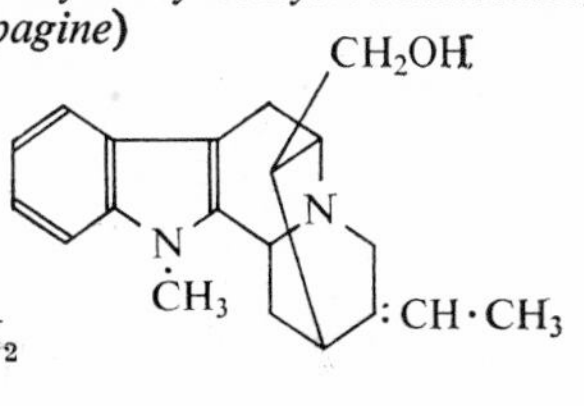

$C_{20}H_{24}ON_2$ MW 308

Alkaloid from *Peschiera affinis* (Muell. Arg) Miers. M.p. 194–6°. $[\alpha]_D^{30}$ 19° (c, 0·778 in $CHCl_3$).
O-*Ac*: m.p. 179–80°. $[\alpha]_D^{30}$ 8° (c, 0·82 in $CHCl_3$).

Defay *et al.*, *Bull. soc. chim. Belg.*, 1961, **70**, 475.
Gosset *et al.*, *Bull. soc. chim.*, 1961, 1033.
Bartlett *et al.*, *J. Am. Chem. Soc.*, 1962, **84**, 622.
Cava *et al.*, *Chemistry and Industry*, 1964, 1193.

Aflatoxin B$_1$★ (*Previously B*)

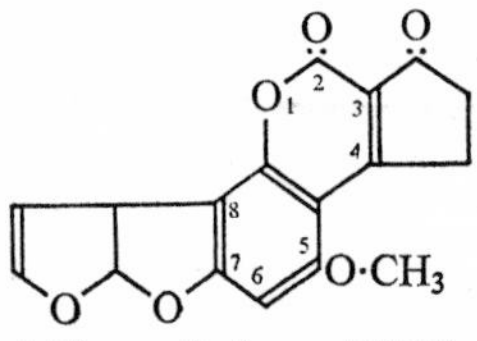

Cryst. from trichloroethylene–$CHCl_3$. H_2(Pt–$BaCO_3$) → Aflatoxin B$_2$.

de Iongh *et al.*, *Biochim. Biophys. Acta*, 1962, **65**, 548.
Hartley, Nesbitt, Kelly, *Nature*, 1963, **198**, 1056.
Asao *et al.*, *J. Am. Chem. Soc.*, 1963, **85**, 1706.

Aflatoxin B$_1$, B$_2$, G$_1$, and G$_2$.
Also isolated from *Penicillium puberulum* Bainer.

Hodges *et al.*, *Science*, 1964, **145**, 1439.

Aflatoxin B$_2$

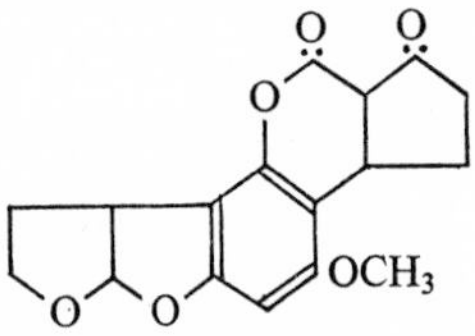

$C_{17}H_{14}O_6$ MW 314
Minor toxin from *Aspergillus flavus*. Cryst. from MeOH. M.p. 306–9°. $[\alpha]_D^{23}$ −492° (c, 0·100 in $CHCl_3$). $\lambda_{max.}$ 265, 363 mμ (ε 11,700, 23,400). Gives blue fluorescence.

Hartley, Nesbitt, Kelly, *Nature*, 1963, **198**, 1056.
Chang *et al.*, *Science*, 1963, **142**, 1191.
van der Merwe, Fourie, Scott, *Chemistry and Industry*, 1963, 1660.

Aflatoxin G$_1$★ (*Previously G*)

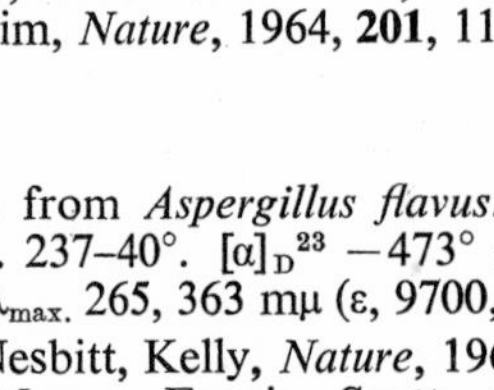

Green fluor. H_2 → Aflatoxin G$_2$.

Hartley, Nesbitt, Kelly, *Nature*, 1963, **198**, 1056.
Asao *et al.*, *J. Am. Chem. Soc.*, 1963, **85**, 1706.
Cheung, Sim, *Nature*, 1964, **201**, 1185.

Aflatoxin G$_2$
$C_{17}H_{14}O_7$ MW 330
Minor toxin from *Aspergillus flavus*. Cryst. from EtOH. M.p. 237–40°. $[\alpha]_D^{23}$ −473° ± 2° (c, 0·084 in $CHCl_3$). $\lambda_{max.}$ 265, 363 mμ (ε, 9700, 21,000).

Hartley, Nesbitt, Kelly, *Nature*, 1963, **198**, 1057.
van der Merwe, Fourie, Scott, *Chemistry and Industry*, 1963, 1660.

Afromosin. *See* 7-Hydroxy-4′ : 6′-dimethoxyisoflavone.

Afrormosin. *See* 7-Hydroxy-4′ : 6-dimethoxyisoflavone.

Agaritine.★
See also:

Levenberg, *J. Am. Chem. Soc.*, 1961, **83**, 503; *J. Biol. Chem.*, 1964, **239**, 2267.

α-Agarofuran

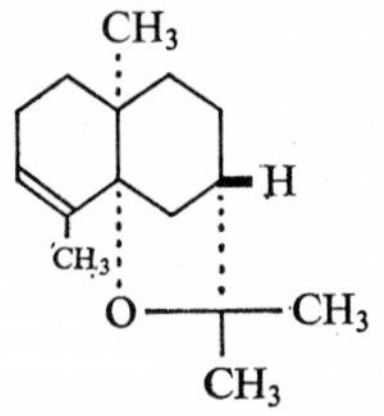

$C_{15}H_{24}O$ MW 220
Constituent of agar wood oil (from fungus infected agar wood, *Aquillaria agallocha* Roxb.). B.p. 134°/6 mm. $[\alpha]_D$ +37·09° (c, 6·12 in $CHCl_3$). n_D^{30} 1·5061.

Maheshwari *et al.*, *Tetrahedron*, 1963, **19**, 1077.

β-Agarofuran

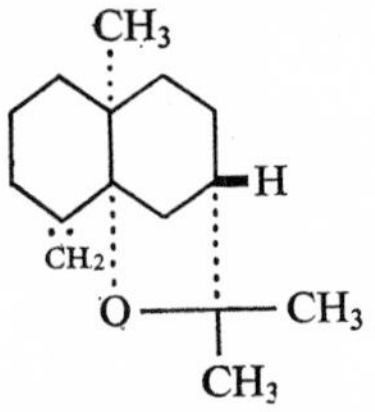

$C_{15}H_{24}O$ MW 220
Constituent of agar wood oil. B.p. 130°/8 mm. $[\alpha]_D^{30}$ −127·1° (c, 8·3 in $CHCl_3$). n_D^{28} 1·4973. D_D^{30} 0·9646. H_2 → dihydro deriv. also present naturally (b.p. 135°/8 mm., $[\alpha]_D$ −77° (c, 4·4 in $CHCl_3$), n_D^{29} 1·4912). Se → eudalene.

Maheshwari *et al.*, *Tetrahedron*, 1963, **19**, 1077.

Agarol

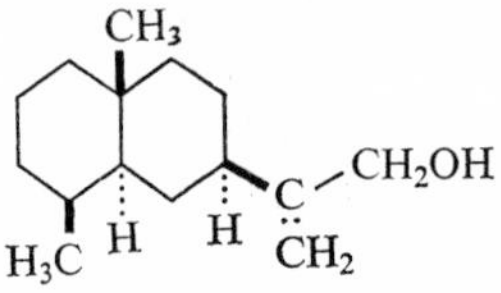

$C_{15}H_{26}O$ MW 222
Constituent of fungus infected *Aquilaria agallocha* Roxb. B.p. 117°/0·9 mm. D_4^{30} 0·9785. n_D^{29} 1·5052. $[\alpha]_D^{23}$ −21·8° (c, 7·25 in $CHCl_3$).
Ac: b.p. 132°/0·3 mm. $[\alpha]_D^{23}$ −10° (c, 1·4 in $CHCl_3$).

Jain, Bhattacharyya, *Tetrahedron Letters*, 1959, No. 9, 13.

Agathic Acid★

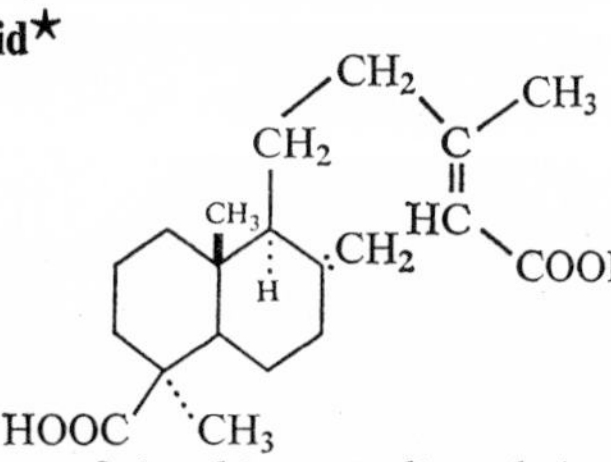

Constituent of *Agathis australis* and *A. microstachya*, but not *A. robusta*.

Carmen, *Austral. J. Chem.*, 1964, **17**, 393.

Stereochemistry:

Bory, Fetizon, Laszlo, *Bull. soc. chim.*, 1963, 2310.

Agrimolide (3 : 4 - *Dihydro* - 6 : 8 - *dihydroxy* - 3 - (4 - *methoxyphenylethyl)isocoumarin*)

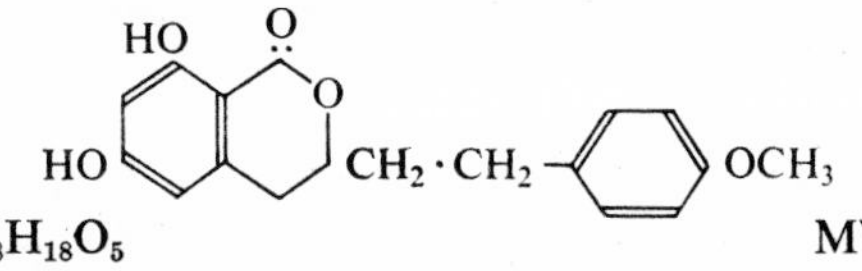

$C_{18}H_{18}O_5$ MW 314

Present in the roots of *Agrimona pilosa*. Columns from MeOH. M.p. 173·5°.

Mono-O-Me ether: needles. M.p. 113–14°.

Di-O-Me ether: needles from MeOH. M.p. 104–6°.

Yamato, *Yakugaku Zasshi*, 1958, **78**, 1086; 1959, **79**, 129, 1069 (*Chem. Abstracts*, 1959, **53**, 5178, 10123; 1960, **54**, 4561).

Ajmalidine.★

Mass spectra:

Biemann *et al.*, *Tetrahedron Letters*, 1963, 1969.

Akrinor.

Circulation analeptic drug containing (—)-7-[2-(β-hydroxy-α-methyl-β-phenethylamino)ethyl]theophylline hydrochloride,

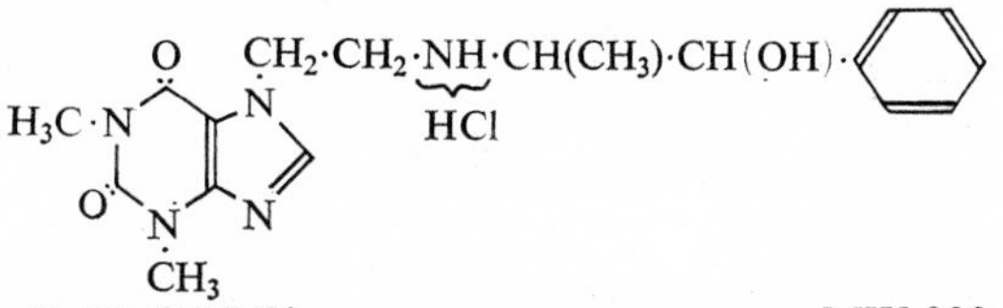

$C_{18}H_{24}O_3N_5Cl$ MW 393·5

M.p. 244–6°.

and 7-{2-[2-(3 : 4-Dihydroxyphenyl)-2-hydroxyethylamino]ethyl}theophylline hydrochloride,

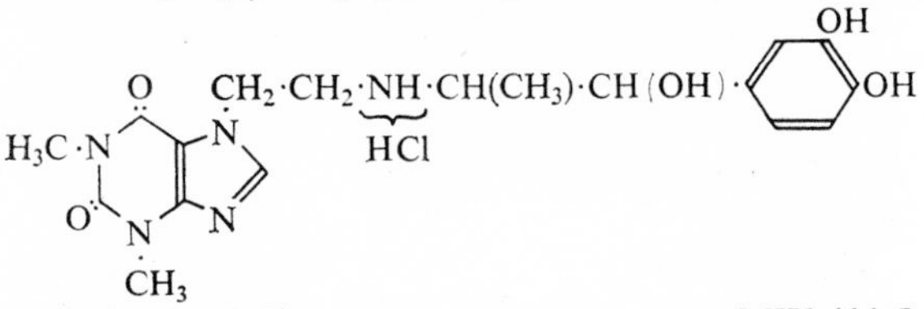

$C_{17}H_{22}O_5N_5Cl$ MW 411·5

M.p. 186–8°.

Chemiewerk (Hamburg), *Report of Therapy Congress and Pharmaceutical Exhibition*, Karlsruhe, 1963 (*Angew. Chem., Int. Ed.*, 1964, **3**, 68).

Akuammigine★

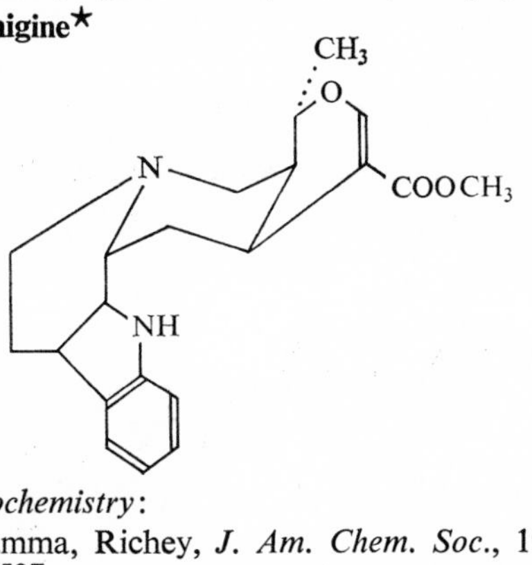

Stereochemistry:

Shamma, Richey, *J. Am. Chem. Soc.*, 1963, **85**, 2507.

5-Alanine-oxytocin. *See* 5-Decarboxamido-oxytocin.

Ala⁵-oxytocin. *See* 5-Decarboxamido-oxytocin.

Albaspidin★

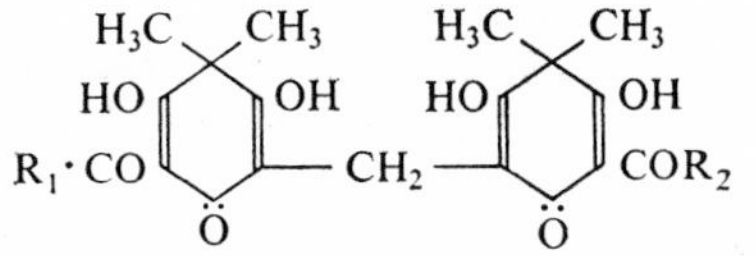

Constituents of male fern (*Dryopteris filix mas*) now shown to be a mixture of homologues.

Albaspidin AA ($R_1 = R_2 = CH_3$).

$C_{21}H_{24}O_8$ MW 404

M.p. 170–1°.

Albaspidin PP ($R_1 = R_2 = \cdot CH_2 \cdot CH_3$).

$C_{23}H_{28}O_8$ MW 432

M.p. 135–7°.

Albaspidin BB ($R_1 = R_2 = \cdot CH_2 \cdot CH_2 \cdot CH_3$).

$C_{25}H_{32}O_8$ MW 460

M.p. 148°.

The following analogues have been synthesised:

Albaspidin i-B i-B ($R_1 = R_2 = \cdot CH(CH_3)_2$.

M.p. 168–9°.

Albaspidin VV ($R_1 = R_2 = CH_2 \cdot CH_2 \cdot CH_2 \cdot CH_3$).

$C_{27}H_{36}O_8$ MW 488

M.p. 121–2°.

Albaspidin CC ($R_1 = R_2 = CH_2 \cdot CH_2 \cdot CH_2 \cdot CH_2 \cdot CH_3$)

$C_{29}H_{40}O_8$ MW 516

M.p. 126–8°.

Pentillä, Sundman, *Acta Chem. Scand.*, 1964, **18**, 344.

Albomaculine

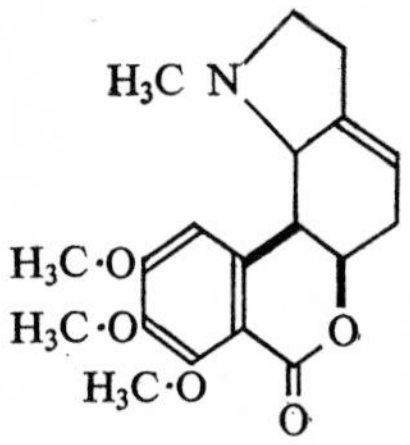

$C_{19}H_{23}O_5N$ MW 345

Alkaloid from *Haemanthus albomaculatus*. M.p. 180–1°. $[\alpha]_D$ +71·1° ($CHCl_3$).

B,HClO₄: prisms from MeOH. M.p. 285–9° decomp.

Picrate: m.p. 189–98°.

Methopicrate: prisms from EtOH.Aq. M.p. 244–6° decomp.

Briggs *et al.*, *J. Am. Chem. Soc.*, 1956, **78**, 2899.

Boit Ehmke, *Chem. Ber.*, 1957, **90**, 57.

Jeffs, Hawksworth, *Tetrahedron Letters*, 1963, 217.

Albonoursin (3-*Benzylidene*-6-*isobutylene*-2 : 5-*dioxopiperazine*)

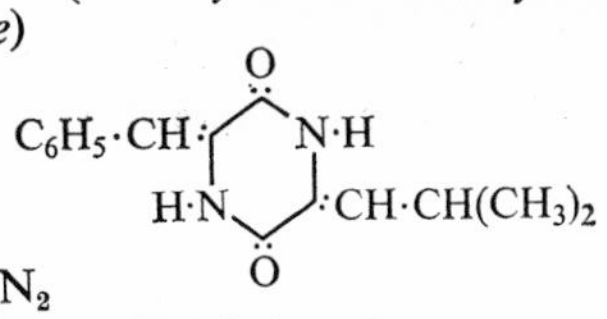

$C_{15}H_{16}O_2N_2$ MW 256

Antibiotic produced by *Streptomyces albus* var. *fungatus* and *S. noursei*. Identical with Component 2 (Brown and Kelley) and B-73 (Rao and Cullen). Plates from AcOEt. M.p. 275–6°.

Khokhlov, Lokshin, *Tetrahedron Letters*, 1963, 1881 (and references there cited).
Brown, Kelley, *Ann. Rep. New York State Dept. Health, Albany*, 1957, 10; 1958, 47; 1959, 52; 1960, 50; 1961, 40.
Rao, Cullen, *J. Am. Chem. Soc.*, 1960, **82**, 1127.
Vondrack, Vanék, *Chemistry and Industry*, 1964, 1686.

Albopetasin. *See* Angelate ester *under* Petasalbin.★

Albopetasol
$C_{15}H_{22}O_3$ MW 250
Constituent of coltsfoot (*Petasites officinalis* Moench.). M.p. 178–80°. $[\alpha]_D$ −24·1°. Light absorption: $\lambda_{max.}$ 220 mμ (log ε, 3·82).
Novotný, Herout, Šorm, *Tetrahedron Letters*, 1963, 697.

Alentin. *See* Carbutamide.★

Alimemazine. *See* Trimeprazine.★

Alkaloid L.9 (Manske, Marion).
A complex of lycopodine and *O*-Acetyl-lofoline.
Manske, Marion, *Can. J. Res.*, 1943, **21B**, 92.
Ayer, Hogg, Soper, *Can. J. Chem.*, 1964, **42**, 949.

Alledryl. *See* Diphenhydramine.★

Allene-1 : 3-dicarboxylic Acid. *See* 2 : 3-Pentadienedioic Acid.★

Alleoside. *See* Erysimine.★

Allergican. *See* Chlorprophenpyridamine.★

Allergin. *See* Diphenhydramine.★

Allo-aromadendrene (α-*Aromadendrene*)

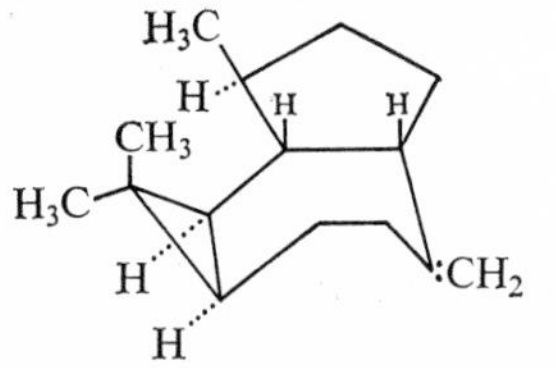

$C_{15}H_{24}$ MW 204
Constituent of many essential oils, *e.g.*, *Eucalyptus-globulus*, *Perovskia scrophullariaefolia*, *Meterosideros scandens*.
$[\alpha]_D^{20}$ −21·6°. n_D^{20} 1·4994. D_4^{20} 0·9224. $O_3 \rightarrow$ α-apo-aromadendrone.
Birch, *J. Chem. Soc.*, 1953, 715.
Dolejš *et al.*, *Chemistry and Industry*, 1959, 566.
Birch *et al.*, *Tetrahedron Letters*, 1959, No. 3, 15.
Büchi *et al.*, *Tetrahedron Letters*, 1959, No. 6, 14.

Allo-thiobinupharidine
$C_{30}H_{42}O_2N_2S$ MW 494
Alkaloid from the rhizome of the yellow water lily (*Nuphar luteum* (L.) Sm.).
B,2HClO₄: plates. M.p. 320–5°.
Achmatowicz, Bellen, *Tetrahedron Letters*, 1962, 1121.

Alloxan.★
See also:
Hartman, Shepperd, *Organic Syntheses*, Coll. Vol. **3**, 37.
Speer, Dabovich, *Organic Syntheses*, Coll. Vol. **3**, 39.
Holmgren, Wenner, *Organic Syntheses*, Coll. Vol. **4**, 23.
Tipson, *Organic Syntheses*, 1953, **33**, 3; Coll. Vol. **4**, 25.

Allyl Alcohol.★
Present in garlic (*Allium sativum*).
Bernhard *et al.*, *Arch. Biochem. Biophys.*, 1964, **107**, 137.

4-Allyl-2 : 6-dimethoxyphenol (*Methoxyeugenol*)

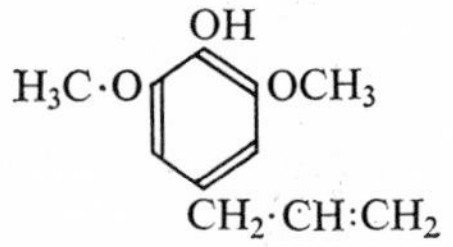

$C_{11}H_{14}O_3$ MW 194
Constituent of oil of nutmeg. B.p. 168–9°/11 mm.
Benzoyl: m.p. 76–7°.
Me ether: *see* Elemicin.★
Mauthner, *Ann.*, 1918, **414**, 244.
Hahn, Wassmuth, *Ber.*, 1934, **67B**, 696.
Shulgin, Kerlinger, *Naturwiss.*, 1964, **51**, 360.

(−)-*N*-Allyl-3-hydroxymorphinan. *See* Levallorphan.★

5-Allyl-5-neopentylbarbituric Acid. *See* Nealbarbitone.★

Almarckine. *See* *N*-Me ether *under* Cephaeline.

Aloe-emodin.★
8-*Mono*-β-D-*glucoside*: $C_{21}H_{20}O_{10}$. MW 432. Constituent of the rhizome of *Rheum palmatum* var. tangut and *Rhamnus purshiana* DC. Cryst. from MeOH. M.p. 237–8°. Light absorption: $\lambda_{max.}$ 223 (log ε, 4·42), 255 (4·32), and 410 mμ (3·87). *Penta-Ac*: m.p. 187°.
Hörhammer *et al.*, *Chem. Ber.*, 1964, **97**, 1662.
Hörhammer, Bittner, Hörhammer, *Naturwiss.*, 1964, **51**, 310.

Alstovenine. *See* Isovenenatine.

Althiomycin★
$C_{27}H_{28}O_{10}N_8S_3$ MW 722
Cryst. from CH_2Cl_2–EtOH (1 : 1). M.p. 180–1·6° decomp. $[\alpha]_D^{25}$ +37·8° (c, 2 in EtOH–$CHCl_3$ (1 : 1)). Ac_2O–Py → acetylalthiomycin.
Cram *et al.*, *J. Am. Chem. Soc.*, 1963, **85**, 1430.

Alurene. *See* Chlorothiazide.★

Alvaxanthone
$C_{23}H_{24}O_6$ MW 396
Pigment from osage orange (*Maclura pomifera* Raf.). M.p. 155°.
Wolfrom *et al.*, *Tetrahedron Letters*, 1963, 749.

Amechol. *See* Methacholine chloride.★

Amicetamine

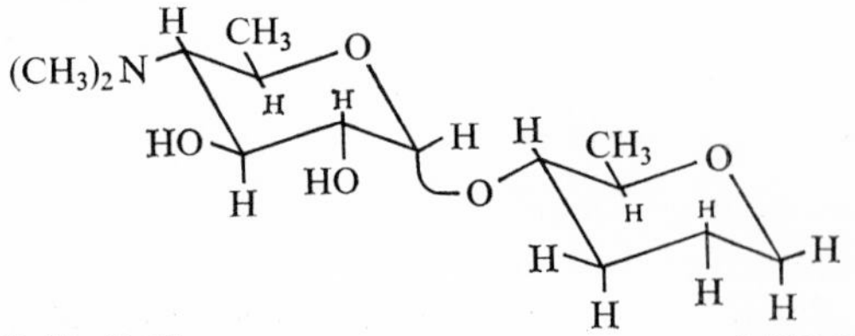

$C_{14}H_{26}O_5N$ MW 288

Fragment of the antibiotic, amicetin.
B,HCl: cryst. M.p. 170·5–171·5°.

Stevens *et al.*, *J. Am. Chem. Soc.*, 1956, **78**, 6212.

Amicetin★

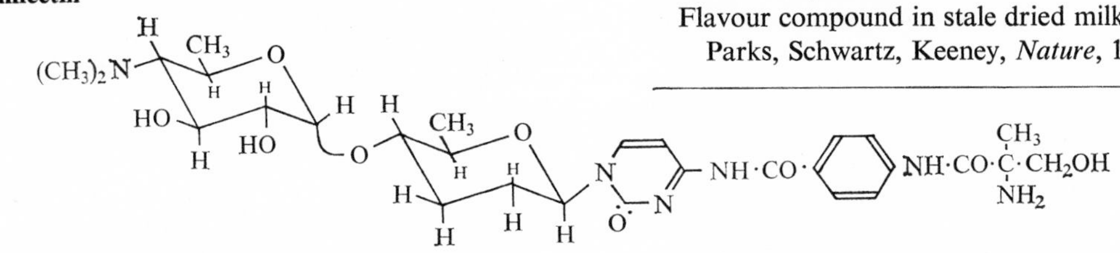

Revised structure and stereochemistry:

Stevens, Blumbergs, Daniher, *J. Am. Chem. Soc.*, 1963, **85**, 1552.
Hanessian, Haskell, *Tetrahedron Letters*, 1964, 2451.

Amicetose (2 : 3 : 6-*Trideoxy*-D-erythro-*aldohexose*)

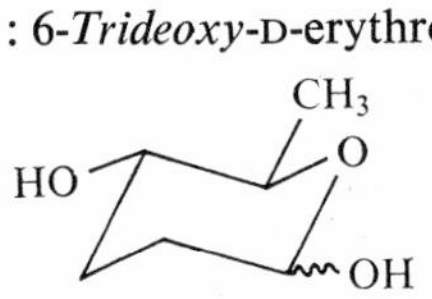

$C_6H_{12}O_3$ MW 132
Fragment of the structure of amicetin. B.p. 70–80° (bath)/0·1 mm. n_D^{25} 1·4680. $[\alpha]_D^{22}$ +43·6° (c, 1 in Me_2CO).
2 : 4-*Dinitrophenylhydrazone*: m.p. 156–156·5°. $[\alpha]_D^{27}$ −9·2° (c, 0·9 in Py).
Me glycoside: $C_7H_{14}O_3$. MW 146. B.p. 55–60° (bath)/5 mm. n_D^{25} 1·4484. $[\alpha]_D^{25}$ +75·1° (c, 0·87 in H_2O).

Stevens, Nagarajan, Haskell, *J. Org. Chem.*, 1962, **27**, 2991.
Stevens, Blumbergs, Wood, *J. Am. Chem. Soc.*, 1964, **86**, 3592.

***N*-(2′-Amidinoethyl)-3-aminocyclopentanecarboxamide.** *See* Amidinomycin.

Amidinomycin (N-(2′-*Amidinoethyl*)-3-*aminocyclopentanecarboxamide*)

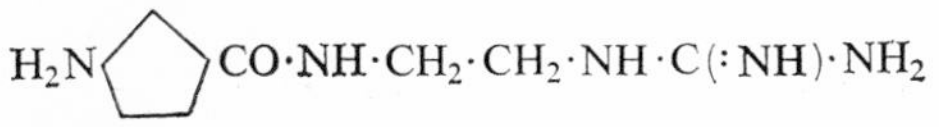

$C_9H_{18}ON_4$ MW 206
Antibiotic from *Streptomyces* spp.
B,H₂SO₄: plates or needles. M.p. 285–8° decomp.
Reineckate: pink needles. M.p. 208–11°.

Nakamura *et al.*, *J. Antibiotics* (Japan), 1961, **14A**, 103.

Amidinothiourea (*Guanylthiourea*)

$NH_2·C(=NH)·NH·CS·NH_2$

$C_2H_6N_4S$ MW 118
Colourless prisms. M.p. 170–2° decomp.

Bamberger, *Ber.*, 1883, **16**, 1460.
Slotta, Tschesche, *Ber.*, 1929, **62**, 1402.
Birtwell *et al.*, *J. Chem. Soc.*, 1948, 1653.
Kurzer, *J. Chem. Soc.*, 1955, 1; *Organic Syntheses*, 1955, 69; Coll. Vol. **4**, 502.

Amidryl. *See* Diphenhydramine.★

Amimycin. *See* Oleandomycin.★

Aminazine. *See* Chlorpromazine.★

***o*-Aminoacetophenone.★**
Flavour compound in stale dried milk.

Parks, Schwartz, Keeney, *Nature*, 1964, **202**, 185.

2-Amino-3-(2-aminoethylamino)propionic Acid (4-*Azalysine*)

$H_2N·CH_2·CH_2·NH·CH_2·CH(NH_2)·COOH$

$C_5H_{13}O_2N_3$ MW 217
Lysine antimetabolite.
B,2HCl,0·5H₂O: extremely hydroscopic. M.p. 175–8° decomp.

McCord, Cook, Smith, *Arch. Biochem. Biophys.*, 1964, **105**, 349.

2-Amino-1-*p*-aminophenyl-1 : 3-propanediol

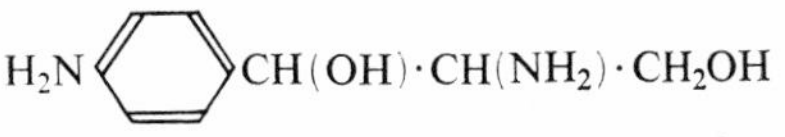

$C_9H_{14}O_2N_2$ MW 182
Threo-.
D-.
M.p. 136°. $[\alpha]_D^{26}$ +28°.
L-.
M.p. 136°. $[\alpha]_D^{22}$ −29°.

Shemyakin *et al.*, *Doklady Akad. Nauk U.S.S.R.*, 1952, **86**, 565.

***p*-Aminobenzaldehyde.★**
See also:

Campaigne, Budde, Schaefer, *Organic Syntheses*, Coll. Col. **4**, 31.

***o*-Aminobenzophenone.★**
See also:

Scheifele, De Tar, *Organic Syntheses*, Coll. Vol. **4**, 34.

***N*-{*N*-[*N*-(*p*-Aminobenzyl)-*p*-aminobenzyl]-*p*-aminobenzyl}-*p*-aminobenzyl Alcohol**

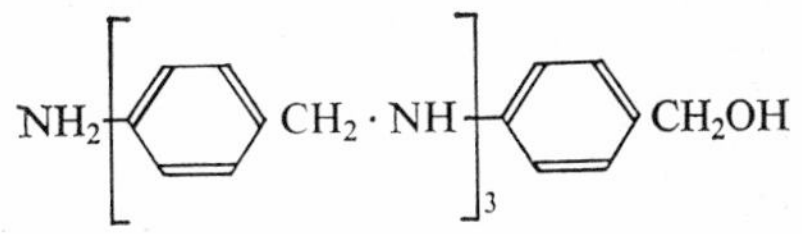

$C_{28}H_{30}ON_4$ MW 438
Cryst. from MeOH or C_6H_6. M.p. 238–42° (preheated bath at 140°) (198–9°). Depends on conditions used.

Sloane, Unteh, *Biochemistry*, 1964, **3**, 1160.

5-Amino-1 : 3-*bis*[ethylhexyl]-5-methylhexahydropyrimidine. *See* Hexetidine.★

2-Aminobutyric Acid.★
L(+)-.
A component of the crystalline globulin from the seed of *Salvia officinalis* L.
Brieskorn, Glasz, *Naturwiss.*, 1964, **51**, 216.

4-α-Aminobutyric Acid-oxytocin. *See* 4-Decarboxamido-oxytocin.

N^ε-(DL-2-Amino-2-carboxyethyl)-L-lysine (*Lysinoalanine*)
HOOC·CH(NH$_2$)·CH$_2$·NH·CH$_2$·CH$_2$·CH$_2$·CH$_2$·CH(NH$_2$)·COOH
$C_9H_{19}O_4N_3$ MW 233
Formed by alkaline treatment of ribonuclease.
B,HCl: cryst. from Py–EtOH.Aq.
Bohak, *J. Biol. Chem.*, 1964, **239**, 2878.

2-Amino-6-carboxy-10-methylphenazinium betaine. *See* Aeruginosin A.

2-Amino-6-carboxy-10-methyl-8-sulphophenazinium betaine. *See* Aeruginosin B.

2-Amino-5-chlorobenzoxazole (*Flexin, Zoxazolamine*)

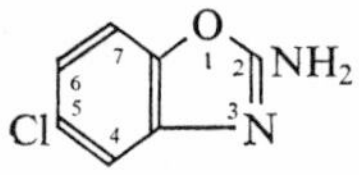

$C_7H_5ON_2Cl$ MW 168·5
Skeletal muscle relaxant. Plates from 50% EtOH.Aq. M.p. 182–3°.
B,HCl: needles. M.p. 229° decomp.
B,HBr: plates. M.p. 240° decomp.
Nagana *et al.*, *J. Am. Chem. Soc.*, 1953, **75**, 2770.
Marsh, Sam, U.S.P. 2,780,633 (*Chem. Abstracts*, 1958, **52**, 444); U.S.P. 2,890,985 (*Chem. Abstracts*, 1959, **53**, 17441).

4-Amino-5-cyanopyrrolo[2,3-*d*]pyrimidine

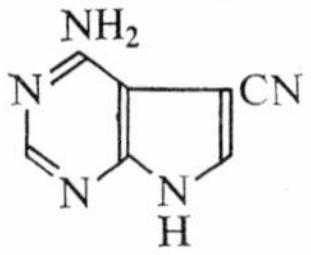

$C_7H_5N_5$ MW 159
Aglycone of the antibiotic Toyocamycin. M.p. >360°. Light absorption: $\lambda_{max.}$ 226 (ε, 10,700), 277 (13,700), and 287 mμ (9750).
Taylor, Hendess, *J. Am. Chem. Soc.*, 1964, **86**, 951.

3′-Amino-3′-deoxyadenosine.★
Also isolated from *Cordyceps militaris*. Cryst. from H_2O. M.p. 275–8°.
Guarino, Kredich, *Biochim. Biophys. Acta*, 1963, **68**, 317.

6-Amino-6-deoxy-D-glucose.★
See also:
Hardegger, Zanetti, Sterner, *Helv. Chim. Acta*, 1963, **46**, 282.

2-Amino-2-deoxygulose. *See* D-Gulosamine.

2-Amino-6-diazo-5-oxohexanoic Acid. *See* 6-Diazo-5-oxonorleucine.★

2-Amino-2 : 6-dideoxygalactose★ (*Fucosamine*).
D-.
Present in polysaccharides from *Bacillus* sp.
L-.
Present in certain enteric bacteria. $[\alpha]_D^{24}$ −93·4° (c, 1·29 in H_2O).
Sharon, Shif, Zehari, *Biochem. J.*, 1964, **93**, 210.
Wheat, Rollins, Leatherwood, *Nature*, 1964, **202**, 492.
Barry, Roark, *Nature*, 1964, **202**, 493.

4-Amino-4 : 6-dideoxy-D-galactose (*Thomosamine*)

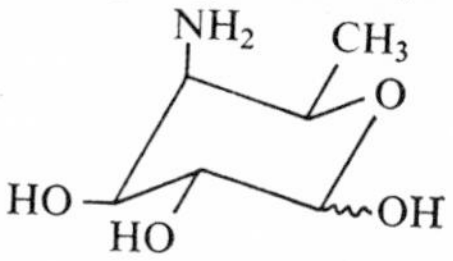

$C_6H_{13}O_4N$ MW 163
Constituent of *Escherichia coli* strain Y-10. Amorph.
Me α-galactopyranoside, B,HCl: m.p. 233–4°. $[\alpha]_D^{25}$ +209° (c, 1·81 in H_2O). N-*Ac*: amorph. M.p. 72–84°. $[\alpha]_D^{25}$ +170·5° (c, 1·86 in H_2O).
Tetra Ac: two forms: (α) m.p. 207–8°, $[\alpha]_D^{25}$ +95° (c, 1·1 in $CHCl_3$), and (β) cryst. M.p. 85–7°, $[\alpha]_D^{25}$ +21·3° (c, 1·1 in $CHCl_3$).
Strominger, Scott, *Biochim. Biophys. Acta*, 1959, **35**, 552.
Okazaki *et al.*, *J. Biol. Chem.*, 1962, **237**, 3014.
Stevens *et al.*, *J. Am. Chem. Soc.*, 1964, **86**, 2937.

4-Amino-4 : 6-dideoxy-D-glucose (*Viosamine*)

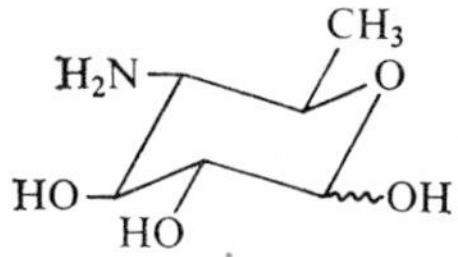

$C_6H_{13}O_4N$ MW 163
Constituent of *Escherichia coli* Strain B and *Chromobacterium violaceum.*
B,HCl: m.p. 132–8°. $[\alpha]_D^{27}$ −9° → +21° (24 hr.; c, 1 in H_2O).
Methyl α-glucopyranoside: $C_7H_{15}O_4N$. MW 177. M.p. 117–18°. $[\alpha]_D$ +144° (c, 0·85 in H_2O). N-*Ac*: m.p. 188–9·5°. $[\alpha]_D$ +151° (c, 0·43 in H_2O).
Wheat, Rollins, Leatherwood, *Biochem. Biophys. Research Commun.*, 1962, **9**, 120.
Stevens *et al.*, *J. Am. Chem. Soc.*, 1963, **85**, 3061; 1964, **86**, 2939.

2-Amino-2 : 6-dideoxy-L-talose.★
Synthesis:
Collins, Overend, *Chemistry and Industry*, 1963, 375.

5-Amino-2 : 3-dihydro-1 : 4-phthalazinedione. *See* Luminol.

2-Amino-1-(2 : 5-dimethoxyphenyl)propanol. *See* Methoxamine.★

2-Amino-3-dimethylaminopropionic Acid (4-*Azaleucine*)
$(CH_3)_2NHCH_2·CH(NH_2)·CO_2H$
$C_5H_{12}O_2N_2$ MW 132
Antimetabolite.
B,2HCl: white cryst. from MeOH–Et$_2$O. M.p. 154–7° decomp.
Smith, Baylis, McCord, *Arch. Biochem. Biophys.*, 1963, **102**, 313.

β-Aminoethylbenzene★ (β-2-*Phenylethylamine*).
Present in Australian *Acacia* spp.
N-*Me*: present in Australian *Acacia* spp.
Fitzgerald, *Austral. J. Chem.*, 1964, **17**, 160.

3-Amino-α-ethyl-3-(2 : 4 : 6-tri-iodophenyl)propionic Acid. *See* Iopanoic Acid.★

2-Aminoheptanoic Acid★

$CH_3\cdot[CH_2]_4\cdot CH(NH_2)\cdot COOH$

$C_7H_{15}O_2N$ MW 145

Produced by *Claviceps purpurea.*

Steiner, Hartmann, *Biochem. Z.*, 1964, **340**, 436.

6-Aminohexanoic Acid.

See also:

Meyers, Miller, *Organic Syntheses*, Coll. Vol. **4**, 39.

4-Amino-3-hydroxybutyric Acid.★

(±)-.

1-^{14}C.

Linstedt, Linstedt, *Arkiv. Kemi*, 1964, **15**, 93.

4-Amino-5-hydroxymethyl-2-methoxypyrimidine. *See* Bacimethrin.

(−)-2-Amino-1-*m*-hydroxyphenylpropanol. *See* Metaraminol.★

3α-Amino-20α-hydroxy-5α-pregnane. *See* Funtumidine.★

20α-Amino-3β-hydroxy-5α-pregnane. *See* Funtuphyllamine A.

4-Amino-5-hydroxypyrimidine

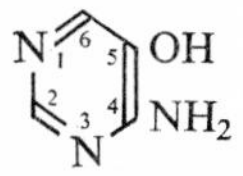

$C_4H_5ON_3$ MW 111

M.p. >250°. Subl. $FeCl_3$ → deep red col.
O-*Me*: needles from C_6H_6. M.p. 118°.
O-*Benzyl*: needles from C_6H_6. M.p. 142–3°. N-*Benzoyl*: cryst. from EtOH. M.p. 176–8°.
N-*Ac*: cryst. from C_6H_6. M.p. 179–80°.
O : N-*Dibenzoyl*: cryst. from EtOH. M.p. 194–5°.
N-*Benzoyl*: cryst. from C_6H_6. M.p. 159–60°.

McOmie, Turner, *J. Chem. Soc.*, 1963, 5590.

2-Amino-4-hydroxy-6-(D-*erythro*-1 : 2 : 3-trihydroxypropyl)pteridine. *See* Neopterin.

2-Amino-5-hydroxyvaleric Acid.★

L-.

Present in Jack bean seeds (*Canavalia ensiformis*). M.p. 216° decomp. $[\alpha]_D^{25}$ 6·19° (c, 4 in H_2O).

Thompson, Morris, Hunt, *J. Biol. Chem.*, 1964, **239**, 1122.

2-Amino-3-*H*-isophenoxazin-3-one. *See* 2-Aminophenoxazin-3-one.

1-(3-Amino-4-methylbenzenesulphonyl)-3-cyclohexylurea. *See* Metahexamide.★

α-Aminomethyl-*p*-hydroxybenzyl Alcohol.★

(−)-.

Present in leaves and juice of lemons. $[\alpha]_D$ −4° (0·5*N*-HCl).

Stewart, Wheaton, *Science*, 1964, **145**, 60.

2-Amino-4-oxohexanoic Acid. *See* 4-Oxonorleucine.

3α-Amino-20-oxo-5α-pregnane. *See* Funtumine.★

6-Aminopenicillanic Acid.★

See also:

Nathorst-Westfelt, Schatz, Thelin, *Acta Chem. Scand.*, 1963, **17**, 1164.

1-Aminophenazine.★

2-Aminophenazine.★

New syntheses:

Gray, Gaertner, Holliman, *Tetrahedron Letters*, 1959, No. 7, 24.

Erratum p. 193

***m*-Aminophenol.★**

N-*Ac*: should read *see* *m*-Acetamidophenol.
N-*Benzoyl*: should read *see* *m*-Benzoylhydroxyaniline.

Erratum p. 193

***o*-Aminophenol.★**

N-*Ac*: should read *see* *o*-Acetamidophenol.
N-*Benzoyl*: should read *see* *o*-Benzoylhydroxyaniline.

Erratum p. 194

***p*-Aminophenol.★**

N-*Ac*: should read *see* *p*-Acetamidophenol.
ON-*Di-Ac*: should read *see under* *p*-Acetamidophenol.
N-*Benzoyl*: should read *see* *p*-Benzoylhydroxyaniline.

2-Aminophenoxazin-3-one (2-*Amino*-3H-*isophenoxazin-3-one*)

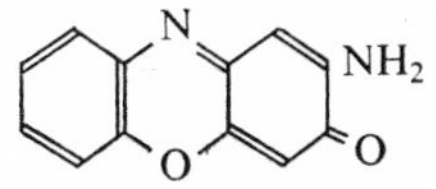

$C_{12}H_8O_2N_2$ MW 212

Metabolite of *Streptomyces* spp. and *Waksmania* spp. Dark-brown. M.p. 254–6° with sublimation. Sometimes occurs in amorph. form which does not liquefy at 296–7°. Light absorption: $\lambda_{max.}$ 238 (ε, 29,200), 422 (24,400), and 437 mμ (25,000).
N-*Ac*: metabolite of *Waksmania* spp. Fine orange needles. M.p. 295–7°. Light absorption: $\lambda_{max.}$ 240, 405 mμ ($E_{1\,cm.}^{1\%}$ 1400, 1100).

Nagasawa, Gutmann, Morgan, *J. Biol. Chem.*, 1959, **234**, 1600.
Anzai *et al.*, *J. Antibiotics* (Tokyo), 1960, **13A**, 125.
Osman, Bassiouni, *J. Am. Chem. Soc.*, 1960, **82**, 1607.
Cavill, Clezy, Whitfield, *Tetrahedron*, 1961, **12**, 139.
Gerber, Lechevalier, *Biochemistry*, 1964, 3, 598.

***Threo*-1-*p*-Aminophenyl-2-dichloroacetamido-1 : 3-propanediol**

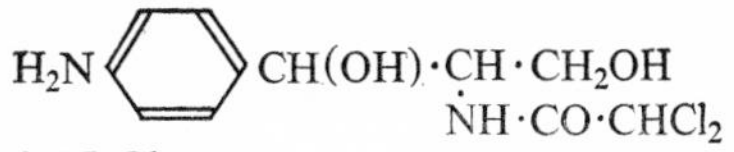

$C_{11}H_{14}O_3N_2Cl_2$ MW 293

D-.
Produced together with chloramphenicol by *Streptomyces venezuelae* P.D. 04745. $[\alpha]_D^{28}$ 10·92° (EtOH). Light absorption: $\lambda_{max.}$ 241 mμ ($E_{1\,cm.}^{1\%}$ 307) in ethanolic NaOH.
B,HCl: m.p. 100° decomp. $[\alpha]_D^{28}$ 8°.
N-p-*Nitrobenzylidene*: cryst. from EtOH.Aq. M.p. 171–2°.
L-.
B,HCl: $[\alpha]_D$ −8°.

Sullivan, U.S.P. 2,568,571 (*Chem. Abstracts*, 1952, **46**, 3567).
Shemyakin *et al.*, *Dokl. Akad. Nauk U.S.S.R.*, 1952, **86**, 565.

2-Amino-5-pyrazinecarboxylic Acid

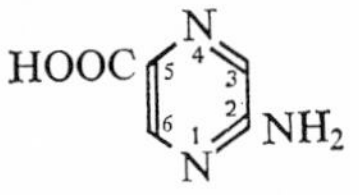

$C_5H_5O_2N_3$ MW 139
Cryst. from H_2O. M.p. 282–3° decomp. Light absorption: $\lambda_{max.}$ 262 (log ε, 4·15) and 319 mμ (3·86).
Me ester: $C_6H_7O_2N_3$. MW 153. Cryst. from H_2O. M.p. 230–1°.
Et ester: $C_7H_9O_2N_3$. MW 167. Cryst. from H_2O. M.p. 172–3°.
Amide: $C_5H_6ON_4$. MW 138. Colourless needles from H_2O. M.p. 266–7°.

Felder, Pitré, Grabitz, *Helv. Chim. Acta*, 1964, **47**, 873.

3-Aminopyridine.★
See also:

Allen, Wolf, *Organic Syntheses*, 1950, **30**, 3; Coll. Vol. **4**, 45.

4-Aminopyrrolo[2,3-*d*]pyrimidine

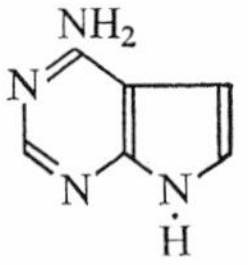

$C_6H_6N_4$ MW 134
Aglycone of the antibiotic, tubercidin. Needles from H_2O. M.p. 252–4°.

Davoll, *J. Chem. Soc.*, 1960, 131.
Suzuki, Marumo, *J. Antibiotics* (Tokyo), 1961, **14A**, 34.
Taylor, Hendess, *J. Am. Chem. Soc.*, 1964, **86**, 951.

α-(3-Amino-2 : 4 : 6-tri-iodobenzyl)butyric Acid. *See* Iopanoic Acid.★

Amorphigenin★

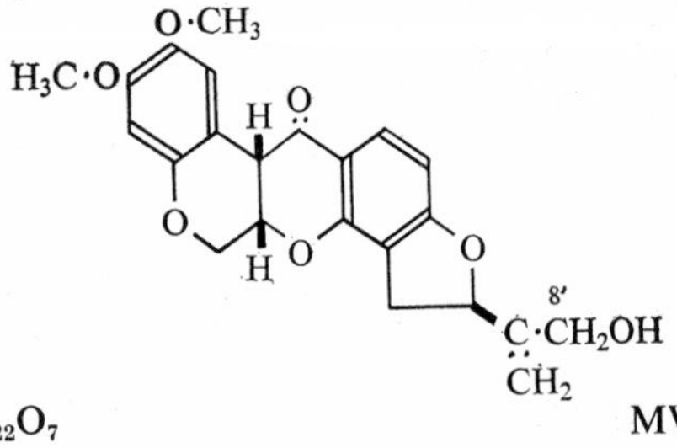

$C_{23}H_{22}O_7$ MW 410
Structure:

Crombie, Peace, *Proc. Chem. Soc.*, 1963, 246.

Amorphin★
See also:

Crombie, Peace, *Proc. Chem. Soc.*, 1963, 246.

Amosamine (4 : 6-*Dideoxy*-4-*dimethylamino*-D-*glucose*)

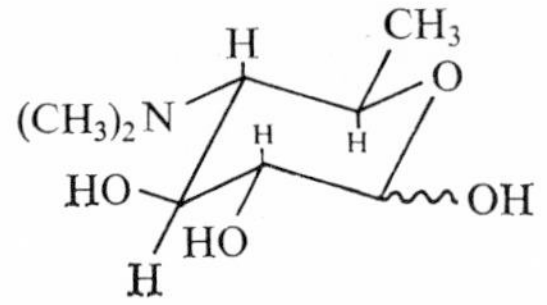

$C_8H_{17}O_4N$ MW 191
Component of the antibiotic, amicetin.
B,HCl: cryst. M.p. 192–3°. $[\alpha]_D^{25}$ +45·5° (c, 1 in H_2O). pK$_a$′ 7·2 (50% MeOH.Aq.).
α-Me amosaminide: $C_9H_{19}O_4N$. MW 205. Needles from Et_2O–hexane. M.p. 93–4°. $[\alpha]_D^{25}$ +138·2° (c, 0·5 in H_2O) +146°, (c, (1·1 in 0·1*N*-HCl), pK$_a$′ 7·2 (50% MeOH.Aq.). *B,HCl*: needles from Et_2O–EtOH. M.p. 195–6° decomp. $[\alpha]_D^{25}$ +113·7° (c, 0·7 in H_2O). *B,HI*: m.p. 193–4°. *Mono-O-benzoyloxycarbonyl deriv.*: m.p. 157–9° decomp.
β-Me amosaminide: thick cubes from EtOH–Et_2O. M.p. 209–10° decomp. $[\alpha]_D^{25}$ −32·4° (c, 0·5 in H_2O). pK$_a$′ 7·2 (50% MeOH.Aq.).

Stevens *et al.*, *J. Am. Chem. Soc.*, 1956, **78**, 6212.
Stevens, Nagarajan, Haskell, *J. Org. Chem.*, 1962, **27**, 2991.
Stevens, Blumbergs, Daniher, *J. Am. Chem. Soc.*, 1963, **85**, 1552.

Ampicillin.★
See also:

Dane, Dockner, *Angew. Chem.*, 1964, **76**, 342; *Int. Ed.*, 1964, **3**, 439.

^{14}C-.

Sjöberg, Undheim, *Acta Chem. Scand.*, 1963, **17**, 933.

Erratum p. 266
Amurensin. Alternative name should read (4′ : 5 : 7-*Trihydroxy*-8-[-3-*hydroxy*-3-*methylbutyl*]*flavonol*).

Anadil. *See* *p*-Acetamidophenol.

Anahist. *See* Thonzylamine.★

Anahygrine

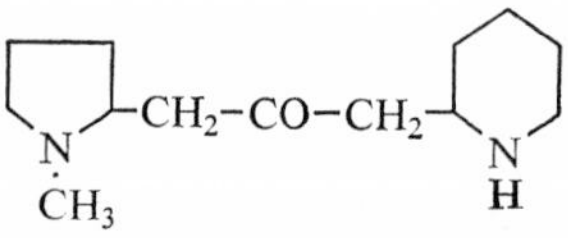

$C_{13}H_{24}ON_2$ MW 224
Alkaloid from the roots of *Withania somnifera* Dunal. Pale yellow oil. B.p. 106°/0·2 mm.
B,2HCl: m.p. 216·5–217·5°.
Dipicrate: m.p. 173–4·5°.

Leary *et al.*, *Chemistry and Industry*, 1964, 283.

Anatabine.★
(±)-.
Total synthesis:

Quan, Karns, Quin, *Chemistry and Industry*, 1964, 1553.

Andantol. *See* Isothipendyl.★

Andirobin

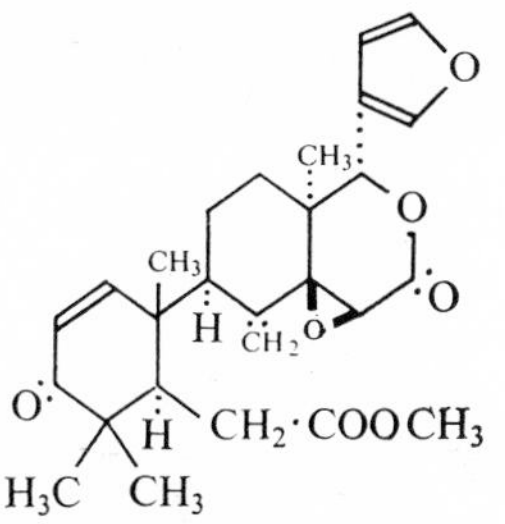

$C_{27}H_{32}O_7$ MW 468

Constituent of the seeds of *Carapa guayanensis*. M.p. 195–7°.

Ollis, Ward, Zelnik, *Tetrahedron Letters*, 1964, 2607.

Andromedol. *See* Grayanotoxin III.★

13 : 14-*seco*-4-*cis*-13(17)-Androstadiene-3 : 14-dione

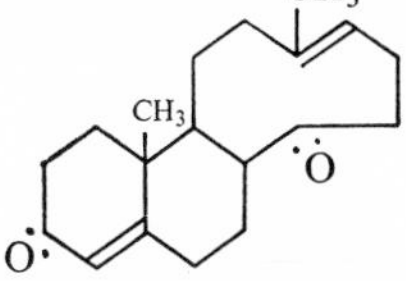

$C_{19}H_{26}O_2$ MW 286

M.p. 149–50°. Light absorption: $\lambda_{max.}$ 238 mμ (ε, 14,900).

Tanabe, Crowe, *Tetrahedron Letters*, 1964, 2955.

Androstalone. *See* 17β-Hydroxy-17-methyl-5α-androstan-3-one.

5α-Androstan-15α-ol

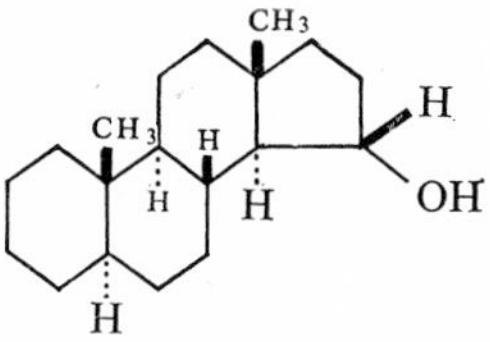

$C_{19}H_{32}O$ MW 276

Cryst. M.p. 161–3°. $[\alpha]_D$ 42° ($CHCl_3$).

Djerassi, v. Mutzenbecher, *Proc. Chem. Soc.*, 1963, 377.

5α-Androstan-15β-ol

$C_{19}H_{32}O$ MW 276

Cryst. M.p. 80·5–81·5°. $[\alpha]_D$ −34° ($CHCl_3$). *Ac*: amorph. $[\alpha]_D$ −45° ($CHCl_3$).

Djerassi, v. Mutzenbecher, *Proc. Chem. Soc.*, 1963, 377.

5α-Androstan-15-one

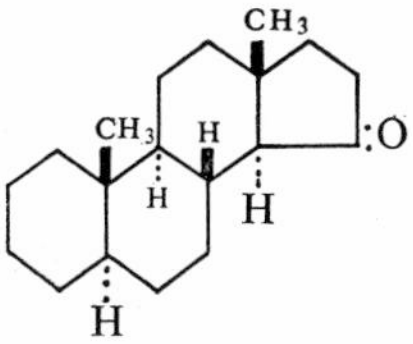

$C_{19}H_{30}O$ MW 274

Cryst. M.p. 92–3°. $[\alpha]_D$ 30° ($CHCl_3$).

Djerassi, v. Mutzenbecher, *Proc. Chem. Soc.*, 1963, 377.

8-(1-Angeloyloxy-1-methylethyl)-8 : 9-dihydro-2*H*-furo-[2,3-*h*]-1-benzopyran-2-one

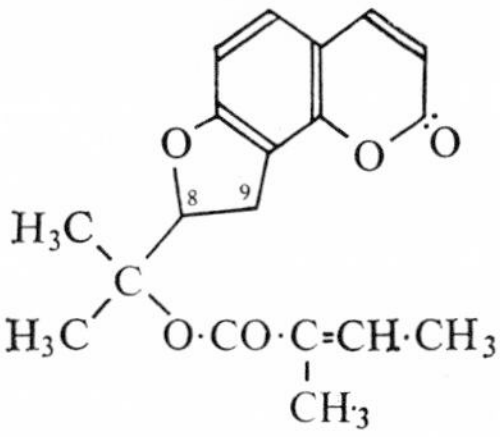

$C_{19}H_{20}O_5$ MW 328

(+)-.

Constituent of the root of *Peucedanum palustre* L. Cryst. from Et_2O. M.p. 118·5–119°. $[\alpha]_D^{22}$ +227° (c, 2·8 in $CHCl_3$). Shows blue fluorescence. Light absorption: $\lambda_{max.}$ 218 sh. (log ε, 4·31), 251 (3·41), 261 (3·46), and 328 mμ (4·20).

Nielsen, Lemmich, *Acta Chem. Scand.*, 1964, **18**, 1379.

Angolensic Acid

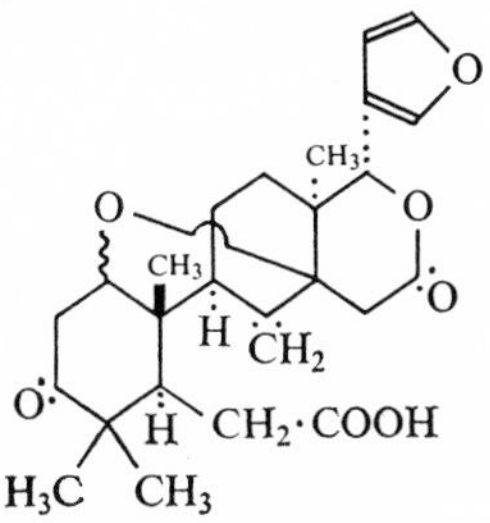

Proposed structure

$C_{26}H_{32}O_7$ MW 456

Hemihydrate from MeOH.Aq. M.p. 272°.

Me ester: $C_{27}H_{34}O_7$. MW 470. Constituent of the wood of *Entandophragma angolense*, *Cedrela odorata*, and *Guarea thompsonii*. Cryst. from MeOH. M.p. 197°. $[\alpha]_D^{20}$ −43° ($CHCl_3$). *Oxime*: needles from EtOH.Aq. M.p. 228–9°. 2 : 4-*Dinitrophenylhydrazone*: golden-yellow prisms from MeOH. M.p. 258° decomp.

Akisanya *et al.*, *J. Chem. Soc.*, 1960, 3827.
Housley *et al.*, *J. Chem. Soc.*, 1962, 5095.
Bevan *et al.*, *Chemistry and Industry*, 1964, 1751.

Angolide

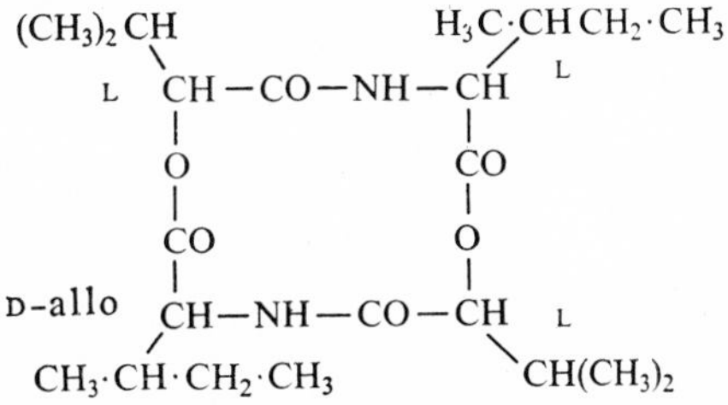

$C_{22}H_{38}O_6N_2$ MW 426

Constituent of *Pithomyces* C.M.I. (Herbarium No. 101184). Colourless cryst. from EtOH. M.p. 260°. $[\alpha]_D$ −83° ($CHCl_3$).

Russell, Ward, *Abstr. 1st Meeting European Biochem. Soc.*, 1964, No. A97.
Macdonald, Shannon, *Tetrahedron Letters*, 1964, 3113.

Angustmycin A★ (*Decoyinine*)

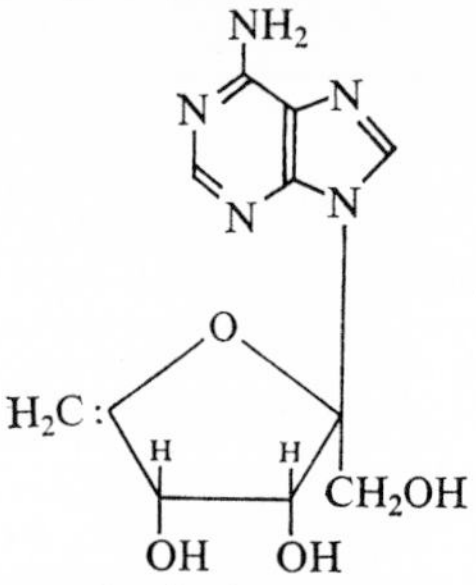

Revised structure

Tri-Ac: m.p. 188–9°.
Tetra-Ac: m.p. *ca.* 65°.
Penta-Ac: m.p. 152–3°.

Hoeksema, Slomp, van Tamelen, *Tetrahedron Letters*, 1964, 1787.

Anhydrodigipurpurogenin.★ Now known as Digipurpurogenin II (*q.v.*).

Anhydro-5-ethyl-4-phenyl-1-thia-2-thio-3 : 4-diazolium thiol

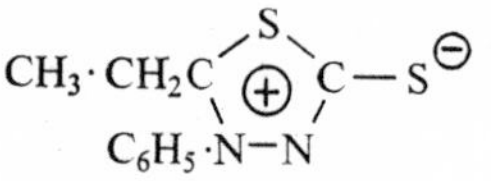

$C_{10}H_{10}N_2S_2$ MW 222

Antimicrobial agent. Cryst. from EtOH. M.p. 191–2°.

Kier *et al.*, *Nature* (Lond.), 1964, **204**, 697.

2 : 5-Anhydro-D-talitol

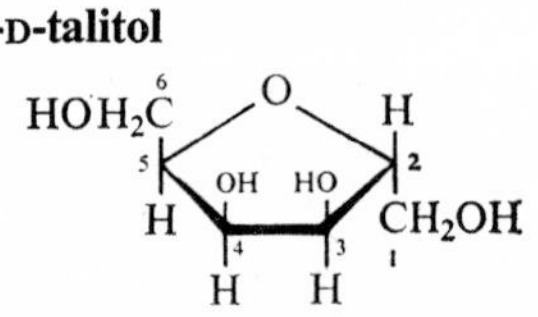

$C_6H_{12}O_5$ MW 164

B.p. 110–15°/5 × 10^{-3} mm. Cryst. M.p. 112–13°. $[\alpha]_D$ +44·5° (c, 1·475 in H_2O).
Tetra-Ac: b.p. 160–5°/0·3 mm. n_D^{22} 1·4512.

Defaye, *Bull. soc. chim.*, 1964, 999.

2 : 5-Anhydro-D-talose

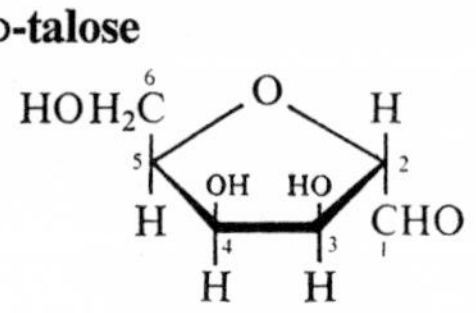

$C_6H_{10}O_5$ MW 162

Colourless glass. $[\alpha]_D^{25}$ +33·9° → +27° (c, 0·44 in H_2O). H_2 → 2 : 5-Anhydro-D-talitol.

Defaye, *Bull. soc. chim.*, 1964, 999.

Aniline.★

Self-consistent Molecular Orbital Calculation:

Kwiatkowski, Wóznicki, *Tetrahedron Letters*, 1964, 2933.

Annofoline.★

Relationship to Lycopodine:

Ayer, Law, Piers, *Tetrahedron Letters*, 1964, 2959.

[18]-Annulene Trisulphide

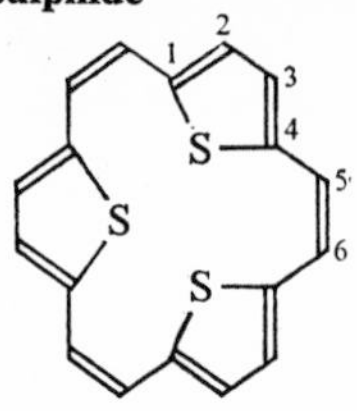

$C_{18}H_{12}S_3$ MW 324

Yellow plates from EtOH.Aq. M.p. 74·5–75·5°. Light absorption: $\lambda_{max.}$ 204 (ε, 18,000), 224 (16,800), and 288 mμ (17,300).

Badger, Elix, Lewis, *Proc. Chem. Soc.*, 1964, 82.
Coulson, Poole, *Proc. Chem. Soc.*, 1964, 220.

Anonaine

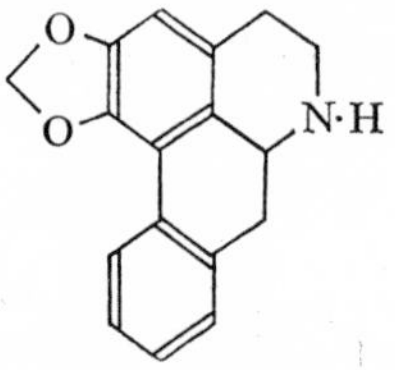

$C_{17}H_{15}O_2N$ MW 265

Alkaloid from *Anona reticulata*. M.p. 122–3°. $[\alpha]_D^{20}$ −52° ($CHCl_3$).
N-*Me*: *see* Roemerine.

Gopinath *et al.*, *Chem. Ber.*, 1959, **92**, 776.

Ansolysen. *See* Pentolium Tartrate.★

Antherospermidine

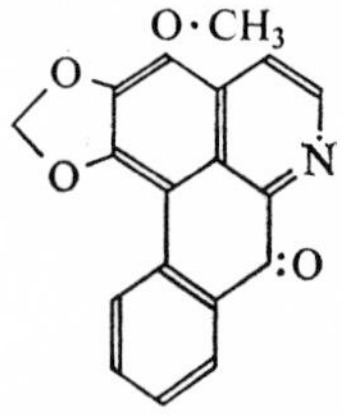

$C_{18}H_{11}O_4N$ MW 305

Alkaloid from *Anthosperma moschatum* Labill. Cryst. from $CHCl_3$. M.p. 275–6° decomp. Light absorption: $\lambda_{max.}$ 247 (log ε, 4·38), 281 (452), and 312 sh. mμ (3·95) in EtOH. $\lambda_{max.}$ 262·2 (4·24), 283 mμ (4·16) in 0·1*N*-HCl.

Bick, Clezy, Crow, *Austral. J. Chem.*, 1956, **9**, 111.
Bick, Douglas, *Tetrahedron Letters*, 1964, 1629.

Anthraceno[2,3-*b*]carbazole (*Anthraceno*[2′ : 3′,2 : 3]-*carbazole*)

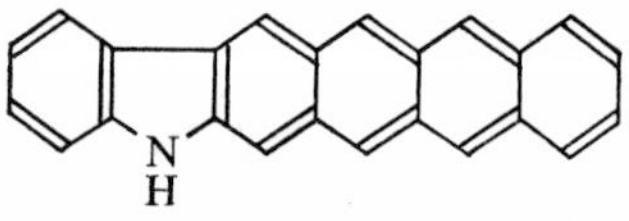

$C_{24}H_{15}N$ MW 317

Red-violet plates from trichlorobenzene. M.p. >400°. Conc. H_2SO_4 → red-brown col., which with HNO_3 → olive-green col. Light absorption: $\lambda_{max.}$ 322 (log ε, 5·00), 364 (4·16), 398 (3·54), 422 (3·54), 485 (3·37), 517 (3·64), and 556 mμ (3·65) in trichlorobenzene.

Zander, Franke, *Chem. Ber.*, 1964, **97**, 212.

Anthraceno[2,3-*c*]carbazole (*Anthraceno*[2′ : 3′,3 : 4]-*carbazole*)

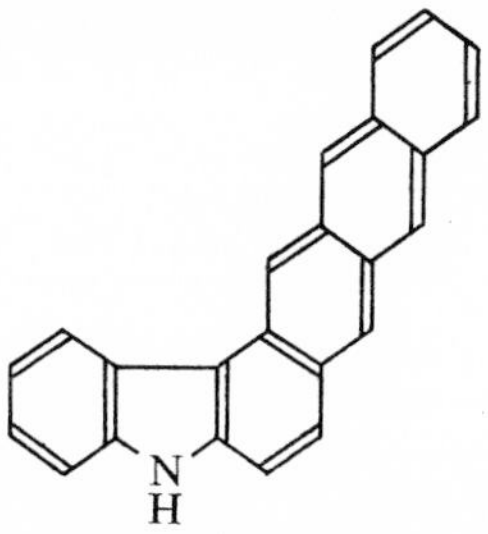

$C_{24}H_{15}N$ MW 317

Red cryst. from trichlorobenzene. M.p. 286° decomp. Conc. H_2SO_4 → violet col., which with HNO_3 → olive-green col. Light absorption: $\lambda_{max.}$ 278 (log ε, 4·76), 304 (4·66), 322 (4·54), 337 (4·48), 388 (3·58), 412 (3·62), 446 (3·42), 475 (3·60), and 508 mμ (3·56) in trichlorobenzene.

Zander, Franke, *Chem. Ber.*, 1964, **97**, 212.

Anthranil★

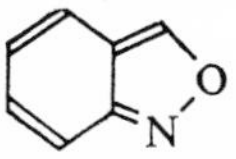

The structure given in the main work should be replaced by that given above.

Bamberger, *Ber.*, 1909, **42**, 1647.
Baker, *J. Chem. Soc.*, 1945, 267.

Anthraniloyl-lycoctonine.★

Also present in *Delphinium consolida* L.

Marion, Edwards, *J. Am. Chem. Soc.*, 1943, **69**, 2016.

Anthryl methyl Ketone (9-*Acetylanthracene*)

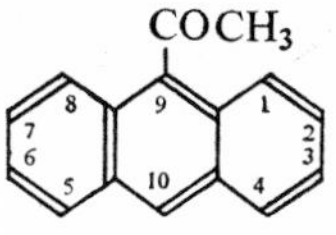

$C_{16}H_{12}O$ MW 220

M.p. 75–6°.

May, Mosettig, *J. Am. Chem. Soc.*, 1948, **70**, 686.
Merritt, Braun, *Organic Syntheses*, 1950, **30**, 1; Coll. Vol. **4**, 8.

Antilusin. *See* Pentamethonium Iodide.★

Apamide. *See* *p*-Acetamidophenol.

Apascil. *See* Meprobamate.★

Aphloïol

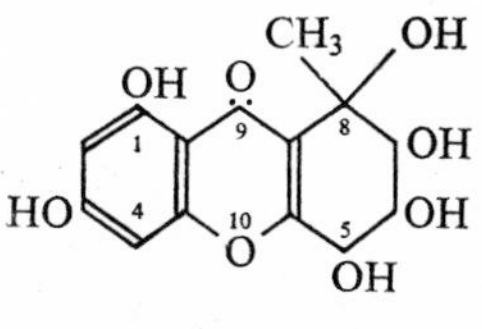

$C_{14}H_{14}O_8$ MW 310

Constituent of the flowers of *Aphloïa madagascariensis* Clos. Small yellow needles. M.p. 304–5° decomp. $[\alpha]_{589}$ 35·6°; $[\alpha]_{578}$ 37·3°; $[\alpha]_{546}$ 43·1°. Light absorption: $\lambda_{max.}$ 241 (log ε, 4·31), 258·5 (4·39), 317 (4·08), and 367 mμ (3·97).

Hexa-Ac: cryst. from EtOH. M.p. 169–70°.

Adjangba, Billet, Mentzer, *Compt. rend.*, 1963, **257**, 1396.
Adjangba, *Bull. soc. chim.*, 1964, 376.

Aphyllidine

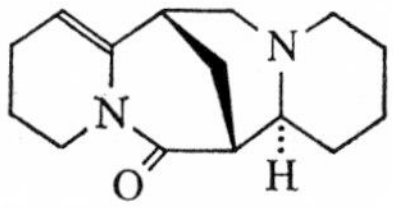

$C_{15}H_{22}ON_2$ MW 246

(+)-.

See Aphylidene.★

(−)-.

Alkaloid present in *Argyrolobium megorhizum* Bol. Prisms from Et_2O–hexane. M.p. 101–6°. $[\alpha]_D$ −9·1° (c, 2·2 in EtOH). Light absorption: $\lambda_{max.}$ 240 mμ (ε, 12,000).

B,HCl: prisms from MeOH–Me_2CO–Et_2O. M.p. 228–30° decomp.

Picrolonate: yellow needles from MeOH. M.p. 241–3° decomp.

Tsuda, Marion, *Can. J. Chem.*, 1964, **42**, 764.

Apiose.★

L-.

Di-O-isopropylidene deriv.: m.p. 56–8°. $[\alpha]_D$ −16° (c, 1·14 in EtOH).

Improved synthesis:

Williams, Jones, *Can. J. Chem.*, 1964, **42**, 69.

Apo-aromadendrone★

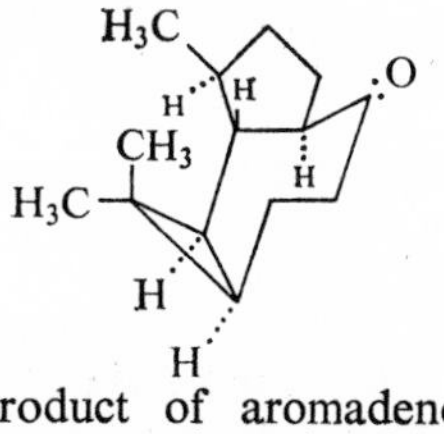

Ozonolysis product of aromadendrene. (Earlier samples were contaminated with alloaromadendrene which gives α-apo-aromadendrene on ozonolysis.)

See also:

Dolejs *et al.*, *Chemistry and Industry*, 1959, 566.
Büchi *et al.*, *Tetrahedron Letters*, 1959, No. 6, 14.

Aquakay. *See* 2-Methyl-1 : 4-naphthoquinone.

Aquocobalamin. *See* Vitamin B_{12b}.

9β-D-Arabinofuranosyladenine. *See* Adenine 9β-D-ribofuranoside.

Arabinose.★

L-.

5-^{14}C:

Hulyalkar, Jones, *Can. J. Chem.*, 1963, **41**, 1898.

Araucarenolone

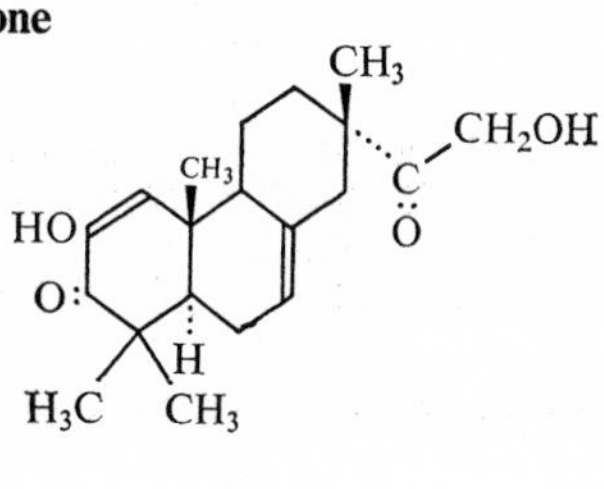

$C_{20}H_{28}O_4$ MW 332

Minor constituent of the wood resin of *Agathis australis* Salis. M.p. 143–4°. $[\alpha]_D$ $-58°$ (c, 2 in $CHCl_3$). Light absorption: $\lambda_{max.}$ 267 mμ (ε, 8000).

Enzell, Thomas, *Tetrahedron Letters*, 1964, 391.

Araucariol

$C_{15}H_{24}O$ MW 220

Minor constituent of oil of Araucaria (from the conifer *Neocallitropsis araucarioides* (Compt.) Florin.). B.p. 146–54°/10 mm.

von Rudloff, *Chemistry and Industry*, 1964, 2126.

Araucarol

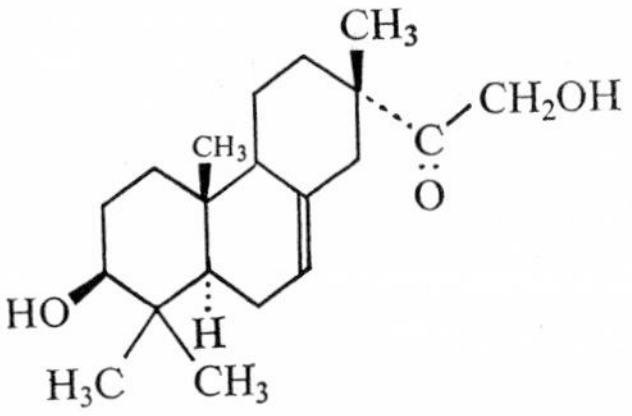

$C_{20}H_{32}O_3$ MW 320

Minor constituent of the wood resin of *Agathis australis* Salis. M.p. 135–6°. $[\alpha]_D$ $-24°$ (c, 1·7 in $CHCl_3$).

Enzell, Thomas, *Tetrahedron Letters*, 1964, 391.

Araucarolone (3 : 16-*Dihydroxyisopimar*-7-*en*-2 : 15-*dione*)

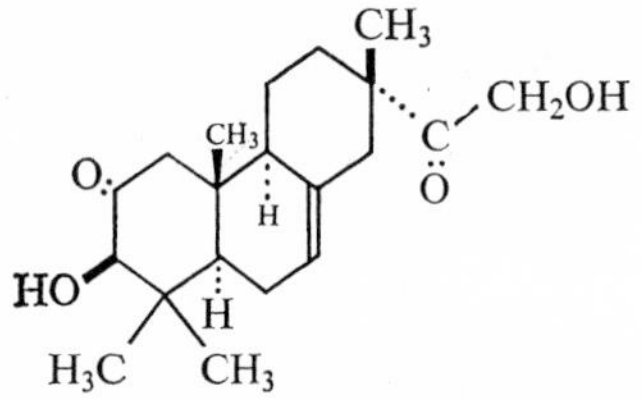

$C_{20}H_{30}O_4$ MW 334

Constituent of the wood resin of *Agathis australis* Salis. M.p. 157–9°. $[\alpha]_D$ $-42°$ (c, 5·4 in $CHCl_3$).

Enzell, Thomas, *Tetrahedron Letters*, 1964, 391.

Araucarone

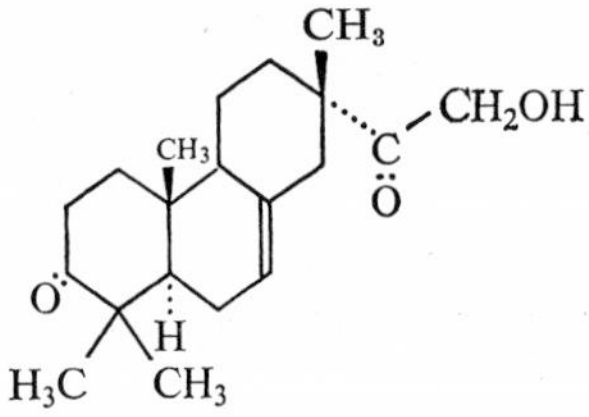

$C_{20}H_{30}O_3$ MW 318

Constituent of the wood resin of *Agathis australis* Salis. M.p. 116°. $[\alpha]_D$ $-51°$ (c, 2·2 in $CHCl_3$).

Enzell, Thomas, *Tetrahedron Letters*, 1964, 391.

Arborinol

$C_{30}H_{48}O$ MW 424

Constituent of the leaves of *Glycosmis arborea*. Cryst. from CH_2Cl_2–MeOH. M.p. 274–274·5°. $[\alpha]_D$ $+34·2°$ (c, 0·75 in $CHCl_3$).

Ac: needles. M.p. 242–3°. $[\alpha]_D$ $+12·7°$ (c, 1·1 in $CHCl_3$).

Vorbrüggen, Pakrashi, Djerassi, *Ann.*, 1963, **668**, 57.

Archangelicin

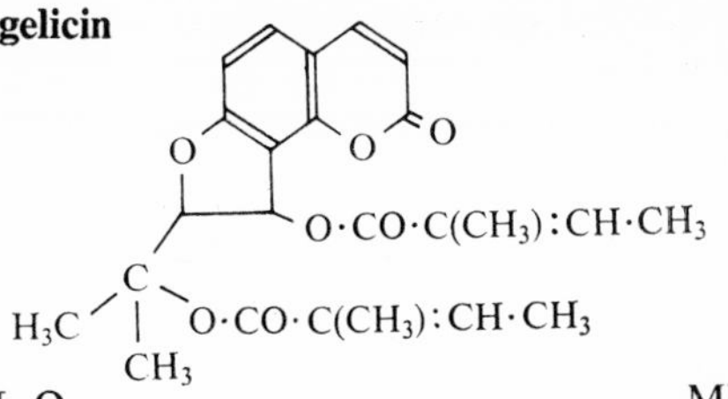

$C_{24}H_{26}O_7$ MW 426

Constituent of the roots of *Angelica archangelica* sub. sp. *litoralis*. Cryst. from cyclohexane. M.p. 100·5–102°. $[\alpha]_D^{26}$ 112·7° (c, 4·5 in MeOH). Light absorption: $\lambda_{max.}$ 258 (log ε, 3·55) and 322 mμ (4·14).

Nielsen, Lemmich, *Acta Chem. Scand.*, 1964, **18**, 932.

Archangelin

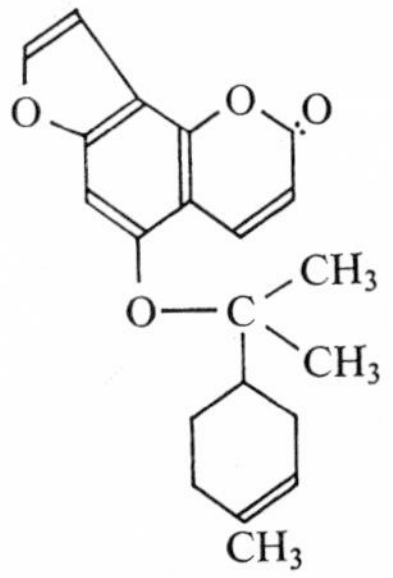

$C_{21}H_{22}O_4$ MW 338

Constituent of the roots of *Angelica archangelica* L. M.p. 132°.

Chatterjee, Sen Gupta, *Tetrahedron Letters*, 1964, 1961.

Arctiopicrin★

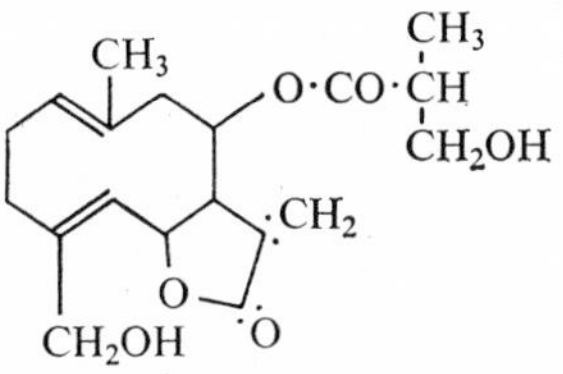

Revised structure:

Suchy *et al.*, *Tetrahedron Letters*, 1964, 3907.

Arenobufagin (3β : 11α : 14-*Trihydroxy*-12-*oxo*-5β-*bufa*-20 : 22-*dienolide*)

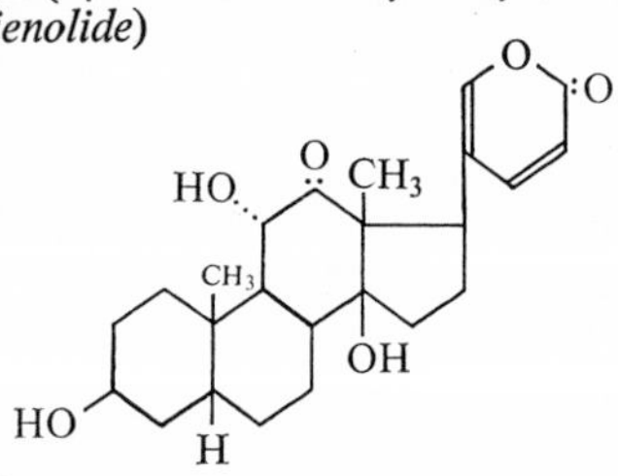

$C_{24}H_{32}O_6$ MW 416

Secretion of the toad, *Bufo arenarum*. M.p. 222–8°. $[\alpha]_D$ 56° (MeOH). Light absorption: $\lambda_{max.}$ 296 mμ (log ε, 3·77).

Di-Ac: m.p. 233–40°. $[\alpha]_D$ 43° ($CHCl_3$).

Jensen, *J. Am. Chem. Soc.*, 1935, **57**, 1765.

Deulofeu, Duprat, Labriola, *Nature*, 1940, **145**, 671.

Hofer, Linde, Meyer, *Tetrahedron Letters*, 1959, No. 7, 8.

Aresin.★ *See* *N*-(4-Chlorophenyl)-*N'*-methoxy-*N'*-methylurea.

Arfonad. *See* (+)-Camphorsulphonate *under* Trimethaphan.★

Arginine.★

DL-.

5-^{14}*C*:

Pichat, Mizon, Herbert, *Bull. soc. chim.*, 1963, 1787.

Arginine Vasopressin.★

Isolation:

Schally *et al.*, *Arch. Biochem. Biophys.*, 1964, **107,** 332.

L-Arginyl-L-prolyl-L-prolylglycyl-L-phenylalanylglycyl-L-prolyl-L-phenylalanyl-L-arginine. *See* 6-Glycinebradykinin.★

L-Arginyl-L-prolyl-L-prolylglycyl-L-phenylalanyl-L-serylglycyl-L-phenylalanyl-L-arginine. *See* 7-Glycinebradykinin.★

Argyrolobine

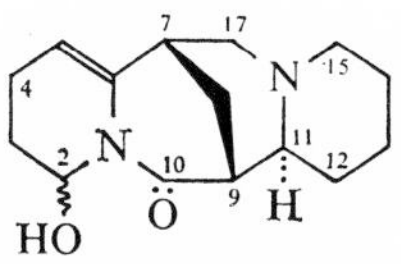

$C_{15}H_{22}O_2N_2$ MW 262

Alkaloid from *Argyrolobium megarhizum* Bol. (Leguminosae). Colourless prisms from Me_2CO. M.p. 168–9°. $[\alpha]_D$ 13·3° (c, 1·4 in $CHCl_3$). Light absorption: $\lambda_{max.}$ 239 mμ (ε, 9400).

B,HCl: prisms from MeOH–AcOEt. M.p. 170–2°.

B,CH_3I: cryst. from MeOH–Et_2O. M.p. 180–3° decomp.

Ac: prisms from hexane. M.p. 61°.

Tsuda, Marion, *Can. J. Chem.*, 1964, **42,** 764.

Aricine★

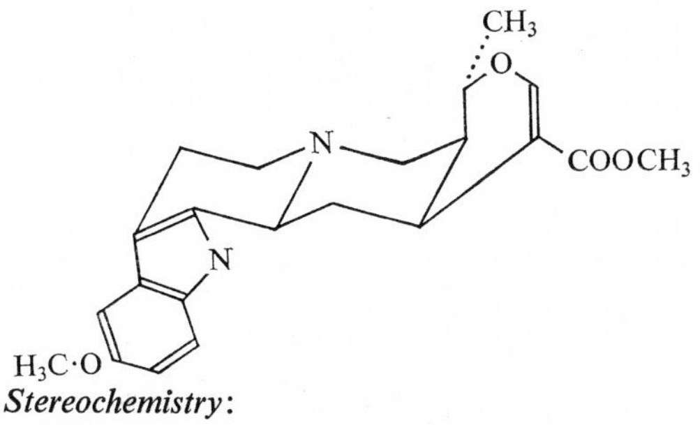

Stereochemistry:

Shamma, Richey, *J. Am. Chem. Soc.*, 1963, **85,** 2507.

Aristolactone★

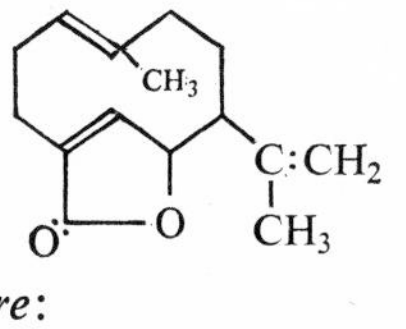

Revised structure:

Martin-Smith *et al.*, *Tetrahedron Letters*, 1964, 2391.

Aristolene

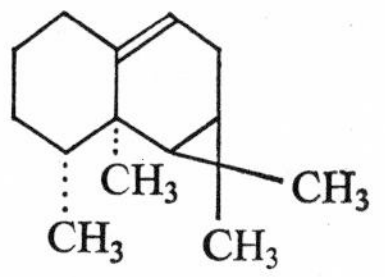

$C_{15}H_{24}$ MW 204

Constituent of calarene from sweet flag oil and essence of nard (*Nardostachys jatamansi*). Oil. D_4^{20} 0·9424. n_D^{20} 1·5047. $[\alpha]_D$ −98·7° (neat). OsO_4 → diol, m.p. 107–8°.

Büchi, Greuter, Tokoroyama, *Tetrahedron Letters*, 1962, 827.

Vrkoč *et al.*, *Tetrahedron Letters*, 1963, 225.

Pesnelle, Ourisson, *Bull. soc. chim.*, 1963, 912.

Armepavine.★

(+)-.

O-Me: cryst. from light petroleum. M.p. 60–2°. $[\alpha]_D^{20}$ +85°. *B,CH_3I*: m.p. 136–8° (sinters at 127–8°). $[\alpha]_D^{20}$ +119° (MeOH).

(±)-.

O-Me: cryst. from light petroleum. M.p. 60–1° rising on storage to 87–8·5°.

Ferrari, Deulofeu, *Tetrahedron*, 1962, **18,** 419.

Arnidenediol (*Arnidiol*)

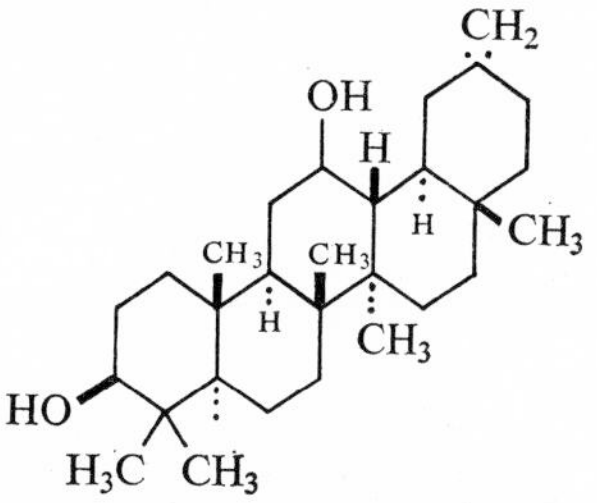

$C_{30}H_{50}O_2$ MW 442

Constituent of the blossoms of *Arnica montana* L. and *Tussilago farfara*. M.p. 257°. $[\alpha]_D$ 81·2°.

Di-Ac: m.p. 193°. $[\alpha]_D$ +79·3° ($CHCl_3$).

Zimmermann, *Helv. Chim. Acta*, 1943, **26,** 642; 1944, **27,** 332; 1946, **29,** 1455.

Santer, Stevenson, *J. Org. Chem.*, 1962, **27,** 3204.

Aromadendrene★

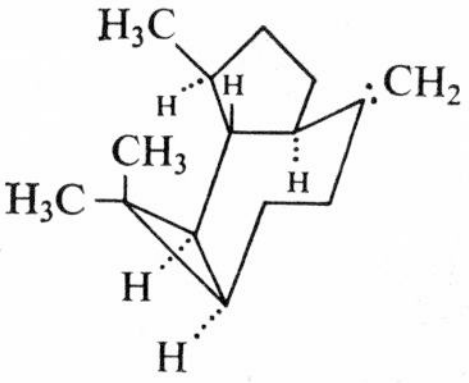

Aromadendrene exists in two diastereomeric forms, aromadendrene and allo-aromadendrene (*q.v.*). Earlier samples being mixtures. Aromadendrene has $[\alpha]_D^{20}$ +24·5°. n_D^{20} 1·4978. D_4^{20} 0·9167. O_3 → apo-aromadendrone.

Dolejš *et al.*, *Chemistry and Industry*, 1959, 566.

Büchi *et al.*, *Tetrahedron Letters*, 1959, No. 6, 14.

Dolejš, Šorm, *Tetrahedron Letters*, 1959, No. 10, 1; 1959, No. 17, 1.

α-Aromadendrene. *See* Allo-aromadendrene.

Aromadendrin.★

7-Me ether: $C_{16}H_{14}O_6$. MW 302. Constituent of the kino of *Eucalyptus maculata* Hook. M.p. 193°. $[\alpha]_D^{22}$ 21° (c, 0·95 in EtOH). $FeCl_3$ → port wine col.

Gell, Pinhey, Ritchie, *Austral. J. Chem.*, 1958, **11**, 372.

Aromaticin (6-*Deoxymexicanin*)

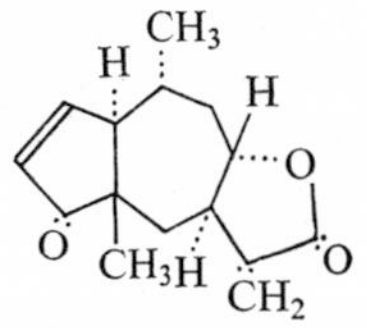

$C_{15}H_{18}O_3$ MW 246

Sesquiterpene lactone from *Helenium aromaticum* (Hook) Bailey. Prisms. M.p. 232–4°. $[\alpha]_D$ +18° ($CHCl_3$). $\lambda_{max.}$ 215 (ε, 15,500), 320 mμ (50).

Romo, Joseph-Nathan, Diaz A., *Chemistry and Industry*, 1963, 1839; *Tetrahedron*, 1964, **20**, 79.

Aromatin (6-*Desoxyhelenalin*)

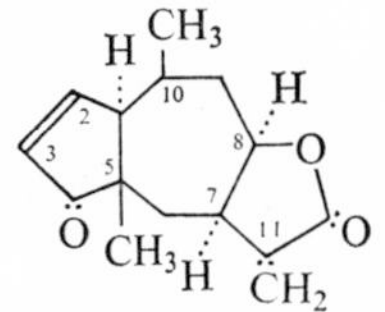

$C_{15}H_{18}O_3$ MW 246

Sesquiterpene lactone from *Helenium aromaticum* (Hook) Bailey. Needles. M.p. 159–60°. $[\alpha]_D$ −6° ($CHCl_3$). $\lambda_{max.}$ 215 (ε, 15,000), 320 mμ (50).

Romo, Joseph-Nathan, Diaz A., *Chemistry and Industry*, 1963, 1839; *Tetrahedron*, 1964, **20**, 79.

Artemisin★

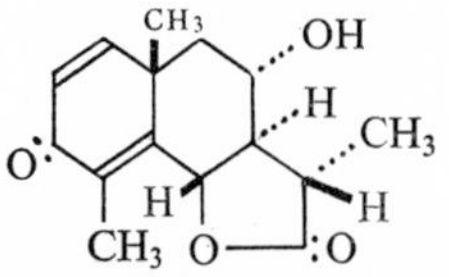

m-*Nitrobenzoyl*: needles from Et_2O. M.p. 179–80°. $[\alpha]_D$ +42·8° (c, 0·76 in $CHCl_3$).
p-*Nitrobenzoyl*: needles from EtOH. M.p. 191–2°. $[\alpha]_D$ +51·6° (c, 0·64 in $CHCl_3$).
3 : 5-*Dinitrobenzoyl*: prisms from EtOH. M.p. 217–18°. $[\alpha]_D$ +34·5° (c, 0·89 in $CHCl_3$).
Revised structure and stereochemistry:

Sumi, *J. Am. Chem. Soc.*, 1958, **80**, 4869.
Bolt, Cocker, McMurray, *J. Chem. Soc.*, 1963, 5235.

Articulol

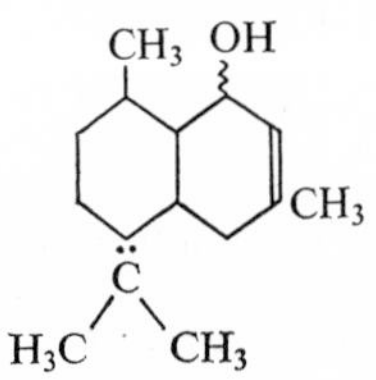

$C_{15}H_{24}O$ MW 220

Constituent of the essential oil of *Cyperus articulatus* L. B.p. 120–2°/1 mm. $[\alpha]_D^{20}$ −22° (c, 5·04 in $CHCl_3$) (impure sample).

Couchman, Pinder, Bromham, *Tetrahedron*, 1964, **20**, 2037.

Articulone

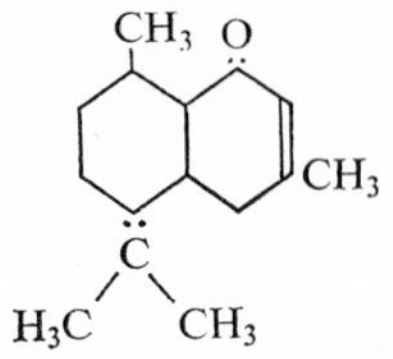

$C_{15}H_{22}O$ MW 218

Constituent of the essential oil of *Cyperus articulata* L. and *C. scaroscus*. B.p. 136–8°/16 mm., 104–6°/0·1 mm. $[\alpha]_D^{20}$ −26·6° (c, 3·5 in $CHCl_3$).
2 : 4-*Dinitrophenylhydrazone*: red needles from EtOH. M.p. 231–2°. Light absorption: $\lambda_{max.}$ 397 mμ (ε, 27,000).

Naves, Ardizio, *Bull. soc. chim.*, 1954, 332.
Couchman, Pinder, Bromham, *Tetrahedron*, 1964, **20**, 2037.

Artosin. *See* Tolbutamide.★

Arundoin (3β-*Methoxy*-D : C-friedo-*oleana*-9(11)*ene*)

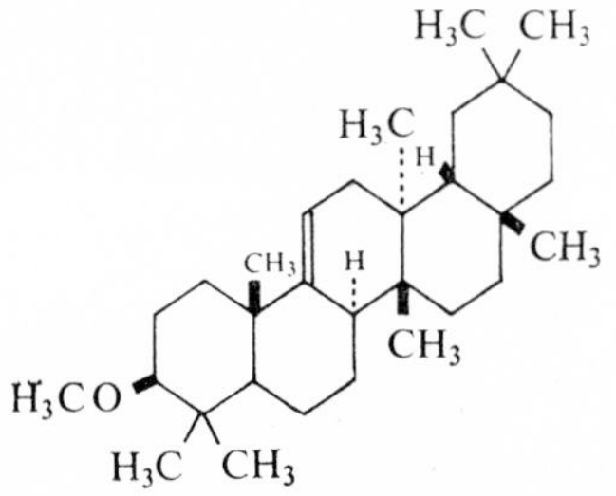

$C_{39}H_{52}O$ MW 440

Constituent of leaf wax of New Zealand toĕ-toĕ grass (*Arundo conspicua*). Dimorphic. M.p. 235–7° and 271–3°. $[\alpha]_D$ −9° (c, 1·7 in $CHCl_3$).

Eglington *et al.*, *Tetrahedron Letters*, 1964, 2323.

Asabaine. *See* Methantheline.★

Äscin. *See* Escin.

Äscinidin. *See* Escinidin.

Ascorbic Acid.★

L-.
5 : 6-O-*Isopropylidene*: cryst. from Me_2CO–hexane. M.p. 223–4° decomp.

Salomon, *Experientia*, 1963, **19**, 619.

Cryst. structure:

Hvoslef, *Acta Chem. Scand.*, 1964, **18**, 841.

Aspartic Acid.★

Carbamoyl: ureidosuccinic acid: cryst. from H_2O. M.p. 162° (sealed capillary) (178–80°).

Nye, Mitchell, *J. Am. Chem. Soc.*, 1947, **69**, 1382.

N-Carbamoyl-^{14}C-aspartic acid:

Wright *et al.*, *J. Am. Chem. Soc.*, 1951, **73**, 1898.
Cooper, Wo, Wilson, *J. Biol. Chem.*, 1955, **216**, 37.

See also:

Dunn, Smart, *Organic Syntheses*, 1950, **30**, 7; Coll. Vol. **4**, 55.

Asperuloside★

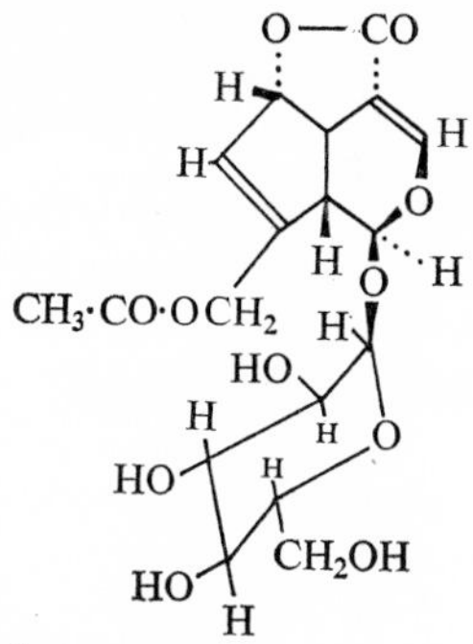

Stereochemistry:

Briggs *et al.*, *Tetrahedron Letters*, 1963, 69.

Aspidoalbidine

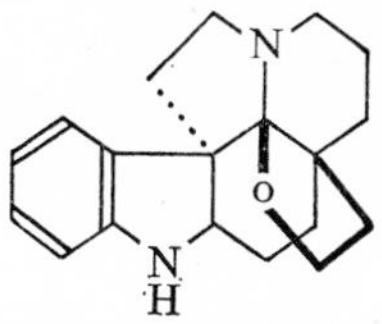

$C_{19}H_{24}ON_2$ MW 296

Basic structure of a group of alkaloids. Poorly cryst. M.p. 180°.

Brown, Budzikiewicz, Djerassi, *Tetrahedron Letters*, 1963, 1731.

Aspidoalbine

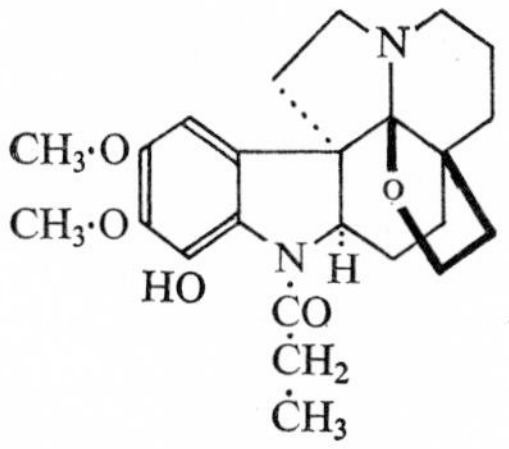

$C_{24}H_{32}O_5N_2$ MW 428

Alkaloid from stem bark of *Aspidosperma album* (Vahl) R. Bent. M.p. 170–2°. $[\alpha]_D$ +159° (MeOH), +148° ($CHCl_3$). Light absorption: $\lambda_{max.}$ 227 (log ε, 4·16), 267 mμ (3·88) (sample possibly contaminated by *N*-Ac isomer).

Me ether: m.p. 118–20°. $[\alpha]_D$ +8° (MeOH) (pure).

Djerassi *et al.*, *Tetrahedron Letters*, 1962, 1001.

Aspidodasycarpine

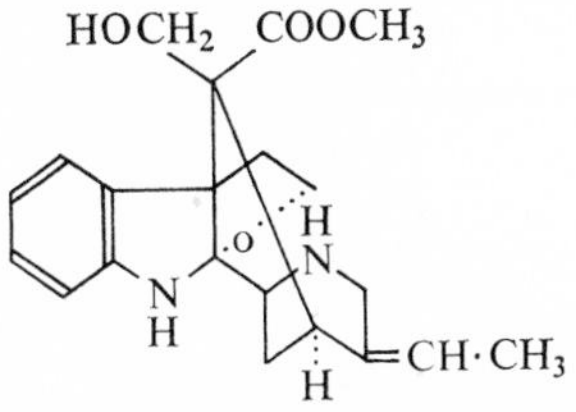

$C_{21}H_{26}O_4N_2$ MW 370

Alkaloid from *Aspidosperma dasycarpon* A. DC. M.p. 207–9°. $[\alpha]_D$ −101° ($CHCl_3$). Light absorption: $\lambda_{max.}$ 240 (log ε, 3·96) and 297 mμ (3·63).

Di-Ac: m.p. 111–14°. $[\alpha]_D$ −35° ($CHCl_3$).

Ohashi, Joule, Djerassi, *Tetrahedron Letters*, 1964, 3899.

Aspidofractinine

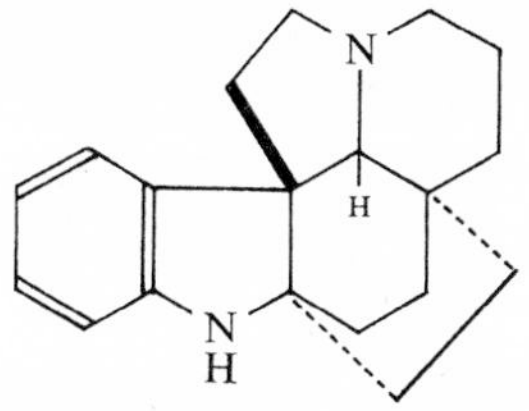

$C_{19}H_{24}N_2$ MW 280

Alkaloid from *Aspidosperma refractum* Mart. and *Pleiocarpa tubicina* Stapf. B.p. 110°/0·001 mm. Prisms from pentane. M.p. 101–2°. $[\alpha]_D^{23}$ −20° (c, 0·58 in $CHCl_3$). Light absorption: $\lambda_{max.}$ 241 (log ε, 3·83), 391 mμ (3·46).

N-*Ac*: b.p. 125°/0·001 mm. Cryst. from Me_2CO. M.p. 127–30°.

Djerassi *et al.*, *Helv. Chim. Acta*, 1963, **46**, 742.

Bycroft *et al.*, *Helv. Chim. Acta*, 1964, **47**, 1147.

Aspidospermatidine

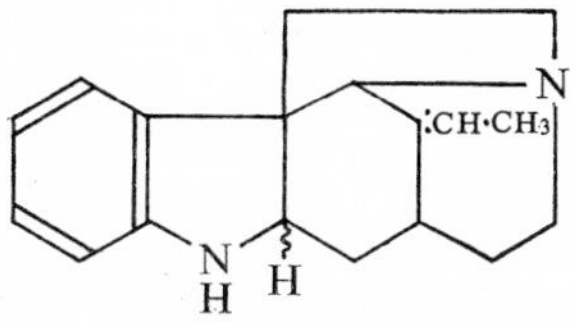

$C_{18}H_{22}N_2$ MW 266

Basic nucleus of a group of alkaloids from *Aspidosperma* spp.

Biemann, Spiteller-Friedmann, Spiteller, *J. Am. Chem. Soc.*, 1963, **85**, 637.

Aspidospermatine

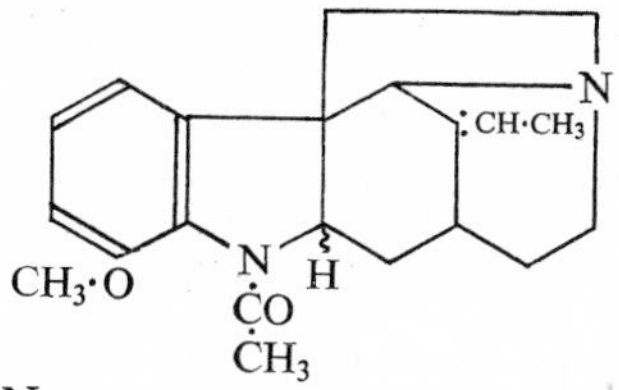

$C_{21}H_{26}O_2N_2$ MW 338

Alkaloid from *Aspidosperma quebracho blanco*. M.p. 162°. $[\alpha]_D$ −72·3° (EtOH).

B_2,H_2PtCl_6,$4H_2O$: amorph.

Hesse, *Ann.*, 1882, **211**, 249.

Biemann, Spiteller-Friedmann, Spiteller, *J. Am. Chem. Soc.*, 1963, **85**, 631.

Aspidospermine★

(±)-.

M.p. 195–195·5°.

Total synthesis:

Stork, Dolfini, *J. Am. Chem. Soc.*, 1963, **85**, 2873.

Asteritol

$C_7H_{14}O_6$ MW 194

Metabolite of the starfish *Asterias rubens*. M.p. 164°. $[\alpha]_D^{24}$ 157·4° (H_2O).

Ackermann, Hoppe-Seyler, *Naturwiss*, 1963, **50**, 733; *Bull. soc. chim. biol.*, 1964, **46**, 167.

Atisine★

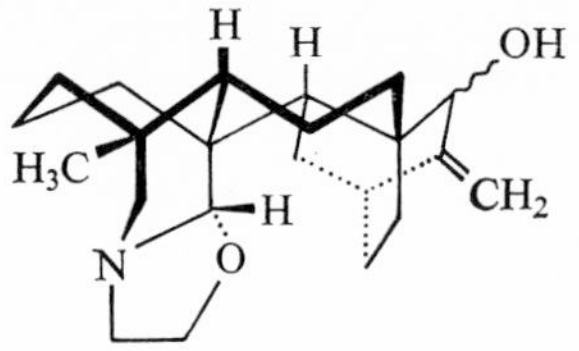

Stereochemistry:

Dvornik, Edwards, *Can. J. Chem.*, 1964, **42**, 137.

Total synthesis:

Nagata *et al.*, *J. Am. Chem. Soc.*, 1963, **85**, 2342.
Masamune, *J. Am. Chem. Soc.*, 1964, **86**, 291.

Atraxin. *See* Meprobamate.★

Aucuparin.

See also:

Nilsson, Norin, *Acta Chem. Scand.*, 1963, **17**, 1157.

Aureothricin★ (*Propiopyrothine*).

Alternative name.

Avagal. *See* Methantheline.★

Avenacin

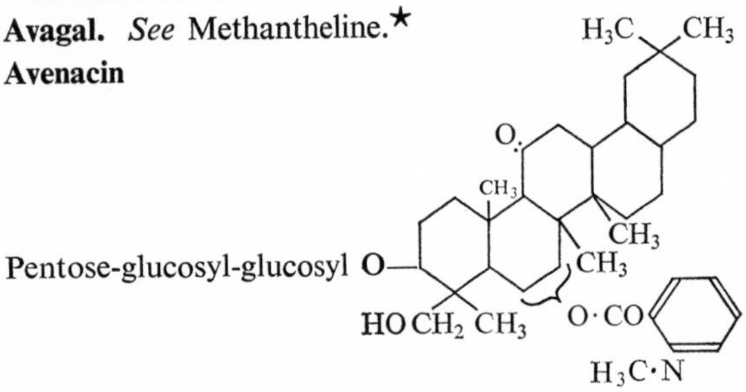

Provisional structure

$C_{55}H_{83}O_{21}N$ MW 1094

Antimicrobial substance from oats (*Avena sativa*). M.p. 248–50° decomp. $[\alpha]_D^{24}$ 35·7° (c, 1 in H_2O). Light absorption: $\lambda_{max.}$ 223, 253, and 357 mμ. Hydrol. → glucose, *N*-methylanthranilic acid, an unidentified pentose, and avenagenin.

Maizel, Burkhardt, Mitchell, *Biochemistry*, 1964, **3**, 424, 426.

Avenaciolide

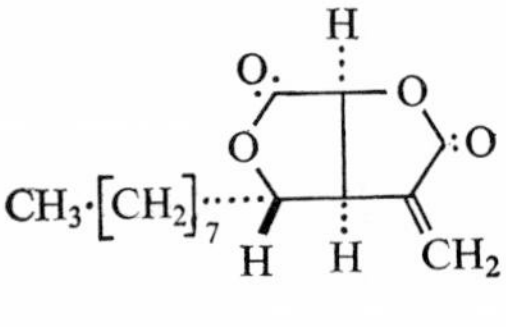

$C_{15}H_{22}O_4$ MW 266

Antifungal metabolite of *Aspergillus avenaceus* G. Smith and *A. fischeri* var. *glaber*. Cryst. from Et_2O–light petroleum with double m.p. 49–50° and 54–6°. $[\alpha]_D^{26·5}$ −41·6° (c, 1·2 in EtOH). Light absorption: $\lambda_{max.}$ 210 mμ (ε, 10,000).

Brookes, Tidd, Turner, *J. Chem. Soc.*, 1963, 5385.
Ellis *et al.*, *Nature*, 1964, **203**, 1382.

Averufin

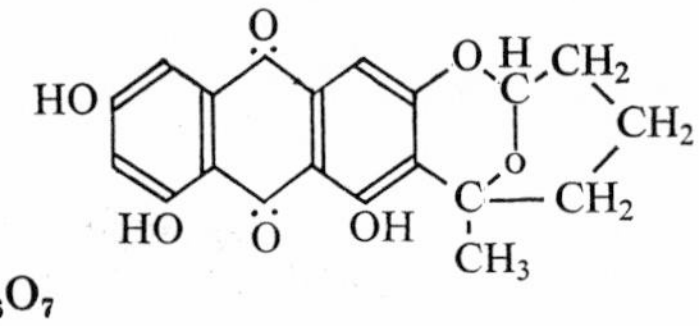

$C_{20}H_{16}O_7$ MW 368

Pigment produced by *Aspergillus versicolor* (Vuillemin) Tiraboschi. Bright orange-red laths from Me_2CO. M.p. 280–2° decomp. $[\alpha]_D$ ≯1°.
Tri-O-Ac: yellow needles from EtOH. M.p. 210–14°. $[\alpha]_D$ −14·9° (c, 0·424 in $CHCl_3$).
Tri-O-Me: yellow prisms. M.p. 190–1°.

Pusey, Roberts, *J. Chem. Soc.*, 1963, 3542.

Avil. *See* Pheniramine.★

Avomine. *See under* Promethazine.★

Ayapin.★

Present in sunflowers treated with 2 : 4-dichlorophenoxyacetic acid.

Dieterman *et al.*, *Arch. Biochem. Biophys.*, 1964, **106**, 275.

Erratum p. 297

1-Azabicyclo[3,2,1]octane.★

Formula should read $C_7H_{13}N$.

2-Azabicyclo[2,2,2]octane (*Isoquinuclidine*)

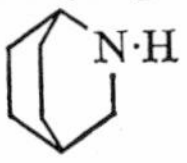

$C_7H_{13}N$ MW 111

Cryst. Unstable, rapidly absorbs CO_2.
B,HCl: m.p. >300°.
N-*Benzoyl*: m.p. 115–18°.
N-*Me,B,CH₃I*: m.p. >300°.
Picrate: yellow needles. M.p. 218° (244–7° decomp.).

Ferber, Bruchner, *Ber.*, 1942, **75**, 425; 1943, **76**, 1019.
Weiner, Ricca, *J. Am. Chem. Soc.*, 1958, **80**, 2733.
Schneider, Dillmann, *Chem. Ber.*, 1963, **96**, 2377.
Cava, Wilkins, *Chemistry and Industry*, 1964, 1422.

5-Azacytidine

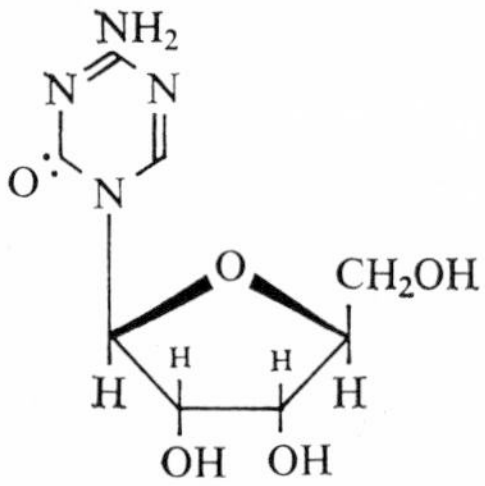

$C_8H_{12}O_5N_4$ MW 244

Cancerostatic agent. M.p. 230°.

Šorm *et al.*, *Experientia*, 1964, **20**, 202.

6-Aza-dihydroequilenin

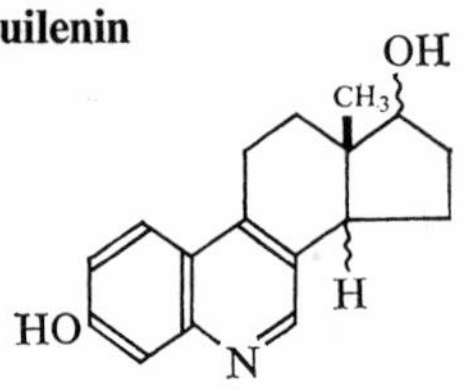

$C_{17}H_{19}O_2N$ MW 269

3-*Me ether*: $C_{18}H_{21}O_2N$. MW 283. M.p. 188–93°. Light absorption: $\lambda_{max.}$ 234 (ε, 52,500), 329 (4850), and 341 mμ (5100).

Smith, Douglas, Walk, *Experientia*, 1964, **20**, 418.

4-Azaleucine. *See* 2-Amino-3-dimethylaminopropionic Acid.

4-Azalysine. *See* 2-Amino-3-(2-aminoethylamino)-propionic Acid.

17-Azapregn-4-ene-3 : 20-dione. *See* 17-Azaprogesterone.

17-Azaprogesterone (17-*Azapregn*-4-*ene*-3 : 20-*dione*)

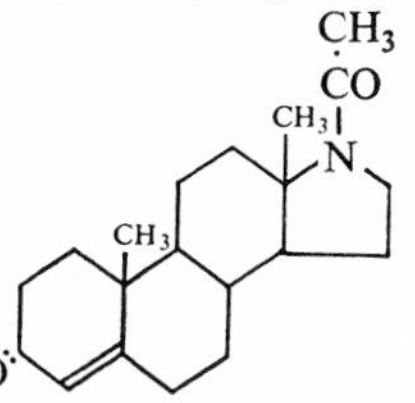

$C_{20}H_{29}O_2N$ MW 315

M.p. 179–81°. Light absorption: $\lambda_{max.}$ 240 mμ (ε, 16,500).

Rahkit, Gut, *Tetrahedron Letters*, 1964, 223.

Azatriptyrene

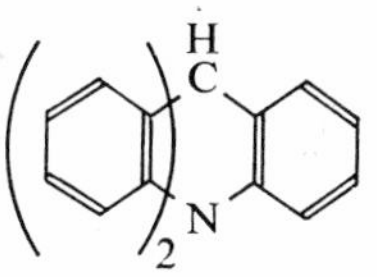

$C_{19}H_{13}N$ MW 255

M.p. 266–7°.

Metho (*tetraphenyl borate*): m.p. 289·5–291° decomp.

Wittig, Steinhoff, *Chem. Ber.*, 1962, **95**, 203; *Angew. Chem.*, 1963, **75**, 453; *Int. Ed.*, 1963, **2**, 396.

Azelaic Acid.★

Dinitrile:★

Cope, Cotter, Estes, *Organic Syntheses*, 1954, **34**, 5; Coll. Vol. **4**, 62.

Aziridine.★

Allen, Spangler, Webster, *Organic Syntheses*, 1950, **30**, 38; Coll. Vol. **4**, 433.

Azoxybenzene.★

Trans-.★

Cis-.

M.p. 69–71°. Light absorption: $\lambda_{max.}$ 239 (ε, 11,200) and 327 mμ (3900).

Webb, Jaffé, *J. Am. Chem. Soc.*, 1964, **86**, 2419.

B

B-73 (Rao and Cullen). *See* Albonoursin.

Bacimethrin (*4-Amino-5-hydroxymethyl-2-methoxypyrimidine*)

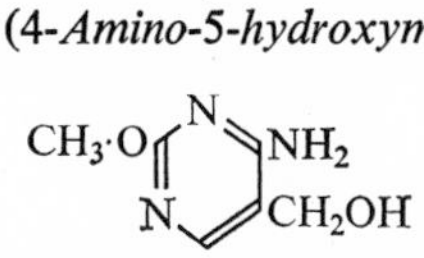

$C_6H_9O_2N_3$ MW 155

Antibiotic from *Bacillus megatherium*. Cryst. from MeOH. M.p. 174°. pK_a' 5·2.

Yonehara, Umezawa, Sumiki, *J. Antibiotics* (Japan), 1961, **14A**, 161.

Balchanin (*1β-Hydroxy-4 : 5 : 7α(H) : 6β(H)eudesm-11(13)en-6 : 12-olide*)

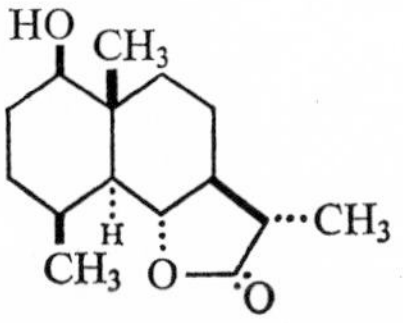

$C_{15}H_{22}O_3$ MW 250

Constituent of *Artemisia balchanorum* H. Krash. Cryst. from Pr^i_2O–Me_2CO. M.p. 142°. $[\alpha]_D^{20}$ +96·6° ($CHCl_3$).

Suchý, *Coll. Czech. Chem. Commun.*, 1962, **27**, 2925.

Band 510. *See* 4-*O*-Caffeoylquinic Acid.

ψ-Baptigenin.★

7-(*3-Methylbut-2-enyl*) *ether*: maxima isoflavone B. Constituent of the roots of *Tephrosia maxima*. Cryst. from C_6H_6–light petroleum. M.p. 132–3° (126–8°).

Rangaswami, Sastry, *Current Sci.*, 1954, **23**, 397; 1955, **24**, 337.
Kukla, Seshadri, *Tetrahedron*, 1962, **18**, 1443.

Baratol. *See under* 3-(3-Dimethylaminopropyl)-1 : 8 : 8-trimethyl-3-azabicyclo[3,2,1]octane.

Barnol (*5-Ethyl-4 : 6-dimethylpyrogallol*)

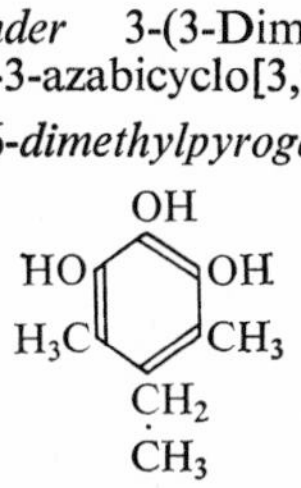

$C_{10}H_{14}O_3$ MW 182

Metabolite of a *Penicillium* spp. (*P. baarnense* v. Beyma). Cryst. from CCl_4. M.p. 145–6°.

Tri-Ac: cryst. from AcOH.Aq. M.p. 130–1°.

Ljungcrantz, Mosbach, *Acta Chem. Scand.*, 1964, **18**, 638.
Mosbach, Ljuncrantz, *Arch. Biochem. Biophys.*, 1964, **86**, 203.

Bayin.★

In view of the amended structure for vitexin, involving an 8-(β-D-glucopyranosyl) grouping, it would appear that the structure for bayin requires modification in the same sense.

Beaumontoside

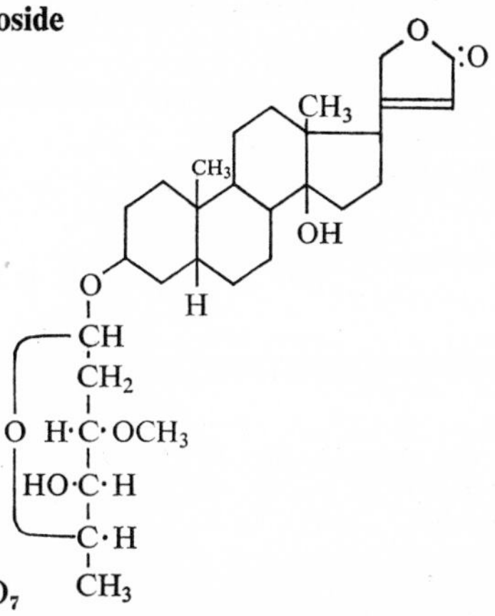

$C_{30}H_{46}O_7$ MW 548

Present in the seeds of *Beaumontia grandiflora* Wallich. M.p. 202–3°. $[\alpha]_D$ −32·5° ($CHCl_3$). Acid hyd. → digitoxigenin + L-oleandrose.

Mono-O-Ac: m.p. 185–7°. $[\alpha]_D$ −34·4° ($CHCl_3$).

Krasso, Weiss, Reichstein, *Helv. Chim. Acta*, 1963, **46**, 1691; *Pharm. Acta Helv.*, 1964, **39**, 168.

Beauwalloside

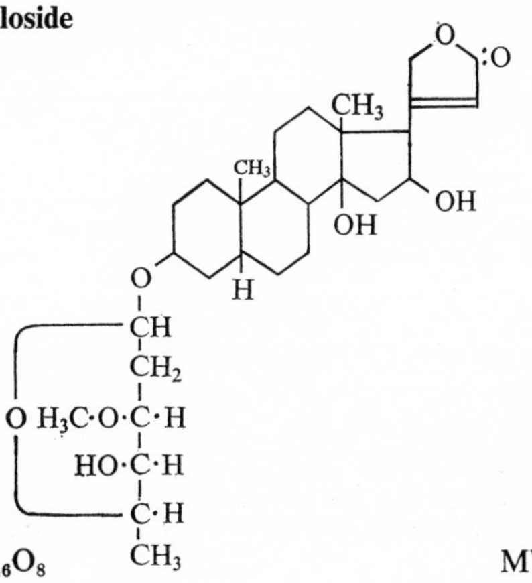

$C_{30}H_{46}O_8$ MW 564

Present in the seeds of *Beaumontia grandiflora* Wallich. M.p. 223–6°. $[\alpha]_D$ −80·7° ($CHCl_3$). Acid hyd. → oleandrigenin + L-cymarose.

Krasso, Weiss, Reichstein, *Helv. Chim. Acta*, 1963, **46**, 1691; *Pharm. Acta Helv.*, 1964, **39**, 168.

Bellidifolium (1 : 5 : 8-*Trihydroxy-3-methoxyxanthane*)

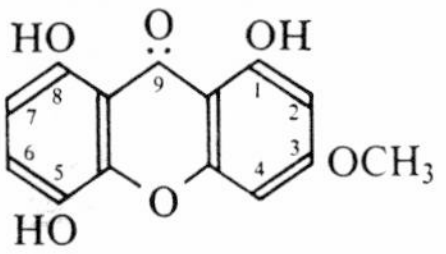

$C_{14}H_{10}O_6$ MW 274

Constituent of *Gentiana bellidifolia*. Yellow needles from Me_2CO or EtOH. M.p. 270–1°. Light absorption: $\lambda_{max.}$ 230–7 (log ε, 4·1), 255 (4·2), 279 (4·1), 302 sh. (3·7), and 334 mμ (3·9).

Tri-Ac: m.p. 240°.

5-Me ether: $C_{15}H_{12}O_6$. MW 288. Constituent of *G. bellidifolia*. M.p. 185–6°. Probably identical with Swerchirin (*q.v.*).

Di-Me ether: $C_{16}H_{14}O_6$. MW 302. Yellow needles from EtOH–$CHCl_3$. M.p. 206–7°.

Markham, *Tetrahedron*, 1964, **20**, 993.

Benodaine. *See* Piperoxan.★

Benzedrex. *See* 1-Cyclohexyl-2-methylaminopropane.

Erratum p. 338

4 : 5-Benzisocoumaranone. *See* Naphtho[2,1-*b*]-furan-2-one.

Benzocyclobutene.★

N.M.R. spectrum:

Fraenkel *et al.*, *Tetrahedron*, 1964, **20**, 1179.

Benzo[*j*]fluoranthene.★

Light absorption: $\lambda_{max.}$ 223 (ε, 49,000), 240 (45,000), 279 (13,200), 291 (19,050), 307 (28,200), 318 (31,600), 332 (12,900), 347 (4170), 365 (8130), and 384 mμ (12,450).

Crawford, Supanekar, *J. Chem. Soc.*, 1964, 2380.

Benzofuroxan.★

See also:

Mallory, *Organic Syntheses*, 1957, **37**, 1; Coll. Vol. **4**, 74.

Smith Boyer, *Organic Syntheses*, Coll. Vol. **4**, 75.

1 : 2-Benzophenanthreno-[9′,10 : 3,4]-tetracene

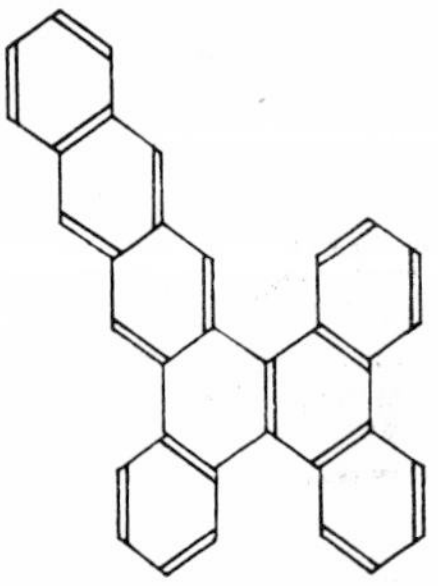

$C_{34}H_{20}$ MW 428

Orange-yellow needles. M.p. 247–8°. H_2SO_4 → green-brown soln. Light absorption: $\lambda_{max.}$ 254 (log ε, 5·00), 268 (4·91), 304 (4·92), 328 (5·12), 345 (4·78), 362 (4·76), 388 (3·78), 412 (3·94), 438 (4·12), and 466 mμ (4·04).

Clar, Guye-Vuillème, Stephen, *Tetrahedron*, 1964, **20**, 2107.

Benzo[*c*]picene. *See* Fulminene.

1 : 4-Benzoquinone-tetracarboxylic Acid-dianhydride

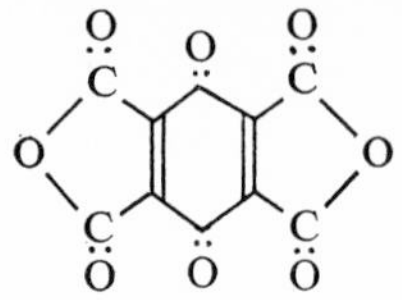

$C_{10}O_8$ MW 248

Very reactive π acid which gives unstable complexes with aromatic hydrocarbons.

C_6H_6 adduct: (1 : 1) deep red. Light sensitive.

Hammond, *Science*, 1963, **142**, 502.

Benzothioindoxyl. *See* Naphthothiophen-3-ol.★

1-Benzoxepin

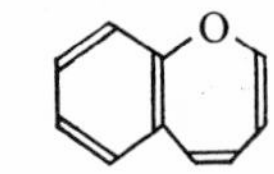

$C_{10}H_8O$ MW 144

Yellow-green liquid. B.p. 50°/0·5 mm. Light absorption: $\lambda_{max.}$ 211 (ε, 14,700), 231 (10,700), and 288 mμ (2900).

Sondheimer, Shani, *J. Am. Chem. Soc.*, 1964, **86**, 3168.

Benzoylacetic Acid.★

Et ester:★

Schriner, Schmidt, Roll, *Organic Syntheses*, Coll. Vol. **2**, 266.

McElvain, Weber, *Organic Syntheses*, Coll. Vol. **3**, 379.

Straley, Adams, *Organic Syntheses*, 1957, **37**, 32; Col. Vol. **4**, 415.

Anilide:

Allen, Humphlet, *Organic Syntheses*, 1957, **37**, 2; Coll. Vol. **4**, 80.

Benzoylmalonic Acid.★

Di-Et ester:

Price, Tarbell, *Organic Syntheses*, 1957, **37**, 20; Coll. Vol. **4**, 285.

1-Benzoyl-2-phenylpyrazolo[1,2-*a*]pyrazole

$C_{19}H_{14}ON_2$ MW 286

M.p. 193–4° decomp. $\lambda_{max.}$ 400 mμ. H_2SO_4 → red soln.

Solomons, Fowler, *Chemistry and Industry*, 1963, 1462.

3-Benzoylpyridine.★

Villani, King, *Organic Syntheses*, 1957, **37**, 6; Coll. Vol. **4**, 88.

2-Benzylaminopyridine

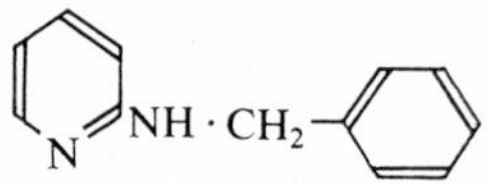

$C_{12}H_{12}N_2$ MW 184

Cryst. from isopropanol. M.p. 97–8°.

Mangini, Colonna, *Gazz. chim. ital.*, 1943, **73**, 313 (*Chem. Abstracts*, 1947, **41**, 1224).

Huntrer *et al.*, *J. Am. Chem. Soc.*, 1946, **68**, 1999.

Bristow *et al.*, *J. Chem. Soc.*, 1954, 616.

Sprinzak, *Organic Syntheses*, 1958, **38**, 3; Coll. Vol. **4**, 91.

N-(2-Benzylcarbamoylethyl)-N′-isonicotinoylhydrazine. See Nialamide.★

2-(N-Benzyl-2-chloroethylamino)-1-phenoxypropane. See Phenoxybenzamine.★

O-Benzyl-O : O-diethylphosphorothionate

$$CH_3 \cdot CH_2 \cdot O{>}P(S) \cdot O \cdot CH_2 \cdot C_6H_5$$
$$CH_3 \cdot CH_2 \cdot O$$

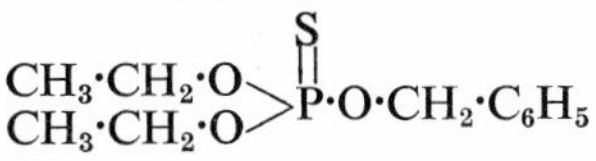

$C_{11}H_{17}O_3PS$　　　　　　　　　MW 260

B.p. 122·5–123·5°/2·5 mm. D_{20} 1·1301. n_D^{20} 1·5152.

Kabachnik, Mastryukova, *Zhur. Obshcheĭ Khim.*, 1955, **25**, 1925 (*Chem. Abstracts*, 1956, **50**, 8499).

Se-Benzyl-O : O-diethylphosphoroselenolate (*Benzyl ethyl phosphoroselenoate, benzyl ethyl selenophosphate*)

$$CH_3 \cdot CH_2 \cdot O{>}P(O) \cdot Se \cdot CH_2 \cdot C_6H_5$$
$$CH_3 \cdot CH_2 \cdot O$$

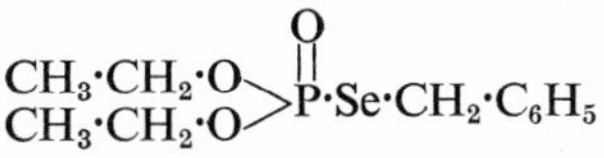

$C_{11}H_{17}O_3PSe$　　　　　　　　MW 307

Insecticide. B.p. 154°/2 mm.

Schrader, Lorenz, B.P. 691,267 (*Chem. Abstracts*, 1954, **48**, 7047); U.S.P. 2,680,132 (*Chem. Abstracts*, 1954, **48**, 9402); Ger. P. 824,046 (*Chem. Abstracts*, 1954, **48**, 11481).

S-Benzyl-O : O-diethylphosphorothiolate (*Benzyl ethyl phosphorothioate, benzyl ethyl thiophosphate*)

$$CH_3 \cdot CH_2O{>}P(O) \cdot S \cdot CH_2 \cdot C_6H_5$$
$$CH_3 \cdot CH_2O$$

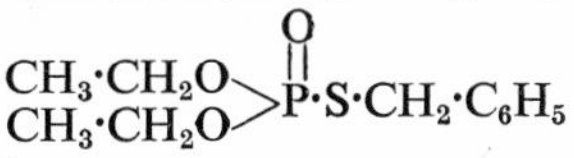

$C_{11}H_{17}O_3PS$　　　　　　　　　MW 260

Contact insecticide. B.p. 165–70°/2 mm., 137·5–8°/2·5 mm. D_{20} 1·1569. n_D^{20} 1·5258.

Schrader, U.S.P. 2,640,847 (*Chem. Abstracts*, 1954, **48**, 5206).

Kabachnik, Mastryukova, *Zhur. Obshcheĭ Khim.*, 1955, **25**, 1925 (*Chem. Abstracts*, 1956, **50**, 8499).

N-Benzyl-N′ : N-dimethyl-N-2-pyridylethylenediamine. See Tripelennamine.★

Benzyl ethyl phosphoroselenoate. See Se-Benzyl-O : O-diethylphosphoroselenolate.

Benzyl ethyl phosphorothioate. See S-Benzyl-O : O-diethylphosphorothiolate.

Benzyl ethyl selenophosphate. See Se-Benzyl-O : O-diethylphosphoroselenolate.

Benzyl ethyl thiophate. See S-Benzyl-O : O-diethylphosphorothiolate.

2-O-Benzylglucose

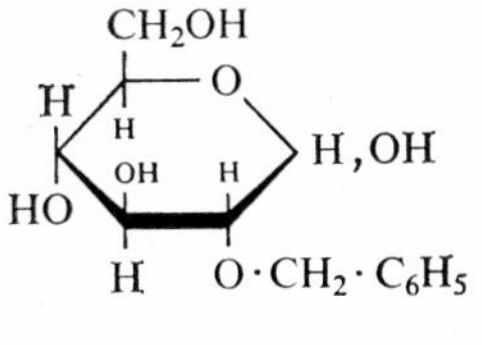

$C_{13}H_{18}O_6$　　　　　　　　　　MW 270

Cryst. from EtOH. M.p. 176–7°. $[\alpha]_D^{23}$ 56° (15 min.) → 47° (24 hr.) (c, 1 in MeOH).

Klemer, *Chem. Ber.*, 1963, **96**, 634.

3-Benzylidene-6-isobutylene-2 : 5-dioxopiperazine. *See* Albonoursin.

2-Benzylimidazoline★ (*Priscol, Tolazoline*)

See also:

Scholz, *Ind. Eng. Chem.*, 1945, **37**, 120.

Benzylpenicillinic Acid.★

2 - *Diethylaminoethyl ester*: B,HI: Penethamate Hydroiodide, Estopen. M.p. 178–9°.

Carpenter, *J Am. Chem. Soc.*, 1948, **70**, 2964.

2-Benzylphenol.★

2-Dimethylamino ethyl ether: *see* Phenyltoloxamine.★

9-Benzyl-1 : 2 : 3 : 4-tetrahydro-3-methyl-γ-carboline. See Mebhydrolin.★

5-Benzyl-1 : 2 : 3 : 4-tetrahydro-2-methylpyrid[4,3-b]-indole. See Mebhydrolin.★

N-Benzyl-m-toluidine.

See also:

Allen, VanAllan, *Organic Syntheses*, Coll. Vol. **3**, 827.

Benzyne

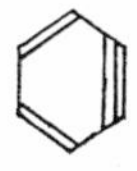

C_6H_4　　　　　　　　　　　　MW 76

Very reactive intermediate in the elimination and fragmentation reactions of certain mono- and o-disubstituted benzenes. Reacts with dienes, *e.g.*, furan, anthracene, and with nucleophiles.

Wittig, *Naturwiss.*, 1942, **30**, 696.

Roberts *et al.*, *J. Am. Chem. Soc.*, 1953, **75**, 3290.

Huisgen, Rist, *Ann.*, 1955, **594**, 137.

Stiles, Miller, Burckhardt, *J. Am. Chem. Soc.*, 1963, **85**, 1792.

Friedmann, Logullo, *J. Am. Chem. Soc.*, 1963, **85**, 1549.

Berry, Clardy, Schafer, *J. Am. Chem. Soc.*, 1964, **86**, 2738.

Campbell, Rees, *Proc. Chem. Soc.*, 1964, 296.

Berculon A. *See* Thiosemicarbazone *under* p-Acetamidobenzaldehyde.

β-Bergamotene★

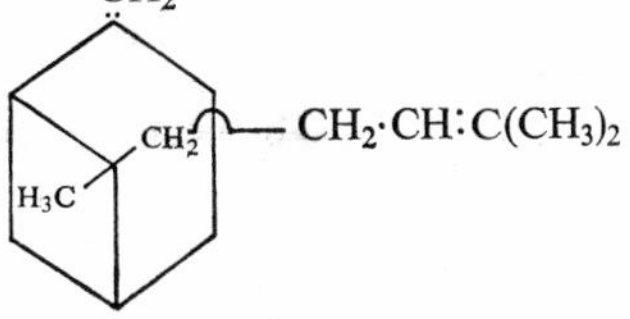

$C_{15}H_{24}$　　　　　　　　　　　MW 204

Sesquiterpene from *Valeriana wallichi*. B.p. 120–30°/1 mm. D^{27} 0·8841. n_D^{27} 1·4949. $[\alpha]_D$ 35·8° (c, 4).

Kulkarni *et al.*, *Tetrahedron Letters*, 1963, 505.

Bergapten.★

Also present in *Dictamnus albus* L.

Berrens, von Dijk, *Experientia*, 1964, **20**, 615.

Bergenin★ (*Corylopsin, Vakerin*)

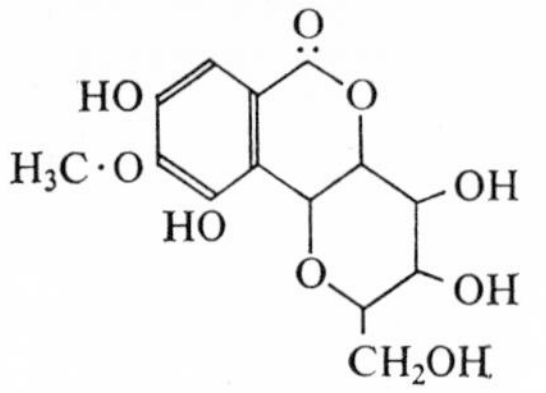

Revised structure

Tri-Me ether: $C_{17}H_{22}O_9$. MW 370. Needles from MeOH. M.p. 240–2°.
Penta-Me ether: $C_{19}H_{26}O_9$. MW 398. Needles from H_2O. M.p. 106°.

Hay, Haynes, *J. Chem. Soc.*, 1958, 2231.
Posternak, Durr, *Helv. Chim. Acta*, 1958, **41**, 1159.
Barry, *Chem. Revs.*, 1964, **64**, 247.

Bervulcine

$C_{18}H_{19}O_3N$ MW 297

Alkaloid from *Berberis vulgaris* L. M.p. 125–6° decomp. $[\alpha]_D^{24}$ −185° (c, 0·2 in $CHCl_3$).
B,HI: prisms from H_2O. M.p. 236° decomp.
B,HClO₄: prisms from H_2O. M.p. 258–60° decomp.
Picrate: fine needles from MeOH. M.p. 188–90° decomp.
B,CH₃I: cryst. from H_2O. M.p. 269° decomp.

Döpke *Naturwiss.*, 1963, **50**, 595.

Betanidin

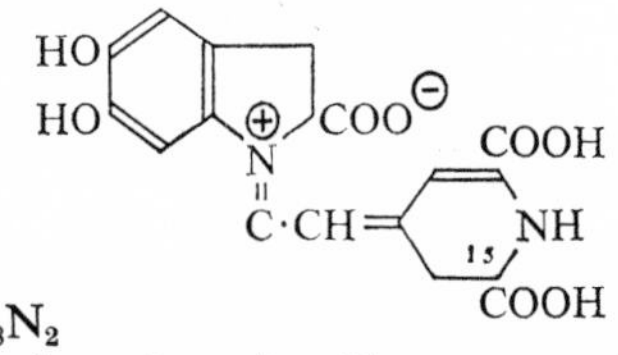

$C_{18}H_{16}O_8N_2$ MW 388

Aglycone from betanin. Forms cryst. K and NH_4 salts.
B,HCl: cryst. Light absorption: $\lambda_{max.}$ 271–2 (ε, 8530), 295 sh. (7170), and 542–6 mμ (51,000).
Di-Ac: isolated as K salt.

Wyler, Dreiding, *Helv. Chim. Acta*, 1959, **42**, 1699; 1962, **45**, 638.
Mabry *et al.*, *Helv. Chim. Acta*, 1962, **45**, 640.
Wyler, Mabry, Dreiding, *Helv. Chim. Acta*, 1963, **46**, 1745.

Betanin

$C_{24}H_{26}O_{13}N_2$ MW 550

Red pigment from beetroot *Beta vulgaris* L. var. *rubra* and other *Centrospermae* spp. Cryst. Hyd. → glucose, betanidin, and isobetanidin.

Ainley, Robinson, *J. Chem. Soc.*, 1937, 446.
Wyler, Dreiding, *Helv. Chim. Acta*, 1957, **40**, 191.
Piattelli, Minale, *Phytochemistry*, 1964, **3**, 307, 547.

Betonicine★

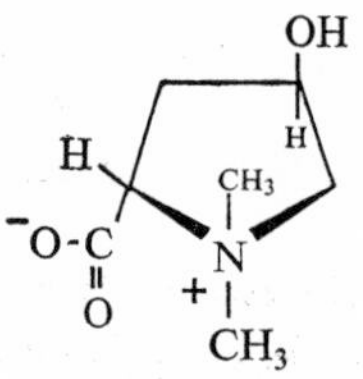

Also present in horehound (*Marrubium vulgare* L.).

Paudler, Wagner, *Chemistry and Industry*, 1963, 1693.

Beyerol

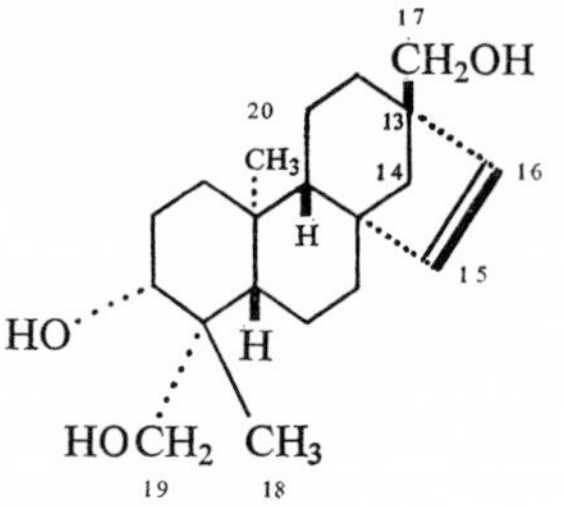

$C_{20}H_{32}O_3$ MW 320

Laths from EtOH. M.p. 242–3°. $[\alpha]_D^{20}$ +61° (c, 1·1 in Py).
Triformate: needles from MeOH.Aq. M.p. 118–19°. $[\alpha]_D^{20}$ +50° (c, 1·1 in $CHCl_3$).
Tri-Ac: plates from EtOH.Aq. M.p. 84–5°. $[\alpha]_D^{20}$ +39° (c, 1·54 in $CHCl_3$).
Tribenzoyl: plates from $CHCl_3$–MeOH. M.p. 153°. $[\alpha]_D^{20}$ −12° (c, 0·92 in $CHCl_3$).
Trimethanesulphonyl: plates from MeOH. M.p. 160° decomp. $[\alpha]_D^{20}$ +34° (c, 0·67 in $CHCl_3$).
17-*Cinnamyl ester*: $C_{29}H_{38}O_4$. MW 450. Constituent of the leaves of *Beyeria leschenaultii* (DC.) Baill var. *drummondii* (Muell. Arg.). Plates from MeOH. M.p. 145–6°. $[\alpha]_D^{20}$ +66° (c, 0·81 in $CHCl_3$). *Ethylidene deriv.*: needles from light petroleum. M.p. 167–8°. $[\alpha]_D^{20}$ −75° (c, 2·56 in $CHCl_3$).

Jefferies *et al.*, *Austral. J. Chem.*, 1962, **15**, 521.
Jefferies, Rosich, White, *Tetrahedron Letters*, 1963, 1793.

8 : 8″-Biapigeninyl. *See* Cupressuflavone.

Bicuculline★

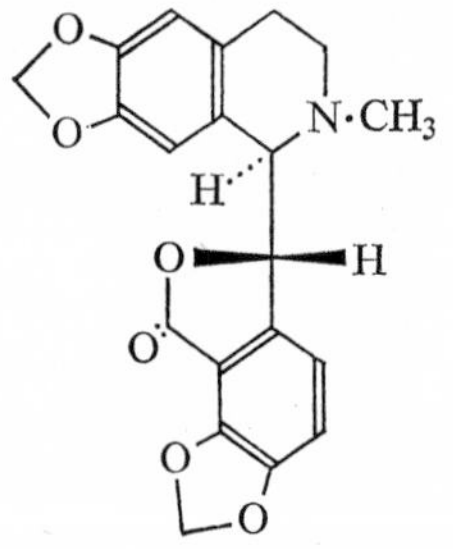

See also:

Edwards, Handa, *Can. J. Chem.*, 1961, **39**, 1801.

Stereochemistry:

Safe, Moir, *Can. J. Chem.*, 1964, **42**, 160.

Bicyclo[1,1,0]butane

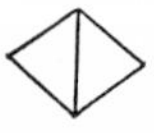

C_4H_6 MW 54

B.p. 7·8° ± 0·5°.

Lemal, Menger, Clark, *J. Am. Chem. Soc.*, 1963, **85**, 2529.
Wiberg, Lampman, *Tetrahedron Letters*, 1963, 2173.

Bicyclo[3,3,1]nonane.★

See also:

Buchta, Billenstein, *Naturwiss.*, 1964, **51**, 383.

Bicyclo[3,2,1]octa-2 : 6-diene

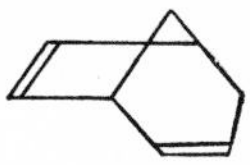

C_8H_{10} MW 106

B.p. 50°/120 mm. n_D^{20} 1·4918.

Moore, Moser, La Prade, *J. Org. Chem.*, 1963, **28**, 2200.

Cupas, Watts, Schleyer, *Tetrahedron Letters*, 1964, 2503.

Bicyclo[5,1,0]octa-3 : 5-dien-2-one. *See* Homotropone.

Bicyclo[3,2,1]octane

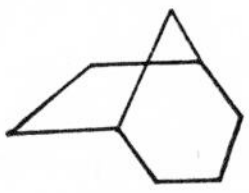

C_8H_{14} MW 110

M.p. 139·5–141°.

Barrett, Linstead, *J. Am. Chem. Soc.*, 1936, **58**, 611.

Doering, Tarber, *J. Am. Chem. Soc.*, 1949, **71**, 1514.

Cope, Grisar, Peterson, *J. Am. Chem. Soc.*, 1960, **82**, 4299.

Buchta, Billenstein, *Naturwiss.*, 1964, **51**, 383.

American Institute of Petroleum Infrared Spectrum No. 2037.

Bicyclo[2,2,2]octane-2 : 6 : 7-trione

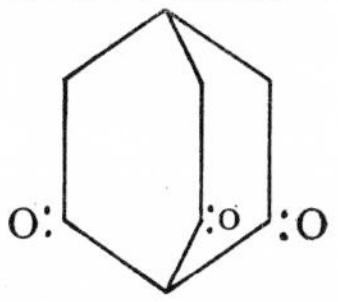

$C_8H_8O_3$ MW 152

M.p. 244–5°. Light absorption: $\lambda_{max.}$ 240 and 295 mμ (log ε, 2·94 and 2·58) in dioxan.

Theilacker, Schmid, *Ann.*, 1950, **570**, 15.

Theilacker, Wegner, *Ann.*, 1963, **664**, 125.

Bicyclo[1,1,1]pentane

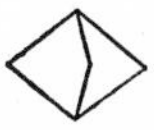

C_5H_8 MW 68

Oil.

Wiberg, Connor, Lampman, *Tetrahedron Letters*, 1964, 531.

Bikhaconite

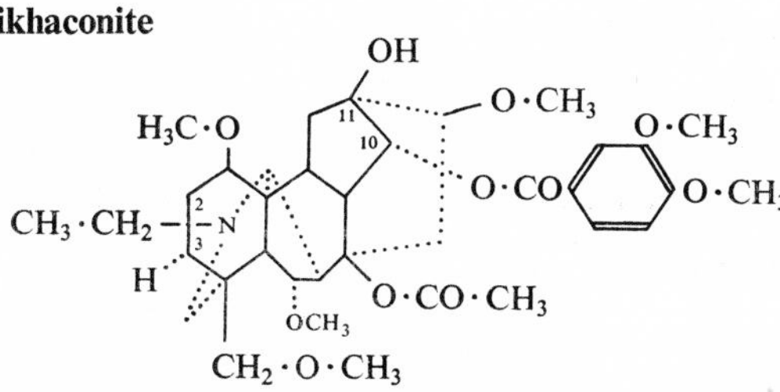

$C_{36}H_{51}O_{11}N$ MW 673

Constituent of *Aconitum spicatum* Stapf. Cryst. from hexane, m.p. 163·5–164°. *Hydrate*: colourless needles. M.p. 105–10° (118–23°). $[\alpha]_D$ +16° (c, 1·6 in EtOH).

B,HBr: prisms from EtOH. M.p. 173–5°. $[\alpha]_D$ −12·4° (H_2O).

B,HClO₄: needles from EtOH. M.p. 240–2°. $[\alpha]_D$ −5·2° (c, 1·6 in $CHCl_3$).

Ac: prisms from MeOH. B.p. 197–9°. $[\alpha]_D$ +21·6° (c, 1·5 in $CHCl_3$).

Dunstan, Andrews, *J. Chem. Soc.*, 1905, **87**, 1636.

Tsuda, Marion, *Can. J. Chem.*, 1963, **41**, 3055.

Biobamat. *See* Meprobamat.★

Biopterin★ (6 - (L - erythro - 1′ : 2′ - *Dihydroxypropyl*) - *pterin*).

Widely distributed in fruit-fly, crayfish, royal jelly, fish, and red ants, etc.

Synthesis:

Patterson, Milstrey, Stokstad, *J. Am. Chem. Soc.*, 1956, **78**, 5868.

8a-^{14}*C*:

Rembold, Metzger, *Chem. Ber.*, 1963, **96**, 1395.

Biphenylene.★

N.M.R. spectrum:

Fraenkel *et al.*, *Tetrahedron*, 1964, **20**, 1179.

3-*p*-*Bis*(2-chloroethyl)aminophenylalanine. *See* Melphalan.★

Bisdechlorogeodin.★

See also:

Mahmoodian, Stickings, *Biochem. J.*, 1964, **92**, 369.

Bisgalvinoxyl

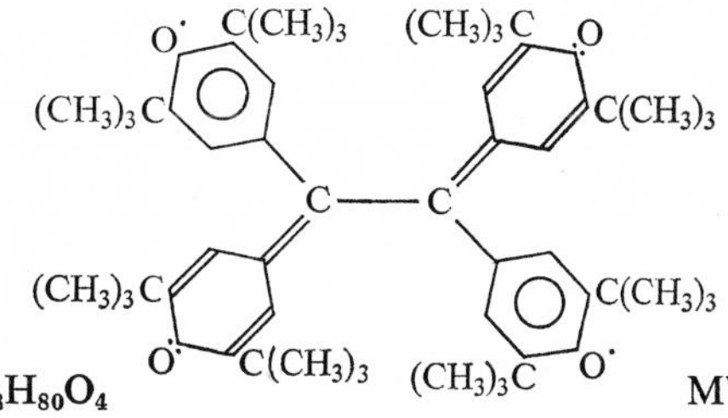

$C_{58}H_{80}O_4$ MW 840

Free radical. Dark cryst. solid with metallic lustre. Redn. → brick red bisquinone methide, m.p. 306–8°.

Chandross, *J. Am. Chem. Soc.*, 1964, **86**, 1262.

***Bis*-(3-hydroxy-4-hydroxymethyl-2-methylpyrid-5-yl-methyl) disulphide.** *See* Pyrithioxin.★

***Bis*-γ-L-glutamyl-L-cystinyl-*bis*-β-alanine**

γ-L-Glu-L-Cy-S-β-Ala
γ-L-Glu-L-Cy-S-β-Ala

$C_{22}H_{36}O_{12}N_6S_2$ MW 640

Peptide present in the seeds of the mung bean (*Phaseolus aureus* Roxb.). Colourless needles from H_2O. M.p. 194–7° decomp. $[\alpha]_D^{20·5}$ −59·5° ± 0·6° (c, 0·5 in H_2O). Redn. → γ-L-glutamyl-L-cysteinyl-β-alanine.

Carnegie, *Arch. Biochem. Biophys.*, 1963, **101**, 364; *Biochem. J.*, 1963, **89**, 459, 471.

***N* : *N′* - *Bis* - (trimethylammoniumphenoxycarbonyl) - *N* : *N′*-dimethyldecamethylene dibromide.** *See* Demecarium bromide.★

Blepherin.★

Hyd. → D-glucose + blepherigenin (*q.v.*).

Blepherigenin

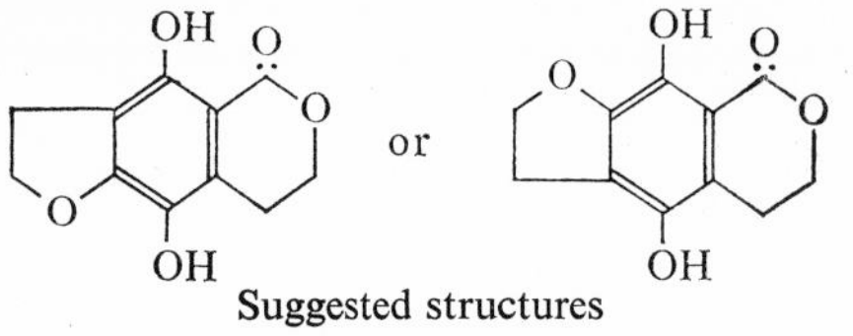

Suggested structures

$C_{11}H_{10}O_5$ MW 222

Aglycone from blepherin. Yellow needles. M.p. 207°. Light absorption: $\lambda_{max.}$ 250 (ε, 13,400) and 280 mμ (7500).

Di-Ac: cryst. from MeOH. M.p. 177°.

Dibenzoyl: cryst. from MeOH and AcOEt. M.p. 207°.

Di-O-Me: cryst. from MeOH.Aq. M.p. 71°. B.p. 180–5°/1 mm.

Lal, *J. Indian Chem. Soc.*, 1936, **13**, 109; 1940, **17**, 269.

Chaudhury, *J. Indian Chem. Soc.*, 1958, **35**, 612.

Bonamine. *See* Meclozine.★

Bonine. *See* Meclozine.★

5 : 6-Borazarobenz[*a*]anthracene

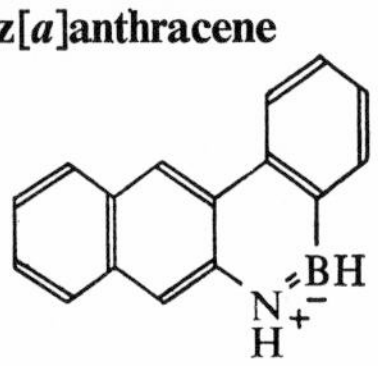

$C_{16}H_{12}BN$ MW 229

M.p. 139° decomp.

Dewar, Poesche, *J. Am. Chem. Soc.*, 1963, **85**, 2253.

6 : 5-Borazarobenz[*a*]anthracene

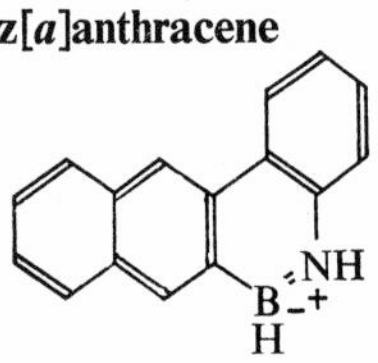

$C_{16}H_{12}BN$ MW 229

M.p. 136·5–137° decomp.

Dewar, Poesche, *J. Am. Chem. Soc.*, 1963, **85**, 2253.

Bradykinin.★

Syntheses:

Merrifield, *J. Am. Chem. Soc.*, 1964, **86**, 302; *Biochemistry*, 1964, **3**, 1385.

Review:

Schröder, Hempel, *Experientia*, 1964, **20**, 529.

Brazilin.★

(+)-.

Tribenzyl ether: cryst. from C_6H_6–C_6H_{12}. M.p. 117–19°. *Ac*: Cryst. from EtOH–AcOEt. M.p. 146–7°.

(±)-.

Tri-Me ether: cryst. from C_6H_6. M.p. 133–4°. *Ac*: m.p. 185°.

Tetra-Ac: cryst. from C_6H_6. M.p. 164–6°.

Tribenzylether, Ac: m.p. 135–6·5°.

Dann, Hofmann, *Ann.*, 1963, **667**, 116.

Braziliolic Acid

$C_{14}H_{28}O_5$ MW 276

Present in Vera Cruz jalap resin. Cryst. from H_2O. M.p. 151·5°. Probably a trihydroxytetradecanoic acid.

Shellard, *Planta Med.*, 1961, **9**, 141.

Brefeldin A

$C_{16}H_{24}O_4$ MW 280

Metabolite of *Penicillium brefeldianum* Dodge. Prisms from MeOH–Et_2O. M.p. 204–5°. $[\alpha]_D^{22}$ +96° (MeOH). Light absorption: $\lambda_{max.}$ 215 mμ (log ε, 4·05). H_2 → tetrahydro deriv. M.p. 134°.

Härri *et al.*, *Helv. Chim. Acta*, 1963, **46**, 1235.

Brefeldin B

$C_{15}H_{22}O_4$ MW 266

Metabolite of *Penicillium brefeldianum* Dodge. Needles from Et_2O–pentane. M.p. 163–5°. $[\alpha]_D^{21}$ −109° (dioxan) −119° (MeOH).

Me ester: oil. *Mesyl deriv.*: m.p. 140°.

Härri *et al.*, *Helv. Chim. Acta*, 1963, **46**, 1235.

Brevifolin.★

See also:

Bernauer, Schmidt, *Ann.*, 1955, **591**, 153.

Grimshaw, Haworth, Pindred, *J. Chem. Soc.*, 1955, 833; 1956, 418.

Brevifolincarboxylic Acid.★

See additional references under Brevifolin.

Bristamin. *See* Phenyltoloxamine.

5-(2-Bromoallyl)-5-isopropyl-1-methylbarbituric Acid. *See* Pronarcon.★

***N*-Bromoacetamide.★**

See also:

Oliveto, Gerold, *Organic Syntheses*, Coll. Vol. **4**, 104.

2-Bromo-2-chloro-1 : 1 : 1-trifluoroethane (*Fluothane, Halothane*)

$HBrClC{\cdot}CF_3$

C_2HF_3ClBr MW 197·5

Anaesthetic. B.p. 50·2°/760 mm., 20°/243 mm. D_4^{20} 1·86°. Light sensitive. Solubility in H_2O 0·345%.

Raventos, *Brit. J. Pharmacol.*, 1956, **11**, 394.

1-^{14}C:

Van Dyke, Chenoweth, Larsen, *Nature* (Lond.), 1964, **204**, 471.

Bromocyanoacetylene

$Br{\cdot}C{:}C{\cdot}CN$

C_3NBr MW 130

M.p. 96°.

Kloster-Jensen, *Acta Chem. Scand.*, 1963, **17**, 1862.

3-Bromoindole

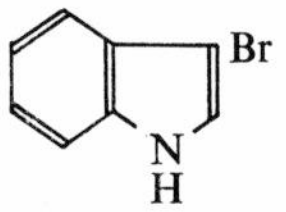

C_8H_5NBr MW 195

M.p. 65–6° decomp.

Weissgerber, *Ber.*, 1913, **46**, 652.

Piers *et al.*, *Can. J. Chem.*, 1963, **41**, 2399.

p-Bromomandelic Acid.★
Klingenberg, *Organic Syntheses*, 1955, **35**, 11; Coll. Vol. **4**, 110.

4-Bromo-3-methylisothiazole-5-carboxaldehyde thiosemicarbazone (*M & B* 7714)

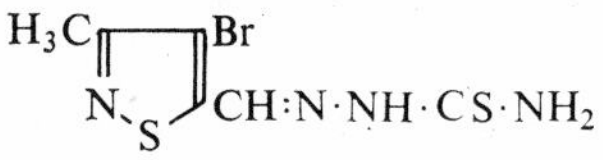

$C_6H_7N_4S_2Br$ MW 279
Antiviral agent. Yellow cryst. M.p. 228–30° decomp.
Buttimore *et al.*, *J. Chem. Soc.*, 1963, 2032.
Slack *et al.*, *Nature* (Lond.), 1964, **204**, 587.

***p*-Bromophenylurea.★**
See also:
Kurzer, *Organic Syntheses*, Coll. Vol. **4**, 49.

2-Bromo-*m*-toluic Acid

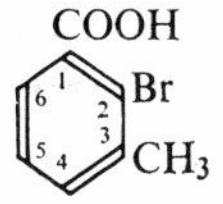

$C_8H_7O_2Br$ MW 215
Cryst. from light petroleum or C_6H_6. M.p. 135–7°.
Cavill, *J. Soc. Chem. Ind.* (London), 1926, **65**, 124.
Bunnett, Rauhut, *J. Org. Chem.*, 1956, **21**, 934; *Organic Syntheses*, 1958, **38**, 11; Coll. Vol. **4**, 114.

Bruceol

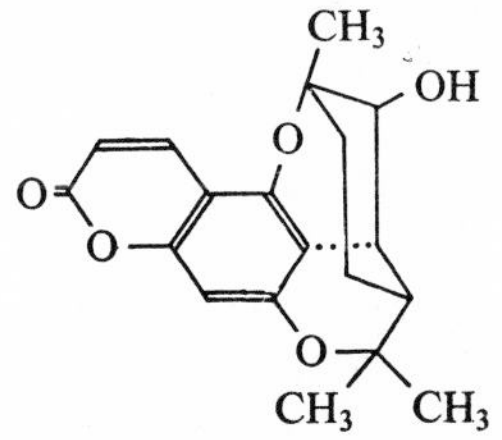

$C_{19}H_{20}O_5$ MW 328
Constituent of *Eriostemon brucei* (Rutaceae). Prisms from MeCOEt and EtOH. M.p. 201°. $[\alpha]_D$ −297° ($CHCl_3$). Light absorption: $\lambda_{max.}$ 218 (log ε, 4·43), 235 sh. (4·02), 254 (3·69), 260 (3·69), 330 mμ (4·13). Br_2 → monobromide needles from C_6H_6. M.p. 184·5° decomp. $[\alpha]_D$ −291° ($CHCl_3$).
Ac: needles from Pr^i_2O. M.p. 175°. $[\alpha]_D$ −357° ($CHCl_3$).
Benzoyl: cubes from EtOH. M.p. 221°. $[\alpha]_D$ −360°.
p-*Nitrobenzoyl*: cream needles from EtOH. M.p. 197°. $[\alpha]_D$ −370° ($CHCl_3$).
Duffield *et al.*, *Tetrahedron*, 1963, **19**, 593.

Bryogenin

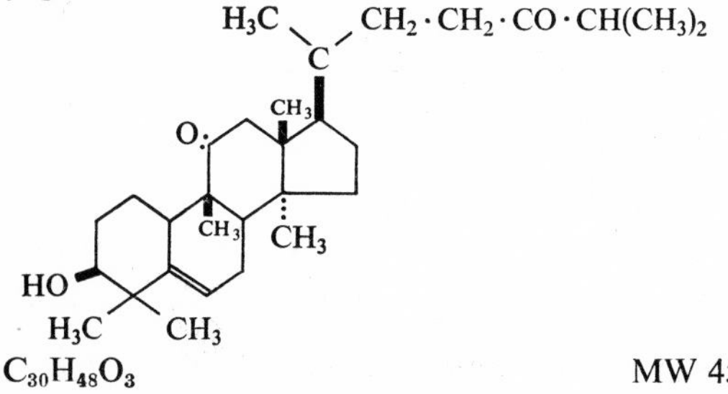

$C_{30}H_{48}O_3$ MW 456
Aglucone from the roots of *Bryonia dioica* Jacq. M.p. 157°.
Ac: m.p. 130°.
Biglino, Lehn, Ourisson, *Tetrahedron Letters*, 1963, 1651.

Bryonin.
Bitter glucoside from the roots of *Bryonia dioica* Jacq. M.p. 203°. Hydrol. → Bryogenin.
Vauquelin, *Berl. Jahr. Pharm.*, 1807, 14.
Biglino, Lehn, Ourisson, *Tetrahedron Letters*, 1963, 1651.

Bufonic Acid I
$C_{27}H_{44}O_5$ MW 448
Bile acid from toad (*Bufo vulgaris formosus*). M.p. 168–70°. H_2 → 3α : 7α : 12α-Trihydroxy-25α-coprostanic acid (m.p. 175–8°).
Okuda *et al.*, *J. Biochem.* (Japan), 1963, **54**, 97.

Bufonic Acid II.
Me ester: m.p. 170°.
Okuda *et al.*, *J. Biochem.* (Japan), 1963, **54**, 97.

Bullvalene (*Tricyclo*[3,3,2,$0^{4\cdot6}$]*deca*-2 : 7 : 9-*triene*)

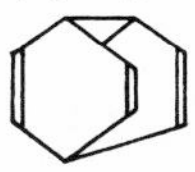

$C_{10}H_{10}$ MW 130
M.p. 96°. Light absorption: $\lambda_{max.}$ 238 sh. mμ (ε, 1700).
Doering, Roth, *Angew. Chem., Int. Ed.*, 1963, **2**, 115.
Schröder, *Angew. Chem.*, 1963, **75**, 722; *Int. Ed.*, 1963, **2**, 481; *Chem. Ber.*, 1964, **97**, 3140.
Schröder, Merényi, Oth, *Tetrahedron Letters*, 1964, 773.
Infrared spectrum:
Schröder, *Chem. Ber.*, 1964, **97**, 3140.

Burnamine (*Deacetylpicraline*)

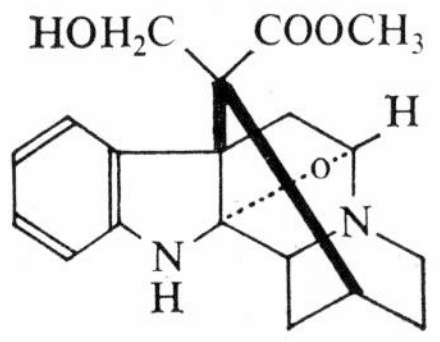

Suggested structure

$C_{21}H_{24}O_4N_2$ MW 368
Alkaloid present in *Hunteria eburna* and *Picralima nitida*. M.p. 197–8°. [α] −131° (−119°) ($CHCl_3$). Light absorption: $\lambda_{max.}$ 234, 288 mμ (log ε, 3·83, 3·47). pK_a 5·80 (50% EtOH).
Picrate: needles from MeOH. M.p. 147–9°.
Bartlett *et al.*, *J. Org. Chem.*, 1963, **28**, 2197.
Britten, Smith, *J. Chem. Soc.*, 1963, 3850.
Taylor *et al.*, *Bull. soc. chim.*, 1964, 392.

1-Buten-3-yne.★
Hennion, Price, McKeon, *Organic Syntheses*, 1958, **38**, 70; Coll. Vol. **4**, 683.

5-(3-Buten-1-ynyl)-2 : 2′-bithienyl

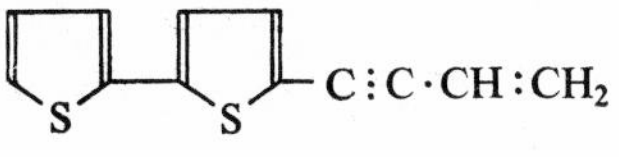

$C_{12}H_8S_2$ MW 216

Nematocidal constituent of *Tagetes erecta* (African marigold). Colourless liquid. Light absorption: λ_{max}. 251 (log ε, 3·96), 341 mμ (4·45).

Uhlenbroek, Bijloo, *Rec. trav. chim.*, 1959, **78**, 382.

Bohlmann, Herbst, *Chem. Ber.*, 1962, **95**, 2945.

Horn, Lamberton, *Austral. J. Chem.*, 1963, **16**, 475.

Atkinson, Curtis, Phillips, *Tetrahedron Letters*, 1964, 3159; *Chemistry and Industry*, 1964, 2101.

Butolic Acid. *See* (−)-6-Hydroxytetradecanoic Acid.

Butropine.★

Add:

Deckers, Maier, *Chem. Ber.*, 1953, **86**, 1424.

Se-Butyl-O : O-diethylphosphoroselenolate (*Butyl ethyl phosphoroselenoate, butyl ethyl selenophosphate*)

$$CH_3 \cdot CH_2O \!\!\! \diagdown \!\!\! \underset{\underset{O}{\|}}{P} \cdot Se \cdot CH_2 \cdot CH_2 \cdot CH_2 \cdot CH_3$$
$$CH_3 \cdot CH_2O \diagup$$

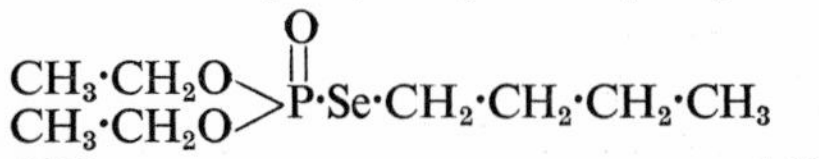

$C_8H_{19}OPSe$ MW 241

Insecticide. B.p. 122°/3 mm.

Schrader, Lorenz, B.P. 691,267 (*Chem. Abstracts*. 1954, **48**, 7047); U.S.P. 2,680,132 (*Chem, Abstracts*, 1954, **48**, 9402); Ger. P. 824,046 (*Chem. Abstracts*, 1954, **48**, 11481).

S-Butyl-O : O-diethylphosphorothiolate

$$CH_3 \cdot CH_2O \!\!\! \diagdown \!\!\! \underset{\underset{O}{\|}}{P} \cdot S \cdot CH_2 \cdot CH_2 \cdot CH_2 \cdot CH_3$$
$$CH_3 \cdot CH_2O \diagup$$

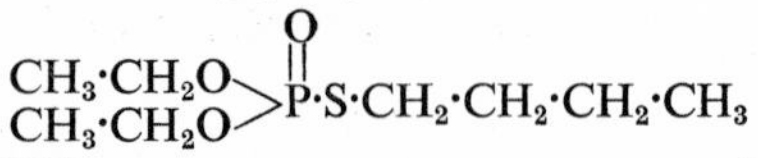

$C_8H_{19}OPS$ MW 194

Insecticide. B.p. 100–15°/5 mm.

Gilbert, McGough, U.S.P. 2,690,451 (*Chem. Abstracts*, 1955, **49**, 11683).

S-tert-Butyl-O : O-diethyl phosphorothiolothionate

$$CH_3 \cdot CH_2O \!\!\! \diagdown \!\!\! \underset{\underset{S}{\|}}{P} \cdot S \cdot C(CH_3)_3$$
$$CH_3 \cdot CH_2O \diagup$$

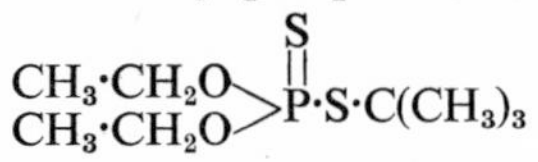

$C_8H_{19}PS_2$ MW 210

B.p. 78–80°/0·4 mm. n_D^{20} 1·502.

Bacon, Le Suer, *J. Am. Chem. Soc.*, 1954, **76**, 670.

1-tert-Butyl-3 : 3-dimethylaziridinone

$$H_3C \diagdown \hspace{2cm} :O$$
$$H_3C \diagup$$
$$N$$
$$C(CH_3)_3$$

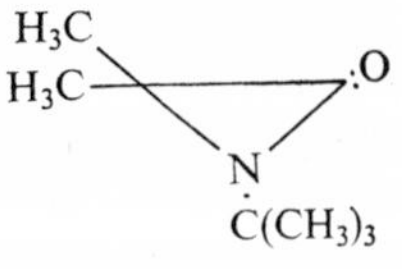

$C_8H_{15}ON$ MW 141

M.p. 22–4°. Decomposed on attempted distillation.

Sheehan, Lengyel, *J. Am. Chem. Soc.*, 1964, **86**, 1356.

tert-Butyl ethyl malonate

$$H_3C \cdot CH_2 \cdot OOC \cdot CH_2 \cdot COOC(CH_3)_3$$

$C_9H_{16}O_4$ MW 188

B.p. 98–100°/22 mm., 107–9°/24 mm. n_D^{25} 1·4128.

Hauser, Abramovitch, Adams, *J. Am. Chem. Soc.*, 1942, **64**, 2714.

Breslow, Baumgarten, Hauser, *J. Am. Chem. Soc.*, 1944, **66**, 1287.

Strube, *Organic Syntheses*, 1957, **37**, 34; Coll. Vol. **4**, 417.

Butyl ethyl phosphoroselenoate. *See Se*-Butyl-*O* : *O*-diethylphosphoroselenolate.

Butyl ethyl selenophosphate. *See Se*-Butyl-*O* : *O*-diethylphosphoroselenolate.

n-Butyl glyoxylate. *See under* Glyoxylic Acid.

tert-Butyl hypochlorite.★

See also:

Teeter, Bell, *Organic Syntheses*, Coll. Vol. **4**, 125.

3-Butylidene phthalide

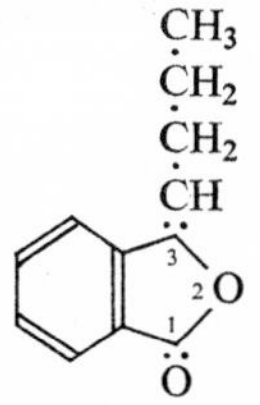

$C_{12}H_{12}O_2$ MW 188

Constituent of *Ligusticum acutilobum* Sieb et Zucc., *Levisticum officinale* Koch. Prisms. from EtOH. M.p. 161–2°.

Bromberg, *Ber.*, 1896, **29**, 1434.

Mitsuhashi, Nagai, Murumatsu, *Chem. Pharm. Bull. Japan*, 1960, **8**, 243.

Butylphosphonic Acid

$$CH_3 \cdot CH_2 \cdot CH_2 \cdot CH_2 \cdot \underset{\underset{O}{\|}}{P}(OH)_2$$

$C_4H_{11}O_3P$ MW 138

Dichloride: $C_4H_9OCl_3P$. MW 175. B.p. 68–70°/3·5 mm.

Graf, *Chem. Ber.*, 1952, **85**, 9.

3-Butyl phthalide

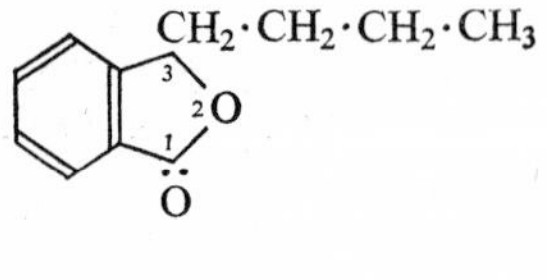

$C_{12}H_{14}O_2$ MW 190

(−)-.

Constituent of celery oil. B.p. 106–8°/0·1 mm. n_D^{22} 1·5528. $[\alpha]_D$ −57° (c, 1·96 in $CHCl_3$). $H_2 \rightarrow$ hexahydro deriv.: m.p. 48–9°. $[\alpha]_D$ −18° (c, 1·10 in $CHCl_3$).

Naves, *Helv. Chim. Acta*, 1943, **26**, 1281.

Barton, de Vries, *J. Chem. Soc.*, 1963, 1916.

1-Butyl-3-(p-tolylsulphonyl)urea. *See* Tolbutamide.★

2-Butyn-1-ol.★

See also:

Ashworth, Mansfield, Whiting, *Organic Syntheses*, Coll. Vol. **4**, 128.

3-(2-Butynyl)isocoumarin. *See* Capillarin.

Buxamine

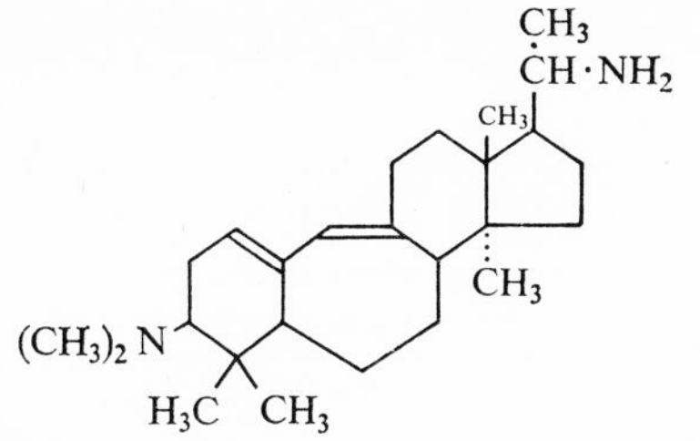

$C_{26}H_{44}N_2$ MW 384

Alkaloid from *Buxus sempervirens* L. Amorph. $[\alpha]_D^{20}$ +32° (c, 0·57 in $CHCl_3$). Light absorption: $\lambda_{max.}$ 238 (log ε, 4·42), 246 (4·45), and 254 mμ (4·24).

B,(COOH)₂: m.p. 263–7°. $[\alpha]_D^{20}$ +18° (c, 0·5 in MeOH : H_2O, 1 : 1).

Bis-*Hydrogen tartrate*: needles from EtOH.Aq. M.p. 210° decomp. $[\alpha]_D^{20}$ +26° (c, 0·52 in EtOH : H_2O, 1 : 1).

20-N-*Ac'*: m.p. 237°. $[\alpha]_D^{20}$ +5° (c, 0·5 in $CHCl_3$).

N-*Isopropylidene deriv.*: m.p. 187°. $[\alpha]_D^{20}$ +48° (c, 0·5 in $CHCl_3$).

Stauffacher, *Helv. Chim. Acta*, 1964, **47**, 968.

Buxaminol

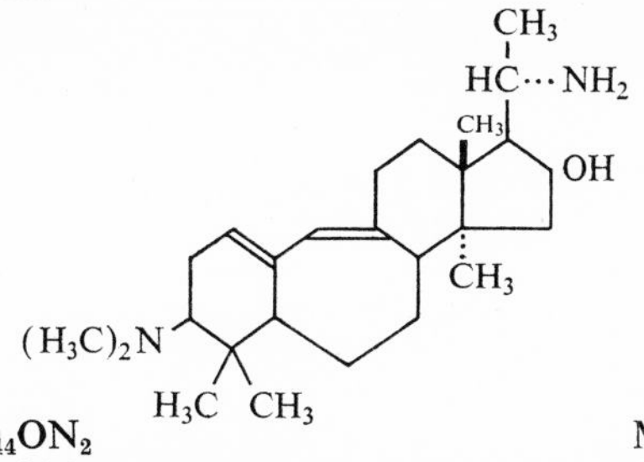

$C_{26}H_{44}ON_2$ MW 400

Alkaloid from *Buxus sempervirens* L. Needles from C_6H_6–hexane and short needles from MeOH.Aq. Sublimes at 200°. M.p. 199–200°. $[\alpha]_D^{20}$ +38° (c, 0·5 in $CHCl_3$). Light absorption: $\lambda_{max.}$ 238 (log ε, 4·45), 245 (4·49), 254 (4·28), 277 (2·68), and 287 mμ (2·58).

Bis-*Hydrogen tartrate*: needles. M.p. 210°. $[\alpha]_D^{20}$ +14° (c, 0·5 in 50% EtOH.Aq.).

N-*Isopropylidene deriv.*: prisms. M.p. 206–9°. $[\alpha]_D^{20}$ +95° (c, 0·5 in $CHCl_3$).

Stauffacher, *Helv. Chim. Acta*, 1964, **47**, 968.

Buxenine G. *See* Nor-buxamine.

C

Caaverin (5-*Hydroxy*-6-*methoxynoraporphine*)

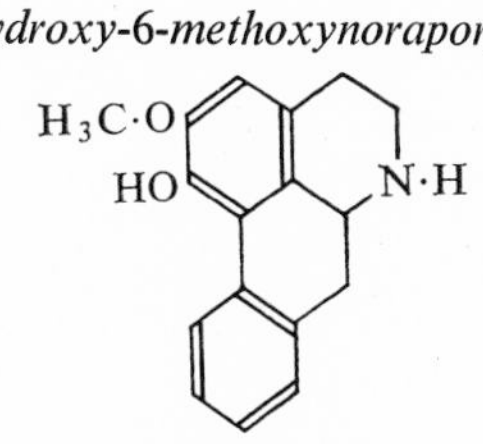

$C_{17}H_{17}O_2N_2$ MW 267

Alkaloid from the bark of *Symplocos celastrinea* Mart. Cryst. from C_6H_6. M.p. 208–10° decomp. $[\alpha]_D^{25}$ −89° (c, 1 in MeOH).

Di-Ac: fine needles from MeOH. M.p. 236–8°.

Tschesche *et al.*, *Tetrahedron*, 1964, **20**, 1435.

Cacalol

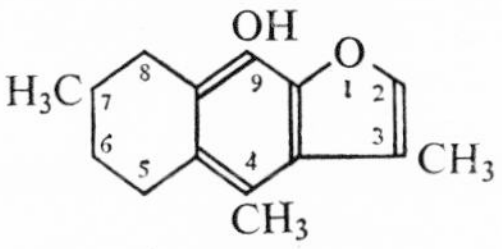

$C_{15}H_{18}O_3$ MW 230

Constituent of the roots of *Cacalea decomposita* A. Gray. Cryst. from Et_2O–pentane. M.p. 92–4°. $[\alpha]_D^{20}$ +10° ($CHCl_3$). Light absorption: $\lambda_{max.}$ 218 (ε, 30,400), 256 (10,500), 264 (10,000), and 286 mμ (1840). H_2 → dihydro deriv., m.p. 78–9°.

Ac: prisms from Me_2CO–hexane. M.p. 103–4°. $[\alpha]_D$ −9° ($CHCl_3$).

Me ether: $C_{16}H_{20}O_2$. MW 244. Oil. $[\alpha]_D$ +7° ($CHCl_3$).

Romo, Joseph-Nathan, *Tetrahedron*, 1964, **20**, 2331.

Cacalone

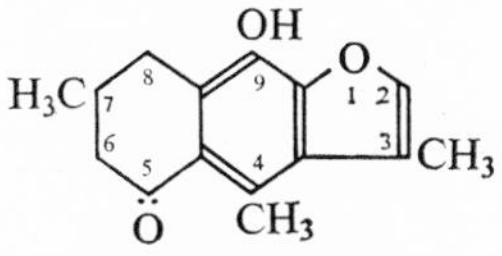

$C_{15}H_{16}O_3$ MW 244

Constituent of the roots of *Cacalea decomposita*. Prisms from Me_2CO–hexane. M.p. 120–1°. $[\alpha]_D$ +84° ($CHCl_3$). Light absorption: $\lambda_{max.}$ 212 (ε, 6600), 250 (11,200), and 320 mμ (8500).

Romo, Joseph-Nathan, *Tetrahedron*, 1964, **20**, 2331.

ε-Cadinene.★

(+)-.

The compound previously assigned this structure has been shown to have *cis*-fused ring system and has been called ε-Muurolene (*q.v.*).

(−)-.

Oil. $[\alpha]_D^{22}$ −15·9° (c, 1·5 in $CHCl_3$). n_D^{22} 1·5032.

Westfelt, *Acta Chem. Scand.*, 1964, **18**, 572.

δ-Cadinol.★

(+)-. Sesquigoyol, Torreyol.

Constituent of *Pinus parviflora* (var. *pentaphylla*), *P. formosana*, and the Siberian cedar. M.p. 137–8°. B.p. 285–9°. $[\alpha]_D^{37}$ +101·96°.

Ac: b.p. 152–5°/4 mm. n_D^{32} 1·4902. $[\alpha]_D^{22}$ +22·2°.

Note. Sesquigoyol and Torreyol have been shown to be identical with (+) δ-cadinol, and the name Torreyol has now been given to another compound (*q.v.*).

(−)-. Brown Alga Cadinol.

See Main work.

Sebe, *J. Chem. Soc., Japan*, 1935, **56**, 1137; 1940, **61**, 1269.

Pentegova, Motl, Herout, *Coll. Czech. Chem. Commun.*, 1961, **26**, 1362.

Wang, Weinstein, *Experientia*, 1963, **19**, 519.

α-Caesalapin

$C_{22}H_{32}O_8$ MW 424

Bitter principle from seeds of *Caesalapinia bonducella* Flen. White rectangular plates. M.p. 187°. $[\alpha]_D^{23}$ +37°. Hyd. → 2AcOH + β-caesalapin.

Ali, Qudrat-i-Khuda, *Chemistry and Industry*, 1960, 463.

β-Caesalapin

$C_{18}H_{26}O_5$ MW 322

Bitter principle from seeds of *Caesalapinia bonducella*. Hexagonal plates. M.p. 243°.

Ac: needles from C_6H_6. M.p. 218°.

Ali, Qudrat-i-Khuda, *Chemistry and Industry*, 1960, 463.

γ-Caesalpin

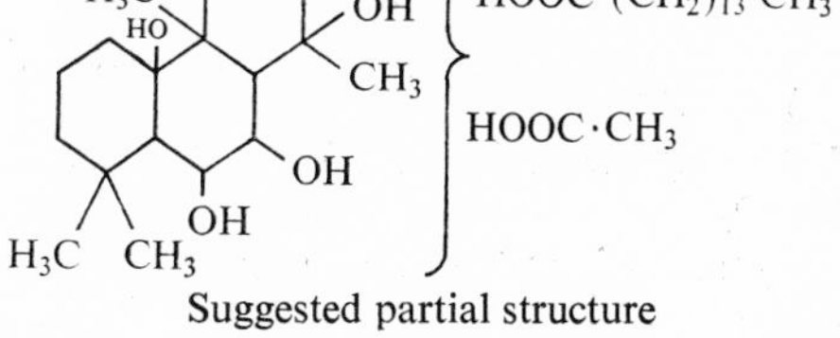

Suggested partial structure

$C_{36}H_{58}O_8$ MW 618

Bitter principle from the seeds of *Caesalpinia bonducella*. Amorph. M.p. 104–20°. Hydrolysis → AcOH, tetradecanoic acid and a cryst. product $C_{20}H_{30}O_6$. MW 366. Cryst. from Me_2CO. M.p. 251°. $[\alpha]_D^{25}$ +40·7° (MeOH). *Di-Ac*: m.p. 148–50°.

Ali, Qudrat-i-Khuda, *Chemistry and Industry*, 1960, 463.

Canonica *et al.*, *Tetrahedron Letters*, 1963, 2079.

1-Caffeoyl 22-feruloyl docosanediol

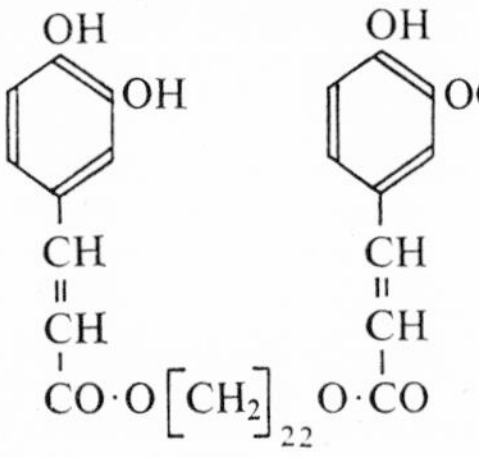

$C_{41}H_{60}O_8$ MW 680

Anti-oxidant isolated from oats. M.p. 85–6°. Hyd. → caffeic acid, ferulic acid, and 1 : 22-docosanediol and/or 1 : 24-docosanediol, m.p. 107·6°.

Daniels, King, Martin, *J. Sci. Food Agric.*, 1963, **14**, 385.

Daniels, Martin, *Nature* (Lond.), 1964, **203**, 298; *Chemistry and Industry*, 1964, 2058.

1-*O*-Caffeoylquinic Acid

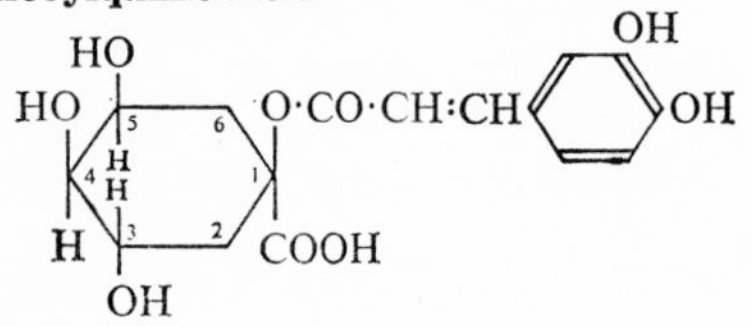

$C_{16}H_{18}O_9$ MW 354

Hemihydrate. Not cryst. $[\alpha]_D^{15}$ −8·3° (c, 3 in H_2O).

Me ester: not cryst.

Anhydride: quinide. M.p. 205–8°. $[\alpha]_D^{25}$ −17° (c, 2 in EtOH).

Monohydrate: m.p. 205–8° (sintering at 160°). 4 : 5-*Acetonide*: m.p. 155°.

Scarpati, Oriente, Panizzi, *Ann. chim.* (Rome), 1958, **48**, 997.

Waiss, Lundin, Corse, *Chemistry and Industry*, 1964, 1984.

3-*O*-Caffeoylquinic Acid. *See* Chlorogenic Acid.

4-*O*-Caffeoylquinic Acid (*Band* 510)

$C_{16}H_{18}O_9$ MW 354

Constituent of coffee and other plants. Not cryst. $[\alpha]_D^{15}$ −69°. Forms tri-*O*-me ether.

Sondheimer, *Arch. Biochem. Biophys.*, 1958, **74**, 131.

Sondheimer, Szymanski, Corse, *J. Agric. Food Chem.*, 1961, **9**, 146.

Scarpati, Esposito, *Tetrahedron Letters*, 1963, 1147.

Waiss, Lundin, Corse, *Chemistry and Industry*, 1964, 1984.

5-*O*-Caffeoylquinic Acid (*Neochlorogenic acid*)

$C_{16}H_{18}O_9$ MW 354

Constituent of coffee and many other plants. Needles from EtOH–AcOEt. M.p. 218–19°. $[\alpha]_D^{21}$ 2·4° (c, 2·1 in 50% EtOH).

Caffeine complex: m.p. 128–30°.

Lactone (Hauschild's substance HS): m.p. 236–8°. $[\alpha]_D^{21}$ +48·5° (10 min.) → 11·4° (40 min.) (c, 0·17 in EtOH).

Tri-O-Me: m.p. 83–5°.

Corse, *Nature*, 1953, **172**, 771.

Sondheimer, *Arch. Biochem. Biophys.*, 1958, **74**, 131.

Sondheimer, Szymanski, Corse, *J. Agric. Food Chem.*, 1961, **9**, 146.

Scarpati, Esposito, *Tetrahedron Letters*, 1963, 1147.

Ruveda, Deulofeu, Galmarini, *Chemistry and Industry*, 1964, 239.

Haslam *et al.*, *J. Chem. Soc.*, 1964, 2137.

Waiss, Lundin, Corse, *Chemistry and Industry*, 1964, 1984.

3-*O*-Caffeoylshikimic Acid (*Dactylifric acid*)

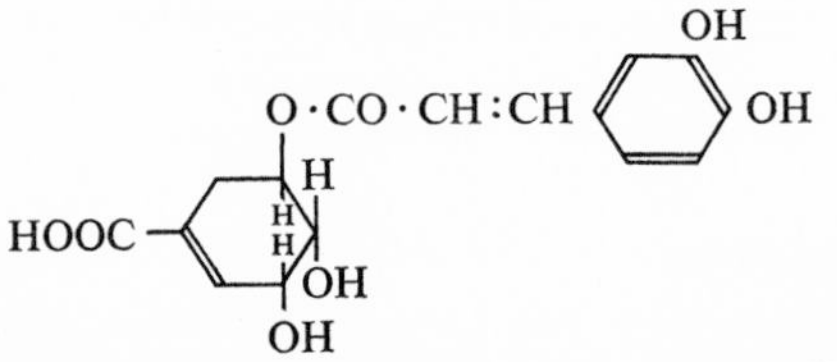

$C_{16}H_{16}O_8$ MW 336

Isolated from dates (*Phoenix dactylifera*). Cryst. from H_2O. M.p. 224–5° decomp. $[\alpha]_D^{25}$ −124° (c, 1·16 in 62·5% EtOH.Aq.). Light absorption: $\lambda_{max.}$ 303 and 332 mμ in EtOH; 304 and 331 mμ in EtOH–NaOH; 306 and 349 mμ in EtOH + NaOAc + H_3BO_3. Responsible for much of the enzymic browning reaction.

Maier, Metzler, Huber, *Biochem. Biophys. Research Commun.*, 1964, **14**, 124.

Calabacin

$C_{17}H_{25}O_3N_3$ MW 319

Alkaloid from the calabar bean. M.p. 138°. $[\alpha]_D^{27}$ −198° (c, 0·2 in $CHCl_3$).

Picrate: prisms from MeOH. M.p. 215°.

Salicylicate: cryst. from MeOH. M.p. 138°.

Döpke, *Naturwiss.*, 1963, **50**, 713.

Calabatin

$C_{17}H_{25}O_2N$ MW 303

Alkaloid from the calabar bean. M.p. 119°. $[\alpha]_D^{24}$ −98° (c, 0·2 in $CHCl_3$).

Picrate: needles from MeOH. M.p. 128°.

Salicylicate: needles from MeOH. M.p. 211°.

Döpke, *Naturwiss.*, 1963, **50**, 713.

Calactin.★

This is probably impure uscharidin.★

Crout, Hassall, Jones, *J. Chem. Soc.*, 1964, 2187.

Calebassine.★

17 : 17′-^2H-.

Grdinic, Nelson, Boekelheide, *J. Am. Chem. Soc.*, 1964, **86**, 3357.

C-Alkaloid-A.★

17 : 17′-^2H-.

Grdinic, Nelson, Boekelheide, *J. Am. Chem. Soc.*, 1964, **86**, 3357.

C-Alkaloid E★

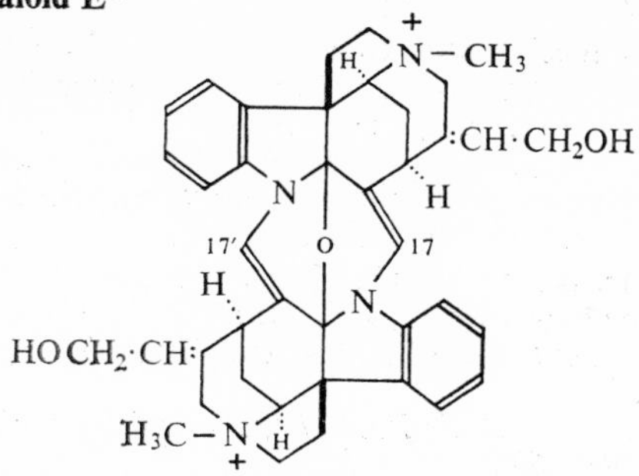

Nagyvary *et al.*, *Tetrahedron*, 1961, **14**, 138.
17 : 17′-^{2}H-.
Grdinic, Nelson, Boekelheide, *J. Am. Chem. Soc.*, 1964, **86**, 3357.

C-Alkaloid Y★

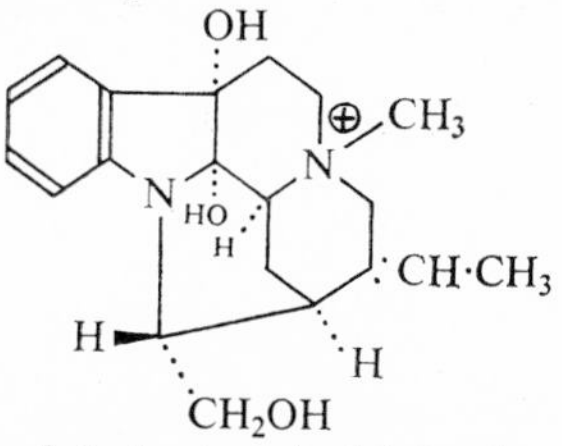

With ceric sulphate → red-violet col.
Revised structure:
Asmis *et al.*, *Helv. Chim. Acta*, 1954, **37**, 1968.
Hesse *et al.*, *Helv. Chim. Acta*, 1964, **47**, 878.

Callengoside

$C_{30}H_{46}O_{20}$ MW 566

Cardenolide from *Strophanthus vanderijstii* Staner. Colourless prisms from MeOH–Me_2CO. M.p. 255–6°. $[\alpha]_D^{25}$ +29·8° (c, 1·2 in MeOH).
O-*Ac*: small plates from Me_2CO–Et_2O. M.p. 227–30°. $[\alpha]_D^{26}$ −8·8° (c, 0·8 in $CHCl_3$).
Brenneisen *et al.*, *Helv. Chim. Acta*, 1964, **47**, 799, 814.

Calmiren. *See* Meprobamate.★

Calotoxin★

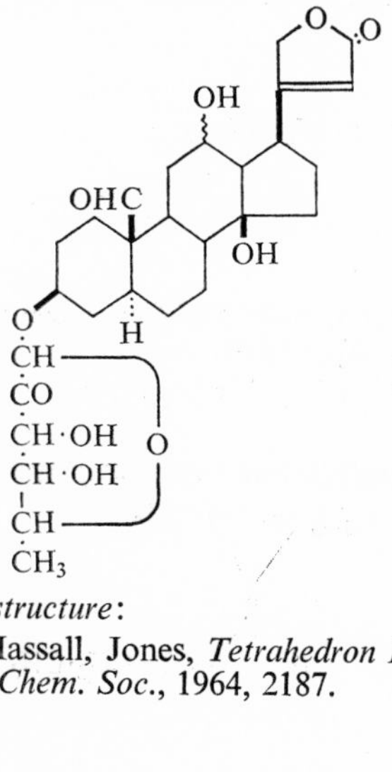

Suggested structure:
Crout, Hassall, Jones, *Tetrahedron Letters*, 1963, 63; *J. Chem. Soc.*, 1964, 2187.

Calotropin★

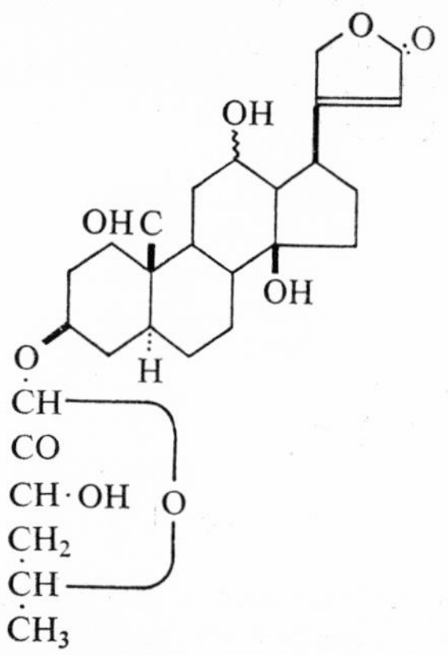

Constituent of *Asclepias curassavira* L.
Kupchan, Knox, Kelsey, *Science*, 1964, **146**, 1685.
Suggested structure:
Crout, Hassall, Jones, *Tetrahedron Letters*, 1963, 63; *J. Chem. Soc.*, 1964, 2187.

Calpol. *See p*-Acetamidophenol.

Calpurnine.★

See also:
Gerrans, Harley-Mason, *J. Chem. Soc.*, 1964, 2202.

Calycanthine.★

(±)-.
M.p. 253–8°.
(+)-.
M.p. 250–1°. $[\alpha]_D$ +684°.
See also:
Woodward *et al.*, *Proc. Chem. Soc.*, 1960, 76.
Hodson, Robinson, Smith, *Proc. Chem. Soc.*, 1961, 465.
Hendrickson, Goichke, Rees, *Tetrahedron*, 1964, **20**, 565.

1-Camphenyl *tert*-butylnitroxide

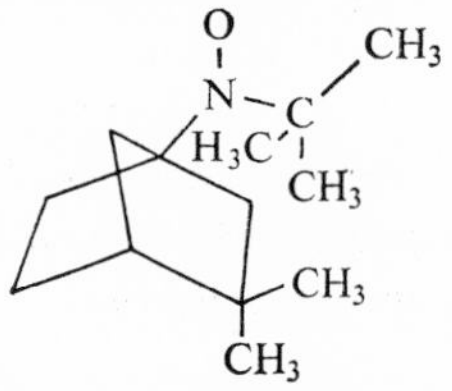

$C_{14}H_{24}ON$ MW 222

Stable optically active free radical. M.p. 56° (after sublimation).
Brunel, Lemaire, Rassat, *Bull. soc. chim.*, 1964, 1895.

Canaric Acid

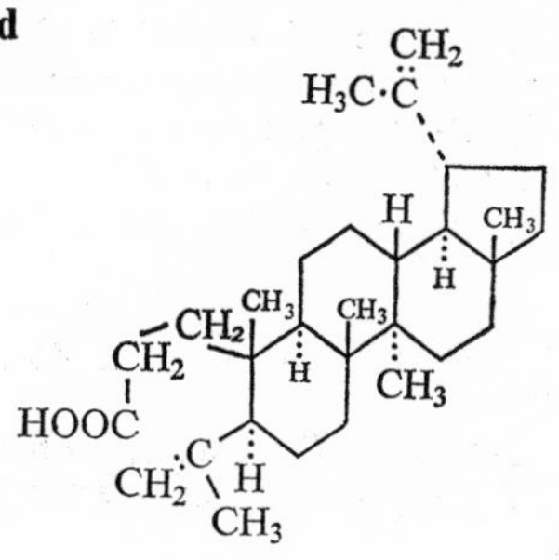

$C_{30}H_{52}O_2$ MW 444

Constituent of the oleoresin of *Canarium Muelleri*. M.p. 215–16°. $[\alpha]_D$ 56·5° ($CHCl_3$).
Me ester: m.p. 119–20°. $[\alpha]_D$ 50·2° ($CHCl_3$).

Carman, Cowley, *Tetrahedron Letters*, 1964, 627.

Candimine

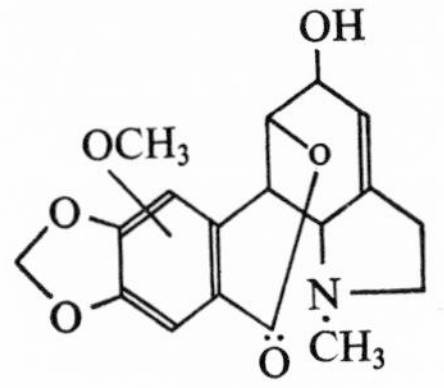

Partial structure

$C_{18}H_{19}O_6N$ MW 345

Constituent of *Hippeastrum candidum*. Cryst. from MeOH. M.p. 218–20°. $[\alpha]_D^{24}$ 220° (c, 0·2 in $CHCl_3$).
B,HClO₄: cryst. from H_2O. M.p. 177–9°.
Picrate: cryst. from MeOH. M.p. 220°
Ac: m.p. 239–41° decomp. *B,HClO₄*: cryst. from H_2O. M.p. 262° decomp.

Döpke, *Arch. Pharm.*, 1962, **295**, 920.

Cannabidiol★

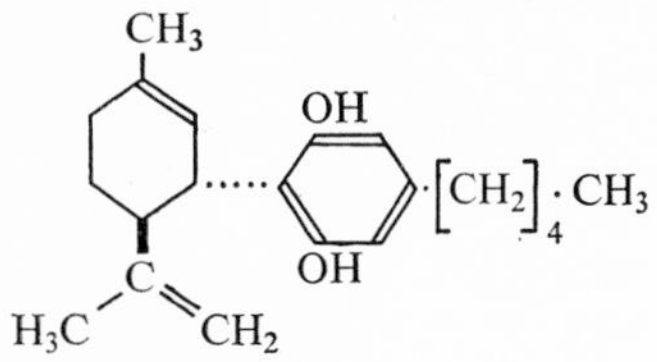

Revised structure:

Mechoulam, Shvo, *Tetrahedron*, 1963, **19**, 2073

Cannabigerol

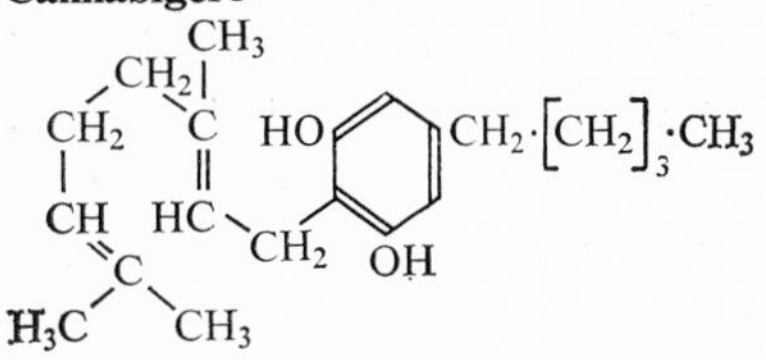

$C_{21}H_{32}O$ MW 316

Constituent of Hashish. M.p. 51–3°.

Gaoni, Mechoulam, *Proc. Chem. Soc.*, 1964, 82.

Capillarin (3-(2-*Butynyl*)*isocoumarin*)

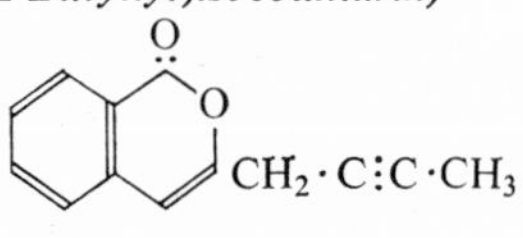

$C_{13}H_{10}O_2$ MW 198

Present in the roots of *Artemisia dracunulua*, *A. capillaris*, and *Chrysanthemum frutescens*. Colourless cryst. from Et_2O–light petroleum. M.p. 124°. H_2 → 3-butylisocoumarin, m.p. 45·5–46·5°.

Bohlmann, Kleine, *Chem. Ber.*, 1962, **95**, 39, 602.

Harada, Ichinomiya, Okada, *Nippon Kagaku. Zasshi*, 1960, **81**, 8548 (*Chem. Abstracts*, 1961, **55**, 8399).

Harada, Noguchi, Sugiyama, *Nippon Kagaku. Zasshi*, 1960, **81**, 654 (*Chem. Abstracts*, 1961, **55**, 8398).

Capreomycin I (*Capromycin*)

$C_{25-27}H_{50-53}N_{13-14}O_{9-10}Cl_4$ MW *ca.* 740

Antibiotic produced by *Streptomyces capreolus* sp. n. $[\alpha]_D$ −29·7°. pK_a' 6·4, 7·9, 9·4, 12·8 (in 66% $H{\cdot}CONMe_2$.Aq.). Hydrol → alanine + serine + 2 : 3-diaminopropionic acid, β-lysine, and α-(hexahydro-2-imino-4-pyrimidyl)glycine.

Herr, Sutton, Stark, *Trans. 21st Res. Conf. Pulmonary Disease*, 1962, 367.

Herr, *Antimicrobial Agents and Chemotherapy*, 1962, 201.

Stark *et al.*, *Antimicrobial Agents and Chemotherapy*, 1962, 596.

Capreomycin II.

Antibiotic produced by *Streptomyces capreolus* sp. n. $[\alpha]_D$ +2·5° (c, 1 in H_2O).
Hydrol. → alanine, serine, 2 : 3-diaminopropionic acid and α-(hexahydro-2-imino-4-pyrimidyl)glycine.

Herr, *Antimicrobial Agents and Chemotherapy*, 1962, 201.

Capromycin. *See* Capreomycin.

Capsanthin★

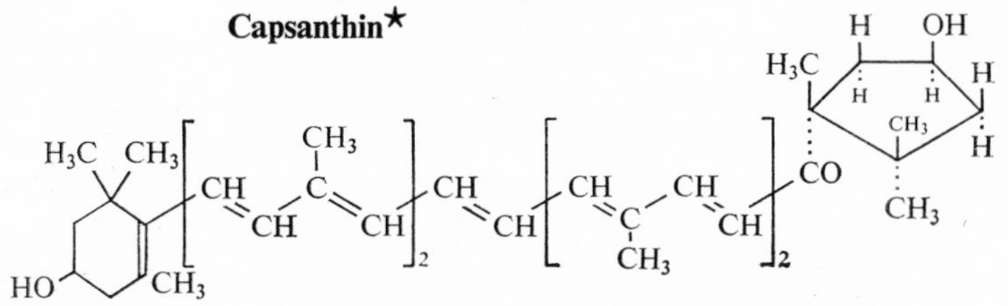

Configuration:

Faigle *et al.*, *Helv. Chim. Acta*, 1964, **47**, 741.

Capsorubin★

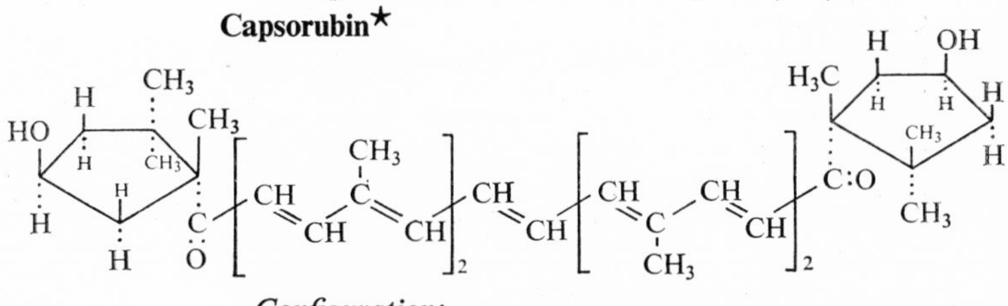

Configuration:

Faigle *et al.*, *Helv. Chim. Acta*, 1964, **47**, 741.

Carabrone

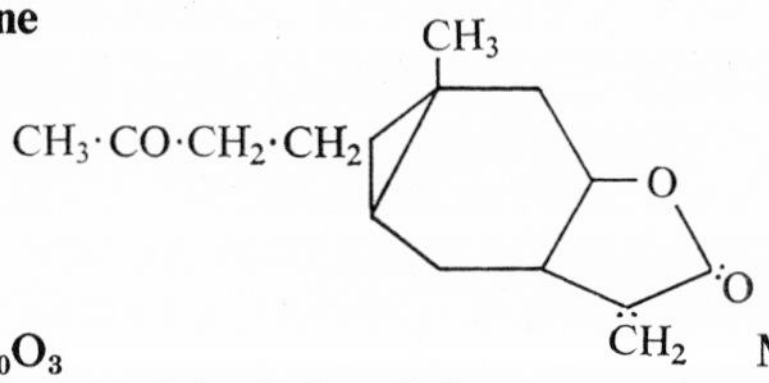

$C_{15}H_{20}O_3$ MW 248

Constituent of the fruits of *Carpesium abrotanoids* L. M.p. 90–1°. $[\alpha]_D$ 116·9°.

Minato, Nosaka, Horibe, *Proc. Chem. Soc.*, 1964, 120.

3-Carbethoxymethylene-1 : 2-diphenylcyclopropene

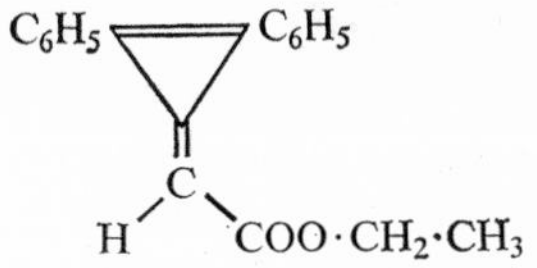

$C_{19}H_{16}O_2$ MW 276

Bright yellow cryst. from hexane. M.p. 72–5°. Light absorption: $\lambda_{max.}$ 244 (log ε, 4·42), 254 (4·43), 268 (4·33), 286 (4·24), 299 (4·26), 312 (4·12), 382 (3·89), 400 (3·87), 423 sh. (3·71), and 452 sh. mμ (3·23) (in iso-octane).

Battiste, *J. Am. Chem. Soc.*, 1964, **86**, 942.

α-Carbethoxy-α-phenylglutaronitrile. *See* Et ester *under* 2 : 4-Dicyano-2-phenylbutyric Acid.

Carbomycin★ (*Magnamycin*)

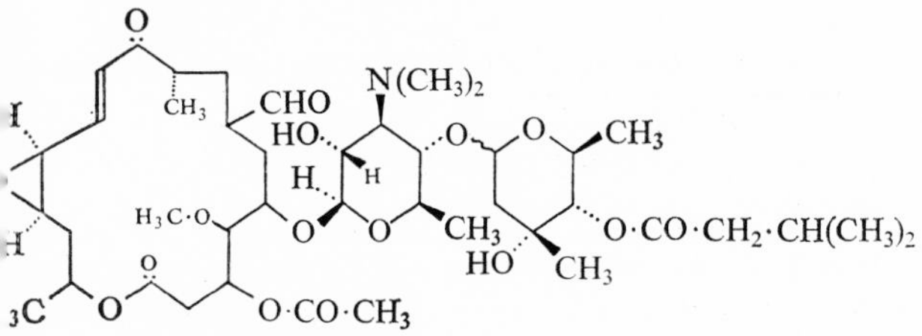

Configuration:

Hofheinz, Grisebach, *Chem. Ber.*, 1963, **96**, 2867.

α-Carboxy-γ-decalactone

$CH_3{\cdot}[CH_2]_5{\cdot}CH{\cdot}CH_2{\cdot}CH{\cdot}COOH$
O——CO

$C_{11}H_{18}O_4$ MW 214

Latent butter aroma compound. M.p. 60·5–62·5°. Heat → CO_2 + γ-decalactone (*see* Lactone *under* 4-Hydroxydecanoic acid★).

Stoll *et al.*, *Nature*, 1964, **202**, 350.

α-Carboxy-δ-decalactone

$CH_3{\cdot}[CH_2]_4{\cdot}CH{\cdot}CH_2{\cdot}CH_2{\cdot}CH{\cdot}COOH$
O——CO

Latent butter aroma compound. M.p. 77–8°. Heat → CO_2 + δ-decalactone (*see* Lactone *under* 5-Hydroxydecanoic acid★).

Stoll *et al.*, *Nature*, 1964, **202**, 350.

2-Carboxy-5 : 7-dimethyl-4-octalactone

$(CH_3)_2{\cdot}CH{\cdot}CH_2{\cdot}CH(CH_3){\cdot}CH{\cdot}CH_2{\cdot}CH{\cdot}COOH$
O——CO

$C_{11}H_{18}O_4$ MW 214

Latent butter aroma compound. M.p. 100·5–105°.

Stoll *et al.*, *Nature*, 1964, **202**, 350.

α-Carboxy-γ-dodecalactone

$CH_3{\cdot}[CH_2]_7{\cdot}CH{\cdot}CH_2{\cdot}CH{\cdot}COOH$
O——CO

$C_{13}H_{22}O_4$ MW 242

Latent butter aroma compound. M.p. 68·5–70·5°. Heat → CO_2 + γ-dodecalactone (*see* Lactone *under* 4-Hydroxydodecanoic acid★).

Stoll *et al.*, *Nature*, 1964, **202**, 350.

3-Carboxy-2-hydroxyadipic Acid. *See* Homoisocitric Acid.

3-Carboxy-3-hydroxyadipic Acid. *See* Homocitric Acid.

6-Carboxy-8-hydroxy-2-methylchromanone. *See* Rosellic Acid.

3-(3-Carboxy-4-hydroxyphenyl)-alanine★ (m-*Carboxytyrosine*)

$C_{10}H_{11}O_5N$ MW 225

Amino acid also present in seeds of *Lunaria annua* L.

Larsen, *Acta Chem. Scand.*, 1962, **16**, 1511.

(3-Carboxy-4-hydroxyphenyl)glycine

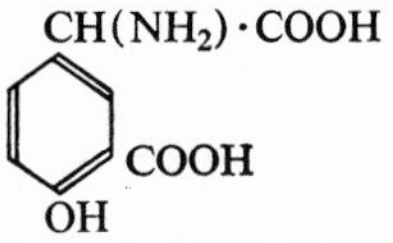

$C_9H_9O_5N$ MW 211

D-.

Amino acid in the seeds of Dyer's weed, weld (*Reseda luteola* L.) (isolated in a partially racemised form). The pure racemate formed a hydrate. $[\alpha]_D^{22}$ −121° (c, 0·75 in 1*N*-HCl), $[\alpha]_D^{25}$ −105° (c, 0·7 in 1*N*-H·COOH), −90·3° (c, 0·88 in 1*N*-NH_3.Aq.), −90·3° (c, 0·68 in 1*N*-NaOH), $[\alpha]_D^{22}$ −95° (c, 0·71 in H_2O), $[\alpha]_D^{24}$ −90·1° (c, 0·7 in 0·21*M*-phosphate buffer soln. pH 7).

L-.

$[\alpha]_D^{24}$ +85·6° (c, 0·72 in 0·2*M*-phosphate buffer soln. pH 7).

DL-.

Cryst. from H_2O as dihydrate. M.p. >250° decomp.

Nienburg, Tauböck, *Z. physiol. Chem.*, 1937, **250**, 80.

Kjaer, Larsen, *Acta Chem. Scand.*, 1963, **17**, 2397.

***S*-Carboxymethyl-L-cysteine**

$HOOC{\cdot}CH_2{\cdot}S{\cdot}CH_2{\cdot}CH(NH_2){\cdot}COOH$

$C_5H_9NO_4S$ MW 179

Present in radish (*Raphanus sativus*) seedlings.

Buziassy, Mazelis, *Biochim. Biophys. Acta*, 1964, **86**, 185.

2-Carboxy-6-methyl-4-heptalactone

$(CH_3)_2{\cdot}CH{\cdot}CH_2{\cdot}CH{\cdot}CH_2{\cdot}CH{\cdot}COOH$
O——CO

$C_9H_{14}O_4$ MW 186

Latent butter aroma compound. M.p. 51–4°.

Stoll *et al.*, *Nature*, 1964, **202**, 350.

α-Carboxy-γ-nonalactone

$CH_3{\cdot}[CH_2]_4{\cdot}CH{\cdot}CH_2{\cdot}CH{\cdot}COOH$
O——CO

$C_{10}H_{16}O_4$ MW 200

Latent butter aroma compound. M.p. 46–8°. Heat → CO_2 + γ-nonalactone (*see* Lactone *under* 4-Hydroxynonanoic acid★).

Stoll *et al.*, *Nature*, 1964, **203**, 350.

α-Carboxy-δ-nonalactone

$CH_3{\cdot}[CH_2]_3{\cdot}CH{\cdot}CH_2{\cdot}CH_2{\cdot}CH{\cdot}COOH$
O——CO

Latent butter aroma compound. M.p. 79–80°. Heat → CO_2 + δ-nonalactone.

Stoll *et al.*, *Nature*, 1964, **202**, 350.

2-Carboxy-7-noneno-4-lactone

$CH_3·CH{:}CH·CH_2·CH_2·CH·CH_2·CH·COOH$ (O———CO ring between the two CH)

$C_{10}H_{14}O_4$ MW 198

Trans-.

Latent butter aroma compound. M.p. 52·5–54°.

Stoll *et al.*, *Nature*, 1964, **202**, 350.

α-Carboxy-γ-octalactone

$CH_3·[CH_2]_3·CH·CH_2·CH·COOH$ (O———CO ring between the two CH)

$C_9H_{14}O_4$ MW 186

Latent butter aroma compound. M.p. 48–50°. Heat → CO_2 + γ-octalactone (*see* Lactone *under* 4-Hydroxyoctanoic Acid★).

Stoll *et al.*, *Nature*, 1964, **202**, 350.

***m*-Carboxyphenylalanine**

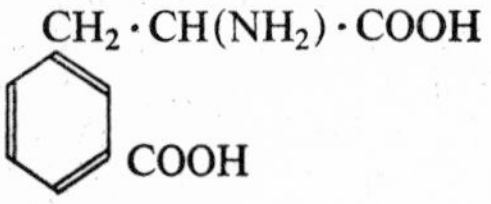

$C_{10}H_{11}O_4N$ MW 209

L-.

Amino acid present in *Lunaria annua* L., *Reseda luteola* L., and *Iris tingitana*. Cryst. from H_2O. $[\alpha]_D^{25}$ −17·2° (c, 1 in H_2O). $[\alpha]_D^{27}$ +4·1° (c, 0·97 in 1*N*-HCl). $[\alpha]_D^{24}$ −1·1° (c, 0·48 in 1*N*-NaOH). $[\alpha]_D^{22}$ −25·4° (c, 0·68 in 0·2*M*-phosphate buffer soln. pH 7).

Thompson *et al.*, *J. Biol. Chem.*, 1961, **236**, 1183.
Larsen, *Acta Chem. Scand.*, 1962, **16**, 1511.
Kjaer, Larsen, *Acta Chem. Scand.*, 1963, **17**, 2397.

***m*-Carboxyphenylglycine**

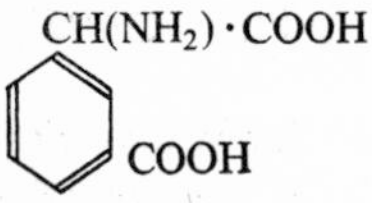

$C_9H_9O_4N$ MW 195

D-.

Amino acid present in the bulbs of *Iris tingitana* var. Wedgewood. Colourless cryst. Decomp. *ca.* 215°. $[\alpha]_D$ −89° (c, 0·6 in H_2O) (the sample isolated from the natural product was partially racemised and had $[\alpha]_D$ −6° (H_2O)).

L-*Arginine salt*: cryst. from MeOH.Aq. M.p. 203° decomp. $[\alpha]_D^{26}$ −40·4° (c, 0·8 in H_2O).

m-*Nitrile*: $C_9H_8O_2N_2$. MW 176. Cryst. from EtOH.Aq. M.p. 170° decomp. $[\alpha]_D^{23}$ −127° (c, 0·93 in *N*-HCl).

DL-.

Cryst. from EtOH.Aq. M.p. 210–11°.

m-*Nitrile*: m.p. 181°.

Morris *et al.*, *J. Am. Chem. Soc.*, 1959, **81**, 6069.
Irreverre *et al.*, *J. Biol. Chem.*, 1961, **236**, 1093.
Friis, Kjaer, *Acta Chem. Scand.*, 1963, **17**, 2391.

3-*o*-Carboxyphenylpropionic Acid.★

Page, Tarbell, *Organic Syntheses*, 1954, **34**, 8; Coll. Vol. **4**, 136.

β-(6-Carboxy-α′-pyron-3-yl) alanine. *See* Stizolobinic Acid.

β-(6-Carboxy-α′-pyron-4-yl) alanine. *See* Stizolobic Acid.

3-Carboxy-2-quinoxalinylpenicillinic Acid (3-*Carboxy-2-quinoxalinylpenicillin*)

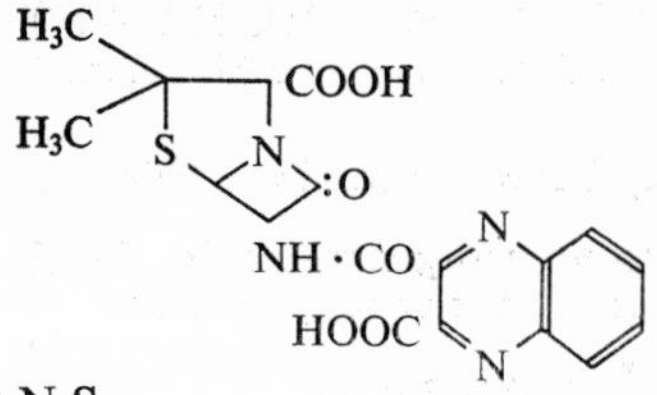

$C_{18}H_{16}O_6N_4S$ MW 416

Antibiotic particularly active against penicillinase-producing bacteria, $FeSO_4$ → deep violet col. Cuprous salts → red col.

Bis-*triethylammonium salt*: cryst. + $1H_2O$ from Me_2CO. M.p. 135–7° decomp. $[\alpha]_D^{20}$ 142° (c, 0·376 in H_2O).

Na salt: quinacillin: cream-coloured needles. M.p. 260° decomp. Anhyd. M.p. 261–2° decomp. $[\alpha]_D^{23}$ 183·5° (H_2O).

Richards, Housley, Spooner, *Nature*, 1963, **199**, 354.

3-Carboxy-2-quinoxalinylpenicillin. *See* 3-Carboxy-2-quinoxalinylpenicillinic Acid.

α-Carboxy-γ-tridecalactone

$CH_3·[CH_2]_8·CH·CH_2·CH·COOH$ (C———CO ring between the two CH)

$C_{14}H_{24}O_4$ MW 256

Latent butter aroma compound. M.p. 68·5–69·5°.

Stoll *et al.*, *Nature*, 1964, **202**, 350.

***m*-Carboxytyrosine.** *See* 3-(3-Carboxy-4-hydroxyphenyl)alanine.

α-Carboxy-γ-undecalactone

$CH_3·[CH_2]_6·CH·CH_2·CH·COOH$ (O———CO ring between the two CH)

$C_{12}H_{20}O_4$ MW 228

Latent butter aroma compound. M.p. 58–60°. Heat → CO_2 + γ-undecalactone (*see* Lactone *under* 4-Hydroxyundecanoic Acid★).

Stoll *et al.*, *Nature*, 1964, **202**, 350.

5-Carboxyvanillin (3-*Carboxy-4-hydroxy-5-methoxybenzaldehyde*, 6-*hydroxy-5-methoxyisophthalaldehydic acid*)

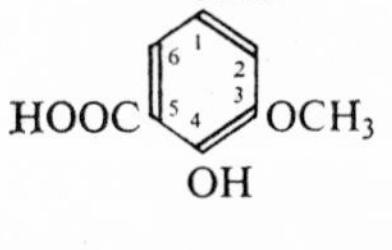

$C_9H_8O_5$ MW 196

Colourless cryst. from EtOH.Aq. M.p. 256–8°. Light absorption: $\lambda_{max.}$ 230 (ε, 18,000), 290 (10,700), and 320 mμ (11,600).

Pearl, Beyer, *J. Am. Chem. Soc.*, 1952, **74**, 4263.
Morita, *Can. J. Chem.*, 1964, **42**, 2362.

Cardiazole. *See* Metrazole.★

Caridan. *See under* Oxyphencyclimine.★

Carlina oxide.★

Alternative synthesis:

Atkinson, Curtis, Phillips, *Chemistry and Industry*, 1964, 2101.

Carnitine.★
(±)-.
Carboxy [14]*C*.
(−)-.
Methyl [14]*C*.
Lindstedt, Lindstedt, *Arkiv. Kemi*, 1964, **15**, 93.

Carolic Acid.★
See also:
Duncanson, *J. Chem. Soc.*, 1953, 1207.
Plimmer, *J. Org. Chem.*, 1964, **29**, 511.

Carone.★
(±)-.
Synthesis:
Medina, Manjarrez, *Tetrahedron*, 1964, **20**, 1807.

ζ-Carotene

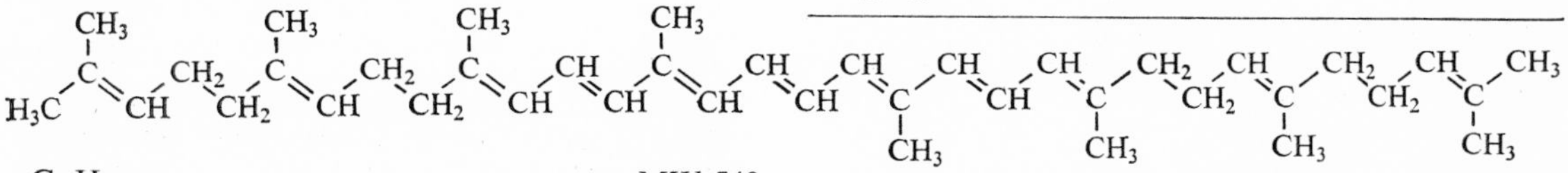

$C_{40}H_{60}$ MW 540
All *trans*-.
Constituent of carrot oil. M.p. 38–42°. Light absorption: $\lambda_{max.}$ 380, 401, 425 mμ.
Central *cis*-.
Light absorption: $\lambda_{max.}$ 286, 296, 378, 398, 422 mμ.
Rabourn, Quackenbush, *Arch. Biochem. Biophys.*, 1956, **61**, 111.
Davis *et al.*, *Proc. Chem. Soc.*, 1961, 261.

Carotol★

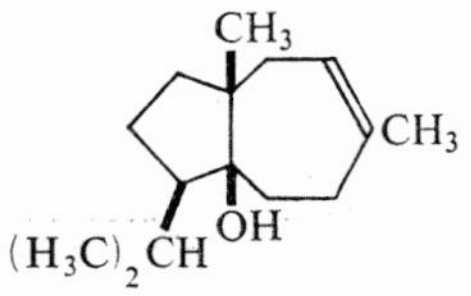

Stereochemistry:
Levisalles, Rudler, *Bull. soc. chim.*, 1964, 2020.

κ-Carrageenan.
Polysaccharide from the marine algae *Chondrus crispus* or *C. ocellatus*. Partial methanolysis → carrobiose.
Schmidt, *Ann.*, 1844, **51**, 29.
Smith, Cook, *Arch. Biochem. Biophys.*, 1953, **45**, 232.
O'Neill, *J. Am. Chem. Soc.*, 1955, **77**, 2837, 6324.

Carrobiose (3 : 6-*Anhydro*-4-O-β-D-*galactopyranosyl*-D-*galactose*)

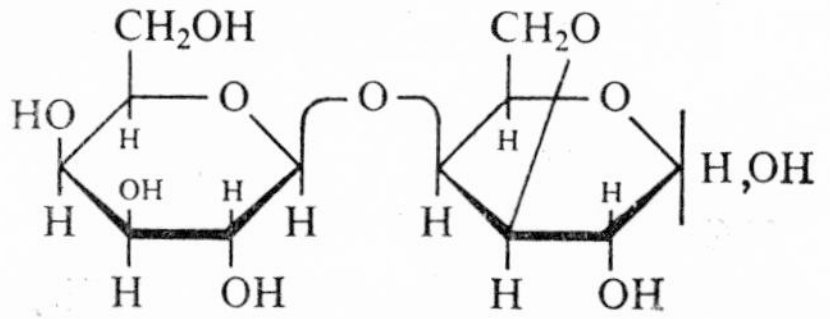

$C_{12}H_{20}O_{10}$ MW 324
Produced by partial methanolysis of the polysaccharide from marine alga *Chondrus crispus* (κ-carrageenan) and the red alga *Furcellaria fastigiata* (Huds.) Lamour. Redn. → carrobi-itol, m.p. 173°.
Di-Me Acetal: $C_{14}H_{26}O_{11}$. MW 370. Syrup. $[\alpha]_D^{17}$ +17° (c, 1 in H_2O). *Hexa-Ac*: from EtOH.Aq. M.p. 154–5°. $[\alpha]_D$ −8·5° (c, 1 in C_6H_6).
Di-Et Mercaptal: $C_{16}H_{30}O_9S_2$. MW 430. Cryst. from EtOH–Et_2O. M.p. 116–17°. $[\alpha]_D$ +14° (c, 2 in H_2O). *Hexa-Ac*: cryst. from EtOH.Aq. M.p. 121–121·5°. $[\alpha]_D$ +12° (c, 4 in $CHCl_3$).
O'Neill, *J. Am. Chem. Soc.*, 1955, **77**, 2837, 6324.
Painter, *Can. J. Chem.*, 1960, **38**, 112; *J. Chem. Soc.*, 1964, 1396.

Caryolysine. *See under* Mustine.★

α-Caryophyllene Alcohol

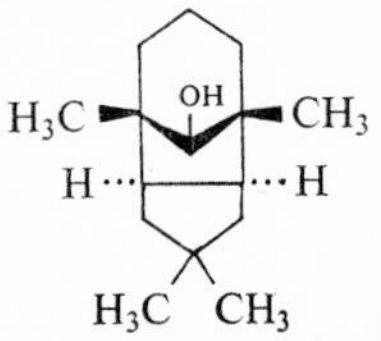

$C_{15}H_{26}O$ MW 222
Product of acid treatment of humulene. M.p. 117°. p-*Bromobenzene sulphonate*: monoclinic cryst. from Et_2O. M.p. 147·5–148°.
Asahina, Tsukamoto, *J. Pharm. Soc. Japan*, 1922, **484**, 463.
Dev, *Current Sci.* (India), 1951, **20**, 296.
Nickson *et al.*, *J. Am. Chem. Soc.*, 1964, **86**, 1437.
Gemmell *et al.*, *J. Am. Chem. Soc.*, 1964, **86**, 1438.
Corey, Nozoe, *J. Am. Chem. Soc.*, 1964, **86**, 1652.

Caryophyllene Chlorohydrin

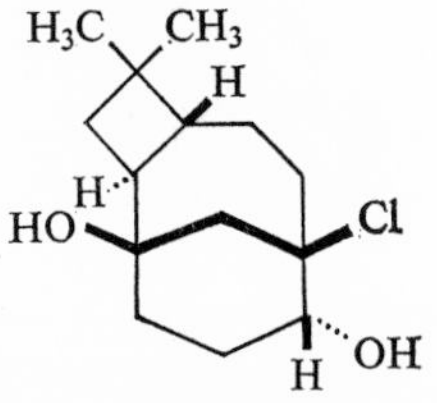

$C_{14}H_{23}O_2Cl$ MW 258·5
Cryst. from $CHCl_3$–light petroleum. M.p. 145–7° decomp.
Barton, Lindsey, *J. Chem. Soc.*, 1951, 2988.
Rogers, Mazhar-ul-Haque, *Proc. Chem. Soc.*, 1963, 371.
Greenwood, Qurreshi, Sutherland, *Proc. Chem. Soc.*, 1963, 372.

Cascarillin

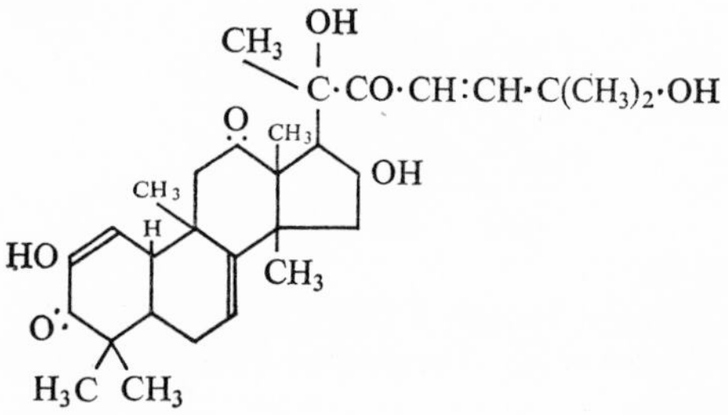

$C_{22}H_{32}O_7$ MW 413

Bitter principle of cascarilla bark (*Croton eleuteria*). Cryst. from EtOH. M.p. 203·5°.

Naylor, Littlefield, *Pharm. J.*, 1896, **57**, 95.
Birtwistle *et al.*, *Proc. Chem. Soc.*, 1962, 329.

Casimiroedine (N$^{\alpha}$-*Cinnamoyl*-N$^{\alpha}$-*methylhistamine* N-*glucoside*)

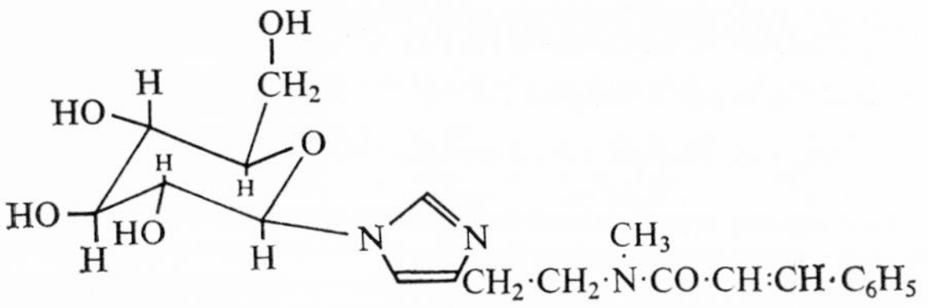

$C_{21}H_{27}O_6N_3$ MW 417
Alkaloid from the seeds of *Casimiroa edulis* La Llave et Lej. Cryst. from EtOH. M.p. 223–4°. $[\alpha]_D$ −27° (1% HCl). Light absorption: $\lambda_{max.}$ 219 (log ε, 4·26) and 280 mμ (4·30). H_2 → dihydro deriv. M.p. 176–7°. $[\alpha]_D$ +12° (EtOH).
Tetra-Ac: cryst. M.p. 80°.
Tetrabenzoyl: cryst. from MeOH.Aq. M.p. 97–105°.
$[\alpha]_D$ +29° (EtOH).
Picrate: yellow needles from MeOH. M.p. 110–12°.

Power, Callan, *J. Chem. Soc.*, 1911, 1993.
Aebi, *Helv. Chim. Acta*, 1956, **39**, 1495.
Djerassi *et al.*, *J. Org. Chem.*, 1956, **21**, 1510; *Tetrahedron*, 1958, **2**, 168a.
Ramm *et al.*, *Tetrahedron Letters*, 1962, 357.

Casimiroin (4-*Methoxy*-1-*methyl* 7 : 8-*methylenedioxy*-2-*quinolone*)

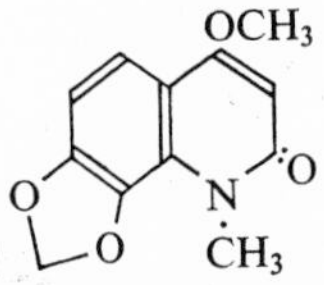

$C_{12}H_{11}O_4N$ MW 233
Constituent of the seed and bark of *Casimiron edulis* Llave et Lex. Cryst. from Me_2CO–hexane. M.p. 202–3°. Light absorption: $\lambda_{max.}$ 227 (log ε, 4·55), 237 (4·49), 252 (4·38), 260 (4·38), and 301 mμ (3·87).

Kincl *et al.*, *J. Chem. Soc.*, 1956, 4163, 4170.
Meisels, Sondheimer, *J. Am. Chem. Soc.*, 1957, **79**, 6328.
Weinstein, Hylton, *Tetrahedron*, 1964, **20**, 1725.

Cassaic Acid★

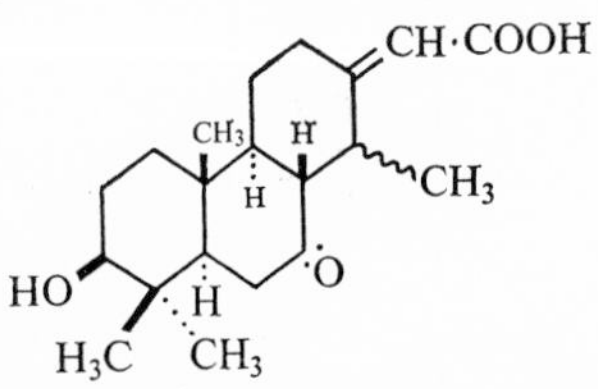

See also:

Humber, Taylor, *J. Chem. Soc.*, 1955, 1044.
Turner *et al.*, *Tetrahedron Letters*, 1959, No. 2, 7.
Chapman *et al.*, *J. Chem. Soc.*, 1963, 4010.

Cassaine★

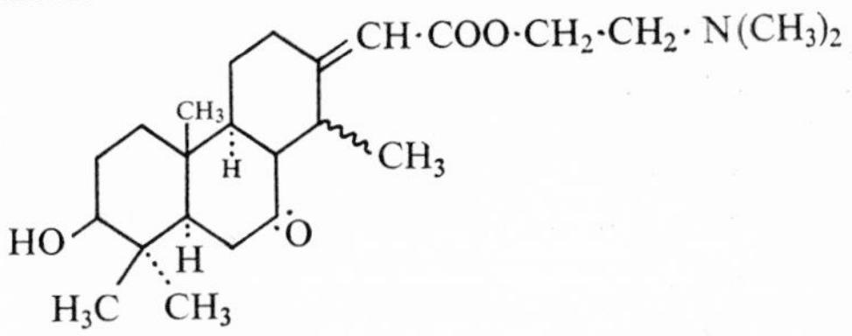

The structure follows from that of Cassaic Acid.

Cassiamin

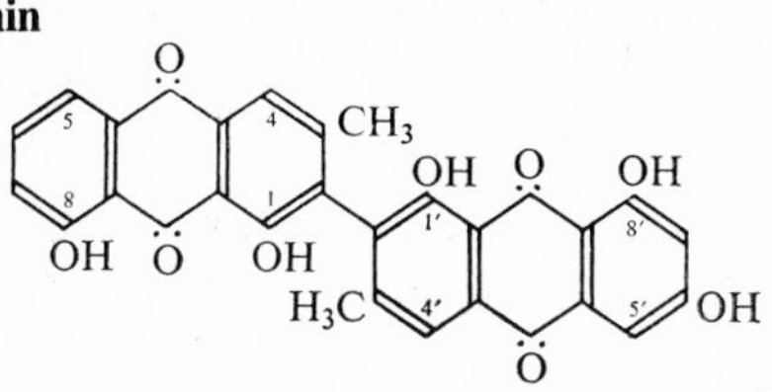

$C_{30}H_{18}O_9$ MW 522
Constituent of the root bark of *Cassia siamea* Lam. (syn. *C. florida* Vahl.). Bright orange-yellow prisms from tetrahydrofuran. M.p. 356–7° decomp. Light absorption: $\lambda_{max.}$ 228, 259, 288, and 445 mμ.
Penta-Ac: m.p. 182–3°. $[\alpha]_D$ −169·5° (c, 0·1 in $CHCl_3$).
Penta-Me ether: $C_{35}H_{28}O_9$. MW 592. M.p. 295–6°.

Dutta *et al.*, *Tetrahedron Letters*, 1964, 3023.

Erratum p. 571

Cassic Acid.★

Should read: *See* Rhein.

Cassine

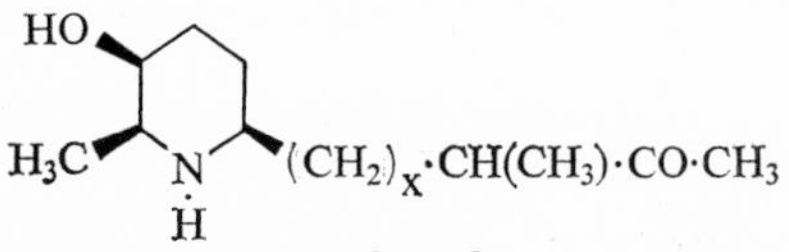

x = 9 or 8

$C_{19}H_{37}O_2N$ ($C_{18}H_{35}O_2N$) MW 311 (297)
Alkaloid present in the leaves of *Cassia excela* Shrad. B.p. 90°/0·001 mm. M.p. 57–8°. $[\alpha]_D^{25}$ −0·6°.
B,HCl: needles from EtOH. M.p. 173–5°.
B,HNO₃: cryst. from AcOEt. M.p. 116–17°.
Di-Ac: oil. B.p. 110°/0·002 mm.
N-*Me*: cryst. from AcOEt. M.p. 110·5–111·5°. $[\alpha]_D^{26}$ 6·5°. *B,CH₃I*: cryst. from AcOEt. M.p. 91–3°. $[\alpha]_D^{26}$ 15·8°.

Highet, *J. Org. Chem.*, 1964, **29**, 471.

Casticin (3′ : 5-*Dihydroxy*-3 : 4′ : 6 : 7-*tetramethoxy*-*flavone*)

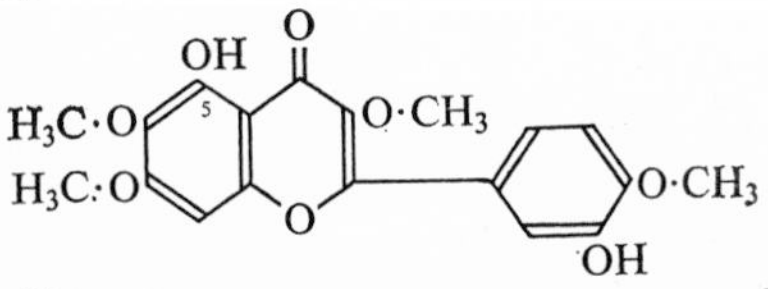

$C_{19}H_{18}O_8$ MW 374
Constituent of *Vitex agnus castus* seeds. Prisms from C_6H_6–light petroleum. M.p. 186–7°. $FeCl_3$ → olive green col.
Di-Ac: needles. M.p. 178–9°.
5-O-*Me*: m.p. 182·5–183·5°.

Di-O-Me: colourless needles. M.p. 141–2°.
Di-O-Et: colourless needles. M.p. 115–16°.

Belič, Bergant-Dolar, Morton, *J. Chem. Soc.*, 1961, 2523.
Hörhammer, Wagner, Graf, *Tetrahedron Letters*, 1964, 323.

Castoreum Pigment I. *See* 2′ : 4 : 4′-Trihydroxybiphenyl-2-carboxylic Acid (2 : 2′) lactone.

Catharine

$C_{46}H_{52}O_9N_4$ MW 804

Minor alkaloid from *Vinca rosea* L. Cryst. with mole MeOH. M.p. 271–5° decomp. $[\alpha]_D$ −54·2° ($CHCl_3$). pK_a' 5·34 (66% H·CONMe₂). Light absorption: $\lambda_{max.}$ 222, 265, 292 mμ.

Svoboda *et al.*, *J. Pharm. Sci.*, 1961, **50**, 409.

Caulophylline.★

Cryst. structure:

Mathews, Rich, *Nature*, 1964, **201**, 179.

Cavodil. *See* B,HCl *under* α-Methylphenethylhydrazine.

Ceanothic Acid.★

See also:

Eade, Kornis, Simes, *Austral. J. Chem.*, 1964, **17**, 141.

Celesticetin★

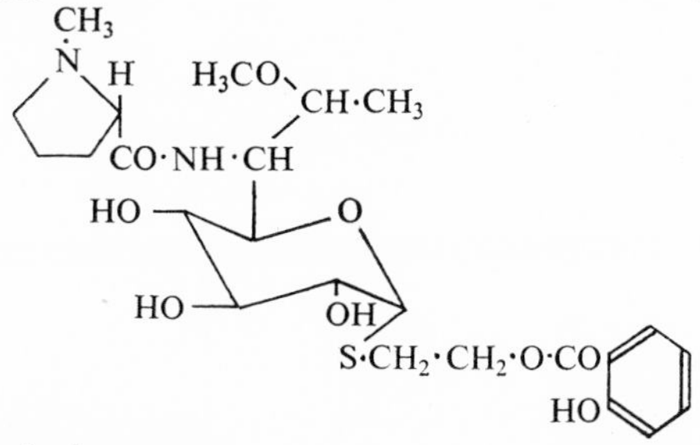

Revised structure:

Hoeksema, *J. Am. Chem. Soc.*, 1964, **86**, 4224.

Celontin. *See* Methsuximide.★

Erratum p. 578

Cembrene.★

Should read: Occurs in the essential oil of *Pinus albicaulis*.

Cenazole. *See* Metrazole.★

Censedal. *See* Nealbarbitone.★

Centaureidin

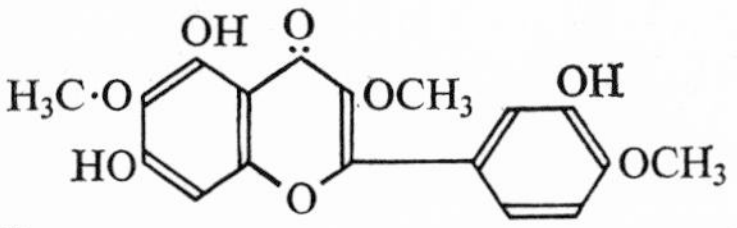

$C_{18}H_{16}O_8$ MW 360

Aglycone from centaureine. Needles from MeOH. M.p. 196°. HI → quercetagetin.
3′ : 5 : 7-*Tri-O-Me ether*: quercetagetin hexa-Me ether: m.p. 142°.
3 : 5-*Di-O-Me ether*: yellow needles. M.p. 228–30°. 7-*O-Et ether*: m.p. 128–30°.

Farkas *et al.*, *Chem. Ber.*, 1964, **97**, 1666.

Centaureine

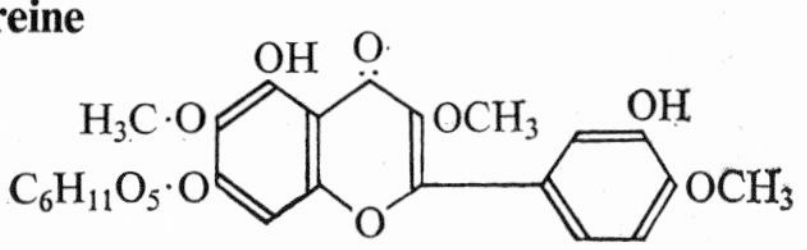

$C_{24}H_{26}O_{13}$ MW 522

Constituent of the root of *Centaurea jacea* L. Cryst. of hydrate. M.p. 208–9°. $[\alpha]_D^{20}$ −76·6° (c, 1·4 in MeOH). Light absorption: $\lambda_{max.}$ 258 (log ε, 4·30) and 349 mμ (4·31). $FeCl_3$ → green col. Hydrol. → centaureidine.
Hexa-Ac: m.p. 192°.

Farkas *et al.*, *Chem. Ber.*, 1964, **97**, 1666.

Cephaeline.★

O-*Me*: *see* Emetine.★
N-*Me*: almarckine. Alkaloid from *Alangium lamarckii*. Cryst. from MeOH. M.p. 191–2°. $[\alpha]_D$ −50·5° (c, 1·14 in $CHCl_3$). O-*Me ether*: $C_{30}H_{42}O_4N_2$. MW 494. Amorph.

Subbaratnam, Siddiqui, *J. Sci. Ind. Res.* (India), 1956, **15B**, 432.
Budzikiewicz, Pakrashi, Vorbrüggen, *Tetrahedron*, 1964, **20**, 399.

Cephalochromin

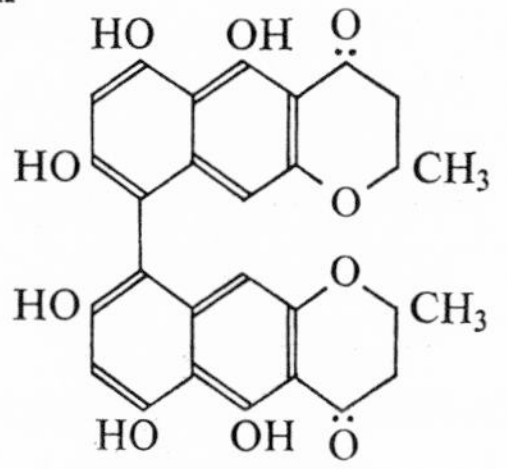

$C_{28}H_{22}O_{10}$ MW 518

Yellow pigment produced by *Cephalosporium* (P.R.L. 2070) sp. Orange cryst. from hexane. M.p. >300°. $[\alpha]_D$ 510° ($CHCl_3$). Light absorption: $\lambda_{max.}$ 234, 270, 295, 329, and 418 mμ.

Tertzakian *et al.*, *Proc. Chem. Soc.*, 1964, 195.

Cephaloridine (7-[(2-*Thienyl*)*acetamido*]-3-(1-*pyridylmethyl*)-3-*cephem*-4-*carboxylic acid betaine*, *Ceporin*)

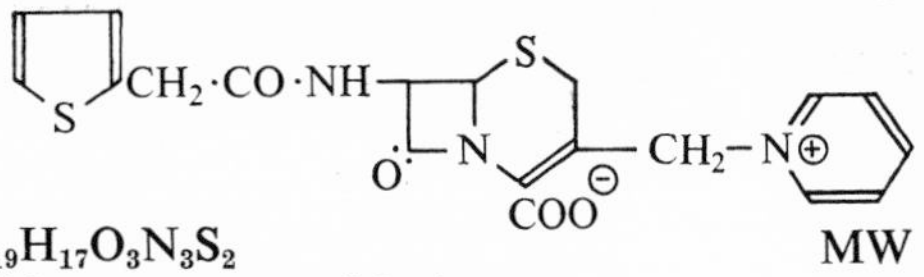

$C_{19}H_{17}O_3N_3S_2$ MW 399

Wide spectrum antibiotic.

Anon, *Chemistry and Industry*, 1964, 1927.

Cephalosporin C.★

For synthetic approaches see:

Green *et al.*, *J. Chem. Soc.*, 1964, 766.
Barrett, Kane, Lowe, *J. Chem. Soc.*, 1964, 783.
Barrett *et al.*, *J. Chem. Soc.*, 1964, 788.

Cephalosporin P_1★

$C_{33}H_{50}O_8$ MW 574

Mass spectra and N.M.R. spectra indicate that the structure given ★ must have an additional angular methyl group.

Melera, *Experientia*, 1963, **19**, 565.

Cephalotaxine

$C_{18}H_{21}O_4N$ MW 315

Alkaloid from *Cephalotaxus drupacea* and *C. fortunei*. Cryst. from C_6H_6. M.p. 131–2°. $[\alpha]_D^{25}$ −204° (c, 1·8 in $CHCl_3$). pK_a 8·95 (95% EtOH). Light absorption: $\lambda_{max.}$ 238, 290 mμ (log ε, 3·56, 3·55).

B,HCl: cryst. from EtOH–Et_2O. M.p. 174–7°, 188° decomp.

B,HClO₄: m.p. 213–16° decomp.

Ac: cryst. from Et_2O. M.p. 140–2°. $[\alpha]_D^{25}$ −97° (c, 2·2 in $CHCl_3$). pK_a 7·97 (95% EtOH).

Paudler, Kerley, McKay, *J. Org. Chem.*, 1963, **28**, 2194.

Ceporin. *See* Cephaloridine.

Cerebellar Factor. *See* Ergothioneine.

Cerebron★ (*Phrenosine*)

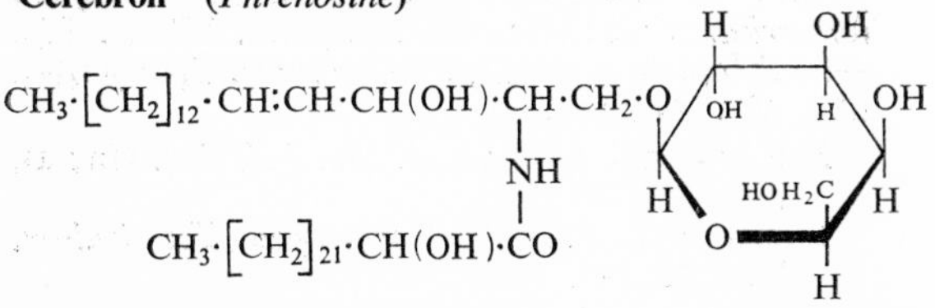

$C_{48}H_{93}NO_9$ MW 827

Galactocebroside. M.p. 195°. $[\alpha]_D^{26}$ +4·4° (Py).

Hexa-Ac: cryst. from MeOH. M.p. 40–1°. $[\alpha]_D^{25}$ −10° (c, 1 in MeOH–$CHCl_3$[1 : 1]).

Shapiro, Flowers, *J. Am. Chem. Soc.*, 1961, **83**, 3327.

Cernuine

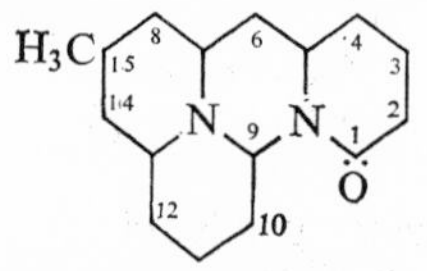

$C_{16}H_{26}ON_2$ MW 262

Alkaloid from *Lycopodium cernuum* L. M.p. 106°. pK 6·3 (50% MeOH).

Note. This name was also given to an aurone. *See* Aureusidin.★

Marion, Manske, *Can. J. Research*, 1948, **26B**, 1.
Ayer *et al.*, *Tetrahedron Letters*, 1964, 2201.

Cervicarcin

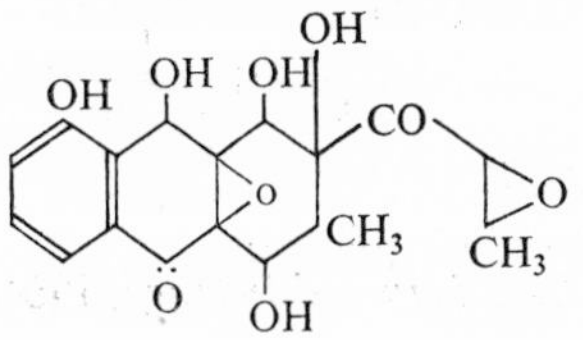

$C_{19}H_{20}O_9$ MW 392

Antitumour antibiotic produced by *Streptomyces ogaensis*. M.p. 205°. $[\alpha]_D^{26}$ −59·7° (c, 1·4 in EtOH). pK_a' 9·00 (60% EtOH). Light absorption: $\lambda_{max.}$ 227 (ε, 14,700), 264 (7860), and 323 mμ (3700).

Me ether: $C_{20}H_{22}O_4$. MW 406. Hemihydrate. M.p. 227°. *Tri-Ac*: m.p. 256°.

Ohkuma *et al.*, *J. Antibiotics* (Tokyo) Ser. A, 1962, **15**, 152, 247.
Itakura *et al.*, *J. Antibiotics* (Tokyo) Ser. A, 1963, **16**, 231.
Marumo, Sasaki, Suzuki, *J. Am. Chem. Soc.*, 1964, **86**, 4507.

Chalcomycin★

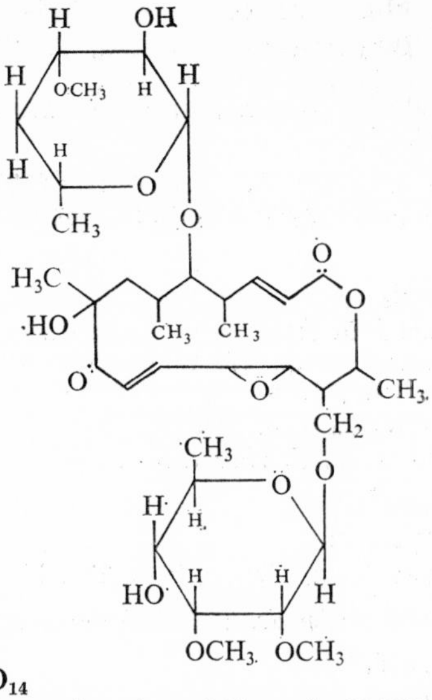

$C_{35}H_{56}O_{14}$ MW 700

Light absorption: $\lambda_{max.}$ 268 mμ (ε, 22,770).

Woo, Dion, Bartz, *J. Am. Chem. Soc.*, 1962, **84**, 1512; 1964, **86**, 2724, 2726.

Chasmaconitine

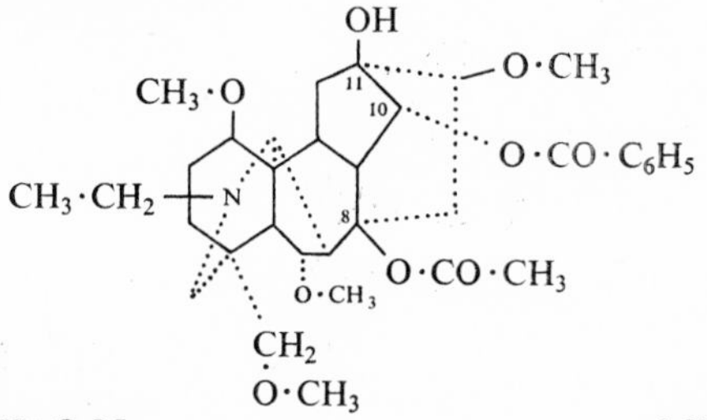

$C_{34}H_{47}O_9N$ MW 613

Alkaloid from roots of *Aconitium chasmanthum* Stapf. Two forms: (i) Colourless prisms from hexane. M.p. 181–2° decomp. (ii) Fine needles from Et_2O. M.p. 165–7°. $[\alpha]_D^{25}$ +10·3° (c, 1·26 in EtOH).

Achmatowicz, Marion, *Can. J. Chem.*, 1964, **42**, 154.

Chasmanthinine

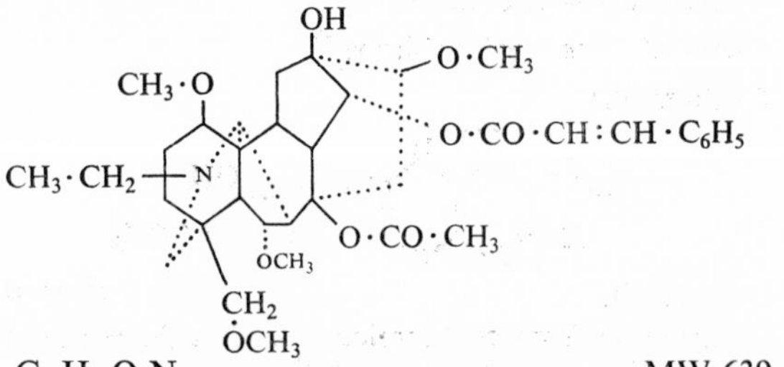

$C_{36}H_{49}O_9N$ MW 639

Alkaloid from the roots of *Aconitium chasmanthum* Stapf. Needles from hexane or Et_2O. M.p. 160–1° decomp. $[\alpha]_D^{25}$ +9·6° (c, 1·09 in EtOH).

Achmatowicz, Marion, *Can. J. Chem.*, 1964, **42**, 154.

Chebulagic Acid★

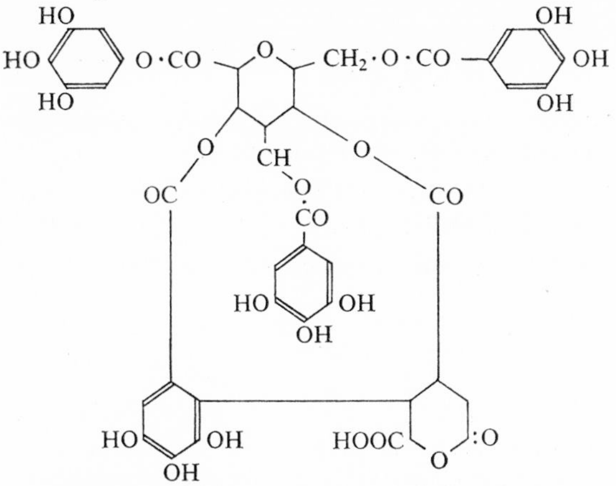

Revised structure:

Schmidt, Hensler, Stephan, *Ann.*, 1957, **609**, 186.

Chelocardin

$C_{23}H_{23}O_8N$ MW 441

Antibiotic from *Nocardia sulphurea* N. spp. Bright yellow needles. Decomp. 215–30° without melting. *B,HCl*: $C_{23}H_{21}NO_7$·HCl. MW 459·5. Decomp. 220–30°. $[\alpha]_D^{22}$ +570° (c, 1 in MeOH). pK_a' 3·4, 7·6, 9·25.

Oliver *et al.*, *Antimicrobial Agents and Chemotherapy*, 1963, 583.

Sinclair *et al.*, *Antimicrobial Agents and Chemotherapy*, 1962, 592.

Chemiofuran. *See* Nitrofuranotoin.★

Childhood Sterol.

Sterol only found in urine of children.

Gupta, Tanner, *Nature*, 1964, **203**, 187.

Chimonanthine.★

(±)-.

M.p. 184°.

See also:

Hendrickson, Göschke, Rees, *Tetrahedron*, 1964, **20**, 565.

Scott, McCapra, Hall, *J. Am. Chem. Soc.*, 1964, **86**, 302.

Chinovosamine. *See* 2-Amino-2 : 6-dideoxy-D-glucose.

Chloroacetonitrile.★

See also:

Reisner, Horning, *Organic Syntheses*, Coll. Vol. **4**, 144.

Chloro-*p*-benzoquinone.★

See also:

Harman, *Organic Syntheses*, 1955, **35**, 22; Coll. Vol. **4**, 148.

2-Chlorocyclopentanol.★

See also:

Donahoe, Vanderwerf, *Organic Syntheses*, Coll. Vol. **4**, 157.

7-Chloro-1 : 3-dihydro-1-methyl-5-phenyl-2*H*-1 : 4-benzodiazepin-2-one. *See* Valium.★

2-Chloro-1 : 3-dinitrobenzene.★

See also:

Gunstone, Tucker, *Organic Syntheses*, Coll. Vol. **4**, 160.

2-Chloro-1 : 3 : 2-dioxaphosphepan (*Tetramethylenephosphorochloridite*)

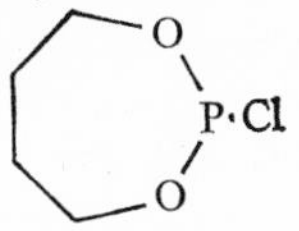

$C_4H_8O_2ClP$ MW 154·5

B.p. 74–5·5°/8 mm. with decomp. D_0^{20} 1·2885. n_D^{20} 1·5010. Inflames in air. Polymerises on standing.

Arbuzov, Zoroastrova, *Izvest. Akad. Nauk S.S.S.R., Otdel. Khim. Nauk*, 1952, 770 (*Chem. Abstracts*, 1953, **47**, 9900).

***p*-Chloro-*N*-ethylaniline.**★

B.p. 108–10°/5 mm., 149–50°/40 mm. n_D^{25} 1·5650–1·5651.

Roberts, Vogt, *Organic Syntheses*, 1958, **38**, 29; Coll. Vol. **4**, 420.

Chloroethylene Oxide. *See* Chloro-oxirane.

Chlorofluoroacetic Acid

ClFCH·COOH

$C_2H_2O_2ClF$ MW 112·5

B.p. 162°. n_D^{25} 1·4085. D_4^{25} 1·532.

Me ester: $C_3H_4O_2ClF$. MW 126·5. B.p. 116°. n_D^{25} 1·3903. D_4^{25} 1·323.

Et ester: $C_4H_6O_2ClF$. MW 140·5. B.p. 129–30°. n_D^{25} 1·3925. D_4^{25} 1·225.

Propyl ester: $C_5H_8O_2ClF$. MW 154·5. B.p. 147°. n_D^{25} 1·3994. D_4^{25} 1·170.

Butyl ester: $C_6H_{10}O_2ClF$. MW 168·5. B.p. 165–6°. n_D^{25} 1·4067. D_4^{25} 1·124.

Chloride: C_2HOCl_2F. MW 131. B.p. 69·5°. n_D^{25} 1·3992. D_4^{25} 1·468.

Amide: C_2H_3ONClF. MW 111·5. B.p. 72°/1 mm. n_D^{25} 1·4535. n_D^{25} 1·510.

Nitrile: C_2HNClF. MW 93·5. B.p. 66°. n_D^{25} 1·3627. D_4^{25} 1·267.

Young, Tarrant, *J. Am. Chem. Soc.*, 1949, **71**, 2432.

Bergmann *et al.*, *J. Am. Chem. Soc.*, 1957, **79**, 4174.

Englund, *Organic Syntheses*, 1954, **34**, 49; Coll. Vol. **4**, 423.

1-Chloro-1-fluorocyclohexane

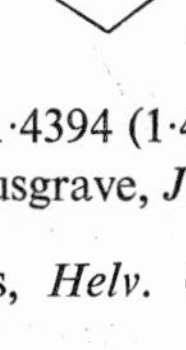

$C_6H_{10}ClF$ MW 136·5

B.p. 141–2°. n_D^{25} 1·4394 (1·4382).

Cuthbertson, Musgrave, *J. Appl. Chem.*, 1957, **7**, 99.

Hopff, Valkanas, *Helv. Chim. Acta*, 1963, **46**, 1818.

Chlorogenic Acid (3-O-*Caffeoylquinic acid*).
N.M.R. spectrum:
Waiss, Lundin, Corse, *Chemistry and Industry*, 1964, 1984.

5-(1-Chloro-2-hydroxy-3-butynyl)-2 : 2′-bithienyl

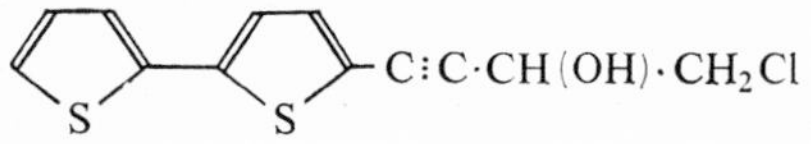

$C_{12}H_9OClS_2$ MW 268·5
Constituent of the roots of *Tagetes minuta* L. M.p. 55°. Light absorption: $\lambda_{max.}$ 245 and 336 mμ.
Atkinson, Curtis, Phillips, *Tetrahedron Letters*, 1964, 3159.

2-Chloro-10{3-[1-(2-hydroxyethyl)-4-piperazinyl]propyl}-phenothiazine. *See* Perphenazine.★

Chloromadinone acetate (*Gestafortin*, 17α-*acetoxy*-6-*chloro*-6-*dehydroprogesterone*)

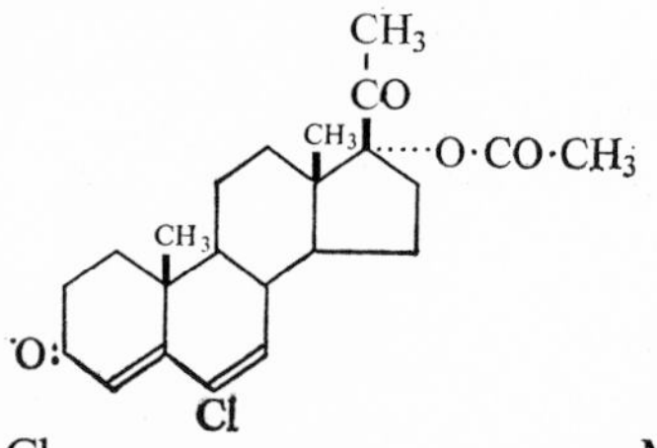

$C_{23}H_{29}O_4Cl$ MW 404·5
Oral progesterone derivative. M.p. 212–14°.
Merck (Darmstadt), *Report of Therapy Congress and Pharmaceutical Exhibition*, Karlsruhe, 1963 (*Angew. Chem., Int. Ed.*, 1964, **3**, 68).

2-Chloromercuri-4-(*p*-nitrophenylazo)phenol

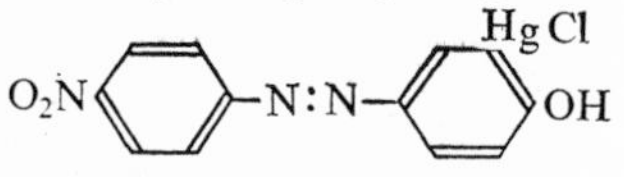

$C_{12}H_9O_3N_3ClHg$ MW 479
Chromogenic reagent for thiol groups. Orange-red cryst. M.p. 218–20°. Light absorption: $\lambda_{max.}$ 385 mμ (ε, 23,300) in 15% EtOH.
Chang, Liener, *Nature*, 1964, **203**, 1065.

2-Chloromercuri-4-phenylazophenol

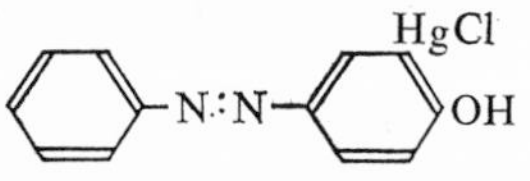

$C_{12}H_9ON_2ClHg$ MW 433·5
Chromopheric reagent for thiol groups. Orange-yellow cryst. from C_6H_6. M.p. 146–7°. Light absorption: $\lambda_{max.}$ 350 mμ (ε, 25,900) in 15% EtOH.
Chang, Liener, *Nature*, 1964, **203**, 1065.

2-Chloro-10-[3-(4-methylpiperazin-1-yl)propyl]phenothiazine. *See* Prochlorperazine.★

Chloro-oxirane (*Chloroethylene oxide*)

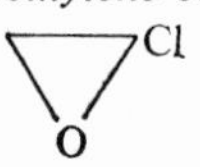

C_2H_3OCl MW 78·5
Colourless oil. B.p. 78–9°. Decomp. on standing → chloroacetaldehyde.
Zief, Schramm, *Chemistry and Industry*, 1964, 660.

α-Chlorophenylacetic Acid.★
See also:
Eliel, Fisk, Prosser, *Organic Syntheses*, 1956, **36**, 3; Coll. Vol. **4**, 169.

1-(4-Chloro-α-phenylbenzyl)-4-(2-[2-hydroxyethoxy]-ethyl)piperazine. *See* Hydroxyzine.★

1-*p*-Chlorophenyl-1-(β-diethylaminoethoxy)cyclohexane. *See* Chlorphenoyclan.

***N*-(4-Chlorophenyl)-*N*′-methoxy-*N*′-methylurea** (*Aresin*®)

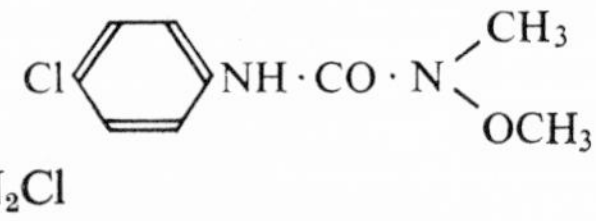

$C_9H_{11}O_2N_2Cl$ MW 214·5
Selective herbicide. M.p. 76–8°.
Scherer, Hörlein, Hartel, *Angew. Chem.*, 1963, **75**, 851; *Int. Ed.*, 1963, **2**, 670.

2-*p*-Chlorophenyl-3-methylbutane-2 : 3-diol. *See* Phenaglycodol.★

2-Chlororesorcinol.★
See also:
Schamp, *Bull. soc. chim. Belg.*, 1964, **73**, 35.

Chlorphencyclan (1-p-*Chlorophenyl*-1-[β-*diethylamino-ethoxy*]*cyclohexane*)

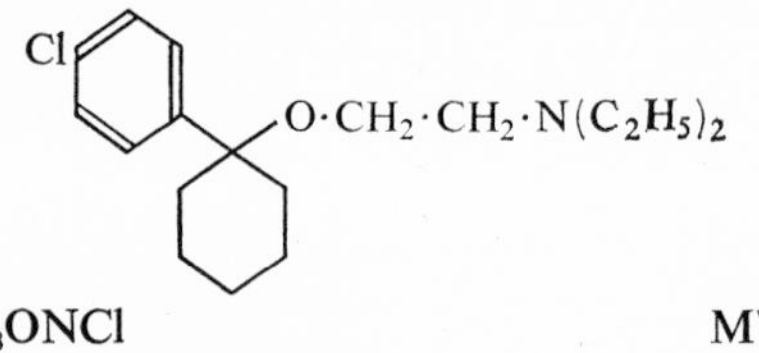

$C_{18}H_{28}ONCl$ MW 309·5
Parasympatholytic drug.
B,HCl: m.p. 143–5°.
Boehringer & Co., *Report of Therapy Congress and Pharmaceutical Exhibition*, Karlsruhe, 1963 (*Angew. Chem., Int. Ed.*, 1964, **3**, 68).

1-(4′-Chlorophenethyl)-1 : 2 : 3 : 4-tetrahydro-6 : 7-dimethoxy-2-methylisoquinoline (*Versidyne*)

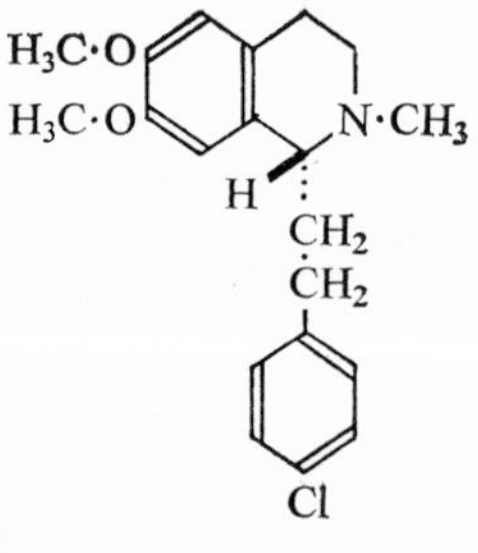

$C_{20}H_{24}O_2NCl$ MW 345·5
R (−)-.
Antitussive, analgesic with spasmolytic activity. B.p. 194°/0·15 mm. $[\alpha]_D^{25}$ −15·9° (c, 1 in MeOH).
(−)-*Dibenzoyl tartrate*: m.p. 148–9°. $[\alpha]_D^{25}$ −69·3° (c, 1 in MeOH).
(+)-.
B.p. 196–8°/0·06 mm. $[\alpha]_D^{25}$ +17·9° (c, 1 in MeOH).

(+)-*Camphor sulphonate*: m.p. 105–6°. $[\alpha]_D$ +27° (c, 1 in MeOH).
(±)-.
B,HCl: cryst. from Me_2CO. M.p. 105–6°. Light absorption: $\lambda_{max.}$ 283 mμ (ε, 3830).

Brossi *et al.*, *Helv. Chim. Acta*, 1960, **43**, 1459.
Besendorf *et al.*, *Experientia*, 1962, **18**, 446.
Rheiner, Brossi, *Experientia*, 1964, **20**, 488.

Chloroxanthin

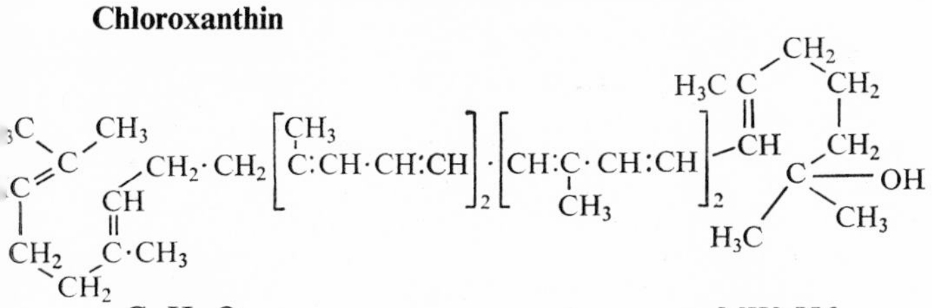

$C_{40}H_{60}O$ MW 556
Carotenoid of photosynthetic purple bacteria. M.p. 140–1°. Light absorption: $\lambda_{max.}$ 415, 439, and 469 mμ.

Goodwin, Land, Sissins, *Biochem. J.*, 1956, **64**, 486.
Nakayama, *Arch. Biochem. Biophys.*, 1958, **75**, 352, 356.
Manchand, Weedon, *Tetrahedron Letters*, 1964, 2603.

5 : 22-Cholestadien-3-β-ol (22-*Dehydrocholesterol*)

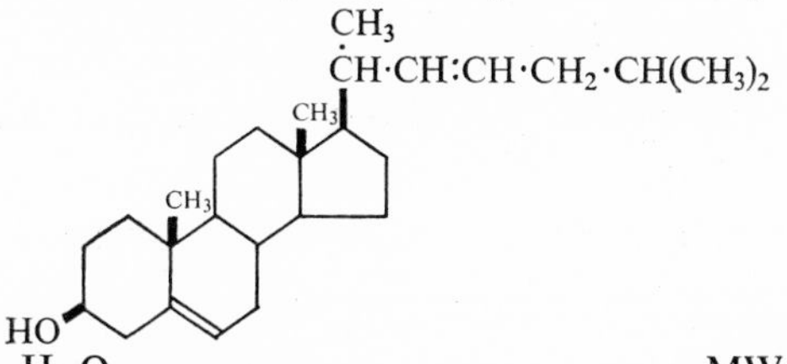

$C_{27}H_{44}O$ MW 384
Constituent of the scallop *Placopecten magellanicus* (Gmelin) and red algae *Hypnea japonica*. M.p. 134–6°. $[\alpha]_D$ −58·5°.
Ac: m.p. 128–31°. $[\alpha]_D$ −62·7°. *Tetrabromide*: m.p. 178–9° decomp.

Bergmann, Dusza, *J. Org. Chem.*, 1958, **23**, 1245.
Tsuda *et al.*, *J. Am. Chem. Soc.*, 1960, **82**, 1442.
Tamura *et al.*, *Can. J. Biochem.*, 1964, **42**, 1331.

4-Cholesten-3-one.★

Eastham, Teranishi, *Organic Syntheses*, Coll. Vol. **4**, 192.
Fieser, *Organic Syntheses*, 1955, **35**, 43; Coll. Vol. **4**, 195.

5-Cholesten-3-one.★

Fieser, *Organic Syntheses*, Coll. Vol. **4**, 195.

Cholesterol.★

See also:
Fieser, *Organic Syntheses*, Coll. Vol. **4**, 195.

Chholografin. *See under* 3-Amino-2 : 4 : 6-tri-iodo-benzoic Acid.★

Chondrine. *See S*-Oxide *under* 1 : 4-Thiazane-3-carboxylic Acid.

Chondrofoline.★
See also:
Bick *et al.*, *J. Chem. Soc.*, 1961, 1896.

Chondrosamine-1-phosphate. *See* α-D-Galactose-1-phosphate.

Chorismic Acid★

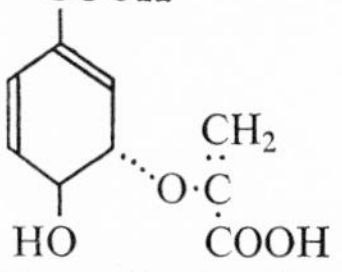

$C_{10}H_{10}O_6$ MW 226
Intermediate in biosynthesis of aromatic compounds isolated from a mutant of *Aerobacter aerogenes*. Light absorption: $\lambda_{max.}$ 272 mμ (H_2O), 282 mμ (Et_2O). Isolated as Ba salt.

Gibson, Gibson, *Biochem. J.*, 1964, **90**, 248, 256.

Chromomycin A$_3$

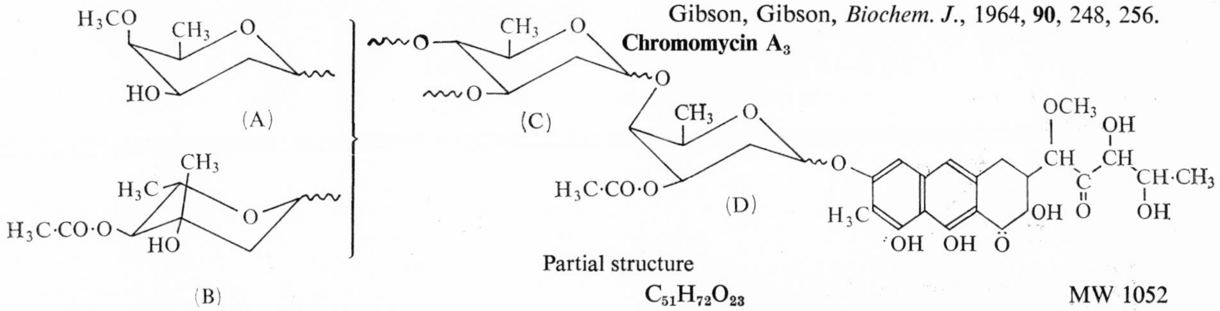

Partial structure

$C_{51}H_{72}O_{23}$ MW 1052
Principal member of a group of cancerostatic antibiotics produced by *Streptomyces griseus* No. 7. Pale yellow cryst. M.p. 183° decomp. $[\alpha]_D^{20}$ −26° (c, 1 in EtOH). Hydrol. → chromycinone + chromose A–D.
Tri-p-toluenesulphonyl: m.p. 117° decomp.

Shibata *et al.*, *J. Antibiotics*, 1963, **16A**, 22.
Miyamoto *et al.*, *Tetrahedron Letters*, 1964, 2355, 2367, 2371.

Chromose A (2 : 6-*Dideoxy*-4-O-*methyl*-D-*galactose*)

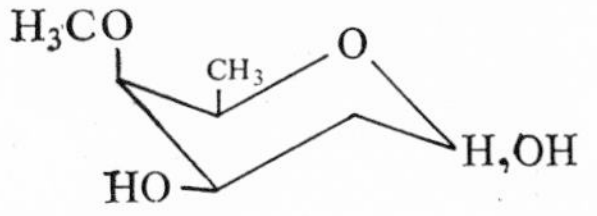

$C_7H_{14}O_4$ MW 162
M.p. 151–3°. $[\alpha]_D^{22}$ 93° → 77° (1 hr.) (c, 1 in H_2O) (+80° equilibrium).
2 : 4-*Dinitrophenylhydrazone*: m.p. 146–7°.
Me chromoside: two forms: (α) m.p. 92°. $[\alpha]_D^{22}$ 122° (c, 1 in EtOH); (β) m.p. 152°. $[\alpha]_D^{22}$ −36° (c, 1 in EtOH).

Miyamoto *et al.*, *Tetrahedron Letters*, 1963, 693.
Brimacombe, Portsmouth, Stacey, *Chemistry and Industry*, 1964, 1758.

Chromose B (4-O-*Acetyl*-2 : 6-*dideoxy*-3-C-*methyl*-L-arabo-*pyranose*)

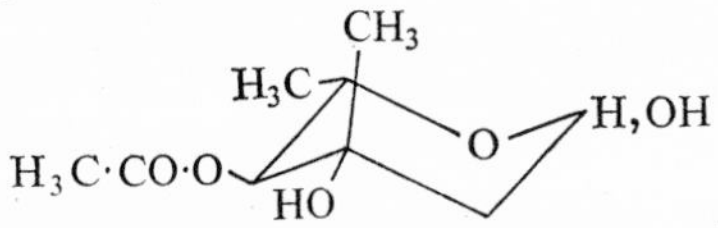

$C_9H_{16}O_5$ MW 204

Sugar from chromomycin A_3. Oil. $[\alpha]_D$ −26° (c, 1·1 in H_2O). Hydrol. → deacetylchromose B. $C_7H_{14}O_4$. MW 162. M.p. 109°. $[\alpha]_D$ −15° (c, 1 in H_2O) → −22° (1 hr.).

Miyamoto *et al.*, *Tetrahedron Letters*, 1964, 2371.

Chromose C (2 : 6-*Dideoxy*-D-arabo-*hexopyranose*)

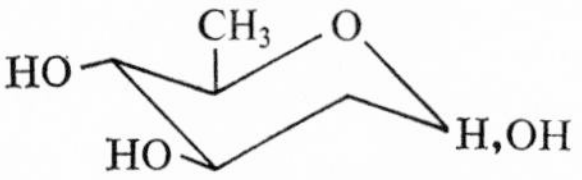

$C_6H_{12}O_4$ MW 148

Sugar from chromomycin A_3. Oil. $[\alpha]_D^{21}$ 22° (c, 1·4 in H_2O). Probably identical with olivose.
Me chromoside: b.p. 126–9°/1 mm. $[\alpha]_D^{23}$ 87° (c, 1·2 in H_2O).

Miyamoto *et al.*, *Tetrahedron Letters*, 1964, 2371.

Chromose D (3-O-*Acetyl*-2 : 6-*dideoxy*-D-lyxo-*hexopyranose*)

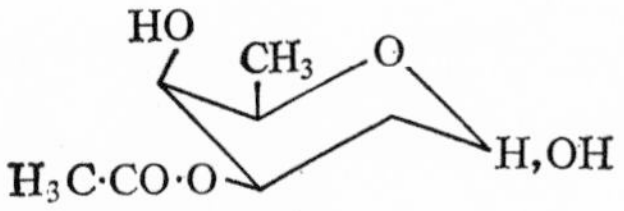

$C_8H_{14}O_5$ MW 190

Sugar from chromomycin A_3. Cryst. M.p. 128°. $[\alpha]_D^{23}$ 87° (c, 1·5 in H_2O).

Miyamoto *et al.*, *Tetrahedron Letters*, 1964, 2371.

Chromycinone

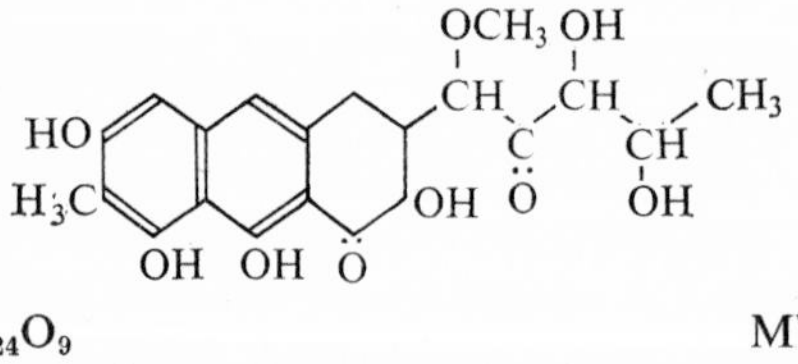

$C_{21}H_{24}O_9$ MW 420

Aglycone from chromomycin A_3. Cryst. from AcOEt. M.p. 184–7°. Light absorption: $\lambda_{max.}$ 232 (log ε, 4·38), 282 (4·60), 326 (3·85), 340 (3·85), and 412 mμ (4·01).

Miyamoto *et al.*, *Tetrahedron Letters*, 1964, 2355.

Chrysergonic Acid.★

A 2 : 1 mixture of secalonic acids A and B.

Franck, Gottschalk, *Angew. Chem.*, 1964, **76**, 438; *Int. Ed.*, 1964, **3**, 441.

Chrysoaphin-*fb*★

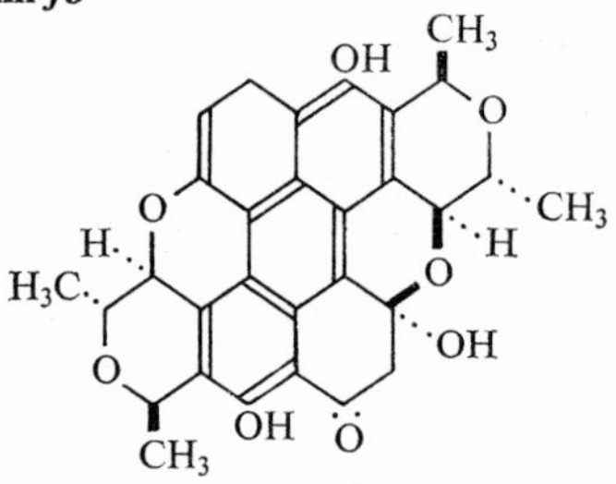

$C_{30}H_{24}O_9$ MW 528

Fine orange plates from Et_2O. M.p. 250° decomp. Light absorption: $\lambda_{max.}$ 268 (log ε, 4·64), 380 (4·30), 402 (4·51), 457 (4·19), and 485 mμ (4·21).
Structure:

Calderbank *et al.*, *J. Chem. Soc.*, 1964, 80.

Chrysoaphin-*sl*★

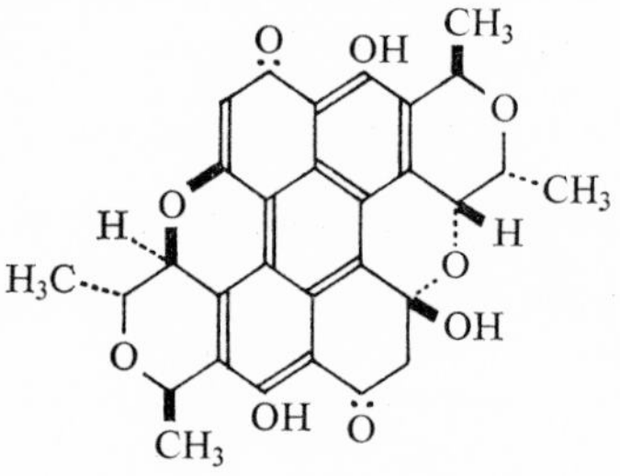

a

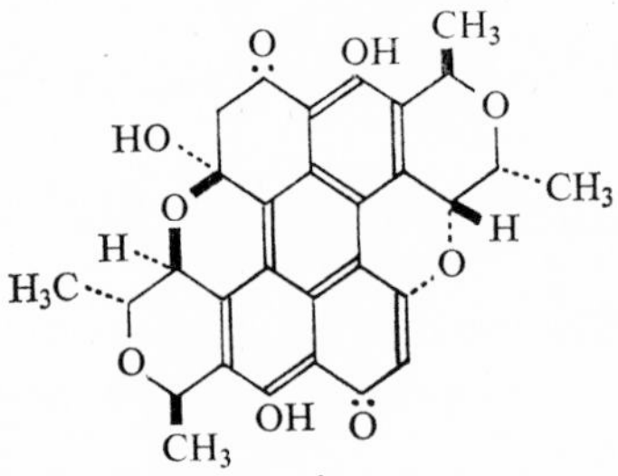

b

$C_{30}H_{24}O_9$ MW 528

Two forms exist:
sl-1.
Orange plates. M.p. 238–9° decomp. Light absorption as Chrysoaphin-*fb*.
sl-2.
Microcryst. powder. M.p. 212–15° decomp.
Note. It is not known which structure (*a* or *b*) corresponds to which form.

Calderbank *et al.*, *J. Chem. Soc.*, 1964, 80.

Cimicidine★

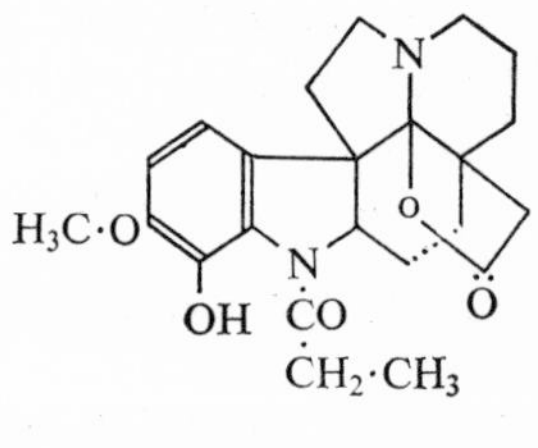

Structure:

Cava *et al.*, *Chemistry and Industry*, 1963, 1875.

Cimicine

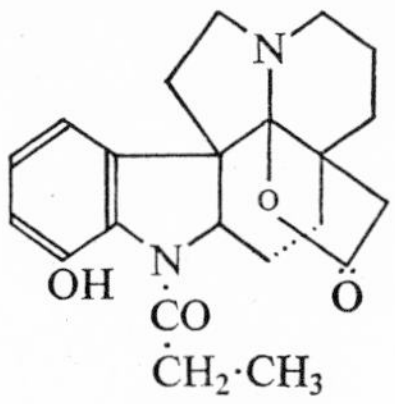

$C_{22}H_{26}O_4N_2$ MW 382

Alkaloid from *Haplophyton cimicidum*. M.p. 229–31°. $[\alpha]_D$ +113° ($CHCl_3$).

Cava *et al.*, *Chemistry and Industry*, 1963, 1875.

Cincholic Acid (3β-*Hydroxyolean*-12-*en*-27 : 28-*dioic acid*)

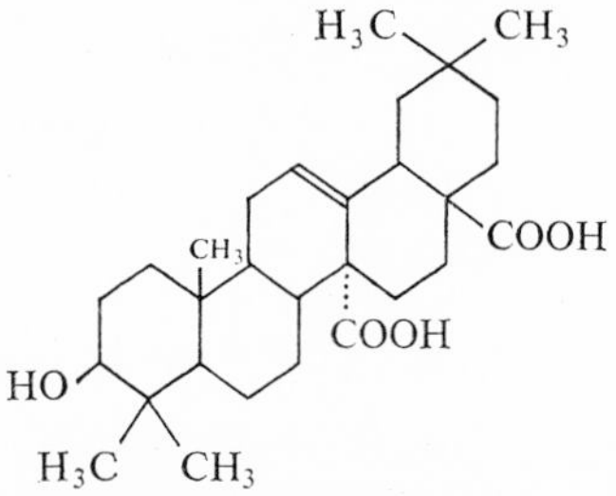

$C_{30}H_{46}O_5$ MW 486

Minor constituent of cinchona bark. Fine needles. M.p. 265–8° decomp. $[\alpha]_D^{20}$ +118° ± 3° (c, 1 in Py).

Di-Me ester: $C_{32}H_{50}O_5$. MW 514. M.p. 213–15°. $[\alpha]_D$ +114° ± 3° (c, 1 in Py). *Ac*: m.p. 248–51°. $[\alpha]_D$ +98° ± 2° (c, 1 in Py).

Ac: cryst. from Py.Aq. M.p. 251–5°. $[\alpha]_D$ +101° ± 2° (c, 1 in Py).

Snatzke, Fehlhaber, *Ann.*, 1963, **663**, 123.
Tschesche, Duphorn, Snatzke, *Ann.*, 1963, **667**, 151.

Cinnamoyl histamine. *See under* Histamine.

N^{α}-Cinnamoyl-N^{α}-methylhistamine N-glucoside. *See* Casimiroedine.

1-*O*-Cinnamoylquinic Acid

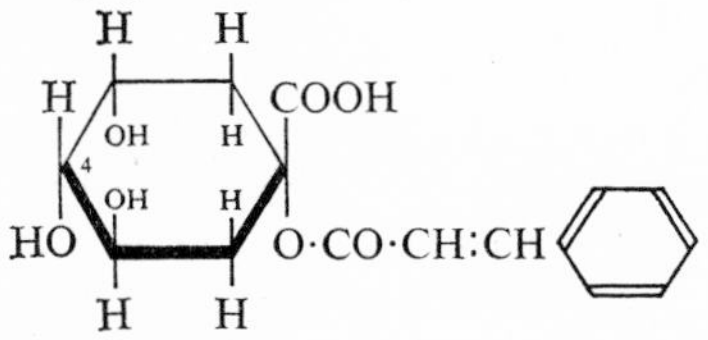

$C_{16}H_{18}O_7$ MW 322

Short prisms from EtOH.Aq. M.p. 195° (188°).

4 : 5-*Isopropylidene deriv.*: needles from EtOH.Aq. M.p. 104°.

Josephson, *Ber.*, 1928, **61B**, 911.
Hanson, *Chemistry and Industry*, 1963, 1691.

3-*O*-Cinnamoylquinic Acid.

Two forms: (*a*) Needles from AcOEt–light petroleum. M.p. 166°. (*b*) Prisms from EtOH.Aq. M.p. 146°.

Hanson, *Chemistry and Industry*, 1963, 1691.

4-*O*-Cinnamoylquinic Acid.

Cryst. from EtOH–AcOEt. M.p. 157°.

Hanson, *Chemistry and Industry*, 1963, 1691.

5-*O*-Cinnamoylquinic Acid.

Cryst. from EtOH–AcOEt. M.p. 204°.

Hanson, *Chemistry and Industry*, 1963, 1691.

Cinnamoylsuccinic Acid. *See* γ-Phenylallylsuccinic Acid.

***O*-Cinnamoyltaxicin I**

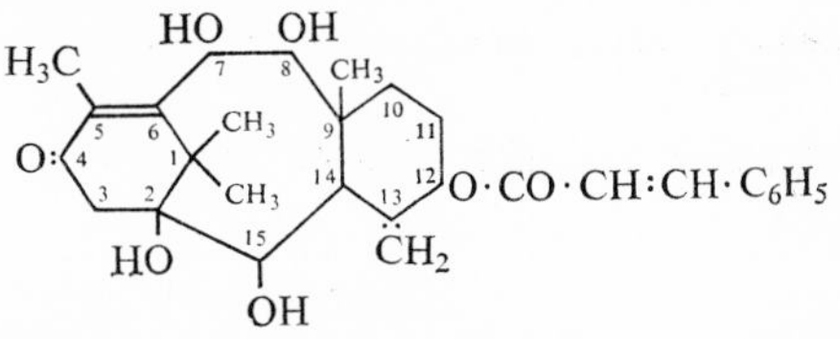

$C_{29}H_{36}O_7$ MW 496

Degradation product of taxine. M.p. 233–4°. $[\alpha]_D^{21}$ 285°. Light absorption: $\lambda_{max.}$ 282 mμ (ε, 28,200).

Tri-Ac: prisms from EtOH. M.p. 237–9°. $[\alpha]_D^{18}$ 218°.

15-*Me ether, di-Ac*: m.p. 194–5°.

7 : 8-*Isopropylidene deriv.*: *Mono-Ac*: m.p. 141–2°. *Me ether*: m.p. 180°.

Baxter *et al.*, *J. Chem. Soc.*, 1962, 2964.
Langley *et al.*, *J. Chem. Soc.*, 1962, 2972.
Eyre *et al.*, *Proc. Chem. Soc.*, 1963, 271.

***O*-Cinnamoyltaxicin II**

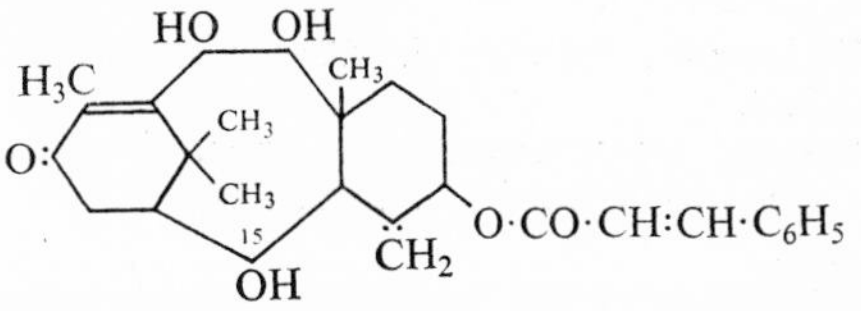

$C_{29}H_{36}O_6$ MW 480

Tri-Ac: taxinine. $C_{35}H_{42}O_9$. MW 606. Constituent of the leaves of *Taxus baccata* L. sub sp. *cuspidata* Pilg. et Zucc. Prisms from EtOH. M.p. 265–7°. $[\alpha]_D^{18}$ 137°. Light absorption: $\lambda_{max.}$ 279 mμ (ε, 28,500).

15-*Mono Ac*: m.p. 224–5°. *Isopropylidene deriv.*: m.p. 195°.

Baxter *et al.*, *J. Chem. Soc.*, 1962, 2964.
Langley *et al.*, *J. Chem. Soc.*, 1962, 2972.
Eyre *et al.*, *Proc. Chem. Soc.*, 1963, 271.
Kurono *et al.*, *Tetrahedron Letters*, 1963, 2153.
Nakanishi, Kurono, Bhacca, *Tetrahedron Letters*, 1963, 2161.
Ueda *et al.*, *Tetrahedron Letters*, 1963, 2167.

Cirpon. *See* Meprobamate.★

Citreorosein.★

8-*Me ether*: *see* Questinol.

See also:

Mahmoodian, Stickings, *Biochem. J.*, 1964, **92**, 369.

Citreoviridin

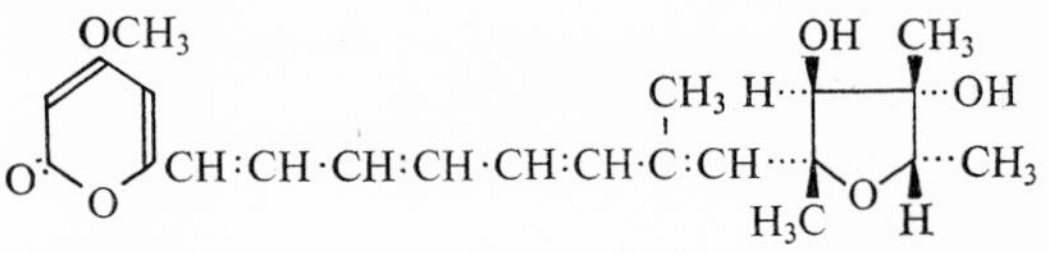

$C_{23}H_{30}O_6$ MW 402

Metabolite of *Penicillium citreoviride*, *P. toxicarium* Miyake, and *P. ochrosalmoneum* Udagawa growing on rice. Yellow cryst. from MeOH. M.p. 107–11°. Light absorption: $\lambda_{max.}$ 204 (ε, 17,000), 234 (10,200), 286 sh. (24,600), 294 (27,100), and 388 mμ (17,000).
Ac: m.p. 99–101°.
Mono-p-*nitrobenzoyl*: m.p. 178–178·5°.
Di-p-*nitrobenzoyl*: m.p. 269–71°.

Sakabe, Soto, Hirata, *Tetrahedron Letters*, 1964, 1825.

Citrostadienol (24-*Ethylidene*-4α-*methyl*-Δ^7-*cholesten*-3β-*ol)*

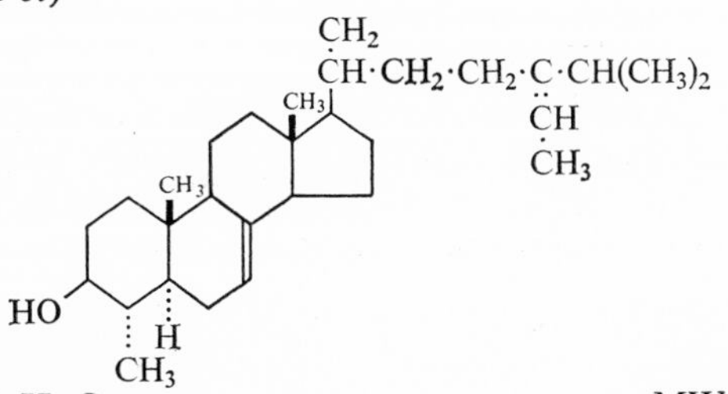

$C_{30}H_{50}O$ MW 426
Constituent of grapefruit peel oil. Cryst. from Et_2O–MeOH. M.p. 162–4°. $[\alpha]_D$ 24° (c, 1 in $CHCl_3$). Give ppt. with digitonin.
Ac: cryst. from MeOH. M.p. 142–3°. $[\alpha]_D$ 43° (c, 1 in $CHCl_3$).

Weizmann, Mazur, *J. Org. Chem.*, 1958, **23**, 832.
Mazur, Weizmann, Sondheimer, *J. Am. Chem. Soc.*, 1958, **80**, 1007, 6293, 6296.

Clovene★

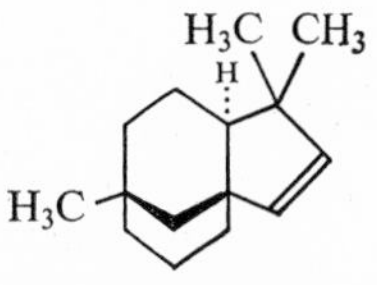

(±)-.
Total synthesis:

Doyle *et al.*, *Proc. Chem. Soc.*, 1963, 239.

Cnidilide

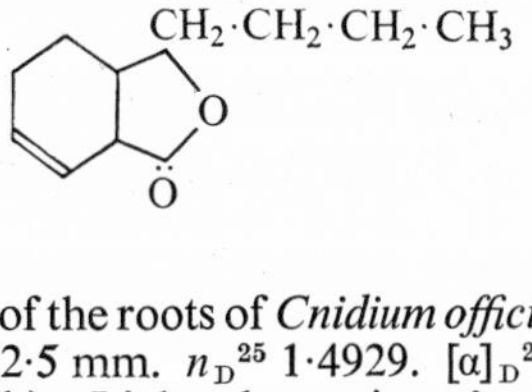

$C_{12}H_{18}O_2$ MW 194
Constituent of the roots of *Cnidium officinale* Makino. B.p. 145–6°/2·5 mm. n_D^{25} 1·4929. $[\alpha]_D^{25}$ −122·5° (c, 3·5 in $CHCl_3$). Light absorption: $\lambda_{max.}$ 227 (log ε, 3·00), 274 (2·30), and 282 mμ (2·27).

Mitsuhashi, Muramatsu, *Tetrahedron*, 1964, **20**, 1971.

Cnidium Lactone.

Cnidium lactone (Noguchi, *J. Pharm. Soc. Japan*, 1934, **54**, 913) is heterogeneous.

Mitsuhashi, Muramatsu, *Tetrahedron*, 1964, **20**, 1971.

Cobastab. *See* Vitamin B_{12}.★

Cobione. *See* Vitamin B_{12}.★

Cocarcinogen A1

$C_{36}H_{56}O_8$ MW 616
Pharmacologically active constituent of croton oil. Colourless resin. $[\alpha]_D^{24}$ 49° (c, 1 in dioxan). Light absorption: $\lambda_{max.}$ 232 (ε, 5400), 333 mμ (73). Hydrol. → AcOH, tetradecanoic acid, and an alcohol. $C_{20}H_{28}O_6$. MW 364. M.p. 238–40°. $[\alpha]_D$ 116° (c, 0·4 in dioxan).
4′-*Nitroazobenzoyl*: m.p. 86–7°.

Hecker, Bresch, Szczepunski, *Angew. Chem.*, 1964, **76**, 225; *Ind. Ed.*, 1964, **3**, 227.

Cocsarmine

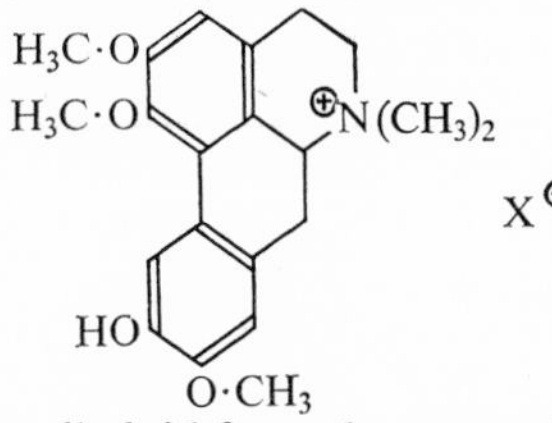

Quaternary alkaloid from the roots of *Cocculus sarmentosus*.
B,I (X = I): $C_{21}H_{26}O_4NI$. MW 483. *Trihydrate*: m.p. 205–7° (after sintering at 185°). $[\alpha]_D^{22}$ +27·9° (EtOH).
Picrate: m.p. 226–7° decomp.

Tomita, Furukawa, *J. Pharm. Soc., Japan*, 1963, **83**, 190.

Codelcortone. *See* Prednisolone.★

Coenzyme A.★
Synthesis:

Michelson, *Biochim. Biophys. Acta*, 1964, **93**, 71.

Coenzyme Q_{10} (*H*-10)

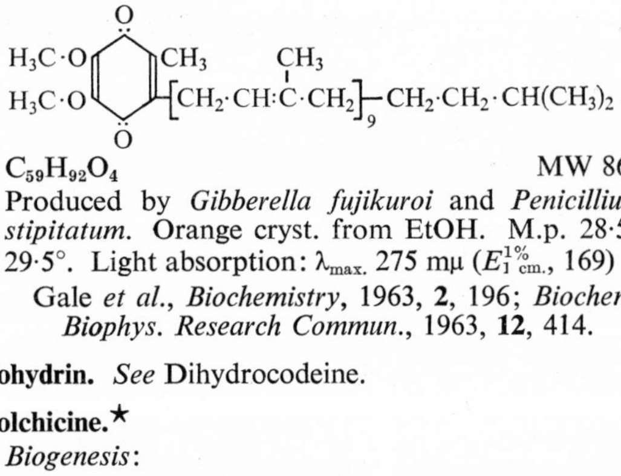

$C_{59}H_{92}O_4$ MW 864
Produced by *Gibberella fujikuroi* and *Penicillium stipitatum*. Orange cryst. from EtOH. M.p. 28·5–29·5°. Light absorption: $\lambda_{max.}$ 275 mμ ($E_{1\,cm.}^{1\%}$, 169)

Gale *et al.*, *Biochemistry*, 1963, **2**, 196; *Biochem. Biophys. Research Commun.*, 1963, **12**, 414.

Cohydrin. *See* Dihydrocodeine.

Colchicine.★
Biogenesis:

Battersby, Herbert, *Proc. Chem. Soc.*, 1964, 260.

Colistin.★

This has now been separated into three components, namely, colistins A, B, and C, by means of counter-current distribution.

Suzuki *et al.*, *J. Biochem.* (Japan), 1963, **54**, 25, 173, 412.
Wilkinson, Lowe, *Nature*, 1963, **200**, 1008.

Colistin A (*Polymyxin E*$_1$)

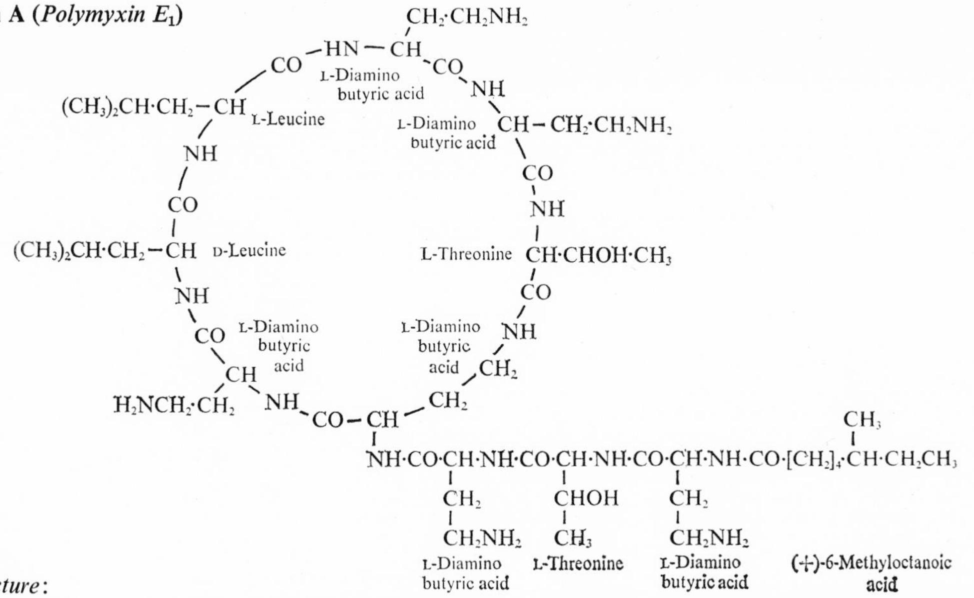

Structure:

Suzuki *et al.*, *J. Biochem.* (Japan), 1963, **54**, 25, 173, 412.

Wilkinson, Lowe, *Nature* (Lond.), 1964, **204**, 993.

Colistin B

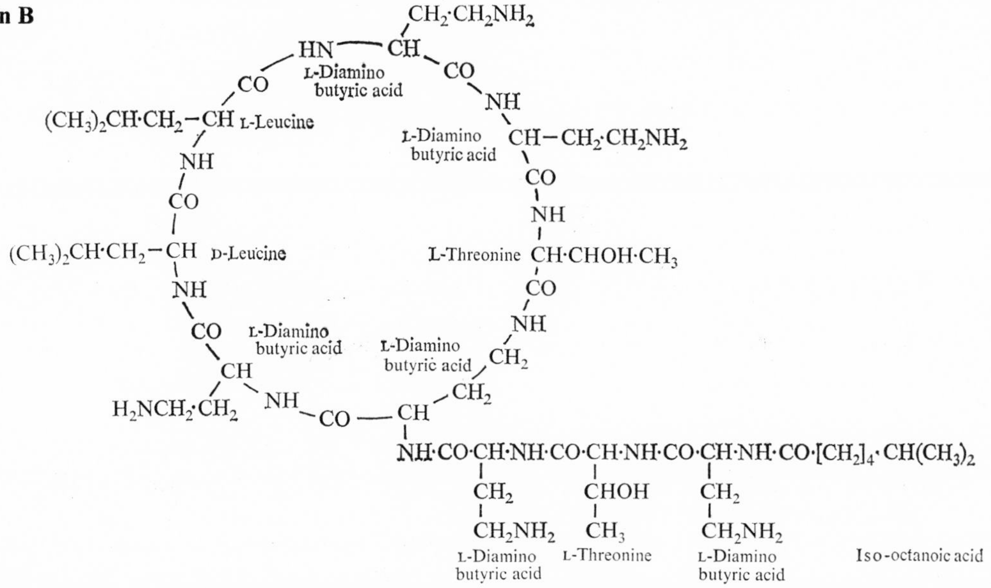

Suzuki, Fukjikawa, *J. Biochem.* (Japan), 1964, **56**, 182.

α-Colubrin★

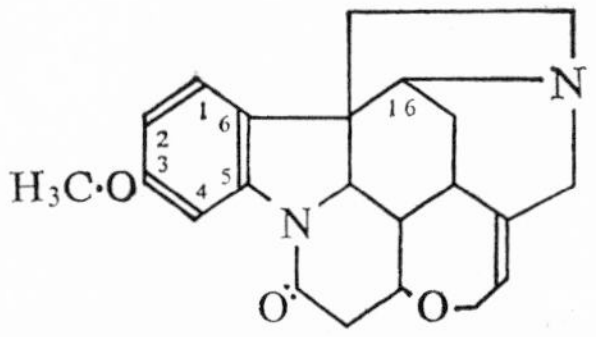

Synthesis from Strychnine:

Rosenmund, Franke, *Chem. Ber.*, 1964, **97**, 1677.

Commic Acid A★

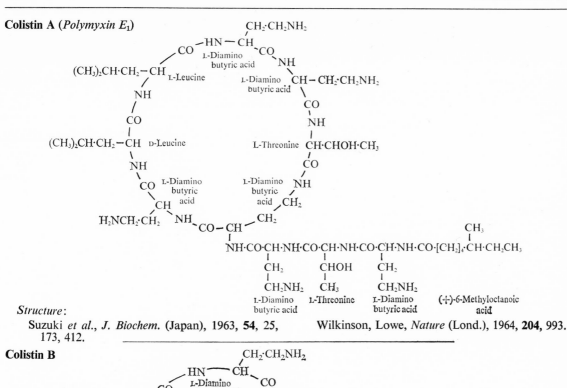

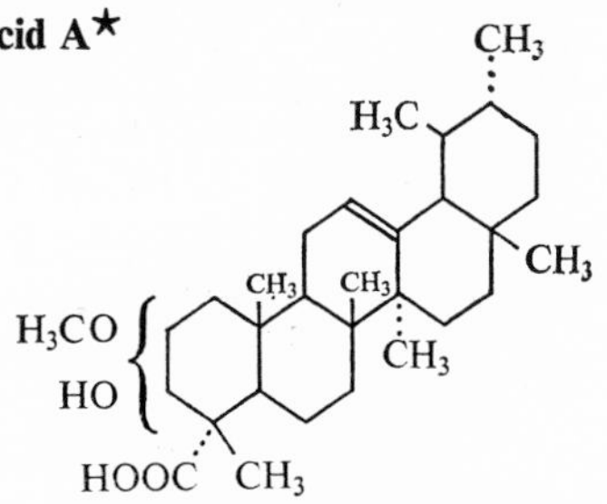

Partial structure

Thomas, Willhalm, *Tetrahedron Letters*, 1964, 3177.

Commic Acid B★ (3β-*Hydroxyurs*-12-*en*-23-*oic acid*)

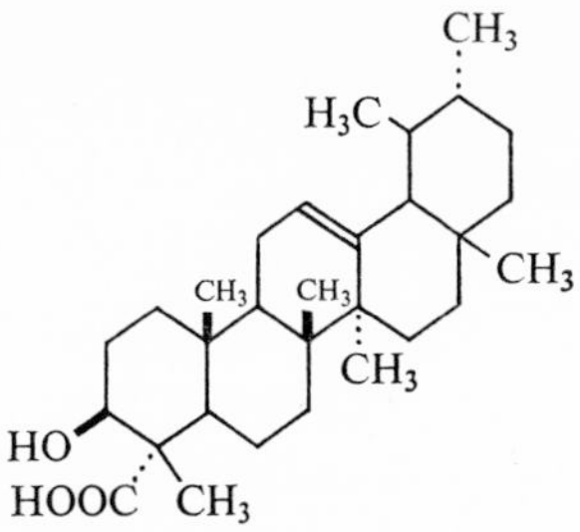

Suggested structure

Thomas, Willhalm, *Tetrahedron Letters*, 1964, 3177.

Communic Acid.★

Present in the cones of *Cupressus sempervirens* L. and oleoresin from *Agathis robusta*.

Ahond, Carnero, Gastambide, *Bull. soc. chim.*, 1964, 348.

Carman, Dennis, *Austral. J. Chem.*, 1964, **17**, 390.

Compactinervine

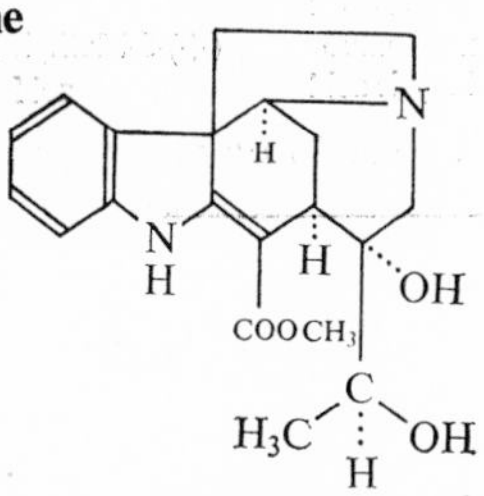

$C_{20}H_{24}O_4N_2$ MW 356

Alkaloid from *Aspidosperma compactinervium* Kuhlm. Occurs only in solvated forms. M.p. 110–20° decomposes at 235–45°. $[\alpha]_D$ −640° (Py). Light absorption: $\lambda_{max.}$ 237, 297, 331 mμ (log ε, 3·97, 3·95, 4·15).

Djerassi *et al.*, *Experientia*, 1963, **19**, 467.

Concurchine.★

Identical with Irehline★ (*q.v.*).

Janot *et al.*, *Compt. rend.*, 1964, **258**, 2089.

Condylocarpine

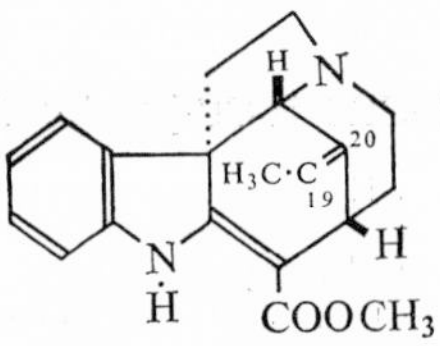

$C_{20}H_{22}O_2N_2$ MW 322

Alkaloid from *Diplorrhynchus condylocarpon*. M.p. 167–8°. $[\alpha]_D$ +876°. H_2 → Tubotaiwin.

Stauffacher, *Helv. Chim. Acta*, 1961, **44**, 2006.

Sandoval *et al.*, *Tetrahedron Letters*, 1962, 409.

Schumann, Schmid, *Helv. Chim. Acta*, 1963, **46**, 1996.

Confertifolin

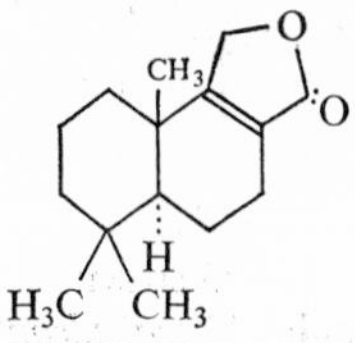

$C_{15}H_{22}O_2$ MW 234

From the bark of *Drimys winteri* Forst. Cryst. from light petroleum. M.p. 152°. $[\alpha]_D$ 72° (c, 2 in $CHCl_3$), 93° (c, 2·10 in C_6H_6).

Appel *et al.*, *J. Chem. Soc.*, 1960, 4685.

Wenkert, Strike, *J. Am. Chem. Soc.*, 1964, **86**, 2044.

Conoduramine★

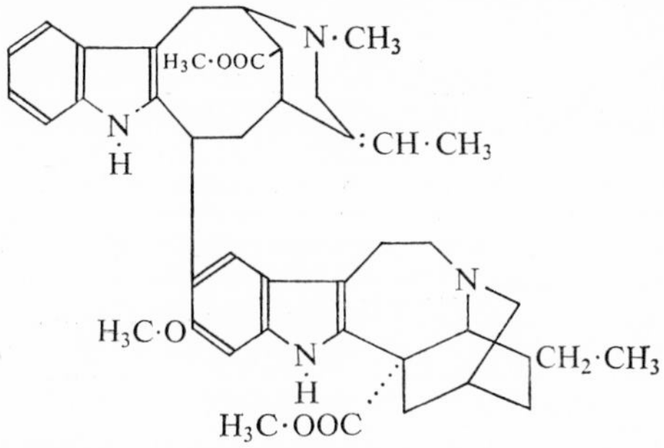

Structure:

Renner, Fritz, *Tetrahedron Letters*, 1964, 283.

Conodurine★

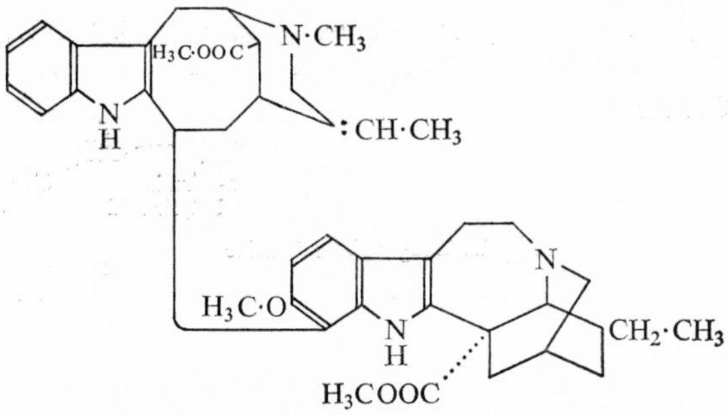

Isomeric with Voacamine.

Renner, Fritz, *Tetrahedron Letters*, 1964, 283.

Conteben. *See* Thiosemicarbazone *under p*-Acetamidobenzaldehyde.★

Copaene★

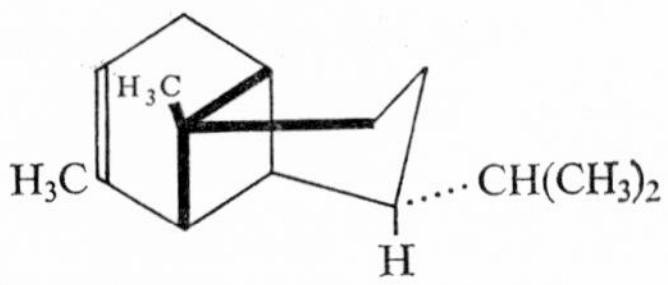

Amended structure:

Kapadia *et al.*, *Tetrahedron Letters*, 1963, 1933.

Coranormol. *See* Metrazole.★

Corazole. *See* Metrazole.★

Cordycepic Acid.★

Isolated from *Cordyceps sinensis* (Berkeley) Saccardo (Chatterjee, Srinivasan, Maiti, *J. Am. Pharm. Assoc.*, 1957, **46**, 114) has been shown to be D-mannitol.

Sprecher, Sprinson, *J. Org. Chem.*, 1963, **28**, 2490.

Cordycepin.★

Cordycepin has been shown to be 3′-Deoxyadenosine (*q.v.*).

Kaczka *et al.*, *Biochem. Biophys. Res. Commun.*, 1964, **14**, 456.

Cordycepose.★
This is therefore 3-Deoxyxylose.★

Coriamyrtin★

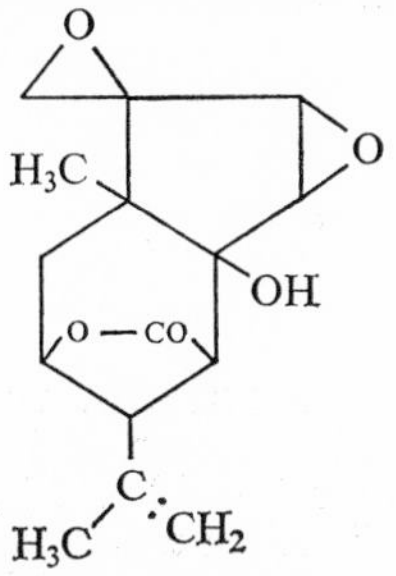

Revised structure:
Okuda Yoshida, *Tetrahedron Letters*, 1964, 439.

Cori ester. *See* Glucose-1-phosphate.

Corlumine★

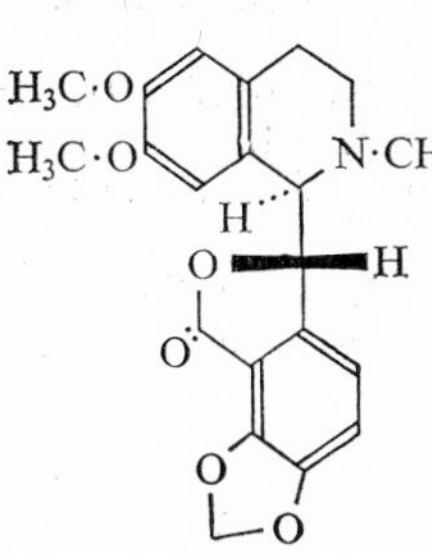

Stereochemistry:
Edwards, Hanola, *Can. J. Chem.*, 1961, **39**, 1801.
Safe, Moir, *Can. J. Chem.*, 1964, **42**, 160.

Cornigereine

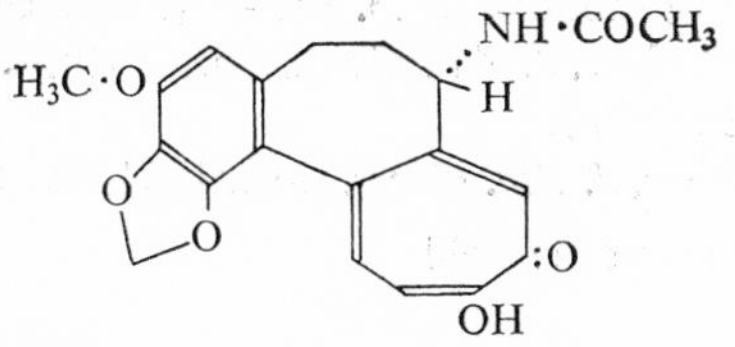

$C_{20}H_{19}O_6N$ MW 369
Yellow prisms from AcOEt or Me_2CO. M.p. 168–70°. $[\alpha]_D^{22}$ −222° (c, 0·758 in $CHCl_3$).
O-*Me ether*: *see* Cornigerine.
El-Hamidi, Šantavý, *Coll. Czech. Chem. Commun.*, 1962, **27**, 2111.
Cross *et al.*, *Coll. Czech. Chem. Commun.*, 1964, **29**, 1187.

Cornigerine

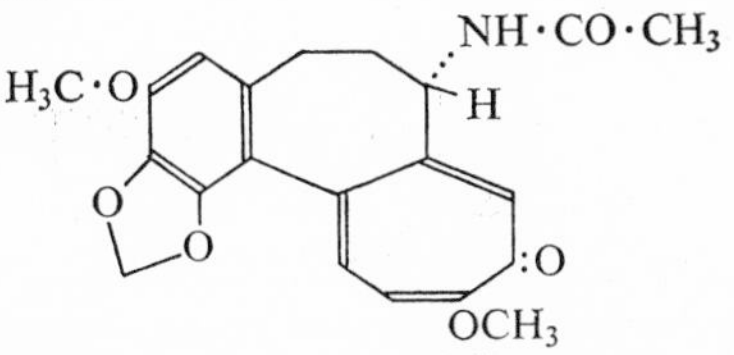

$C_{21}H_{21}O_6N$ MW 383
Alkaloid from the corms of *Colchicum cornigerum* (Schweinf.) Täckh. et Drar. Cryst. from AcOEt–Et_2O. M.p. 268–70°. $[\alpha]_D^{20}$ −150° (c, 0·63 in $CHCl_3$), −233° (c, 0·73 in MeOH). Hydrol. → cornigereine.
El-Hamidi, Šantavý, *Coll. Czech. Chem. Commun.*, 1962, **27**, 2111.
Cross *et al.*, *Coll. Czech. Chem. Commun.*, 1964, **29**, 1187.

Coroglaucigenin.★
3-*Rhamnoside*: present in the seeds of *Maclotus philippinensis* (Lam.) Muell.-Arg. Cryst. from Me_2CO–Et_2O. M.p. 231–5°. $[\alpha]_D^{27}$ −38·1° (c, 1·04 in MeOH). Light absorption: $\lambda_{max.}$ 217 mμ (log ε, 4·17).
Roberts, Weiss, Reichstein, *Helv. Chim. Acta*, 1963, **46**, 2886.

Corticotropin.★
Synthesis of amino acid sequence 11–24.
Sturm, Geiger, Siedel, *Chem. Ber.*, 1963, **96**, 609.

Corylopsin. *See* Bergenin.

Corymbiferin.★
Also present in *Gentiana bellidifolia*.
Markham, *Tetrahedron*, 1964, **20**, 991.

Corynantheine★

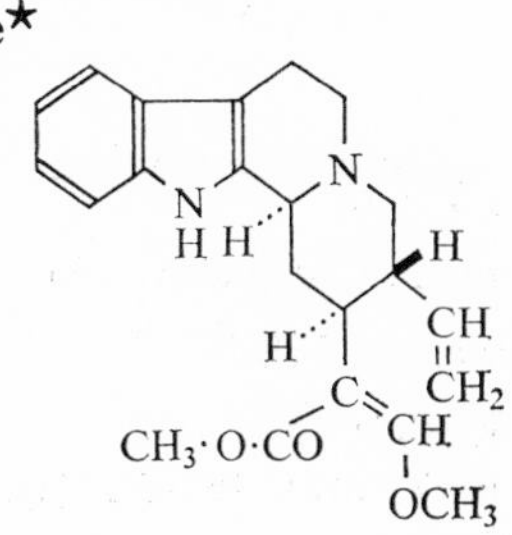

(±)-.
B,HCl: m.p. 176–9°.
Total synthesis:
Van Tamelen, Wright, *Tetrahedron Letters*, 1964, 295.

Corypalmine.★
Also occurs in roots of *Berberis floribunda*, *B. himaloica*, and *Coptis teeta*.
Chatterjee, Juha, das Gupta, *J. Indian Chem. Soc.*, 1952, **29**, 921.

Corytuberine methiodide. *See under* Magnoflorine.

Costaclavine

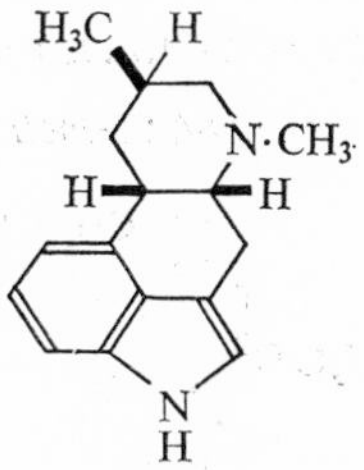

$C_{16}H_{20}N_2$ MW 240
Ergot alkaloid also produced by *Penicillium chermesinum*. M.p. 182–4°. Light absorption: $\lambda_{max.}$ 275, 283, 293 mμ.
Abe *et al.*, *Bull. Agric. Chem. Soc. Japan*, 1956, **20**, 59
Agurell, *Experientia*, 1964, **20**, 25.

Costunolide

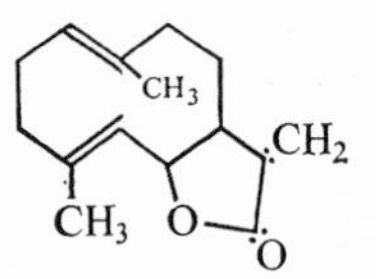

$C_{15}H_{20}O_2$ MW 232

Constituent of costus root oil (*Saussurea lappa* Clarke). Needles from MeOH. M.p. 106–7°. $[\alpha]_D$ 128° (c, 0·45 in $CHCl_3$). Light absorption: $\lambda_{max.}$ 213 mμ (log ε, 4·21).

Rao, Kelkar, Bhattacharyya, *Tetrahedron*, 1960, **9**, 275.

See also under Dihydrocostunolide.

1-*O-p*-Coumaroylquinic Acid (1-O-p-*Hydroxycinnamoylquinic acid*)

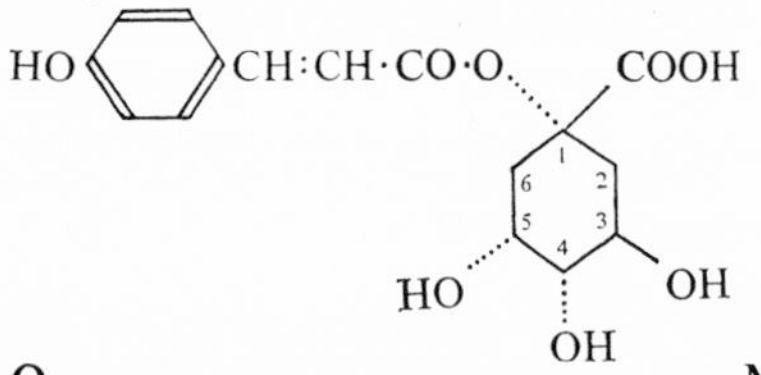

$C_{16}H_{18}O_8$ MW 338

Amorph. $Me_2CO/HCl \rightarrow$ quinide, needles from EtOH.Aq. M.p. 179°.

Haslam *et al.*, *J. Chem. Soc.*, 1964, 2137.

3-*O-p*-Coumaroylquinic Acid.★

4-*O-p*-Coumaroylquinic Acid.

Plates from H_2O. M.p. 192–3°. $[\alpha]_D^{20}$ −47·3° (c, 1·4 in MeOH).

1-*Me ether*: plates. M.p. 193–4°.

Haslam *et al.*, *J. Chem. Soc.*, 1964, 2137.

5-*O-p*-Coumaroylquinic Acid.

Prisms from H_2O. M.p. 194°. $[\alpha]_D^{19}$ −5·6° (c, 0·6 in MeOH).

Haslam *et al.*, *J. Chem. Soc.*, 1964, 2137.

Coumudin. *See* 3-(2-Acetyl-1-phenylethyl)-4-hydroxycoumarin.

Creosol.★

Schwarz, Hering, *Organic Syntheses*, Coll. Vol. **4**, 203.

Crepenyic Acid. *See cis*-9-Octadecen-12-ynoic Acid.

Crocatone (3-*Methoxy*-4 : 5-*methylenedioxy-propiophenone*)

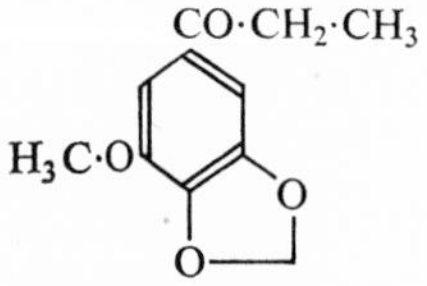

$C_{11}H_{12}O_4$ MW 208

Product from *Oenanthe crocata* L. (Umbelliferae). Needles. M.p. 89°

Plat, le Men, Janot, *Bull. soc. chim. biol.*, 1963, **45**, 1119.

Crodimyl. *See* 3-Methylchromone.★

Crotonosine

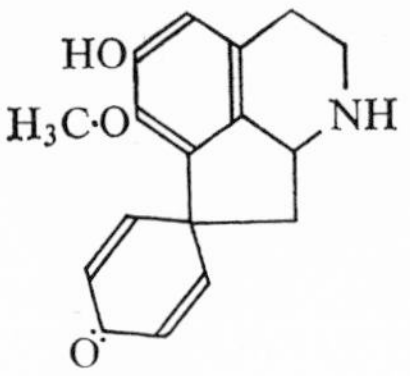

$C_{17}H_{17}O_3N$ MW 283

D(+)-.

Alkaloid from *Croton linearis*. Cryst. from isopropanol which start to decomp. at 165°, soften at 197°, and do not melt below 300°. $[\alpha]_D^{28}$ 180° (c, 0·83 in MeOH). pK_a 7·3. Light absorption: $\lambda_{max.}$ 226 (log ε, 4·30), 235 (4·33), 282 (3·37), and 290 mμ (3·41).

O-*Me*: *see* Stepharine.

N : O-*di-Me*: *see* Pronuciferin.

N : O-*di-Ac*: cubes from AcOEt. M.p. 203–5°.

B,CH₃I: rods from MeOH. M.p. >250° decomp.

L(−)-.

N-*Me*: $C_{18}H_{19}O_3N$. MW 297. Homolinearisine. Plates from EtOH. M.p. 220–3° decomp. *B,HCl*: rods. M.p. >300°. *B,HClO₄*: needles from MeOH–Et_2O. M.p. 184–6°.

Hayes, Stuart, *J. Chem. Soc.*, 1963, 1784, 1789.

Hayes *et al.*, *Proc. Chem. Soc.*, 1963, 280; 1964, 261.

Cubane

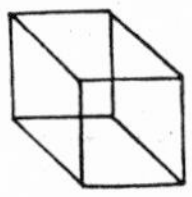

C_8H_8 MW 104

Glistening rhombs. M.p. 130–1° (sealed capillary).

Eaton, Cole, *J. Am. Chem. Soc.*, 1964, **86**, 3157.

Cryst. structure:

Fleischer, *J. Am. Chem. Soc.*, 1964, **86**, 3889.

Cubanedicarboxylic Acid

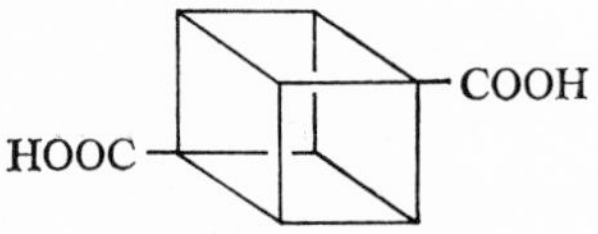

$C_{10}H_8O_4$ MW 192

Di-Me ester: $C_{12}H_{12}O_4$. MW 220. Cryst. from hexane. M.p. 161–2°.

Eaton, Cole, *J. Am. Chem. Soc.*, 1964, **86**, 963.

Cucurbitacin I★

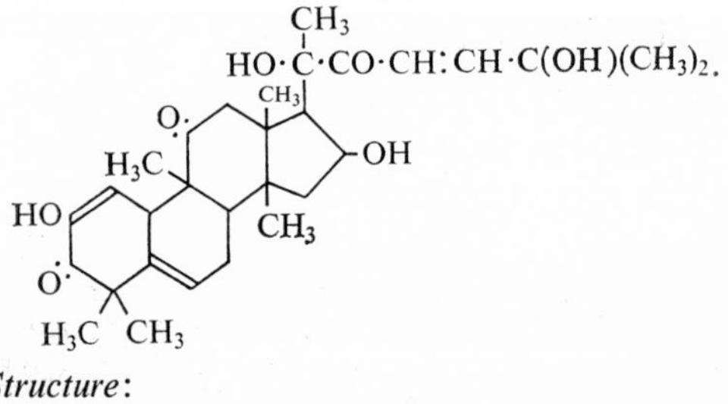

Structure:

de Kock *et al.*, *J. Chem. Soc.*, 1963, 3828.

Cucurbitacin J★

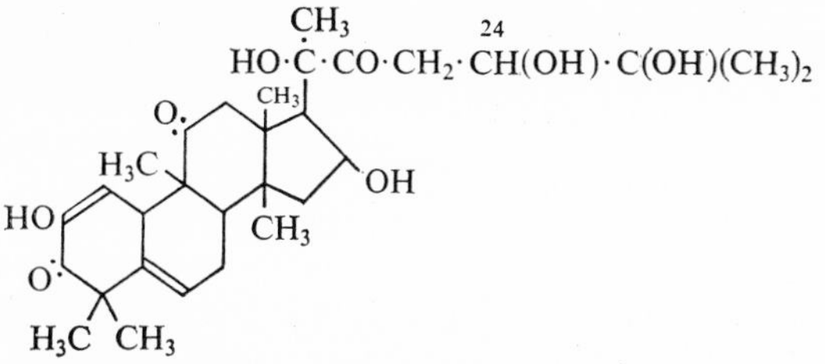

C_{24} epimer of Cucurbitacin K.

Enslin, Norton, *J. Chem. Soc.*, 1964, 529.

Cucurbitacin K★

$C_{30}H_{44}O_8$ MW 532

Hemihydrate. C_{24} epimer of Cucurbitacin J.

Structure:

Enslin, Norton, *J. Chem. Soc.*, 1964, 529.

Cucurbitacin L★ (23 : 24-*Dihydrocucurbitacin I*)

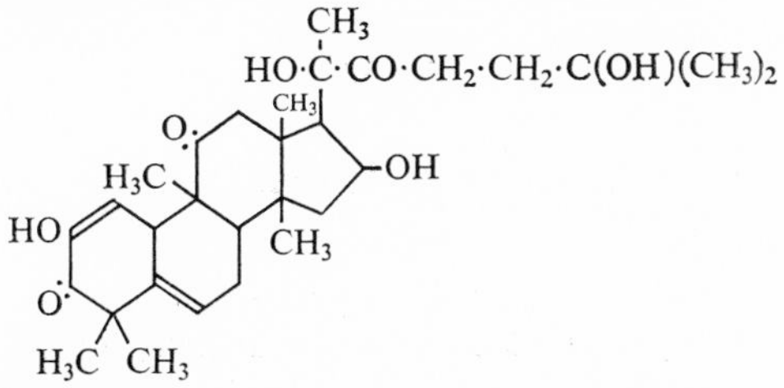

Structure:

Enslin, Norton, *J. Chem. Soc.*, 1964, 529.

Cularimine.★

(±)-.
M.p. 127–8°.
Total synthesis:

Kametani *et al.*, *Tetrahedron Letters*, 1964, 25.

α-Cuparenone

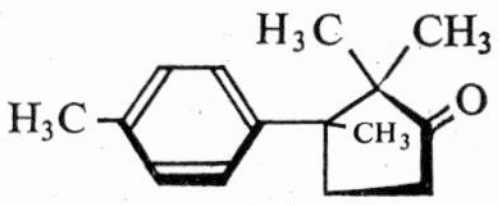

$C_{15}H_{20}O$ MW 216

(+)-.
Constituent of the wood of "Mayur pankhi" (*Thuja orientalis* or *T. compacta*). M.p. 52–3°. $[\alpha]_D^{30}$ +177·1°.
(±)-.
Semicarbazone: prisms from MeOH.Aq. M.p. 212–15°.

Parker, Ramage, Raphael, *J. Chem. Soc.*, 1962, 1558.
Chetty, Dev, *Tetrahedron Letters*, 1964, 73.

β-Cuparenone

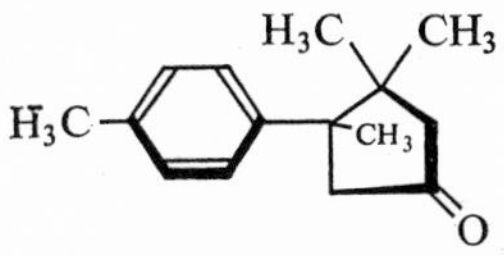

$C_{15}H_{20}O$ MW 216

Constituent of the wood of "Mayur pankhi." B.p. 114–15°/0·8 mm. n_D^{30} 1·5292. $[\alpha]_D^{30}$ +48°.
Semicarbazone: m.p. 213·5–215°.

Chetty, Dev, *Tetrahedron Letters*, 1964, 73.

Cupressene.

Constituent of the essential oil of *Cupressus macrocarpa* and *Podocarpus ferrugineus* G. Benn. Shown to be a mixture of hibaene and isophyllocladene (2:1).

Briggs *et al.*, *Tetrahedron Letters*, 1964, 2223.

Cupressuflavone (8 : 8″-*Biapigeninyl*)

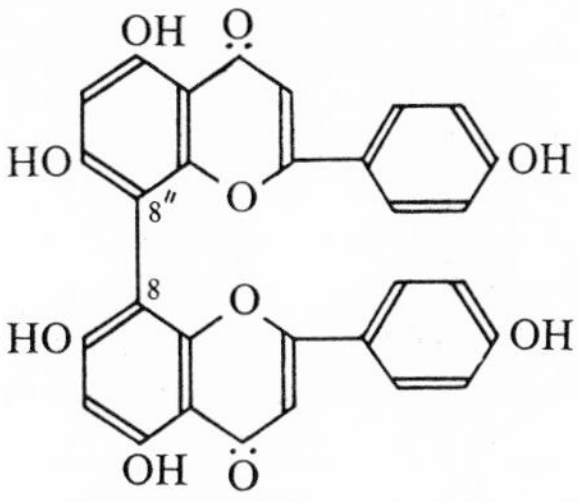

$C_{30}H_{18}O_{10}$ MW 538

Constituent of *Cupressus torulosa* and *C. sempervirens*. Yellow cryst. from Py–MeOH, which do not melt below 360°.
Hexa-Ac: m.p. 251–3°.
Tetra-Me ether: $C_{34}H_{26}O_{10}$. MW 594. M.p. 259–61°.
Hexa-Me ether: $C_{36}H_{30}O_{10}$. MW 622. M.p. 295–7°.
Hexa-Et ether: $C_{42}H_{42}O_{10}$. MW 706. M.p. 267–9°. *Oxime*: m.p. 290–1°.

Nakazawa, *Chem. Pharm. Bull.* (Tokyo), 1962, **10**, 1036.
Murti, Raman, Seshadri, *Tetrahedron Letters*, 1964, 2995.

***C*-Curarine I★**

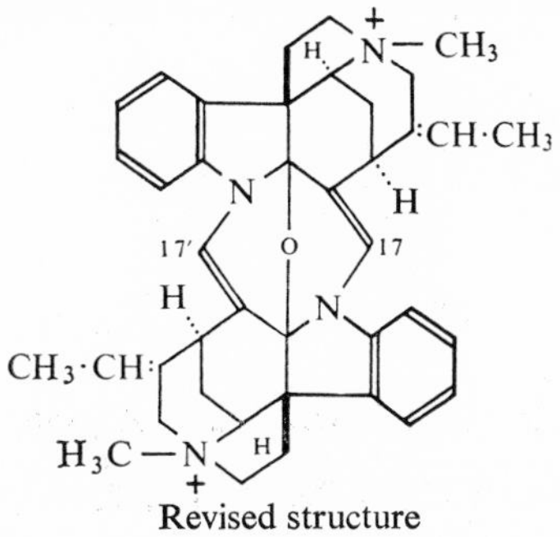

Revised structure

See also:

Grdinic, Nelson, Boekelheide, *J. Am. Chem. Soc.*, 1964, **86**, 3357.

Curvulinic Acid

$C_{10}H_{10}O_5$ MW 210

Metabolite of *Curvularia siddiqui.* M.p. 218° decomp.

Kamal *et al.*, *Tetrahedron*, 1962, **18**, 433.

Curvulin

$C_{12}H_{14}O_5$ MW 238

Metabolite of *Curvularia siddiqui*. M.p. 145°. Light absorption: $\lambda_{max.}$ 270 (ε, 7467), 303 mμ (5640). $Ac_2O \rightarrow$ diacetyldehydro deriv. (prismatic needles, m.p. 120°).

Kamal *et al.*, *Tetrahedron*, 1962, **18**, 433.

Cyanein.

Antibiotic produced by *Penicillium cyaneum*. Cryst. from AcOEt. M.p. 199·8–201·8°. $[\alpha]_D^{23}$ 82·7° (c, 0·317 in AcOEt). Sol. EtOH, Me_2CO, butanol, AcOEt, Et_2O. Spar. sol. H_2O. Insol. C_6H_6, light petroleum. H_2SO_4 → yellow-brown → red col.

Betina *et al.*, *Folia Microbiol.*, 1962, **7**, 353.

Cyanogen Iodide.★

Bak, Hillebert, *Organic Syntheses*, Coll. Vol. **4**, 207.

Cyanoiodoacetylene

I·C⁚C·CN

C_3NI MW 177

M.p. 152–152·5°.

Kloster-Jensen, *Acta Chem. Scand.*, 1963, **17**, 1859.

5-Cyano-1-methyl-2-pyridone. *See* Nudiflorine.

3-Cyanopyridine.★

See also:

Teague, Short, *Organic Syntheses*, Coll. Vol. **4**, 706.

Cycasin

$CH_3 \cdot \overset{\oplus}{N}(O^{\ominus})⁚N \cdot CH_2 \cdot O \cdot$β-D-glucopyranose

$C_8H_{16}O_7N_2$ MW 252

Toxic glycoside from seeds of *Cycas circinalis* L. and *C. revoluta* Thunb. Cryst. from Me_2CO.Aq.–Et_2O. M.p. 154° decomp. $[\alpha]_D^{18}$ −44° (c, 0·62 in H_2O).

Tetra-Ac: plates from Me_2CO–light petroleum. M.p. 137°. $[\alpha]_D^{18}$ −27° (c, 0·98 in $CHCl_3$).

Nishida, Kobayashi, Nagahama, *Bull. Agric. Chem. Soc. Japan*, 1955, **19**, 77.

Riggs, *Chemistry and Industry*, 1956, 926.

Korsch, Riggs, *Tetrahedron Letters*, 1964, 523.

Cycloartocarpin (*Isoartocarpin*)

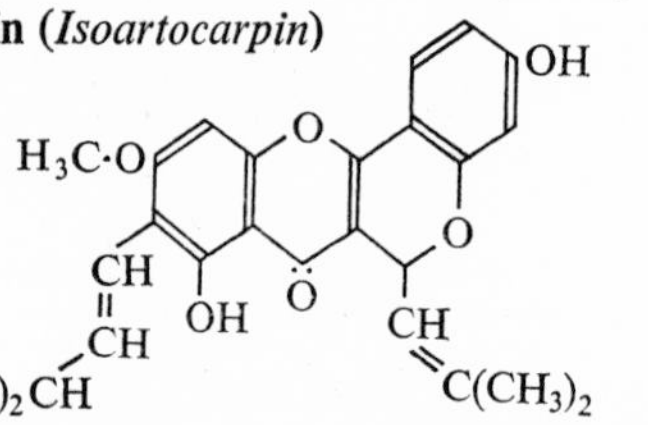

$C_{26}H_{26}O_6$ MW 434

Pigment from the heartwood of *Artocarpus integrifolia*.

Di-Me ether: $C_{28}H_{30}O_6$. MW 462. $[\alpha]_D^{25}$ +1·19° (c, 2·25 in $CHCl_3$).

Dave, Telang, Venkataraman, *Tetrahedron Letters*, 1962, 9.

Nair, Rao, Venkataraman, *Tetrahedron Letters*, 1964, 125.

Cyclobutane-1 : 1-dicarboxylic Acid.★

Di-Et ester:

Mariella, Raube, *Organic Syntheses*, Coll. Vol. **4**, 288.

Cyclocolorenone.★

See also:

Narang, Dutta, *J. Chem. Soc.*, 1964, 1119.

Cyclodecane-1 : 2-dione (*Sebacil*).★

See also:

Blomqvist, Goldstein, *Organic Syntheses*, 1956, **36**, 77; Coll. Vol. **4**, 838.

Cyclodecanone.★

Cope, Barthel, Smith, *Organic Syntheses*, 1956, **36**, 14; Coll. Vol. **4**, 218.

Cyclodecapentaene-1 : 6-epoxide

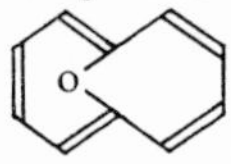

$C_{10}H_8O$ MW 144

Pale yellow cryst. M.p. 52–3°. Light absorption: $\lambda_{max.}$ 257 (ε, 74,500) and 302 mμ (7100).

Vogel *et al.*, *Angew. Chem.*, 1964, **76**, 785; *Int. Ed.*, 1964, **3**, 642.

Cyclodiazomethane. *See* Diazirine.

1 : 5 : 9-Cyclododecatrienene

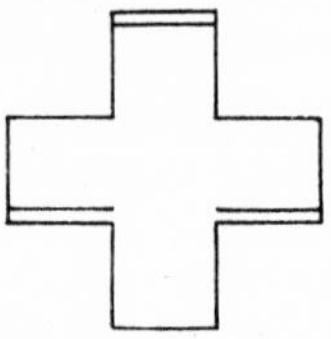

$C_{12}H_{18}$ MW 162

1-*Cis*-5-*trans*-9-*trans*-.

M.p. −18°. B.p. 100–1°/11 mm.

1-*Trans*-5-*trans*-9-*trans*-.

M.p. 34°.

Wilke, *Angew. Chem.*, 1957, **69**, 397.

Ohno, Torimitsu, *Tetrahedron Letters*, 1964, 2259.

Cyclododecene

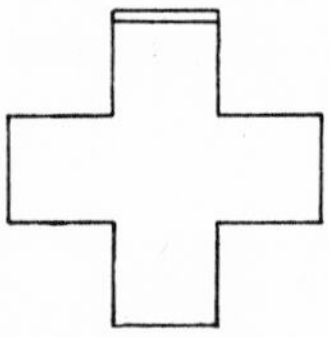

$C_{12}H_{22}$ MW 166

Cis-.

B.p. 64–5°/1 mm., 100–3°/11 mm. n_D^{20} 1·4863. OsO_4 → *cis*-diol, m.p. 157–8°.

Prelog, Speck, *Helv. Chim. Acta*, 1955, **38**, 1786.

Ohno, Okamoto, *Tetrahedron Letters*, 1964, 2423.

Cycloheptane-1 : 3-dione

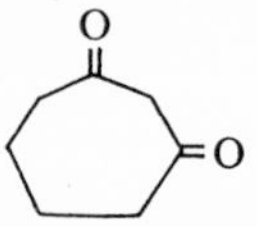

$C_7H_{10}O_2$ MW 126

Oil. B.p. 116°/10 mm. $n_D^{22·5}$ 1·4832. Light absorption: $\lambda_{max.}$ *ca.* 270 mμ (ε, *ca.* 600) in acidic MeOH. $\lambda_{max.}$ 287 mμ (ε, 16,400) in alkaline MeOH.

Bis-*phenylhydrazone*: yellow cryst from MeOH. M.p. 127–8° decomp.

Bis-[2 : 4-*dinitrophenylhydrazone*]: orange cryst. from MeOH. M.p. 205–6°.

Bis-*semicarbazone*: colourless cryst. from EtOH. M.p. 214° decomp.

Bis-*oxime*: cryst. from MeOH. M.p. 162–3°.

Eistert, Haupter, Schank, *Ann.*, 1963, **665**, 55.

Cycloheptanone.★

Dauben *et al.*, *Organic Syntheses*, Coll. Vol. **4**, 221.

Boer, Backer, *Organic Syntheses*, Coll. Vol. **4**, 225.

Cycloheptatriene-1 : 6-dicarboxylic Acid

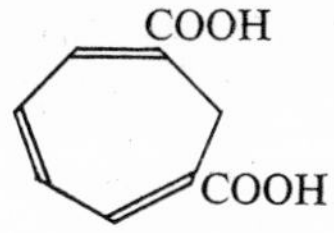

$C_9H_8O_4$ MW 144

Needles from hot dioxan–benzene. M.p. 293–5° decomp. Light absorption: $\lambda_{max.}$ 225 (log ε, 440) and 300 mμ (3·71) in EtOH; 226 (4·44) and 310 mμ (3·68) in EtOH–0·001*N*-HCl; 222 (4·34) and 302 mμ (3·68) in EtOH–0·001*N*-NaOH.

Mono-Me ester: $C_{10}H_{10}O_4$. MW 158. Needles from CH_2Cl_2–hexane. M.p. 122–3°.

Di-Me ester: $C_{11}H_{12}O_4$. MW 172. Needles from Et_2O–hexane. M.p. 53–4°.

Darms *et al.*, *Helv. Chim. Acta*, 1963, **46**, 2893.

1 : 2-Cyclohexanedione.★

B.p. 85°/17 mm., 40°/0·01 mm.

See also:

Borger *et al.*, *Bull. soc. chim. Belg.*, 1964, **73**, 73.

Di-oxime:

Hach, Banks, Diehl, *Organic Syntheses*, Coll. Vol. **4**, 229.

Cycloheximide. *See* Actidione.

1-Cyclohexyl-2-methylaminopropane (*Propyl hexedrine, Benzedrex, Eventin*)

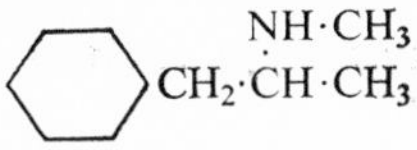

$C_{10}H_{21}N$ MW 155

(±)-.

Inhalant. Oil. B.p. 205°/760 mm., 92–3°/20 mm. D_4^{25} 0·8501. n_D^{20} 1·4600.

B,HCl: m.p. 127–8° decomp.

(+)-.

B.p. 82–3°/10 mm. n_D^{20} 1·4588.

B,HCl: m.p. 137–9°. $[\alpha]_D^{26}$ 14·73°.

(−)-.

B.p. 80–1°/9 mm. n_D^{20} 1·4590.

B,HCl: m.p. 138–9° decomp. $[\alpha]_D^{26}$ −14·74°.

Zenitz, Macks, Moore, *J. Am. Chem. Soc.*, 1947, **69**, 1117.

Ullyot, U.S.P. 2,454,746 (*Chem. Abstracts*, 1949, **43**, 1802).

1-Cyclohexyl-1-phenyl-3-pyrrolidinopropan-1-ol. *See* Procyclidine.★

***Cyclo*-(L-α-hydroxyisohexanoyl-L-valyl-*N*-methyl-L-leucyl-L-α-hydroxyisovaleryl-D-valyl-D-leucyl).** *See* Sporidesmolide IV.

***Cyclo*-(L-α-hydroxyisovaleryl-L-valyl-L-leucyl-L-α-hydroxyisovaleryl-D-valyl-D-leucyl).** *See* Sporidesmolide III.

***Cyclo*-(L-α-hydroxyisovaleryl-L-valyl-*N*-methyl-L-leucyl-L-α-hydroxyisovaleryl-D-*allo*-isoleucyl-D-leucyl).** *See* Sporidesmolide II.

***Cyclo*-(L-α-hydroxyisovaleryl-L-valyl-*N*-methyl-L-leucyl-L-α-hydroxyisovaleryl-D-valyl-D-leucyl).** *See* Sporidesmolide I.★

Cyclokauranoic Acid

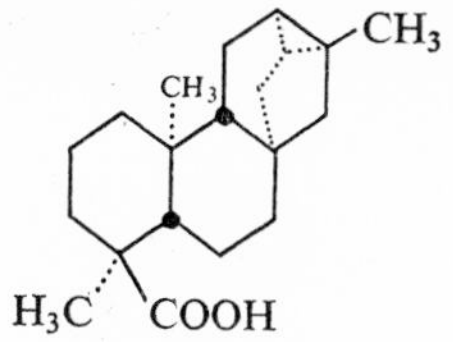

$C_{20}H_{30}O_2$ MW 302

Constituent of the wood *Trachylobium verrucosum* (Gaertn.) Oliv.

Me ester: m.p. 110–12°. $[\alpha]_D$ −41° ($CHCl_3$).

Hugel *et al.*, *Bull. soc. chim.*, 1963, 1974.

Cyclomicrophylline A

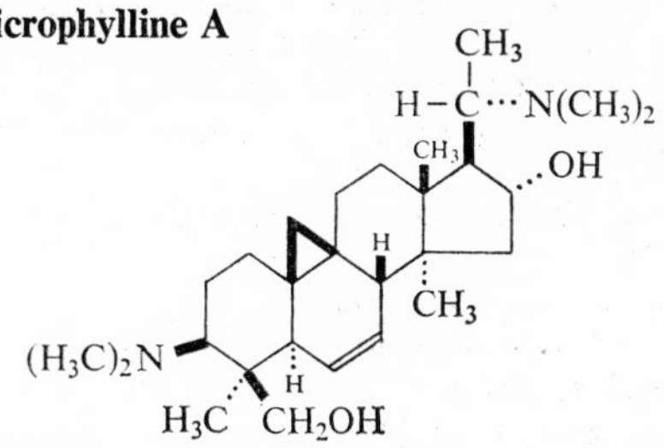

$C_{28}H_{48}O_2N_2$ MW 444

Constituent of *Buxus microphylla* Sieb. et Zucc. var. *suffruticosa* Makino. M.p. 232–3°. $[\alpha]_D$ −93° ($CHCl_3$).

Mono-p-*toluenesulphonyl*: m.p. 176–7°. $[\alpha]_D$ 12° ($CHCl_3$).

Nakano, Tereo, *Tetrahedron Letters*, 1964, 1035, 1045.

Cyclomicrophylline B

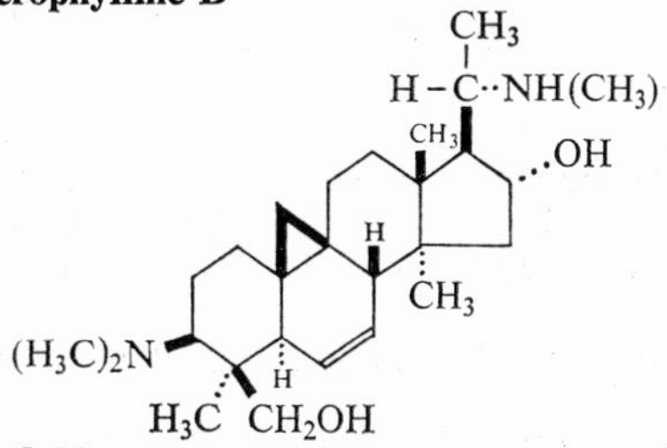

$C_{27}H_{46}O_2N_2$ MW 430

Constituent of *Buxus microphylla* Sieb. et Zucc. var. *suffruticosa* Makino. M.p. 251–2°. $[\alpha]_D$ −65° ($CHCl_3$).

N-*Me*: *see* Cyclomicrophylline A.

Nakano, Tereo, *Tetrahedron Letters*, 1964, 1035, 1045.

Cyclomicrophylline C

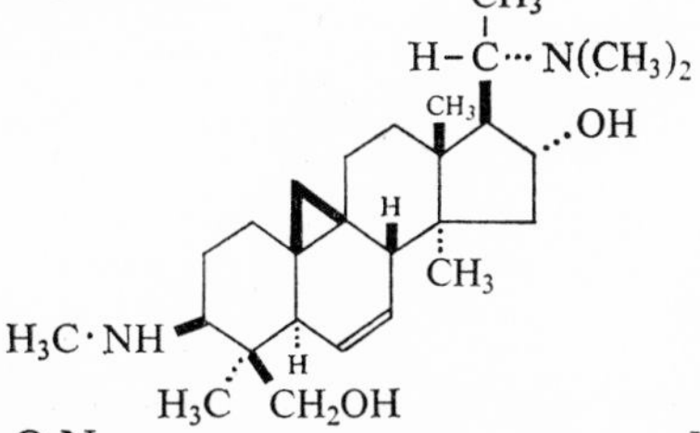

$C_{27}H_{46}O_2N_2$ MW 430

Constituent of *Buxus microphylla* Sieb. et Zucc. var. *suffruticosa* Makino. M.p. 283–4°. $[\alpha]_D$ −40°.

N-*Me*: *see* Cyclomicrophylline A.

Nakano, Tereo, *Tetrahedron Letters*, 1964, 1035, 1045.

1 : 4 : 7-Cyclononatriene

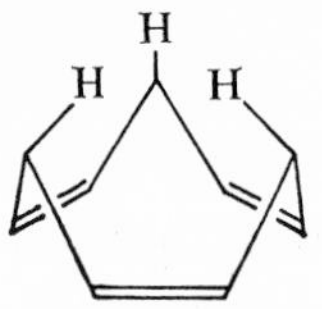

C_9H_{12} MW 120

Cis, cis, cis-.

White needles. M.p. 50–1°. Light absorption: $\lambda_{max.}$ 198 (ε, 9300) and 210 sh. mμ (4600).

$AgNO_3$ complex: m.p. 243° decomp.

Radlick, Winstein, *J. Am. Chem. Soc.*, 1963, **85**, 344.

Untch, Kurland, *J. Am. Chem. Soc.*, 1963, **85**, 345, 346.

Roth, *Ann.*, 1964, **671**, 10.

Roth *et al., J. Am. Chem. Soc.*, 1964, **86**, 3178.

Infra-red spectrum:

Roth, *Ann.*, 1964, **671**, 10.

Cyclo-octadecanonaene

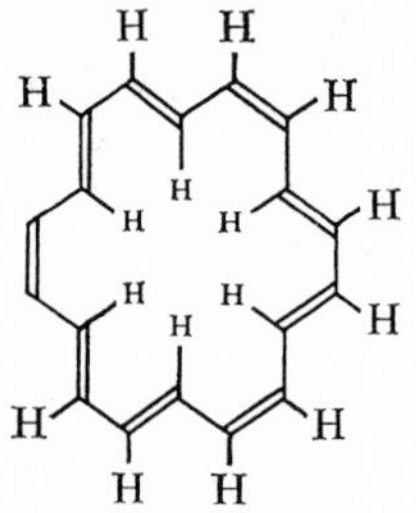

$C_{18}H_{18}$ MW 234

Long red-brown needles from $CHCl_3$. Does not melt below 230°. Light absorption: $\lambda_{max.}$ 278 (ε, 8100), 369 (303,000), 408 (7500), 448 mμ (21,800) in iso-octane.

Sondheimer, Wolovsky, *Tetrahedron Letters*, 1959, No. 3, 3.

Davies, *Tetrahedron Letters*, 1959, No. 8, 4.

Cyclo-octene.★

Cis-.

B.p. 42°/18 mm. M.p. −15·5° to −14·5°. n_D^{25} 1·4682. D_4^{25} 0·8448.

Trans-.

B.p. 75°/78 mm. n_D^{25} 1·4741. D_4^{25} 0·8456.

Cope, Pike, Spencer, *J. Am. Chem. Soc.*, 1953, **75**, 3215.

2-Cyclo-octenone

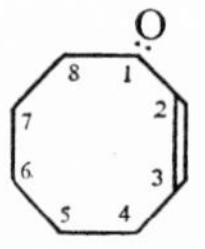

$C_8H_{12}O$ MW 124

Cis-.

B.p. 89°/14 mm. n_D^{25} 1·4953. Light absorption: $\lambda_{max.}$ 223 (ε, 7600), 321 mμ (70). With 1 : 1-dimethoxy-2 : 3 : 4 : 5-tetrachlorocyclopentadiene → adduct. M.p. 118–20°.

Trans-.

Unstable acids → *cis*-isomer with 1 : 1-dimethoxy-2 : 3 : 4 : 5-tetrachlorocyclopentadiene → adduct. M.p. 116–18°.

Cope, Kinter, Keller, *J. Am. Chem. Soc.*, 1954, **76**, 2757.

Eaton, Lin, *J. Am. Chem. Soc.*, 1964, **86**, 2087.

Cyclo-octyne.★

See also:

Wolinsky, Erickson, *Chemistry and Industry*, 1964, 1953.

Cyclopenol

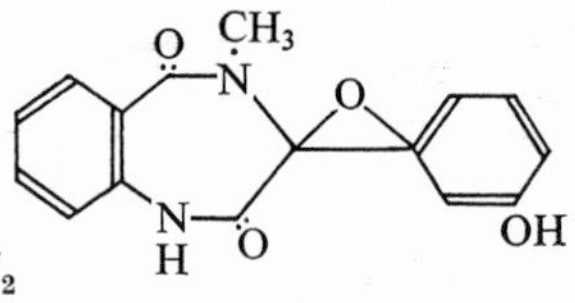

$C_{17}H_{14}O_4N_2$ MW 310

Metabolite of *Penicillium cyclopium* Westling and *P. viridicatum*. Prisms from C_6H_6–AcOEt. M.p. 215° decomp. $[\alpha]_{5461}^{20}$ −309° (c, 1·3 in MeOH). Acid → CO_2, $MeNH_2$, and viridicatol (*q.v.*).

Di-Me: needles from AcOEt–light petroleum. M.p. 167–9°.

Birkinshaw *et al., Biochem. J.*, 1963, **89**, 196.

Mohammed, Lucker, *Tetrahedron Letters*, 1963, 1953.

Cyclopentadecanone (*Exaltolide*).

Syntheses:

Mathur, Bhattacharyya, *J. Chem. Soc.*, 1963, 3505.

Cyclopentadiene.★

Moffett, *Organic Syntheses*, 1952, **32**, 41; Coll. Vol. **4**, 238.

Cyclopenta[*c*]thiapyran. *See* Cyclopenta[*c*]thiin.

Cyclopentanecarboxylic Acid.★

Me ester: $C_7H_{12}O_2$. MW 128. B.p. 70–3°/48 mm. n_D^{25} 1·4341.

Goheen, Vaughan, *Organic Syntheses*, 1959, **39**, 37; Coll. Vol. **4**, 594.

Cyclopenta[*c*]thiin (*Cyclopenta*[c]*thiapyran*)

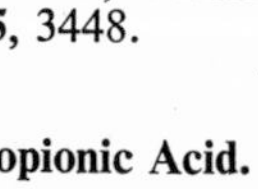

C_8H_6S MW 134

Red plates from pentane. M.p. 89–90·5°. Light absorption: $\lambda_{max.}$ 234 (log ε, 4·15), 249 (4·28), 257 (4·28), 273 (4·34), 283 (4·52), 321 (3·45), 329 (3·38), 344 (3·11), 465 (3·08), 483 (3·04), 500 (2·97), 520 (2·54), 542 (2·54), and 565 mμ (2·26).

Anderson, Harrison, Anderson, *J. Am. Chem. Soc.*, 1963, **85**, 3448.

Erratum p. 801

2-1′-Cyclopentenylpropionic Acid.

Corrected structure

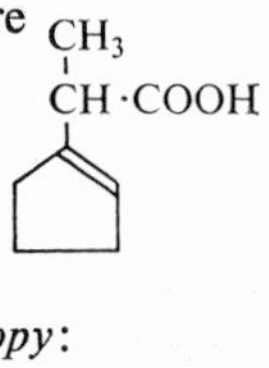

Cyclopropane.★

N.M.R. spectroscopy:

Weitkamp, Korte, *Tetrahedron*, 1964, **20**, 2125.

Cyclopropane-1 : 2-dicarboxylic Acid.★
Trans (−) (1R : 2R)-.
Absolute configuration:
Inouye, Sugita, Walborsky, *Tetrahedron*, 1964, **20**, 1695.

Cyclovirobuxine D

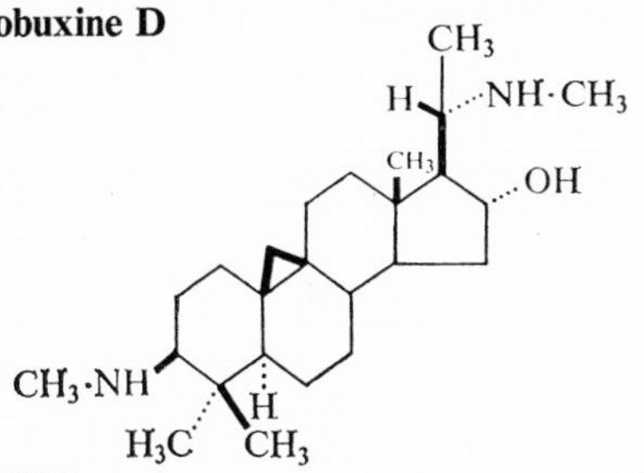

$C_{26}H_{46}ON_2$ MW 402
Alkaloid of common box (*Buxus sempervrens* L.). M.p. 221–4°. $[\alpha]_D$ +63° ($CHCl_3$).
B,2HI: m.p. 313–15° decomp.
B,2HClO₄: m.p. 249–52° decomp.
Tri-Ac, H₂O: m.p. 237–9° decomp. $[\alpha]_D$ −60° ($CHCl_3$).
N : N-*Di-Ac,H₂O*: m.p. 265–6°. $[\alpha]_D$ −43° ($CHCl_3$).
Brown, Kupchan, *Tetrahedron Letters*, 1964, 2895.

Cyperene

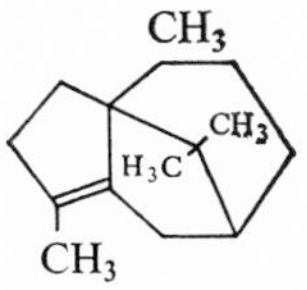

$C_{15}H_{24}$ MW 204
Constituent of the essential oil of *Cyperus rotundus* L. B.p. 104°/5 mm. n_D^{20} 1·5058. D_4^{20} 0·9354. $[\alpha]_D^{20}$ −20° (neat). OsO_4 → diol, m.p. 147·5°.
Trivedi *et al.*, *Tetrahedron Letters*, 1964, 1197.

Cyprinol (3α : 7α : 12α : 26 : 27 - *Pentahydroxycholestane*)

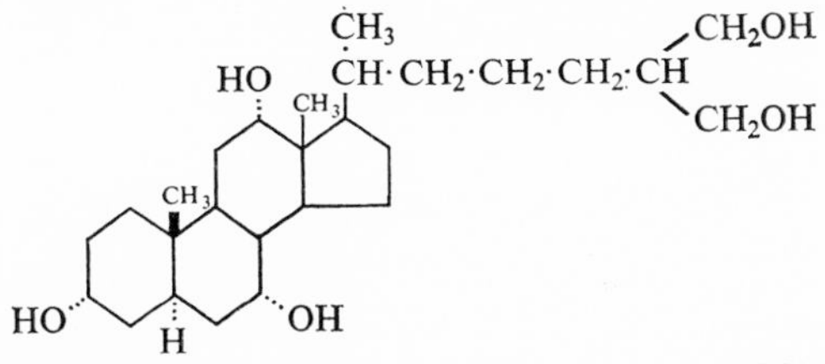

$C_{27}H_{48}O_5$ MW 452
Bile alcohol present in *Cyrinidae* (carp) spp. Colourless prisms from Me_2CO. M.p. 242–4°. $[\alpha]_D^{23}$ 29° ± 2° (c, 1·7 in EtOH).
Tetra-Ac: cryst. from Et_2O with double m.p. 110–15° and 137·5–139°. $[\alpha]_D^{26}$ 10° ± 1° (c, 1·6 in EtOH).
Anderson, Briggs, Haslewood, *Biochem. J.*, 1964, **90**, 303.

Cystamine *S*-monoxide
$NH_2·CH_2·CH_2·SO·S·CH_2·CH_2NH_2$
$C_4H_{12}ON_2S_2$ MW 168
(±)-.
Di-p-toluenesulphonyl: needles from EtOH.Aq. M.p. 160° decomp.
Savige *et al.*, *Tetrahedron Letters*, 1964, 3289.

Cysteine.★
S-*Me*: $C_4H_9O_2NS$. MW 135. Present in human urine and in the kidney bean (*Phaseolus vulgaris*). M.p. 207–11°.
Thompson, Morris, Zacharius, *Nature*, 1956, **178**, 593.
Tominga *et al.*, *J. Biochem* (Japan), 1963, **54**, 220.

L-Cystine (±)-*S*-monoxide
$HOOC·CH(NH_2)·CH_2·SO·S·CH_2·CH(NH_2)·COOH$
$C_6H_{12}O_5N_2S_2$ MW 256
Two forms:
α-.
Ppd. from aq. soln. with EtOH. $[\alpha]_D^{20}$ +62° (c, 2·5 in N-H_2SO_4). Gives pink col. with ninhydrin.
β-.
$[\alpha]_D^{20}$ +14° (in N-H_2SO_4).
Savige *et al.*, *Tetrahedron Letters*, 1964, 3289.

Cytacon. *See* Vitamin B_{12}.★

Cytamen. *See* Vitamin B_{12}.★

Cytidine.★
2′-O-*Me*: present in the ribonucleic acid from various plant, animal, and bacterial sources.
Smith, Dunn, *Biochim. Biophys. Acta*, 1959, **31**, 573.
Hall, *Biochim. Biophys. Acta*, 1963, **68**, 278; *Biochem. Biophys. Research Commun.*, 1963, **12**, 429.
Morisawa, Chargaff, *Biochim. Biophys. Acta*, 1963, **68**, 147.

Cytochrome C
H·Thr·Glu·Phe·Lys·Ala–Gly·Ser·Ala·Lys·Lys·Gly–
(1)
–Ala·Thr·Leu·Phe·Lys·Thr·Arg·CyS·Glu·Leu·CyS–
Haem (bridging the two CyS)
–His·Thr·Val·Glu·Lys·Gly·Gly·Pro·His·Lys·Val·Gly–
–Pro·Asp(NH_2)·Leu·His·Gly·Ileu·Phe·Gly·Arg·His–
–Ser·Gly·Glu(NH_2)·Ala·Glu(NH_2)·Gly·Tyr·Ser·Tyr–
–Thr·Asp·Ala·Asp(NH_2)·Ileu·Lys·Lys·Asp(NH_2)–
–Val·Leu·Try·Asp·Glu·Asp(NH_2)·Asp(NH_2)·Met–
–Ser·Glu·Tyr·Leu·Thr·Asp(NH_2)·Pro·Lys·Lys·Tyr–
–Ileu·Pro·Gly·Thr·Lys·Met·Ala·Phe·Gly·Gly·Leu–
–Lys·Lys·Glu·Lys·Asp·Arg·Asp(NH_2)·Asp·Leu·Ileu–
–Thr·Tyr·Leu·Lys·Lys·Ala·CySH·Glu·OH.
(108)
Complete amino acid sequence of bakers' yeast cytochrome C.
Narita *et al.*, *Biochim. Biophys. Acta*, 1963, **77**, 688.

Cytochrome C-551
Glu·Asp·Pro·Glu·Val·Leu·Phe·Lys·Asp(NH_2)·Lys–
(1)
Haem (bridging Cys and Ala·Cys)
–Gly·Cys·Val·Ala·Cys·His·Ala·Ileu·Asp·Thr·Lys–
–Met·Val·Gly·Pro·Ala·Tyr·Lys·Asp·Val·Ala·Ala–
–Lys·Phe·Ala·Gly·Glu(NH_2)·Ala·Gly·Ala·Glu·Ala–
–Glu·Leu·Ala·Glu(NH_2)·Arg·Ileu·Lys·Asp(NH_2)–
–Gly·Ser·Glu(NH_2)·Gly·Val·Try·Gly·Pro·Ileu·Pro–
–Met·Pro·Pro·Asp(NH_2)·Ala·Val·Ser·Asp·Asp·Glu–
–Ala·Glu(NH_2)·Thr·Leu·Ala·Lys·Try·Val·Leu·Ser–
–Glu(NH_2)·Lys.
(82)

Produced by *Pseudomonas* spp. Amorph. Light absorption: $\lambda_{max.}$ 551, 521, 416, 313 mμ (reduced form).

Horio *et al.*, *Biochem. J.*, 1960, **77**, 194.
Ambler, *Biochem. J.*, 1963, **89**, 341, 349.

Cytohaemin

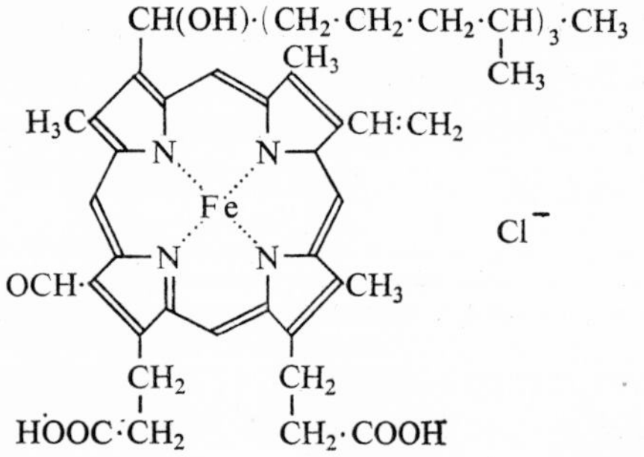

$C_{49}H_{62}O_6N_4ClFe$ MW 894·5

Constituent of beef hearts. Cryst. from Py–iso-octane.

Warburg, Gewitz, Völker, *Z. Naturforsch.*, 1955, **10b**, 541.
Grassl *et al.*, *Biochem. Z.*, 1963, **338**, 771.

Cytolipin H (N-*Lignoceroyl*-1-D-*sphingosyl*-β-*lactoside*)

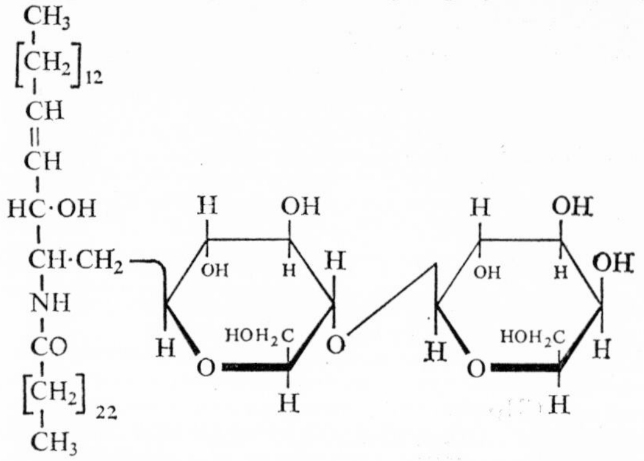

$C_{54}H_{103}O_{12}N$ MW 957

D-.

Lipid isolated from human epidermoid carcinoma. M.p. 230–40° with sintering 180–90°. $[\alpha]_D$ −6·4° (Py).

Rapport *et al.*, *Cancer*, 1959, **12**, 438; *J. Lipid Research*, 1961, **2**, 25, 148.
Shapiro, Bachaman, *Nature*, 1964, **201**, 878.

D

D. 860. *See* Tolbutamide.

Dactylifric Acid. *See* 3-*O*-Caffeoylshikimic Acid.

Daneral. *See p*-Aminosalicylate *under* Pheniramine.★

Dansyl chloride. *See* 5-Dimethylamino-1-naphthalene sulphonyl chloride.

Daphnorin (*Daphnoretin*-7β-*glucoside*)

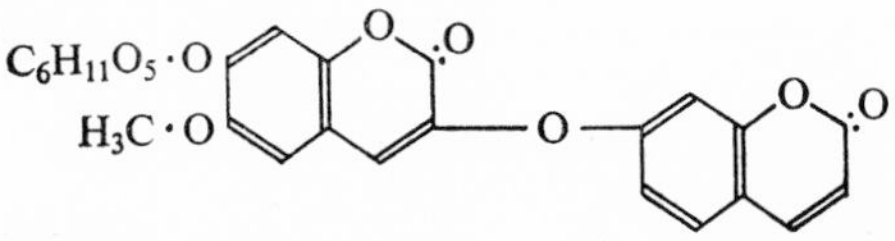

$C_{25}H_{22}O_{12}$ MW 514

Glucoside present in *Thymelaeace*. Colourless fine needles from MeOH–H_2O. M.p. 202–4° decomp. $[\alpha]_D^{20}$ −78° (c, 0·6 in H_2O). Light absorption: $\lambda_{max.}$ 224 sh. (log ε, 4·34), 260 (3·90), 325 (4·31), 339 mμ (4·34). Hyd. → Daphnoretin + glucose.

Tschesche, Schacht, Legler, *Naturwiss.*, 1963, **50**, 521.

Daraprim. *See* Pyrimethamine.★

Daricon. *See under* Oxyphencyclimine.★

Dasycarpidol

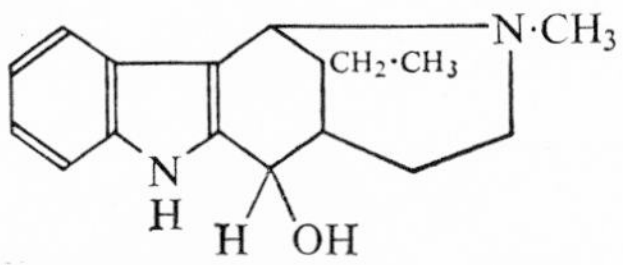

$C_{17}H_{22}ON_2$ MW 270

Alkaloid of *Aspidosperma dasycarpon* A. DC. M.p. 118–22°. $[\alpha]_D$ −54° (EtOH). Light absorption: $\lambda_{max.}$ 220 (log ε, 4·54), 282 (3·89), and 290 mμ (3·81). CrO_3 → dasycarpidone.

Ohashi *et al.*, *Experientia*, 1964, **20**, 363.

Dasycarpidone

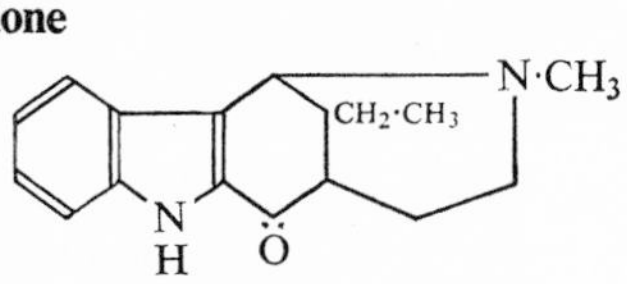

$C_{17}H_{20}ON_2$ MW 268

Alkaloid from *Aspidosperma dasycarpon* A. DC. Amorph. $[\alpha]_D$ 65° ($CHCl_3$). Light absorption: $\lambda_{max.}$ 237 (log ε, 4·15) and 316 mμ (4·29).

Ohashi *et al.*, *Experientia*, 1964, **20**, 363.

Daunomycin

$C_{27}H_{32}O_{11}N$(?) MW 546

Antibiotic from *Streptomyces peucetius*.

B,HCl: thin red needles. M.p. 184–6°. Light absorption: $\lambda_{max.}$ 234 ($E^{1\%}_{1\,cm.}$ 665), 252 (462), 290 (153), 480 (214), 495 (218), and 532 mμ (112).

Di Marco *et al.*, *Nature*, 1964, **201**, 706.

Dauricine.★

(±)-.

Amorph. M.p. 122–4°.

Picrate: m.p. 140–2°.

Styphnate: m.p. 146–9°.

Synthesis:

Kametani, Fukumoto, *Tetrahedron Letters*, 1964, 2771.

Davallic Acid

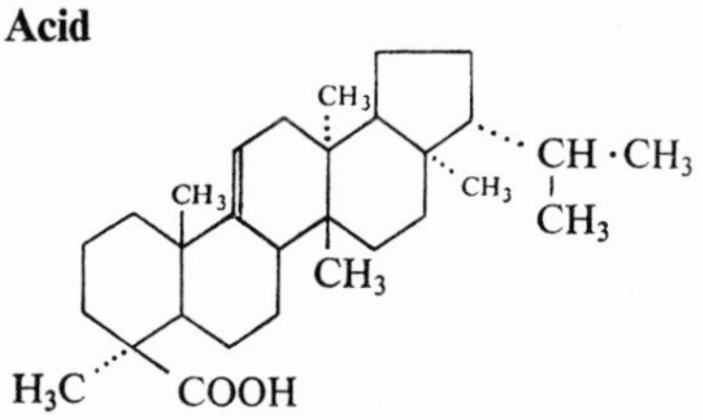

$C_{30}H_{48}O_2$ MW 440

Constituent of the rhizome of the Chinese fern *Davallia divaricata*. M.p. 283°.

Me ester: m.p. 234°.

Nakanishi *et al.*, *Tetrahedron Letters*, 1963, 1451.

7-Deacetoxy-7-oxogedunin

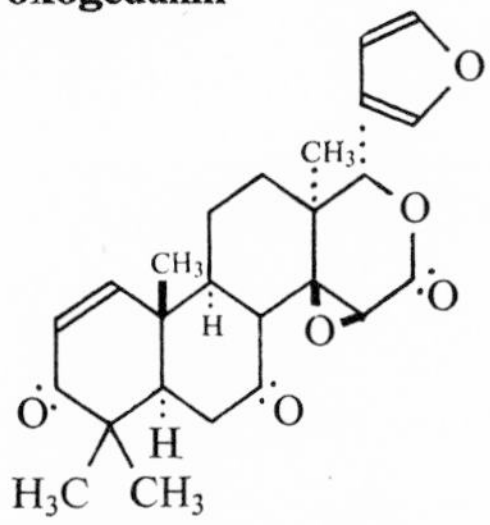

$C_{26}H_{30}O_6$ MW 438

Constituent of *Cedrela odorata* and the seed of *Carapa guayanensis*. M.p. 260–3°. $[\alpha]_D^{20}$ −53° ($CHCl_3$).

Bevan, Powell, Taylor, *J. Chem. Soc.*, 1963, 980.

Ollis, Ward, Zelnik, *Tetrahedron Letters*, 1964, 2607.

Deacetylaspidospermine (*Desacetylaspidospermine*)

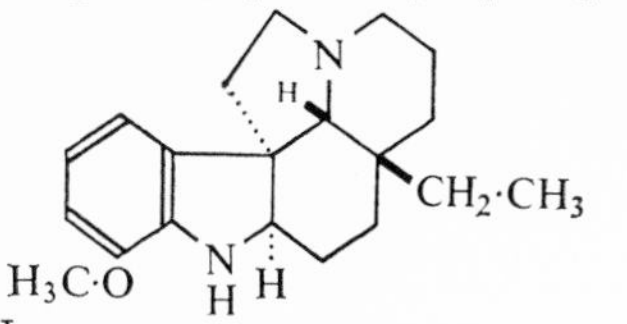

$C_{20}H_{28}ON_2$ MW 312
M.p. 107–8°. $[\alpha]_D^{24}$ +7°.
N-*Formyl*: *see* Vallesin.★
N-*Ac*: *see* Aspidospermine.★
N-*Propionyl*: *see* Palosine.★
B,2HI: m.p. >280°.
Benzoyl: cryst. from MeOH.Aq. M.p. 187–90°.

Ewins, *J. Chem. Soc.*, 1914, **105**, 2738.
Schlittler, *Helv. Chim. Acta*, 1948, **31**, 446.

Deacetylpicraline. *See* Burnamine.

Deamino-oxytocin. *See* Desamino-oxytocin.

4-Decarboxamido-oxytocin (4-α-*Aminobutyric acid-oxytocin*)

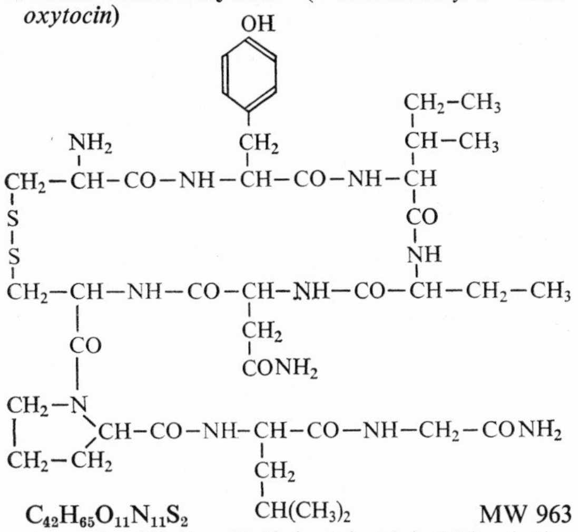

$C_{42}H_{65}O_{11}N_{11}S_2$ MW 963
Amorph. $[\alpha]_D^{20}$ −30·7° (c, 1 in *N*-AcOH). Active avian depressor and rat oxytocic factor.

du Vigneaud *et al.*, *J. Biol. Chem.*, 1964, **239**, 472.

5-Decarboxamido-oxytocin (5-*Alanine-oxytocin*, *Ala*[5]-*oxytocin*)

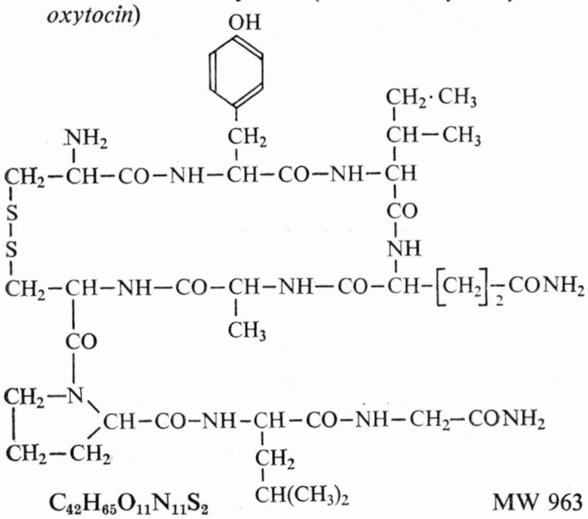

$C_{42}H_{65}O_{11}N_{11}S_2$ MW 963
Amorph. $[\alpha]_D^{19}$ −13·3° (c, 1·5 in *N*-AcOH). Inactive in the avian depressor and rat oxytocic factor tests.

du Vigneaud *et al.*, *J. Biol. Chem.*, 1964, **239**, 472.

2-Decene-4 : 6-diynoic Acid.★
Cis-.
Me ester: also constituent of *Aster spinosus* Benth. Light absorption: $\lambda_{max.}$ 225·3 (log ε, 4·57), 276 (4·08), 292 (4·31), and 310·5 mμ (4·30).

Spitzer, Steelink, *Science*, 1964, **146**, 1461.

See also:

Sorensen, Stauholt, *Acta Chem. Scand.*, 1950, **4**, 1575.

Decentan. *See* Perphenazine.★

7-Dechloro-7-fluorogriseofulvin

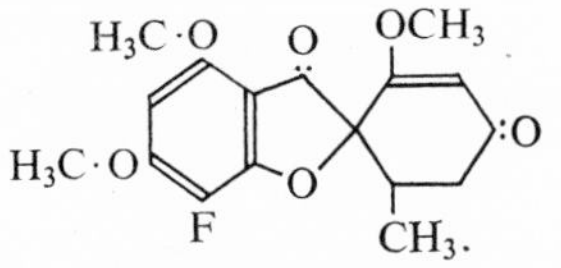

$C_{17}H_{17}O_6F$ MW 336
(+)-.
Cryst. from Me_2CO–Et_2O. M.p. 210–12°. $[\alpha]_D$ +316° (c, 0·61 in $CHCl_3$).

Taub, Kuo, Wendler, *Chemistry and Industry*, 1962, 557; *J. Org. Chem.*, 1963, **28**, 2752.

De Cortisyl. *See* Prednisone.

Decoyinine. *See* Augustmycin A.

Deglucoerysimoside. *See* Erysimine.

Dehacodin. *See* Dihydrocodeine.

Dehydroabietic Acid.★
Me ester: constituent of the concrete of *Cistus labdaniferus*. Needles. M.p. 58–60°. B.p. 152–4°/0·2 mm.

Tabacik-Wlotzka, Mousseron, Chafai, *Bull. soc. chim.*, 1963, 2299; 1964, 618.

Dehydroactidione

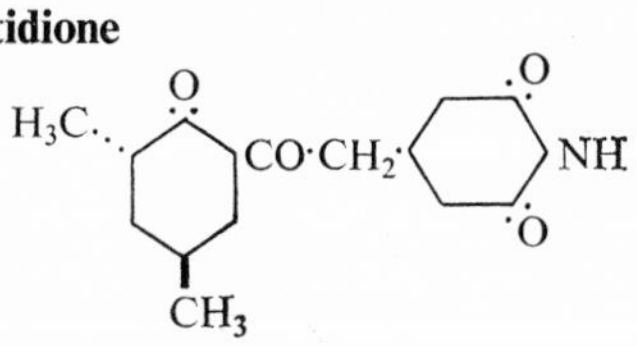

$C_{15}H_{21}O_4N$ MW 289
Metabolite of *Streptomyces noursei*. Cryst. from EtOH. M.p. 178°. $[\alpha]_D^{20}$ −29·8° (c, 2 in dioxan).
Cu complex: m.p. 228–9° decomp.

Kornfeld, Jones, Parker, *J. Am. Chem. Soc.*, 1949, **71**, 150.
Vondráček, Vaněk, *Chemistry and Industry*, 1964, 1686.

1 : 2-Dehydroaspidospermine.★
(−)-.
Alkaloid from the leaves of *Pleiocarpa tubicina*. B.p. 140°/0·01 mm. $[\alpha]_D^{23}$ −212° ± 15° (c, 0·15 in EtOH).

Bycroft *et al.*, *Helv. Chim. Acta*, 1964, **47**, 1147.

22-Dehydrocholesterol. *See* 5 : 22-Cholestadien-3β-ol.

1 : 2-Dehydrocortisone. *See* Prednisone.

1 : 2-Dehydrohydrocortisone. *See* Prednisolone.★

Dehydrolapachone

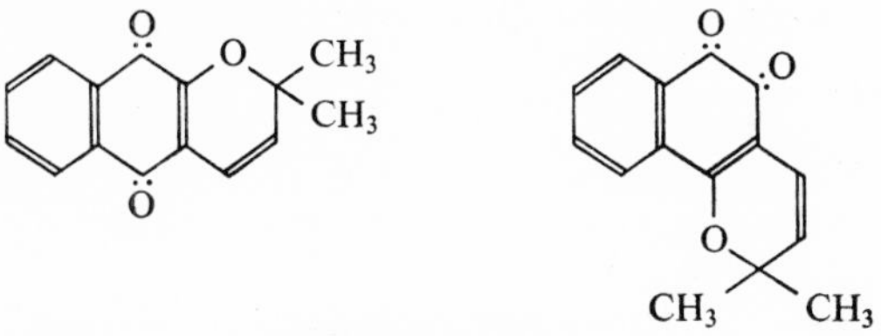

Suggested structures

$C_{15}H_{12}O_3$ MW 240

Constituent of the wood of *Tabebuia avellanedae*. Yellow needles from EtOH. M.p. 142·5–143·5°.

Casinovi *et al.*, *Ann. chim.* (Rome), 1962, **52**, 1184 (*Chem. Abstracts*, 1963, **59**, 7466).

Dehydrolycopene

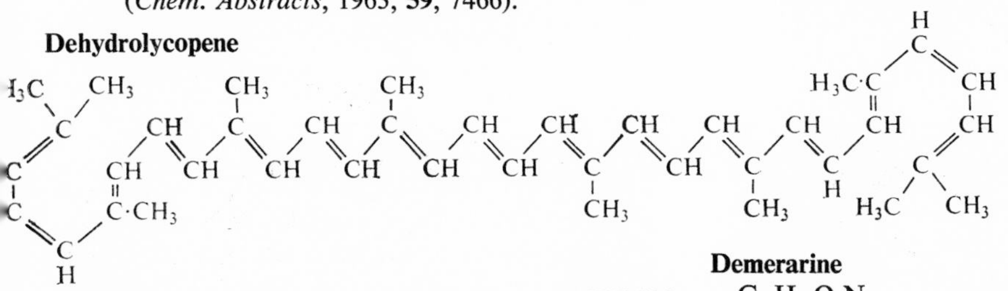

$C_{40}H_{52}$ MW 532

Carotenoid from Spanish oranges. Cryst. from Py. M.p. >200° decomp. Light absorption: $\lambda_{max.}$ 520, 557, and 601 mμ (in CS_2).

Karrer, Rutschmann, *Helv. Chim. Acta*, 1945, **28**, 793.

Winterstein, Studer, Rüegg, *Chem. Ber.*, 1960, **93**, 2951.

Surmatis, Ofner, *J. Org. Chem.*, 1963, **28**, 2735.

Dehydrotectol

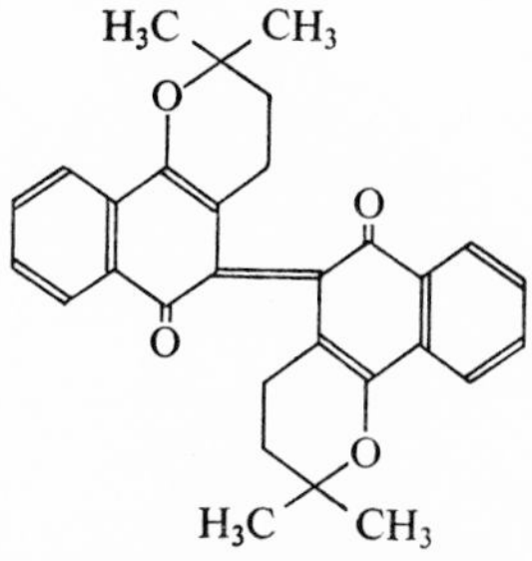

$C_{30}H_{24}O_4$ MW 448

Extractive of teak (*Tecona grandis* L.F.). Blue-green-black cryst. M.p. 195–6°. Zn/AcOH → tectol.

Picrate: m.p. 167–8°.

Trinitrobenzene deriv.: m.p. 214–16°.

Sandermann, Dietrichs, *Holzforschung*, 1959, **13**, 137 (*Chem. Abstracts*, 1960, **54**, 7142).

Sandermann, Simatupang, *Tetrahedron Letters*, 1963, 1269; *Chem. Ber.*, 1964, **97**, 588.

11 : 12-Dehydroursolic Acid Lactone

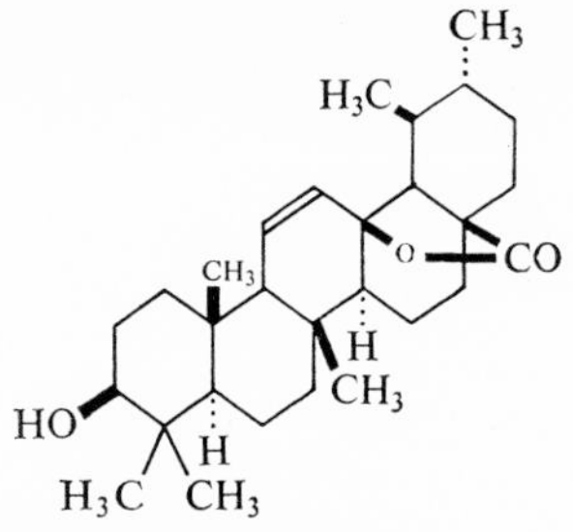

$C_{30}H_{46}O_3$ MW 454

M.p. 278° decomp. $[\alpha]_D^{10}$ 44°.

Ac: $C_{32}H_{48}O_4$. MW 496. Present in the waxes of *Eucalyptus* sp. Colourless cryst. M.p. *ca.* 262° decomp. $[\alpha]_D^{26}$ 39° (c, 0·7 in $CHCl_3$).

Fujii, Osumi, *J. Pharm. Soc. Japan*, 1940, **60**, 291 (*Chem. Abstracts*, 1940, **34**, 7293).

Barton *et al.*, *J. Chem. Soc.*, 1962, 5163.

Horn, Lamberton, *Austral. J. Chem.*, 1964, **17**, 477.

Delta-Cortef. *See* Prednisolone.★

Deltacortone. *See* Prednisone.★

Deltacortril. *See* Prednisolone.★

Delta-Stab. *See* Prednisolone.★

Demerarine

$C_{36}H_{38}O_6N_2$ MW 594

Alkaloid from Greenheart (*Ocotea rodiaei*).

B,HCl: $[\alpha]_D$ −181° (c, 1 in H_2O).

Hearst, *J. Org. Chem.*, 1964, **29**, 466.

Demethoxyaspidospermine

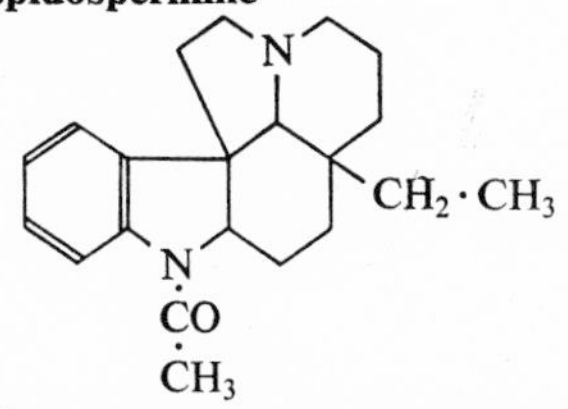

$C_{21}H_{28}ON_2$ MW 324

Alkaloid from *Aspidosperma discolor* A. DC. and *A. eburneum* Fr. All. Amorph. $[\alpha]_D^{25}$ −15° (c, 1·8 in $CHCl_3$). Light absorption: $\lambda_{max.}$ 253 (log ε, 4·12), 280 (3·58), 289 mμ (3·52).

B,HClO₄,0·5H₂O: $[\alpha]_D^{35}$ +21° (c, 1·3 in MeOH).

Ferreira *et al.*, *Experientia*, 1963, **19**, 585.

15-Demethoxyobscurinervidine. *See* Neblinine.

Demethylaspidospermine

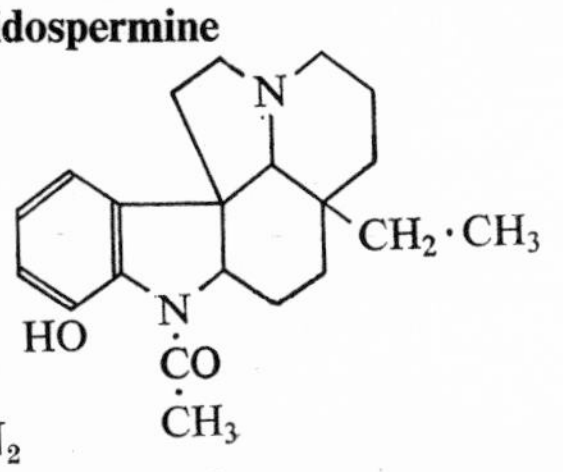

$C_{21}H_{28}O_2N_2$ MW 340

Alkaloid from *Aspidosperma discolor* A. DC. and *A. eburneum* Fr. All. Oil. Light absorption: $\lambda_{max.}$ 220 (log ε, 4·39), 258 (3·52), 293 mμ (3·20).

B,HClO$_4$,MeOH: cryst. M.p. 170° decomp. $[\alpha]_D^{25}$ +94° (c, 0·98 in MeOH).

Witkop, Patrick, *J. Am. Chem. Soc.*, 1954, **76**, 5603.
Ferreira *et al.*, *Experientia*, 1963, **19**, 585.

2-Demethylcolchicine (*Substance C*)

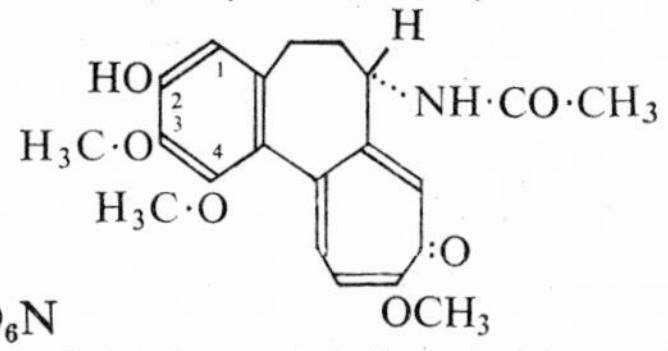

$C_{21}H_{23}O_6N$ MW 385

Minor alkaloid from *Colchicum autumnale* L. M.p. 176–82°. $[\alpha]_D^{22}$ −130·7° ($CHCl_3$).
Me ether: *see* Colchicine.
Et ether: m.p. 232–4°. $[\alpha]_D^{23}$ −135·8° ($CHCl_3$).

Šantavý, Reichstein, *Helv. Chim. Acta*, 1950, **33**, 1606.
Šantavý, Talaš, Tělopilova, *Coll. Czech. Chem. Commun.*, 1953, **18**, 710.

De-*N*-methyldasycarpidone

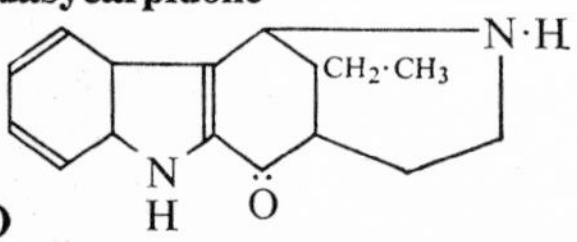

$C_{16}H_{18}N_2O$ MW 254

Alkaloid from *Aspidospermi dasycarpon* A. DC. M.p. 208–10°. Methylation → dasycarpidone.

Okashi *et al.*, *Experientia*, 1964, **20**, 363.

4′-Demethyl-deoxypodophyllotoxin

$C_{21}H_{20}O_7$ MW 384

Plates from MeOH. M.p. 244–9°. $[\alpha]_D^{20}$ −122·6° (c, 0·555 in $CHCl_3$), −183·4° (c, 0·548 in Py).
Ac: m.p. 247–8°. $[\alpha]_D^{20}$ −106·7° (c, 0·483 in $CHCl_3$), −85·2° (c, 0·523 in MeOH).
Me ether: *see* Deoxypodophyllotoxin.

Polonsky, Moron, Pourrat, *Bull. soc. chim.*, 1962, 1722.
von Wartburg, Kuhn, Lichti, *Helv. Chim. Acta*, 1964, **47**, 1203.

4′-Demethyl-desoxypodolophyllotoxin-β-D-glucoside

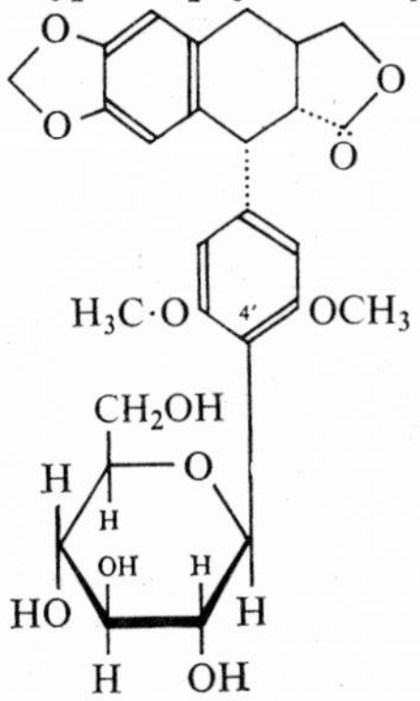

$C_{27}H_{30}O_{12}$ MW 546

Constituent of the root of *Podophyllum emodi* Wall and *P. peltatum* L. Hemihydrate. Amorph. M.p. 146–58°. $[\alpha]_D^{20}$ −77° (c, 0·475 in MeOH). Light absorption: $\lambda_{max.}$ 292 mμ (log ε, 3·66).
Tetra-Ac: colourless needles from MeOH. M.p. 203–6°. $[\alpha]_D^{20}$ −57·9° (c, 0·545 in $CHCl_3$).

von Wartburg, Kuhn, Lichti, *Helv. Chim. Acta*, 1964, **47**, 1203.

Demethylsporidesmolide I. *See* Sporidesmolide III.

De-*N*-methyluleine

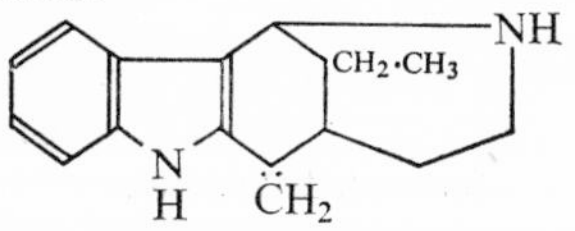

$C_{17}H_{20}N_2$ MW 252

Alkaloid from *Aspidespera dasycarpon* A. DC. M.p. 143–4°. $[\alpha]_D$ −20° (EtOH). Methylation → uleine.

Ohashi *et al.*, *Experientia*, 1964, **20**, 363.

2-Demethyl Vitamin K$_2$ (25)

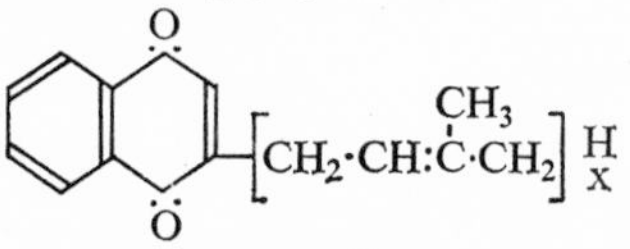

$x = 5$

$C_{35}H_{46}O_2$ MW 498

Minor constituent of *Haemophilus parainfluenzae*.

Lester, White, Smith, *Biochemistry*, 1964, **3**, 949.

2-Demethyl Vitamin K$_2$ (30)

$x = 6$

$C_{40}H_{54}O_2$ MW 566

Constituent of *Haemophilus parainfluenzae*. Oil. Light absorption: $\lambda_{max.}$ 246, 251, 265 sh., and 330 mμ.

Lester, White, Smith, *Biochemistry*, 1964, **3**, 949.

2-Demethyl Vitamin K$_2$ (35)

$x = 7$

$C_{45}H_{62}O_2$ MW 634

Minor constituent of *Haemophilus parainfluenzae*.

Lester, White, Smith, *Biochemistry*, 1964, **3**, 949.

Demissidine.★

Synthesis:

Adam, Schreiber, *Tetrahedron*, 1964, **20**, 1719.

Dendrobine

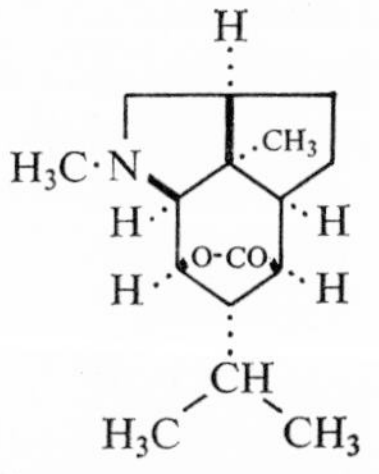

$C_{16}H_{25}O_2N$ MW 263

Alkaloid from *Dendrobium nobile* Lindl. M.p. 135–6°. pK$_a$′ 7·80.

Yamamura, Hirata, *Tetrahedron Letters*, 1964, 79.
Inubushi *et al.*, *Tetrahedron*, 1964, **20**, 2007; *Chemistry and Industry*, 1964, 1689.

Dendrolasin.★

Also present in sweet potato fusel oil and the wood of *Torreya nucifera*.

Sakai, Nishimura, Hirose, *Tetrahedron Letters*, 1963, 1171.

11-Deoxojervine

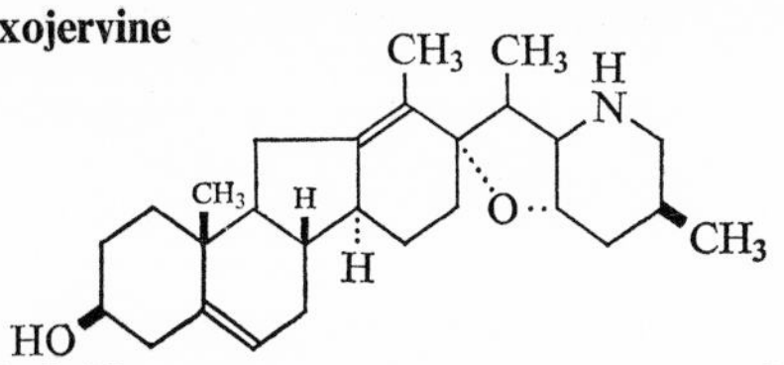

$C_{27}H_{41}O_2N$ MW 411

Alkaloid present in the roots of *Veratrum album* L. var. *glandiflorum* Maxim. Cryst. from MeOH. M.p. 237–8°. $[\alpha]_D$ −44·2° (95% EtOH).

O : N-*Di-Ac*: cryst. from MeOH.Aq. M.p. 163–4°, resolidifies then m.p. 195–7°. $[\alpha]_D^{23}$ 1·1°.

Masamune *et al.*, *Tetrahedron Letters*, 1964, 913.

2′-Deoxyadenosine. *See* Adenine deoxyriboside.

3′-Deoxyadenosine (*Cordycepin*★)

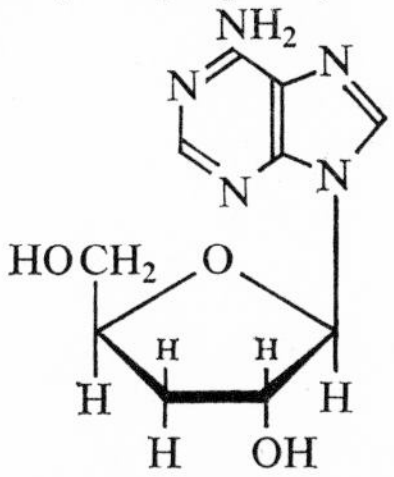

$C_{10}H_{13}O_3N_5$ MW 251

Metabolite of *Cordyceps militaris* and *Aspergillus nidulans*. M.p. 230–1°. $[\alpha]_D^{25}$ −35° (c, 9·425 in H_2O). Light absorption: $\lambda_{max.}$ 259 mμ (ε, 13,100) at pH 4, 260 (ε, 13,700) at pH 11.

5′-Monophosphate: amorph.

Todd, Ulbricht, *J. Chem. Soc.*, 1960, 3275.
Lee *et al.*, *J. Am. Chem. Soc.*, 1961, **83**, 1906.
Rottman, Ibershof, Guarino, *Biochim. Biophys. Acta*, 1963, **76**, 181.
Kaczka *et al.*, *Biochem. Biophys. Research Commun.*, 1964, **14**, 452, 456.
Walton *et al.*, *J. Am. Chem. Soc.*, 1964, **86**, 2952.

Biosynthesis:

Suhadolnik, Weinbaum, Meloche, *J. Am. Chem. Soc.*, 1964, **86**, 948.

5-Deoxy-D-allose. *See* Homoribose.

2′-Deoxy-5-diazouridine (*5-Diazouracil-3-deoxyriboside*)

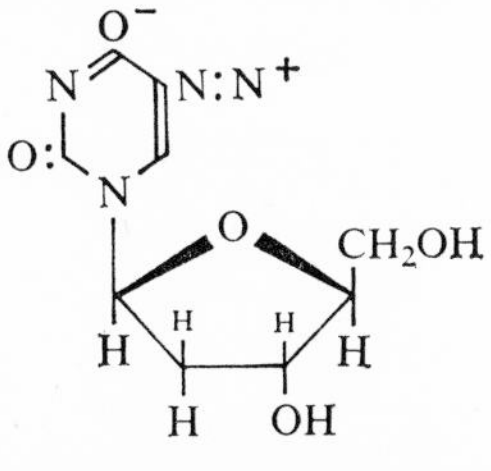

$C_9H_{10}O_5N_4$ MW 264

Cryst. from 95% EtOH. M.p. 163–5° decomp. Light absorption: $\lambda_{max.}$ 261 mμ (ε, 12,600) in MeOH.

Paolini, Robins, Cheng, *Biochim. Biophys. Acta*, 1963, **72**, 114.

Deoxyhelenalin. *See* Aromatin.

2-Deoxy-1 : 3-*myo*-inosadiamine. *See* 2-Deoxystreptamine.

C

14-Deoxylagosin. *See* Filipin.

Deoxylapachol. *See* 2-(γ : γ-Dimethylallyl)-1 : 4-naphthoquinone.

Deoxymexicanin. *See* Aromaticin.

Deoxypicrosalvinic Acid

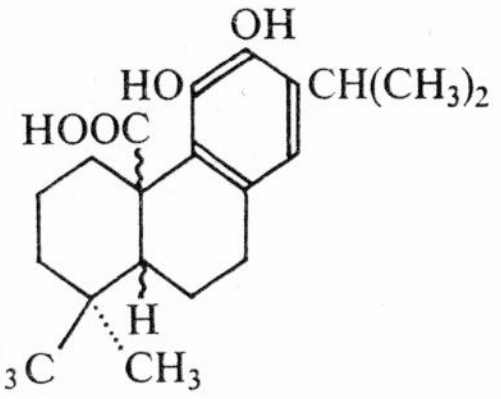

$C_{20}H_{28}O_4$ MW 332

Constituent of *Salvia officinalis* L.

Di-Ac: $C_{24}H_{32}O_6$. MW 416. Prisms. M.p. 196–215° decomp. $[\alpha]_D^{22}$ +139·8° (c, 1·15 in $CHCl_3$). *Me ester*: $C_{25}H_{34}O_6$. MW 430. Prisms. M.p. 158–60°. $[\alpha]_D^{22}$ +143·7° (c, 1·36 in $CHCl_3$).

Di-O-Me, Me ester: amorph.

Linde, *Helv. Chim. Acta*, 1964, **47**, 1234.

Deoxypodophyllotoxin 1-β-D-glucopyranoside ester

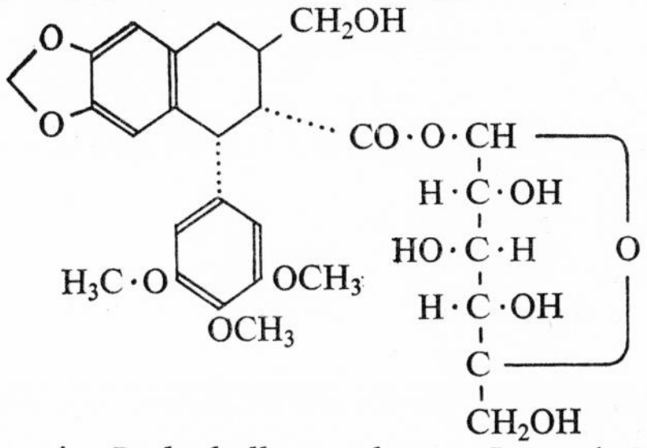

Occurs in *Podophyllum peltatum* L. and *P. emodi* Wall. Antimitotic. M.p. 123–8°. $[\alpha]_D^{22}$ −151·5° (c, 0·575 in MeOH). Light absorption: $\lambda_{max.}$ 289 mμ (log ε, 3·68). *Penta-O-Ac*: m.p. 83–90°. *Pentaphenylurethane*: m.p. 184–97° decomp. $[\alpha]_D^{20}$ −89·3° (c, 0·627 in $CHCl_3$).

Kuhn, Wartburg, *Helv. Chim. Acta*, 1963, **46.**

9-(2′-Deoxyribofuranosyl)adenine. *See* Adenine deoxyriboside.

2-Deoxyribose.★

See also:

Vargha, Kuszmann, *Chem. Ber.*, 96, 411.

2-Deoxystreptamine (*2-Deoxy*-1 : 3-myo-*inosadiamine*)

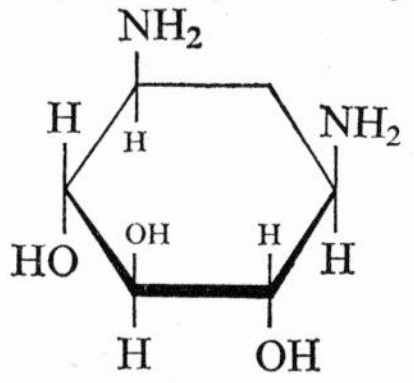

$C_6H_{14}O_3N_2$ MW 162

Hydrolysis product of the antibiotics, kanamycin, neomycin, paromomycin, etc. M.p. 255–8°.

B,2HCl: m.p. 280° decomp.

N : N′-*Dibenzoyl*: m.p. 312–13°.

N : N′-*Dibenzyloxycarbonyl*: m.p. 240° decomp. *Tri-Ac*: m.p. 197°.

Tri-O-Ac, B,2HCl: m.p. >250°.

Dipicrate: cryst. from MeOH.Aq. M.p. 260° decomp.
Mono-N-*Me*: hyosamine. Produced by hydrolysis of hygromycin B. *B,2HCl*: m.p. 170–200° decomp. $[\alpha]_D$ 10·7° (c, 1 in H_2O). pK_a 7·2, 9. *Dipicrate*: m.p. 244° decomp.
N : N-*Tetra-Me*: cryst. from EtOH. M.p. 158–9°. *B,2HCl*: cryst. from EtOH. M.p. 277°. *Dipicrate*: cryst. from H_2O. M.p. 257–8°. *B,2CH₃I*: m.p. 258° decomp.

Kuehl, Bishop, Folkers, *J. Am. Chem. Soc.*, 1951, **73**, 881.
Leach, Tecters, *J. Am. Chem. Soc.*, 1952, **74**, 3187.
Cron *et al.*, *J. Am. Chem. Soc.*, 1958, **80**, 752.
Haskell, French, Butz, *J. Am. Chem. Soc.*, 1959, **81**, 3480.
Daly *et al.*, *J. Am. Chem. Soc.*, 1960, **82**, 5928.
Wiley, Sigal, Weaver, *J. Org. Chem.*, 1962, **27**, 2793.
Nakajima, Hasegawa, Kurihara, *Tetrahedron Letters*, 1964, 967.

Desaspidin

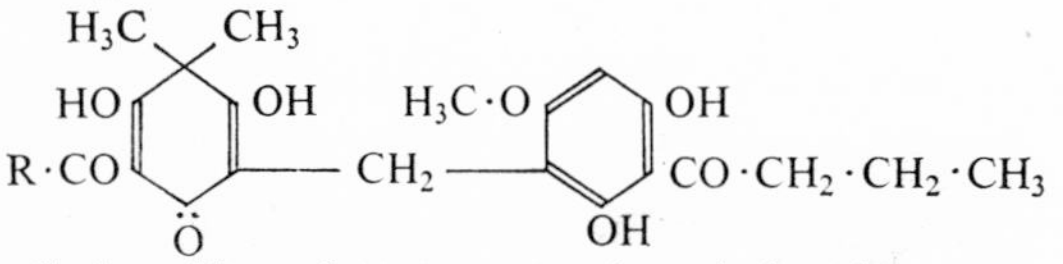

Series of homologues present in male fern (*Dryopteris filix mas*).
BB (R = ·CH_2·CH_2·CH_3)
$C_{24}H_{30}O_8$ MW 446
Cryst. from Et_2O–light petroleum. M.p. 150–150·5°.
PB (R = ·CH_2·CH_3)
$C_{23}H_{28}O_8$ MW 432
M.p. 141–2°.
AB (R = CH_3)
$C_{22}H_{26}O_8$ MW 418
M.p. 145–7°.
The following analogues were synthesised:
i-BB (R = ·$CH(CH_3)_2$)
M.p. 133–5°.
VB (R = CH_2·CH_2·CH_2·CH_3)
$C_{25}H_{32}O_8$ MW 460
M.p. 123–5°.
CB (R = $(CH_2)_4$·CH_3)
$C_{26}H_{34}O_8$ MW 474
M.p. 105–6°.

Büchi, Aebi, Kapoor, *Sci. Pharm.*, 1957, **25**, 248; *Helv. Chim. Acta*, 1957, **40**, 266.
Penttila, Sundman, *Acta Chem. Scand.*, 1964, **18**, 344.

Deserpideine

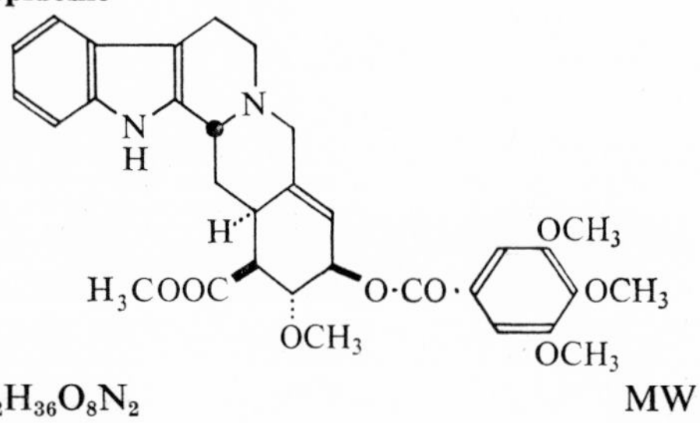

$C_{32}H_{36}O_8N_2$ MW 576

Constituent of *Rauwolfia nitida* Jacq. M.p. 149–52°. $[\alpha]_D^{25}$ −133° (Py).

Smith *et al.*, *J. Am. Chem. Soc.*, 1964, **86**, 2083.

Deshydroxymethylvoachalotinol. *See* Affinisine.

Desmethyl-. *See* Demethyl-.

Desmosine

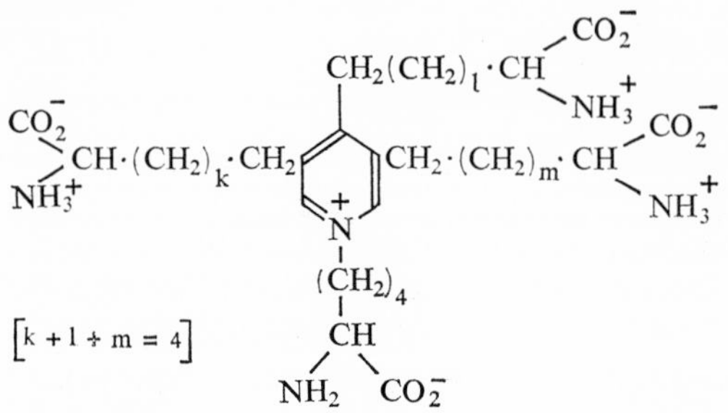

$C_{24}H_{39}O_8N_5$ MW 525
Degradation product of elastin.

Partridge, Elsden, Thomas, *Nature*, 1963, **197**, 1297; 1963, **200**, 651.

Desoxy. *See* Deoxy.

Dethylandiamine. *See* Thenyldiamine.★

Deumacard. *See* Metrazole.★

Devadarool

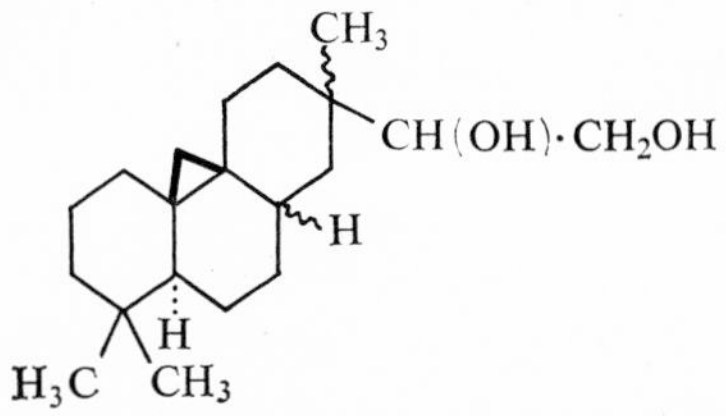

$C_{20}H_{34}O_2$ MW 306
Constituent of the wood of *Erythroxylon monogynum* Roxb. M.p. 124–5°. $[\alpha]_D^{28}$ 11·9° (c, 1·31 in $CHCl_3$). Probably identical with Erythroxydiol X (*q.v.*).

Soman, Dev. *Tetrahedron Letters*, 1964, 1181.

2-Devinyl-2-hydroxyethylphaeophorbid *a*

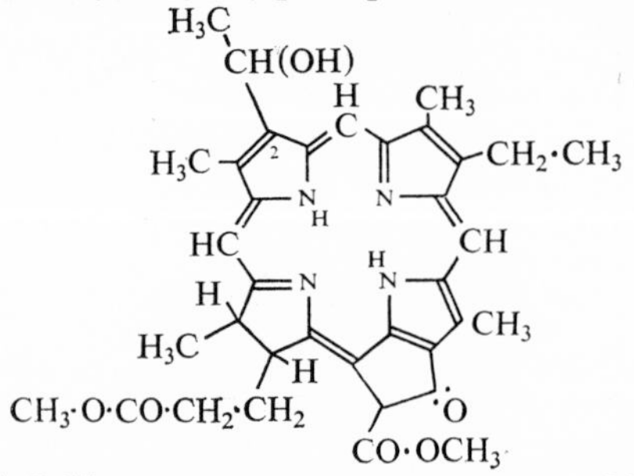

$C_{36}H_{40}O_6N_4$ MW 624
Pigment isolated from *Rhodopseudomonas spheroides*. Light absorption: $\lambda_{max.}$ 406, 469, 502, 532, 554, 603, and 659 mμ.

Jones, *Biochem. J.*, 1964, **91**, 572.

Dhurrin★ (β-D-*Glucopyranosyloxy*-L-p-*hydroxymandelonitrile*).

M.p. 165°.

Penta-Ac: needles from AcOEt–light petroleum. M.p. 132–132·5°. $[\alpha]_D^{20}$ −50·5° (c, 0·235 in EtOH).

Absolute configuration:

Towers, McInnes, Neish, *Tetrahedron*, 1964, **20**, 71.

See also Taxiphyllin.

Erratum p. 846

Diacetyl.★

Should read: *See* Biacetyl.

2 : 3-Diacetylnaphthalene

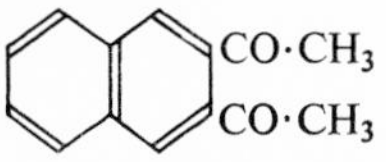

$C_{14}H_{12}O_2$ MW 212

Colourless cryst. from Et_2O. M.p. 117–18°. Gives colour reaction with amino acids.

Ried, Schön, *Chem. Ber.*, 1963, **96**, 3312.

Di-Adreson. *See* Prednisone.★

Di-Adreson-F. *See* Prednisolone.★

Diallyl sulphide.★ Present in garlic (*Allium sativum*).

Bernhard *et al.*, *Arch. Biochem. & Biophys.*, 1964, **107**, 137.

2 : 4-Diamino-5-*p*-chlorophenyl-6-ethylpyrimidine. *See* Pyrimethamine.★

2 : 6-Diamino-2 : 6-dideoxy-L-idose (*Neosamine B, paromose*)

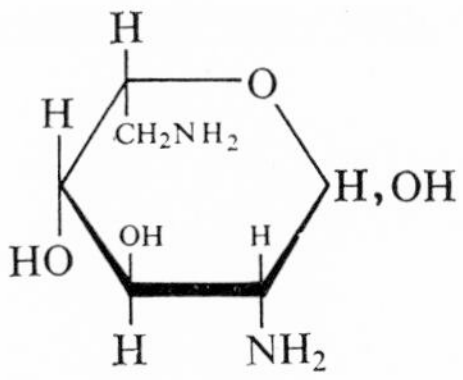

$C_6H_{14}O_4N_2$ MW 178

B,2HCl: m.p. 135–50° decomp. $[\alpha]_D^{24}$ 17·8° (c, 1·18 in H_2O).

N : N-2 : 4-*Dinitrophenyl*: yellow cryst. M.p. 155–8°. $[\alpha]_D^{26}$ −44° (c, 0·31 in MeOH).

N : N - *Di - Ac*: p-*nitrophenylhydrazone*: yellow needles. M.p. 229–31°. $[\alpha]_D^{28}$ 5·9° (c, 0·4 in MeOH).

Picrate: cryst. from H_2O. M.p. 125–6·5°. $[\alpha]_D$ 13° (c, 0·94 in H_2O).

Haskell, French, Bartz, *J. Am. Chem. Soc.*, 1959, **81**, 3480.

Rinehart *et al.*, *J. Am. Chem. Soc.*, 1960, **82**, 3938; 1962, **84**, 3218.

zu Reckendorf, *Angew. Chem.*, 1963, **75**, 573; *Int. Ed.*, 1963, **2**, 398.

Haskell, Hanession, *J. Org. Chem.*, 1963, **28**, 2598.

1 : 2-Diamino-1 : 2-dideoxymannitol

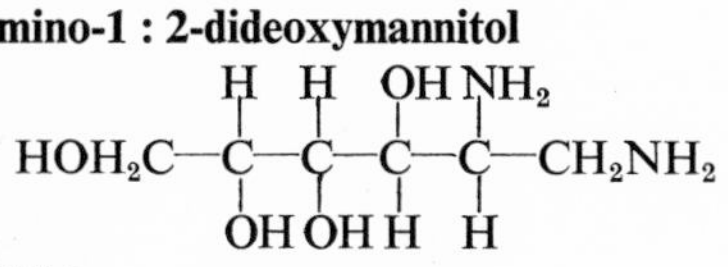

$C_6H_{16}O_4N_2$ MW 180

1 : 2-Bis-*salicylidene*: needles from EtOH or H_2O. M.p. 220–1°. $[\alpha]_D^{20}$ 125° (c, 2 in Py).

Henseke, Neinass, *Chem. Ber.*, 1964, **97**, 733.

1 : 2-Diamino-1 : 2-dideoxysorbitol

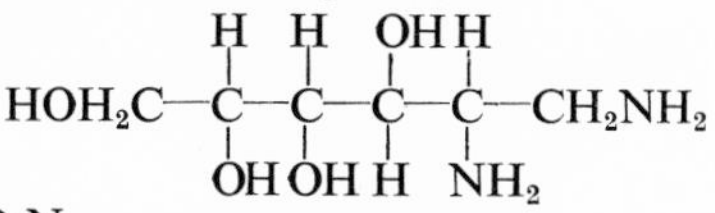

$C_6H_{16}O_4N_2$ MW 180

1 : 2-Bis-*salicylidene*: needles from EtOH. M.p. 205–6°. $[\alpha]_D^{20}$ −139° (c, 2 in Py).

Henseke, Neinass, *Chem. Ber.*, 1964, **97**, 733.

5 : 5′ - Diamino - 4 : 4′ - dihydroxy - 3 : 3′ - diazadipheno - 2 : 2″-quinone (*Indigoidin*)

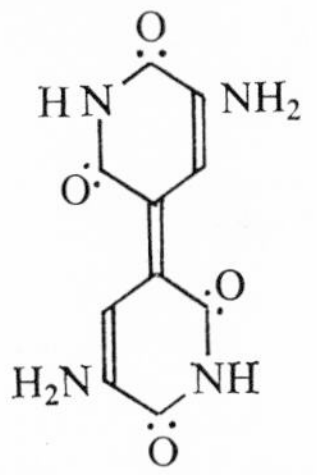

$C_{10}H_8O_4N_4$ MW 248

Blue pigment from *Corynebacterium insidiosum, Pseudomonas indigofera*, and *Arthrobacter atrocyaneus*.

Di-Ac: $C_{14}H_{12}O_6N_4$. MW 332. Blue cryst. Decolour at 304°. Do not melt.

Elazari-Volcani, *Arkiv. Mikrobiol.*, 1939, **10**, 343.
Kuhn, Starr, *Arkiv. Mikrobiol.*, 1960, **36**, 175.
Kuhn *et al.*, *Naturwiss.*, 1964, **51**, 194, 409.

2 : 4-Diamino-5 : 6-dihydroxypyrimidine. *See* Divicine.

4 : 4′-Diamino-2 : 2′-di-iodobiphenyl (2 : 2′-*Di-iodobenzidine*)

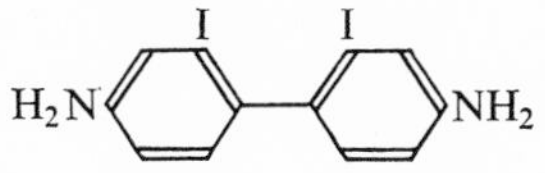

$C_{12}H_{10}N_2I_2$ MW 436

(−)-.

Cryst. $[\alpha]_{546}^{20}$ −10° (c, 5·2 in AcOEt–EtOH, 4 : 1).

(+) - α - *Bromo* - D - *camphorsulphonate*: cryst. from EtOH.Aq. $[\alpha]_{546}^{20}$ 15·4° → 56·4° (c, 3·6 in Me_2CO–H_2O, 4 : 1).

(±)-.

Cryst. from EtOH.Aq. M.p. 170°.

Theilacker, Braune, Strobel, *Chem. Ber.*, 1964, **97**, 880.

4 : 5-Diaminoeicosane. *See* Necrosamine.★

2 : 6-Diamino-4-hexynoic Acid

$NH_2{\cdot}CH_2{\cdot}C{:}C{\cdot}CH_2{\cdot}CH(NH_2){\cdot}CO_2H$

$C_6H_{10}O_2N_2$ MW 142

Lysine antagonist.

Davis *et al.*, *Arch. Biochem. Biophys.*, 1964, **104**, 241.

1 : 3-Diaminoisoquinoline

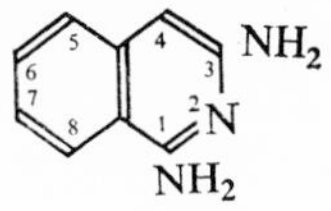

$C_9H_9N_3$ MW 159

Yellow plates from chlorobenzene. M.p. 232°. pK_a 5·70 (in 80% 2-methoxyethanol).
Picrate: orange prisms from nitromethane. M.p. 242°.
Dibenzoyl deriv.: hydrate from EtOH. M.p. 190°.
Di-Ac: hydrate. Needles from EtOH.Aq. M.p. 222°.
Cox, Elvidge, Jones, *J. Chem. Soc.*, 1964, 1423.

Dianabol. *See* 17β-Hydroxy-17α-methylandrosta-1 : 4-dien-3-one.

Diatrin. *See* Methaphenilene.★

4 : 6 - Diaza - 4 : 6 - dibenzyl - 5 - oxo - 1 - thiatricyclo - [6,3,0,0^{3,7}] undecanium. *See* Trimethaphan.★

1 : 4 - Diaza - 2 : 2 : 3 : 3 : 5 : 5 : 6 : 6 - octamethyl - 2 : 3 : 5 : 6-tetrasilacyclohexane

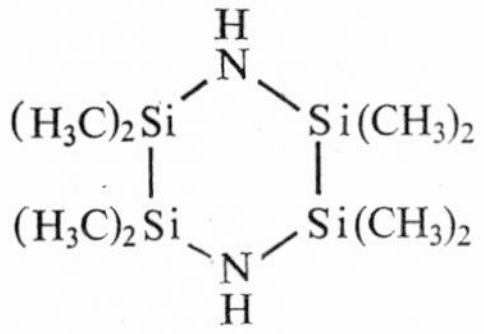

$C_8H_{26}N_2Si_4$ MW 262
M.p. 1°. B.p. 61°/2 mm. D_4^{20} 0·8458. n_D^{20} 1·4760.
Wannagat, Brandstätter, *Angew. Chem., Int. Ed.*, 1963, **2**, 263.

1 : 3-Diaza-6-oxa-adamantane

$C_7H_{12}ON_2$ MW 140
Cryst. from light petroleum. M.p. 239–40·5°.
B,2HCl: m.p. 180° decomp.
Stetter, Meissner, *Chem. Ber.*, 1963, **96**, 2827.

2 : 5-Di-(1-aziridinyl)-3 : 6-dipropoxy-1 : 4-benzoquinone. *See* Inproquone.★

Diazirine (*Cyclodiazomethane*)

CH_2N_2 MW 42
Explosive gas, not to be handled other than in solution. Grignard reagents → *N*-ethyl compounds.
Ohme, Schmitz, *Chem. Ber.*, 1964, **97**, 297.

Diazoacetic Acid.★
See also:
Womack, Nelson, *Organic Syntheses*, Coll. Vol. **3**, 392.
Searle, *Organic Syntheses*, 1956, **36**, 25; Coll. Vol. **4**, 424.

Diazomethane.★
See also:
de Boer, Bucken, *Organic Syntheses*, 1956, **36**, 16; Coll. Vol. **4**, 250.

6-Diazo-5-oxonorleucine.★
N-*Ac*: $C_8H_{12}O_4N_3$. MW 214. Duazomycin A.
Dion *et al.*, *J. Am. Chem. Soc.*, 1956, **78**, 3075.
Rao, *Antimicrobial Agents and Chemotherapy*, 1961, 178.

5-Diazouracil

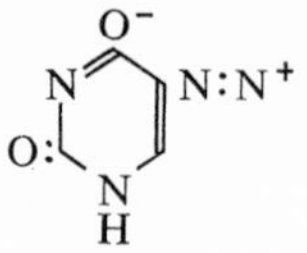

$C_4H_2O_2N_4$ MW 138
Inhibitor of cell division in bacteria. Virostatic and carcinostatic. M.p. 198° decomp.
3-*Deoxyriboside*: *see* 2′-Deoxy-5-diazouridine.
3-*Riboside*: *see* Diazouridine.
Johnson, Baudisch, Hoffmann, *Ber.*, 1931, **64B**, 2629.
Fahr, *Ann.*, 1958, **617**, 11.
Fischer, Fahr, *Ann.*, 1962, **651**, 64.

5-Diazouridine

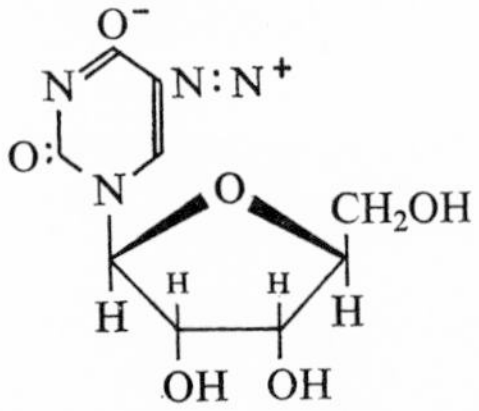

$C_9H_{10}O_4N_4$ MW 248
Cryst. from 95% EtOH. M.p. 178–82° decomp.
Light absorption: $\lambda_{max.}$ 262 mμ (ε, 12,400).
Roberts, Visser, *J. Am. Chem. Soc.*, 1952, **74**, 668.
Paolini, Robins, Cheng, *Biochim. Biophys. Acta*, 1963, **72**, 114.

1 : 2,7 : 8-Dibenzochrysene

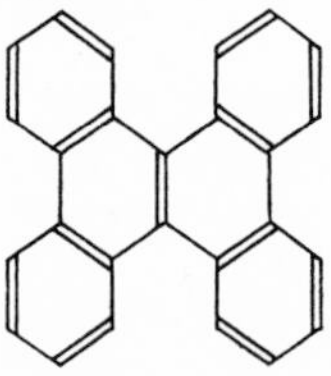

$C_{26}H_{16}$ MW 328
Long needles from AcOH. M.p. 218–20°. Light absorption: $\lambda_{max.}$ 270 (log ε, 4·72), 288 (4·72), 301 (4·9), 336 (4·16), 351 (4·14), and 383 mμ (3·10).
Klinger, Lonnes, *Ber.*, 1896, **29**, 2156.
Lang, Buffleb, Kalowy, *Chem. Ber.*, 1961, **94**, 523.
Clar, Guye-Vuilème, Stephen, *Tetrahedron*, 1964, **20**, 2107.

1 : 2 : 3 : 4-Dibenzo-cyclo-octatetraene

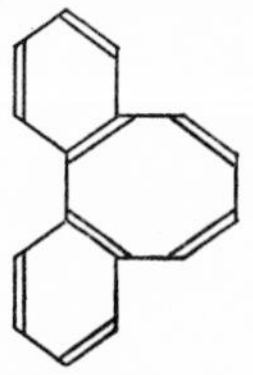

$C_{16}H_{12}$ MW 204
M.p. 123–4°.
Dvorken, Smyth, Mislow, *J. Am. Chem. Soc.*, 1958, **80**, 486.
Vogel, Frass, Wolpers, *Angew. Chem.*, 1963, **75**, 979; *Int. Ed.*, 1963, **2**, 625.

Dibenzotropolone.★
Dioxime: m.p. 212–15°.
Improved synthesis:
Eistert, Minas, *Tetrahedron Letters*, 1964, 1361.

3 : 6-Dibenzylidene-2 : 5-dioxopiperazine

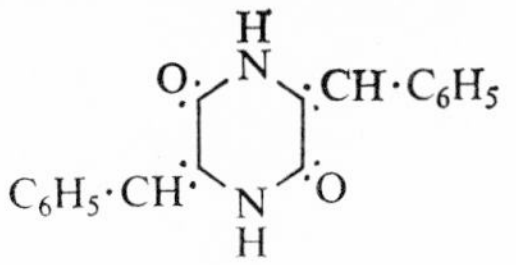

$C_{18}H_{14}O_2N_2$ MW 290
Metabolite of *Streptomyces noursei*. Yellow cryst. M.p. 299–300°. Light absorption: $\lambda_{max.}$ 202, 228, 259, and 337 mμ.
Sasaki, *Ber.*, 1921, **54**, 163.
Vondráček, Vaněk, *Chemistry and Industry*, 1964, 1686.

Dibotin. *See* 1-Phenethyldiguanide.★

Dibromoacetic Acid.★
Nitrile:
Wilt, Diebold, *Organic Syntheses*, 1958, **38**, 16; Coll. Vol. **4**, 254.

4 : 4′-Dibromobiphenyl.★
Buckles, Wheeler, *Organic Syntheses*, Coll. Vol. **4**, 256.

1 : 1-Dibromo-2-butanone
$Br_2CH{\cdot}CO{\cdot}CH_2{\cdot}CH_3$
$C_4H_6OBr_2$ MW 230
B.p. 63–5°/9 mm. n_D^{25} 1·5112.
Rappe, *Acta Chem. Scand.*, 1963, **17**, 2140.

Dibromo - dicyanoethylene. *See* Dibromofumaronitrile.

Dibromofumaronitrile (1 : 2 - *Dibromo* - 1 : 2 - *dicyanoethylene*)

$C_4N_2Br_2$ MW 236
M.p. 110–11°.
Kloster-Jensen, *Acta Chem. Scand.*, 1963, **17**, 1866.

1 : 1-Dibromo-2-pentanone
$C_5H_8OBr_2$ MW 244
B.p. 73–6°/10 mm. n_D^{25} 1·5030.
Rappe, *Acta Chem. Scand.*, 1963, **17**, 2140.

α : α′-Dibromo-*o*-xylene.★
See also:
Stephenson, *Organic Syntheses*, Coll. Vol. **4**, 984.

2 : 3-Di-*tert*-butyl-2 : 3-diazacyclopropanone

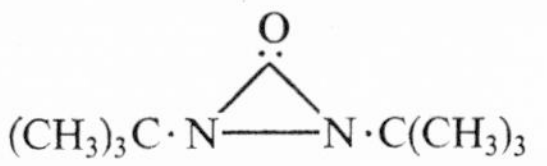

$C_9H_{18}ON_2$ MW 170
M.p. 0–1°. H_2 → N : N′-di-*tert*-butyl urea.
Green, Stowell, *J. Am. Chem. Soc.*, 1964, **86**, 3569.

Di-*tert*-butyl malonate
$(CH_3)_3C{\cdot}OOC{\cdot}CH_2{\cdot}COO{\cdot}C(CH_3)_3$
$C_{11}H_{20}O_4$ MW 216
M.p. −5·9° to −6·1°. B.p. 112–15°/31 mm., 110–11°/22 mm., 65–7°/1 mm. n_D^{25} 1·4159.
Backer, Homan, *Rec. trav. chim.*, 1939, **58**, 1048.
Fonken, Johnson, *J. Am. Chem. Soc.*, 1952, **74**, 831.
Raha, *Organic Syntheses*, 1953, **33**, 20; Coll. Vol. **4**, 263.
McCloskey *et al.*, *Organic Syntheses*, 1954, **34**, 26; Coll. Vol. **4**, 261.

1 : 22-Dicaffeoyl docosanediol

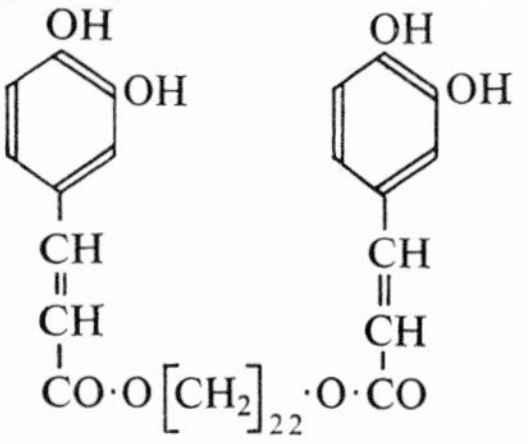

$C_{40}H_{58}O_8$ MW 666
Anti-oxidant isolated from oats. M.p. 140–1°. Hyd. → caffeic acid + 1 : 22-docosanediol and/or 1 : 24-tetracosanol. M.p. 107·6°.
Daniels, King, Martin, *J. Sci. Food Agric.*, 1963, **14**, 385.
Daniels, Martin, *Nature* (Lond.), 1964, **203**, 298; *Chemistry and Industry*, 1964, 2058.

3 : 4-Dicaffeoylquinic Acid (*Compound B*)

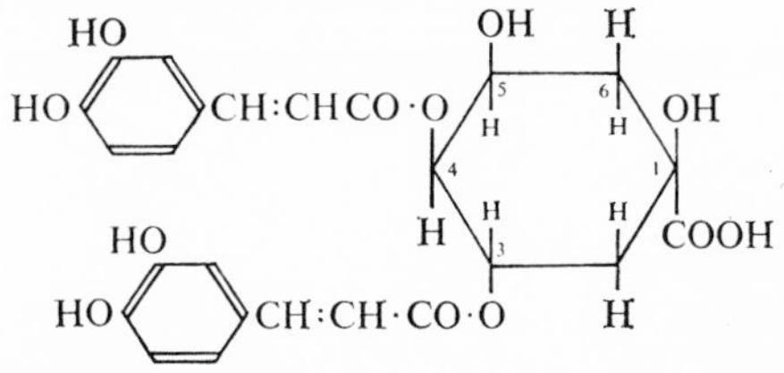

$C_{25}H_{24}O_{12}$ MW 516
Constituent of coffee and maté. Component of isochlorogenic acid. $[\alpha]_D^{28}$ −225° (c, 0·36 in MeOH).
Scarpati, Guiso, *Annali di Chimica*, 1963, **53**, 1315; *Tetrahedron Letters*, 1964, 2851.

3 : 5-Dicaffeoylquinic Acid (*Compound C*)
$C_{25}H_{24}O_{12}$ MW 516
Constituent of coffee and maté. Component of isochlorogenic acid. $[\alpha]_D^{15}$ −198° (c, 0·59 in MeOH).
Scarpati, Guiso, *Annali di Chimica*, 1963, **53**, 1315; *Tetrahedron Letters*, 1964, 2851.
Haslam *et al.*, *J. Chem. Soc.*, 1964, 2137.

4 : 5-Dicaffeoylquinic Acid (*Compound A*)
$C_{25}H_{24}O_{12}$ MW 516
Constituent of coffee and maté. Component of isochlorogenic acid. $[\alpha]_D^{28}$ −170° (c, 0·5 in MeOH).
Scarpati, Oriente, Panizzi, *Annali di Chimica*, 1958, **48**, 997.
Scarpati, Guiso, *Annali di Chimica*, 1963, **53**, 1315; *Tetrahedron Letters*, 1964, 2851.

2 : 2′-Dicarboxy-4 : 4′ : 6 : 6′-tetrahydroxybiphenyl dilactone. *See* Nasutin A.

N : N'-Di-(3-carboxy-2 : 4 : 6-tri-iodophenyl)adipic diamide. *See under* 3-Amino-2 : 4 : 6-tri-iodobenzoic Acid.★

Dichloren. *See under* Mustine.★

1 : 1-Dichloro-2 : 2-difluoroethylene.★
Sauer, *Organic Syntheses*, 1956, **36**, 19; Coll. Vol. **4**, 268.

2 : 2-Dichloroethanol.★
Sroog, Woodburn, *Organic Syntheses*, Coll. Vol. **4**, 271.

N-Di-(2-chloroethyl)methylamine. *See under* Mustine.★

2 : 4-Dichloro-3-hydroxy-7-methoxy-1 : 5 : 8-trimethyl-depsidone. *See* Vicanicin.★

2 : 3-Dichlorophenol.★
See also:
Šťota, Schiessl, *Coll. Czech. Chem. Commun.*, 1964, **29**, 1077.

N-(3 : 4-Dichlorophenyl)-N'-methoxy-N'-methylurea (*Afalon*®)

$$\text{Cl}-\text{C}_6\text{H}_3(\text{Cl})-\text{NH·CO·N}\begin{array}{c}\text{CH}_3\\\text{OCH}_3\end{array}$$

C$_9$H$_{10}$O$_2$N$_2$Cl$_2$ MW 249
Selective herbicide. M.p. 90–1°.
Scherer, Hörlein, Härtel, *Angew. Chem.*, 1963, **75**, 851; *Int. Ed.*, 1963, **2**, 670.

Dichotamine

H$_3$C·O — structure (CHO, N, O, O) —

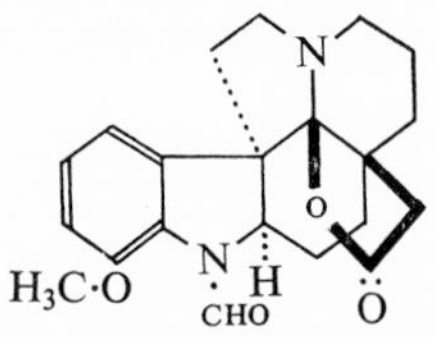

C$_{21}$H$_{24}$O$_4$N$_2$ MW 368
Alkaloid from *Vallesia dichotoma* Ruiz. et Pav. M.p. 262–3° decomp. [α]$_D$ −116° (CHCl$_3$). Light absorption: λ$_{max}$. 217 (log ε, 4·39), 257 mμ (4·08).
Holker *et al.*, *J. Org. Chem.*, 1959, **24**, 314.
Brown, Budzikiewicz, Djerassi, *Tetrahedron Letters*, 1963, 1731.

Dico. *See under* Dihydrocodeine.

Dicodid. *See* Dihydrocodeinone.

Dicodrine. *See under* Dihydrocodeinone.

Dicyano-di-iodoethylene. *See* Di-iodofumaronitrile.

2 : 4-Dicyano-2-phenylbutyric Acid

$$\text{NC·CH}_2\text{·CH}_2\text{·}\underset{\text{CN}}{\overset{\text{C}_6\text{H}_5}{\text{C}}}\text{·COOH}$$

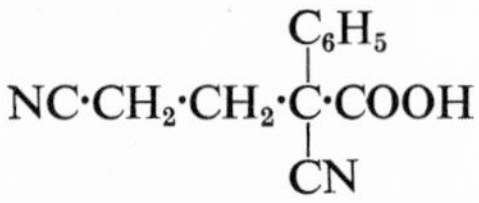

C$_{12}$H$_{10}$O$_2$N$_2$ MW 214
Et ester: C$_{14}$H$_{14}$O$_2$N$_2$. MW 242. α-Carbethoxy-α-phenylglutaronitrile. B.p. 165–7°/1 mm., 195–200°/6 mm. n_D^{25} 1·5100.
Horning, Finelli, *J. Am. Chem. Soc.*, 1949, **71**, 3204; *Organic Syntheses*, 1950, **30**, 80; Coll. Vol. **4**, 776.

2' : 3'-Dideoxyadenosine

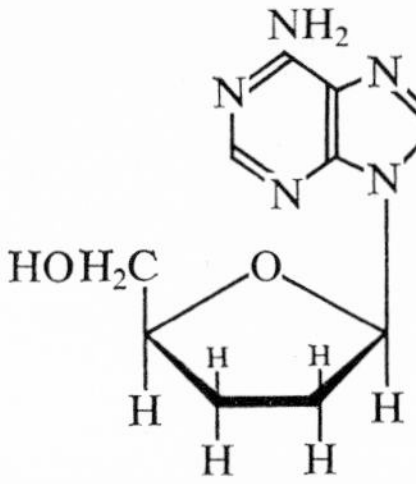

C$_{10}$H$_{13}$O$_2$N$_5$ MW 235
M.p. 184–6°. [α]$_D^{25}$ −25·2° (c, 1·01 in H$_2$O). Light absorption: λ$_{max}$. 259·5 mμ (ε, 14,800).
Robins, Robins, *J. Am. Chem. Soc.*, 1964, **86**, 2585.

2 : 6-Dideoxy-D-*arabo*hexopyranose. *See* Chromose C and Olivose.

4 : 6-Dideoxy-4-dimethylamino-D-glucose. *See* Amosamine.

2 : 6-Dideoxy-4-O-methyl-D-galactose. *See* Chromose A.

2 : 6-Dideoxy-4-O-methyl-D-*lyxo*-hexose. *See* Olivomose.

Didrate. *See* Dihydrocodeine.

1-2'-Diethylaminoethylamino-4-methylthioxanthone. *See* Lucanthone.★

Diethylaminoethyl diphenylthiocarbamate. *See* Escorpal.

3-(β-Diethylaminoethyl)-7-ethoxycarbonylmethoxy-4-methyl-2-oxo-1 : 2-chromene. *See* Intensain.

2-Diethylaminoethyl α-hydroxy-α-cyclopentyl-α-(2-thienyl)acetate. *See* Penthienate.★

2-(2-Diethylaminoethyl-2-phenylglutarimide. *See* Phenglutarimide.★

β-Diethylaminoethyl 9-xanthenecarboxylate metho-bromide. *See* Methantheline.★

N : N'-Diethylbenzidine.★
Rice, Kohn, *Organic Syntheses*, 1956, **36**, 21; Coll. Vol. **4**, 283.

α : α-Diethyl-4 : 4'-dihydroxystilbene. *See* Diethylstilboestrol.★

3 : 3-Diethyl-5-methyl-2 : 4-piperidinedione. *See* Methyprylone.★

Diethyl peroxide.★
B.p. 62–3°. n_D^{14} 1·3724.
Minkoff, *Proc. Roy. Soc.*, 1954, **224A**, 176.
Pryor, Huston, *J. Org. Chem.*, 1964, **29**, 512.

Diethyl pyrocarbonate
$$\text{CH}_3\text{·CH}_2\text{·O·CO·O·CO·O·CH}_2\text{·CH}_3$$
C$_6$H$_{10}$O$_5$ MW 162
B.p. 62–4°/0·2 mm. D$_4^{20}$ 1·119. n_D^{25} 1·3975.
C$_6$H$_5$NH$_2$ → C$_6$H$_5$·NH·COOCH$_2$·CH$_3$.
Boehm, Mehta, *Ber.*, 1938, **71**, 1797.
Degerining, *J. Am. Pharm. Assoc.*, 1950, **39**, 624.
Winterfeld, Buschbeck, *Arch. Pharm.*, 1961, **66**, 472.
Rosnati, *Chem. Ber.*, 1963, **96**, 3098.

Diethylstilboestrol★ (α : α-*Diethyl*-4 : 4′-*dihydroxystilbene, Estilbin MCO,* 3 : 4-*di*-p-*hydroxyphenyl*-3-*hexene*).

Di-D-fructose Anhydride I

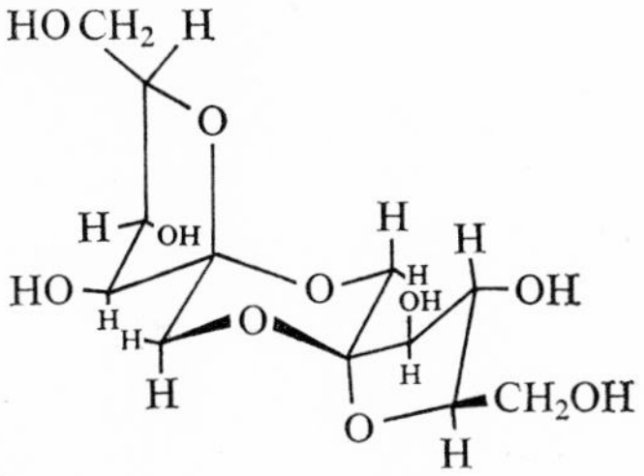

$C_{12}H_{20}O_{10}$ MW 324

Cryst. from EtOH. M.p. 162–4°. $[\alpha]_D$ 27·6° (c, 7·5 in H_2O).

Hexa-Ac: m.p. 137°. $[\alpha]_D$ 1·08°.

3 : 4 : 3′ : 4′-*Tetra-Ac*: m.p. 187–8°. $[\alpha]_D$ −1·94° (−9·9°) ($CHCl_3$). 6 : 6′-*Di-trityl*: m.p. 192–3°. $[\alpha]_D$ 20·1° (c, 8·8 in $CHCl_3$).

Irvine, Stevenson, *J. Am. Chem. Soc.*, 1929, **51**, 2197.
Lemieux, Nagarajan, *Can. J. Chem.*, 1964, **42**, 1270.

Digifologenin.★

See also:

Tschesche, Brügmann, *Tetrahedron*, 1964, **20**, 1469.

Diginigenin.★

See also:

Tschesche, Brügmann, *Tetrahedron*, 1964, **20**, 1469.

Digipurpurogenin I

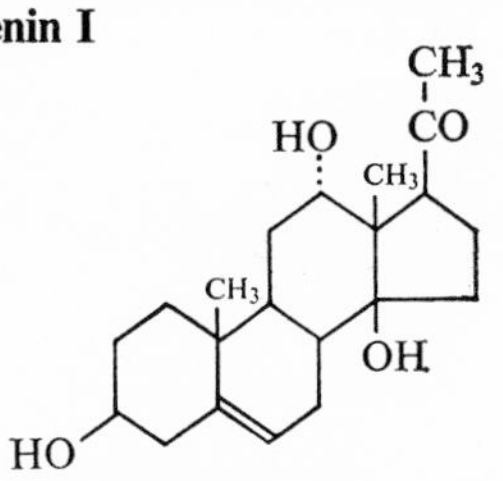

$C_{21}H_{32}O_4$ MW 348

Aglycone from Digipurpurin. Cryst. with a mole Me_2CO. M.p. 167–75°. $[\alpha]_D^{21}$ 51° (c, 1·27 in $CHCl_3$).

Di-Ac: cryst. from EtOH. M.p. 187–8°. $[\alpha]_D^{19}$ 91° (c, 1·33 in $CHCl_3$).

Tschesche *et al.*, *Ann.*, 1961, **648**, 185.
Tschesche, Brügmann, Snatzke, *Tetrahedron Letters*, 1964, 473.

Digipurpurogenin II (*Anhydrodigipurpurogenin*)

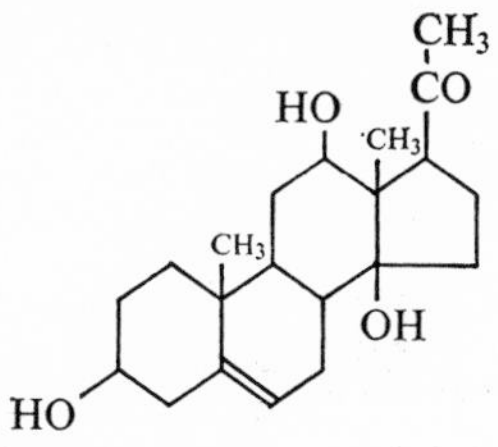

$C_{21}H_{32}O_4$ MW 348

Acid cleavage product of Digipurpurin. M.p. 222–32°. $[\alpha]_D$ 25° (c, 1 in MeOH).

Di-Ac: m.p. 171–4°. $[\alpha]_D^{25}$ 17° (c, 1 in $CHCl_3$). $[\alpha]_D^{20}$ 26° (c, 1 in MeOH).

Tschesche, Grimmer, *Chem. Ber.*, 1955, **88**, 1569.
Tschesche *et al.*, *Ann.*, 1961, **648**, 185.
Tschesche, Brügmann, Snatzke, *Tetrahedron Letters*, 1964, 473.

4 : 6-Di-*O*-(α-D-glucopyranosyl)-D-glucopyranose

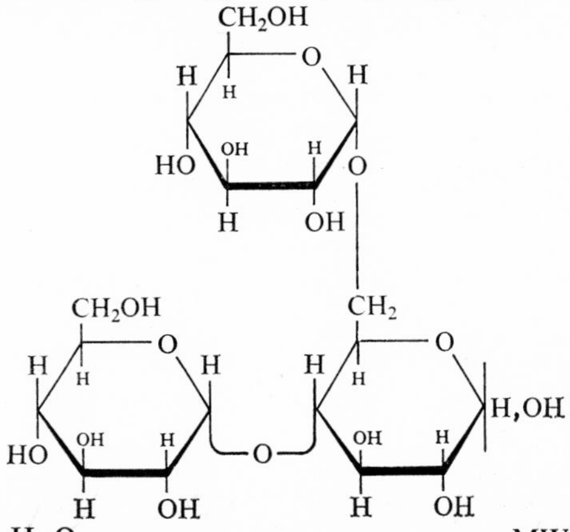

$C_{18}H_{32}O_{16}$ MW 504

Syrup. $[\alpha]_D^{22}$ 125° (c, 0·9 in H_2O).

de Souza, Goldstein, *Tetrahedron Letters*, 1964, 1215.

3 : 5-Di-β-glucosyl petunidin. *See* Petunin.★

Diglyme. *See* Di-Me ether *under* Di-(2-hydroxyethyl) Ether.★

Digoxoside

$C_{47}H_{74}O_{17}$ MW 910

Glycoside from leaves of *Digitatis lanata* Ehrh. M.p. 265–8°. $[\alpha]_D$ +18·5° (Py). Light absorption: $\lambda_{max.}$ 217 mμ (log ε, 4·22). Hydrolysis → digoxigenin and digitoxose.

Kaiser, Haak, Spingler, *Naturwiss.*, 1963, **50**, 668.

Dihydrin. *See* Dihydrocodeine.

9 : 10-Dihydro-9 : 10-*o*-benzenoanthracene. *See* Triptycene.

Dihydrocodeine (*Cohydrin, dehacodin, didrate, dihydrin, dihydroneopine, drocode,* 4 : 5-*epoxy*-6-*hydroxy*-3-*methoxy*-N-*methylmorphinan, hydrocodin, nadocine, novicodin, paracodin, parzone, rapacodin*)

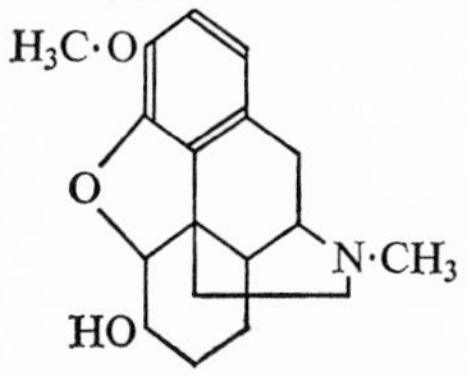

$C_{18}H_{23}O_3N$ MW 301

Cryst. + $1H_2O$ from MeOH.Aq. M.p. 112–13°. B.p. 248°/15 mm.

Hydrogen tartrate: endo-hycodan, dico. Cryst. from MeOH. M.p. 192–3°. $[\alpha]_D^{25}$ −75° (c, 1 in H_2O).

Skita, Franck, *Ber.*, 1911, **44**, 2862.
Wieland, Koralek, *Ann.*, 1923, **433**, 269.
Stein, *Pharmazie*, 1955, **10**, 180.

Dihydrocodeinone (*Hydrocodone, dicodid*)

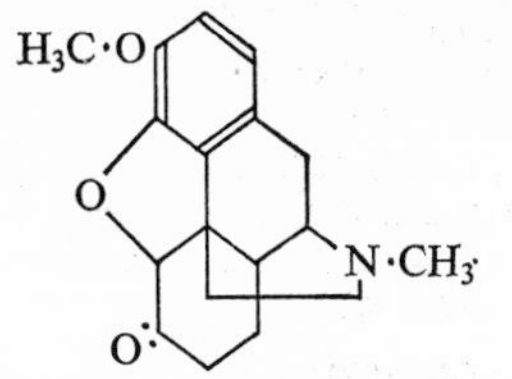

$C_{18}H_{21}O_3N$ MW 299

Prisms from EtOH. M.p. 198°. Light absorption: $\lambda_{max.}$ 280 mμ (ε, 1310).
B,HCl: cryst. + $1H_2O$. M.p. 185–6° decomp. $[\alpha]_D^{27}$ −130° (c, 2·877 in H_2O).
B,HI: m.p. 219–20°.
Hydrogen tartrate: dicodid, mercodinone, synkonin, norgan, dicodrine, hydrokan. Needles. M.p. 146–8°.
Enol-Ac: *see* Acedicon.
Oxime: m.p. 264°.
Phenylhydrazone: cryst. from EtOH. M.p. 106–7°.
Methiodide: m.p. 250–5°.

Small, Lutz, *Chemistry of the Opium Alkaloids*, Suppl. No. 103, Public Health Reports, Washington (1932).
Eddy, Reid, *J. Pharmacol.*, 1934, **52**, 468.
Pfister, Tishler, U.S.P. 2,715,626.

19 : 20-Dihydrocondylocarpin. *See* Tubotaiwin.★

Dihydrocostunolide

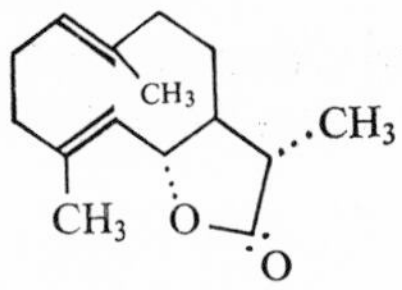

$C_{15}H_{22}O_2$ MW 234

Constituent of costus root oil (*Saussurea lappa* C. B. Clarke). Cryst. from hexane–Et_2O. M.p. 78°. $[\alpha]_D$ +110·8° ($CHCl_3$). Light absorption: $\lambda_{max.}$ 207 mμ (ε, 10,300). Pyrolysis → saussurea lactone.

Rao, Kelkar, Bhattacharyya, *Tetrahedron*, 1960, **9**, 275.
Rao, Sadgopal, Bhattacharyya, *Tetrahedron*, 1961, **13**, 319.
Corey, Hortmann, *J. Am. Chem. Soc.*, 1963, **85**, 4033.

Dihydrocrotonosine. *See* Linearisine.

23 : 24-Dihydrocucurbitacin I. *See* Cucurbitacin L.

3 : 4-Dihydro-6 : 8-dihydroxy-3-(4-methoxyphenylethyl)-isocoumarin. *See* Agrimolide.

2 : 5-Dihydro-2-furoic Acid

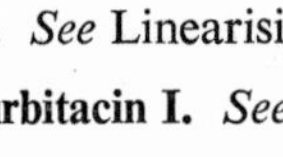

$C_5H_6O_3$ MW 114

Anaerobic decomposition product of ascorbic acid. pK 3·2.
Cyclohexylamine salt: colourless needles. M.p. 160·3° decomp.
Me ester: oil.

Coggiola, *Nature*, 1963, **200**, 954.

β-Dihydroheptachlor (2-exo-4 : 5 : 6 : 7 : 8 : 8-*Heptachloro*-4 : 7-*methylene*-4 : 4a : 7 : 7a-*tetrahydroindane*)

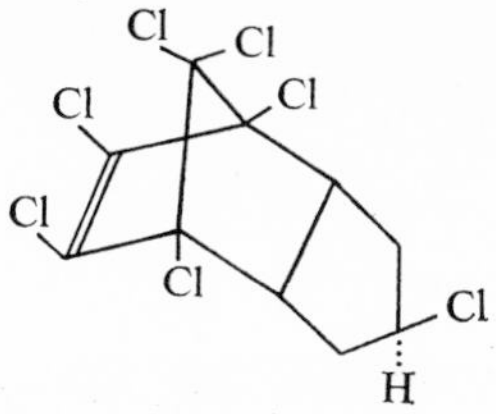

$C_{10}H_7Cl_7$ MW 375·5

Insecticide with lower toxicity to warm blooded mammals. Cryst. from CCl_4. M.p. 135°.

Büchel *et al.*, *Tetrahedron Letters*, 1964, 2267.

7 : 8-Dihydro-14-hydroxycodeinone. *See* Oxycodeine.★

3 : 4-Dihydro-8-hydroxy-3-(3-hydroxy-4-methoxyphenyl)isocoumarin. *See* Phyllodulcinol.

3 : 4-Dihydro-8-hydroxy-3-(4-hydroxyphenyl)isocoumarin. *See* Hydrangenol.

3 : 4-Dihydro-8-hydroxyisocoumarin. *See* Ochracin.★

3 : 4-Dihydro-8-hydroxy-6-methoxy-3-methylisocoumarin

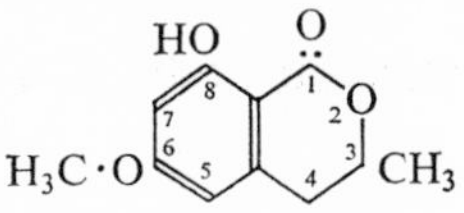

$C_{11}H_{12}O_4$ MW 208

(−)-.
Present in stored carrots. Cryst. from hexane. M.p. 76°. $[\alpha]_D^{24}$ −56° (c, 1 in MeOH). Light absorption: $\lambda_{max.}$ 216 (ε, 22,900), 267 (14,600), and 302 mμ (6000).
Me ether: needles. M.p. 125–8°.
(±)-.
Me ether: needles from C_6H_6–light petroleum. M.p. 102–3·5°.

Sondheimer, *J. Am. Chem. Soc.*, 1957, **79**, 5036; *Phytopathology*, 1961, **51**, 71.
Logan, Newbold, *Chemistry and Industry*, 1957, 1484.

7 : 8-Dihydro-14-hydroxymorphinone. *See* Oxymorphone.★

1 : 3-Dihydro-1-hydroxy-3-oxo-1 : 2-benziodoxole (*o-Iodosobenzoic acid*)

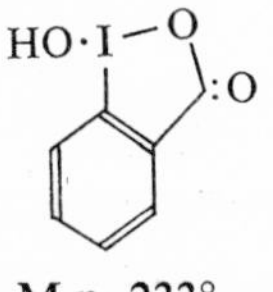

$C_7H_5O_3I$ MW 264

Cryst. from H_2O. M.p. 233°.

Willgerodt, *Ber.*, 1893, **26**, 357.
Askenasy, Meyer, *Ber.*, 1893, **26**, 1354.
Bell, Morgan, *J. Chem. Soc.*, 1960, 1209.
Shefter, Wolf, *Nature*, 1964, **203**, 512.

1 : 13-Dihydro-13-hydroxyuleine

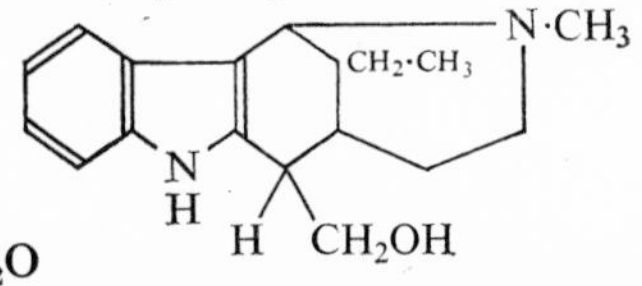

$C_{18}H_{24}N_2O$ MW 284

Alkaloid from *Aspidosperma dasycarpon* A. DC. Amorph. $[\alpha]_D$ −96°. Light absorption: $\lambda_{max.}$ 221 (log ε, 4·56), 282 (3·91), and 289 mμ (3·87).

Ohashi *et al.*, *Tetrahedron Letters*, 1964, **20**, 363.

Dihydroiso-Δ13, 14-abietic Acid (*Dihydropalustric acid*)

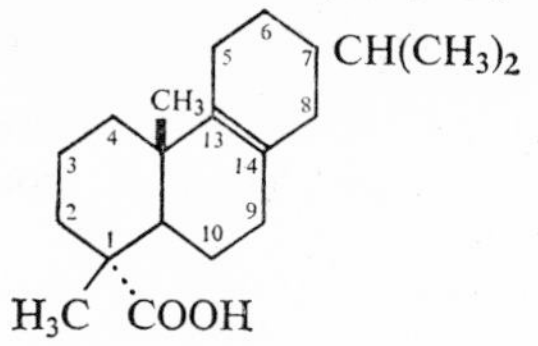

$C_{20}H_{32}O_2$ MW 304

Cryst. from isopropanol.Aq. M.p. 155–8°. From AcOH. M.p. 190–3°.
Cyclohexylamine salt: cryst. from light petroleum. M.p. 185–7°.
Me ester: constituent of the rockrose, *Cistus labdaniferus*. B.p. 153–5°/0·02 mm. $[\alpha]_D^{25}$ +39°.

Tabacik-Wlotzka, Mousseron, Chafai, *Bull. soc. chim.*, 1963, 2299.

3 : 4-Dihydroisocoumarin. *See* 1-Isochromanone.★

3 : 4-Dihydro-1-methyl-3 : 4-methylenequinolin-2-one

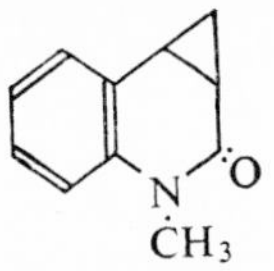

$C_{11}H_{11}ON$ MW 173

B.p. 100–4°/0·005 mm. n_D^{24} 1·6100.

Loev, Kormendy, Snader, *Chemistry and Industry*, 1964, 1710.

Dihydromethylmorphinone. *See* Metapon.★

Dihydromorphine

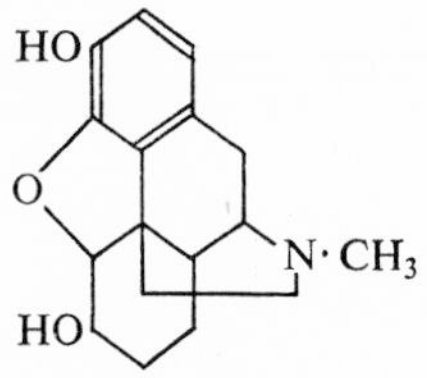

$C_{17}H_{21}O_3N$ MW 287

Prisms + $1H_2O$ from $CHCl_3$. M.p. 157° decomp. (anhyd.).
B,HCl: paramorphan. Prisms. M.p. >280° (*in vacuo*). $[\alpha]_D^{25}$ −112° (c, 1·6 in H_2O). Sol. H_2O. Spar. sol. EtOH.
B,HI: m.p. 275° with softening at 270°.
Picrate: m.p. 139°.

Small, Lutz, *Chemistry of the Opium Alkaloids*, Suppl. No. 103, Public Health Reports, Washington (1932).
Eddy, Reid, *J. Pharmacol.*, 1934, **52**, 468.
Bentley, *The Chemistry of the Morphine Alkaloids*. Oxford University Press, 1954.

Dihydromorphinone (*Hydromorphone, dimorphone*)

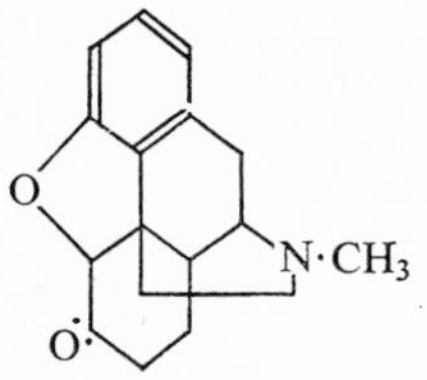

$C_{17}H_{19}O_3N$ MW 285

Narcotic agent. Cryst. M.p. 265–7° decomp. (*in vacuo*).
B,HCl: dilaudid, laudicon, hymorphan. Cryst. M.p. 305–15°. $[\alpha]_D^{25}$ −133° (c, 1 in H_2O).

Bentley, *The Chemistry of the Morphine Alkaloids*. Oxford University Press, 1954.

3 : 4-Dihydro-1(2*H*)-naphthalenone★ (α-*Tetralone*).

Olsen, Bader, *Organic Syntheses*, Coll. Vol. **4**, 898.
Johnson, *Organic Syntheses*, Coll. Vol. **4**, 900.

3 : 4-Dihydro-2(1*H*)-naphthalenone★ (β-*Tetralone*).

Soffer *et al.*, *Organic Syntheses*, 1952, **32**, 97; Coll. Vol. **4**, 903.

Dihydroneopine. *See* Dihydrocodeine.

Dihydro-obscurinervidine

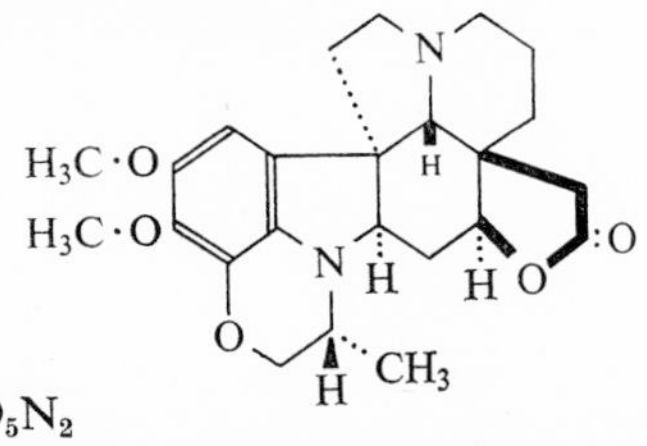

$C_{24}H_{30}O_5N_2$ MW 426

Alkaloid from *Aspidosperma obscurinervium* Azembuja. Cryst. from Me_2CO–hexane. M.p. 189–90°. $[\alpha]_D^{27}$ −44° (c, 0·85 in $CHCl_3$).

Brown, Djerassi, *J. Am. Chem. Soc.*, 1964, **86**, 2451.

Dihydro-obscurinervine

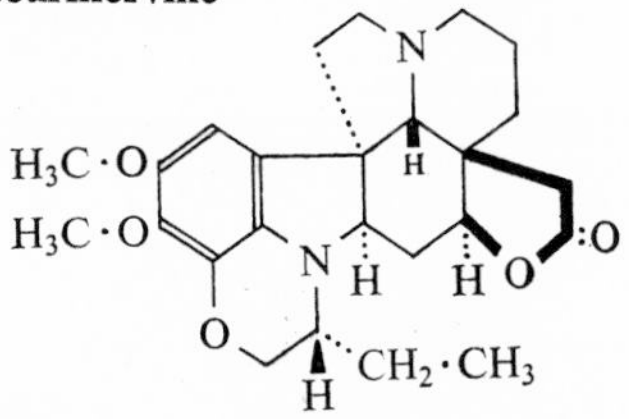

$C_{25}H_{32}O_5N_2$ MW 440

Alkaloid from *Aspidosperma obscurinervium* Azembuja. Cryst. from Me_2CO–hexane. M.p. 184–5° decomp. $[\alpha]_D^{26}$ −61° (c, 0·92 in $CHCl_3$).

Brown, Djerassi, *J. Am. Chem. Soc.*, 1964, **86**, 2451.

Dihydropalustric Acid. *See* Dihydroiso-Δ13, 14-abietic Acid.

9 : 10-Dihydrophenanthrene.★

Phillips, *Organic Syntheses*, Coll. Vol. **4**, 313.

Dihydrositsirikine

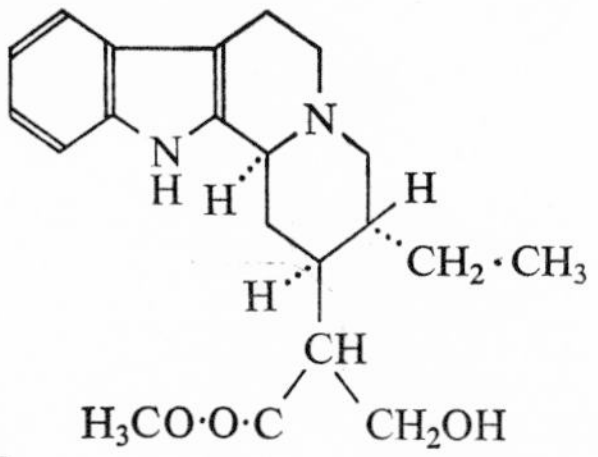

$C_{21}H_{28}O_3N_2$ MW 356

Alkaloid from *Vinca rosea* L. Cryst. from MeOH. M.p. 215°. $[\alpha]_D^{26}$ −55° (MeOH). Light absorption:

$\lambda_{max.}$ 226 (ε, 41,000), 282 (8900), 290 mμ (7500). Solvated cryst. from Me_2CO. M.p. 180°.

Kutney, Brown, *Tetrahedron Letters*, 1963, 1815.

***C*-Dihydrotoxiferine.★**

17 : 17′-^2H-.

Grdinic, Nelson, Boekelheide, *J. Am. Chem. Soc.*, 1964, **86**, 3357.

3 : 7-Dihydroxy-2 : 6-anthraquinone

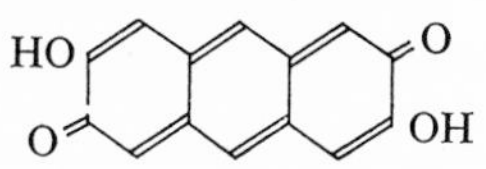

$C_{14}H_8O_2$ MW 240

Light absorption: $\lambda_{max.}$ 356 mμ in dioxan.

Boldt, *Naturwiss.*, 1964, **51**, 108.

5 : 6-Dihydroxy-1 : 2-anthraquinone

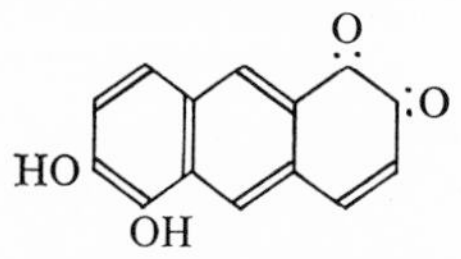

$C_{14}H_{18}O_4$ MW 240

Black cryst. which give red soln. M.p. >320°. Light absorption: $\lambda_{max.}$ 310, 515 mμ (in dimethylsulphoxide).

Di-Ac: brown-red needles. M.p. 225°.

Boldt, *Naturwiss.*, 1964, **51**, 137.

2 : 5-Dihydroxybenzoic Acid★ (*Gentisic acid*).

2 : 5-*Dibenzyl ether*: cryst. from C_6H_6–2 : 2 : 4-trimethylpentane. M.p. 108–9°. *Chloride*: cryst. from hexane. M.p. 86–8°.

Zane, Wender, *J. Org. Chem.*, 1964, **29**, 2078.

2′ : 4′-Dihydroxybiphenyl-2-carboxylic Acid (2 : 2′)-lactone (*Urolithin B*)

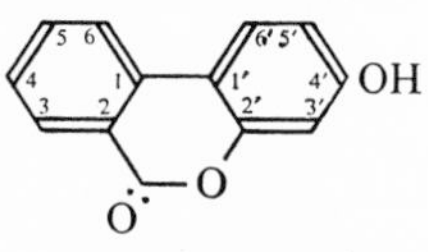

$C_{13}H_8O_3$ MW 212

Constituent of "Clover stone," a type of renal calculus found in sheep. Needles from MeOH. M.p. 223–4°.

Me ether: $C_{14}H_{10}O_3$. MW 226. Needles from AcOEt–light petroleum. M.p. 143°.

Hurtley, *J. Chem. Soc.*, 1929, 1870.
Hey, Leonard, Rees, *J. Chem. Soc.*, 1963, 5251.
Nottle, Pope, *Biochem. J.*, 1963, **89**, 67P.
Pope, *Biochem. J.*, 1964, **93**, 474.

3α : 12α-Dihydroxy-5α-cholan-24-oic Acid (β-*Lagodeoxycholic acid*)

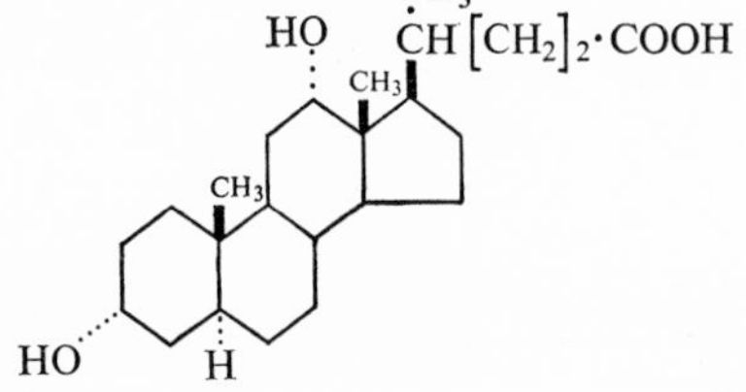

$C_{24}H_{40}O_4$ MW 392

Constituent of rabbit bile and faeces. M.p. 214–15°. $[\alpha]_D^{23}$ 42° (c, 0·75 in 90% EtOH.Aq.).

Me ester: $C_{25}H_{42}O_4$. MW 406. Cryst. from MeOH.Aq. M.p. 174–6°. $[\alpha]_D^{23}$ 35·6° (c, 1 in MeOH).

Kishi, *Z. physiol. Chem.*,1936, **238**, 210.
Danielsson, Kallner, Sjövall, *J. Biol. Chem.*, 1963, **238**, 3846.

3β : 12β-Dihydroxy-5-conanene. *See* Funtuline.

2 : 5-Dihydroxy-3-3′ : 4′-dihydroxyphenyl-6-4′-hydroxyphenyl-1 : 4-benzoquinone. *See* Leucomelone.★

4′ : 5-Dihydroxy-3′ : 7-dimethoxyflavanone

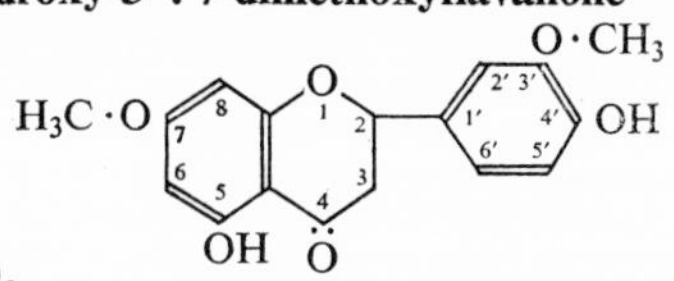

$C_{17}H_{16}O_6$ MW 316

(−)-.

Isolated from the bark of *Melicope sarcococca* Laut. (Rutaceae). Tiny white needles from Me_2CO–MeOH. M.p. 167–8°. $[\alpha]_D^{20}$ −32·2° (c, 1·8 in $CHCl_3$).

4′-*Mono-Ac*: white prisms from Me_2CO–MeOH. M.p. 130–1°.

Di-Ac: cryst. from Me_2CO–MeOH. M.p. 148–9°.

4′[1-3(*Methylbut-2-enyl*)]-*ether*: $C_{22}H_{24}O_6$. MW 384. Constituent of *M. sarcococca* bark. Soft white needles from AcOEt–MeOH. M.p. 165–6°. $[\alpha]_D^{20}$ −34·1° (c, 3·6 in $CHCl_3$). *Ac*: white needles from HOAc.Aq. M.p. 182–3°.

(±)-.

Leaflets from MeOH.Aq. M.p. 147–8°.

Di-Ac: prisms from MeOH. M.p. 159–60°.

Geissman, *Austral. J. Chem.*, 1958, **11**, 376.

4′ : 5-Dihydroxy-6 : 7-dimethoxyisoflavone (*Tectorigenin 7-methyl ether*)

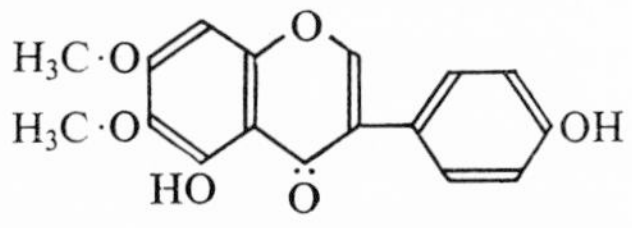

$C_{17}H_{14}O_6$ MW 314

Constituent of the flowers of *Dalbergia sisso*. Pale yellow cryst. M.p. 231–3° (227–8°).

Di-Ac: prisms from MeOH. M.p. 180–1°.

Di-Me ether: colourless prisms from MeOH. M.p. 176–7°.

Di-Et ether: prisms from MeOH. M.p. 144–5°.

Banerji *et al.*, *Indian J. Chem.*, 1963, **1**, 25.
Ghanim, Zaman, Kidwai, *Tetrahedron Letters*, 1964, 185.

11β : 17-Dihydroxy-3 : 20-dioxo-1 : 4-pregnadien-21-yl 2-acetamido-2-deoxy-β-D-glucopyranoside

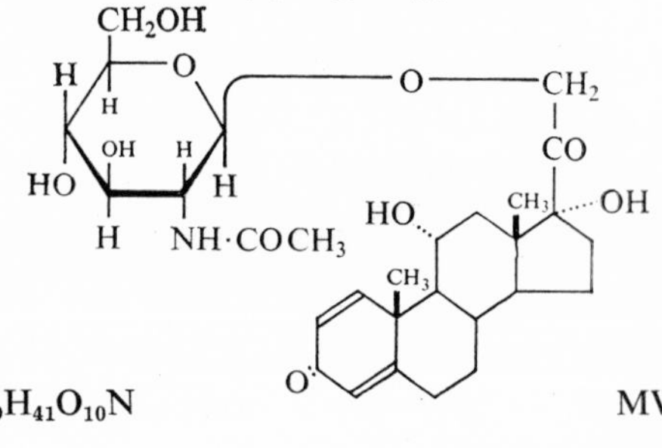

$C_{29}H_{41}O_{10}N$ MW 563

Anti-inflammatory steroid. M.p. 183–4°. $[\alpha]_D^{25}$ $+66°$ (c, 1 in MeOH). Light absorption: $\lambda_{max.}$ 243 mμ (log ε, 4·19).
Tri-O-Ac: m.p. 246–8°. $[\alpha]_D^{25}$ $+36°$ (c, 1 in $CHCl_3$).

Hirschmann *et al.*, *J. Am. Chem. Soc.*, 1964, **86**, 3903.

4 : 5-Dihydroxy-*o*-dithiane

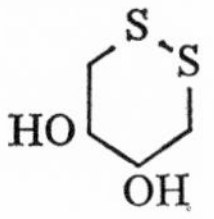

$C_4H_8O_2S_2$ MW 152
Trans-.
Cryst. M.p. 132° (by sublimation at 80°/0·005 mm.). Light absorption: $\lambda_{max.}$ 283 mμ.
Cis-.
M.p. 132°.

Cleland, *Biochemistry*, 1964, **3**, 480.

2 : 3-Dihydroxy-1 : 4-dithiolbutane

HS·CH$_2$·CH(OH)·CH(OH)·CH$_2$SH

$C_4H_{10}O_2S_2$ MW 154
(±)-*Threo* dithiothreitol-.
Protective reagent for SH groups. Fine needles from Et_2O. M.p. 42–3°. B.p. 125–30°/2 mm. Ox. → *trans*-4 : 5-dihydroxy-*o*-dithiane (*q.v.*).
Di-isopropylidene deriv.: needles from MeOH. M.p. 78°.
Tetra-Ac: prisms from MeOH. M.p. 73°.
(±)-*Erythro* dithioerythritol.
Small plates from Et_2O–light petroleum. M.p. 82–3°. Ox. → *cis*-4 : 5-dihydroxy-*o*-dithane (*q.v.*).
Di-isopropylidene deriv.: prisms from light petroleum. M.p. 145°.
Tetra-Ac: plates from C_6H_6 or MeOH. M.p. 126°.

Evans, Fraser, Owen, *J. Chem. Soc.*, 1949, 248.
Cleland, *Biochemistry*, 1964, **3**, 480.

3β : 16α-Dihydroxyeburico-8 : 24(28)-dien-21-oic Acid. *See* Tumulosic Acid.★

2 : 5-Dihydroxy-3-eicosyl-6-methyl-1 : 4-benzoquinone. *See* Polygonaquinone.

5 : 6-Dihydroxyflavone.★

Di-Me ether: constituent of the bark of *Casimiroa edulis* Llave et Lex.

Iriarte *et al.*, *J. Chem. Soc.*, 1956, 4170.

3β : 22-Dihydroxyhopane

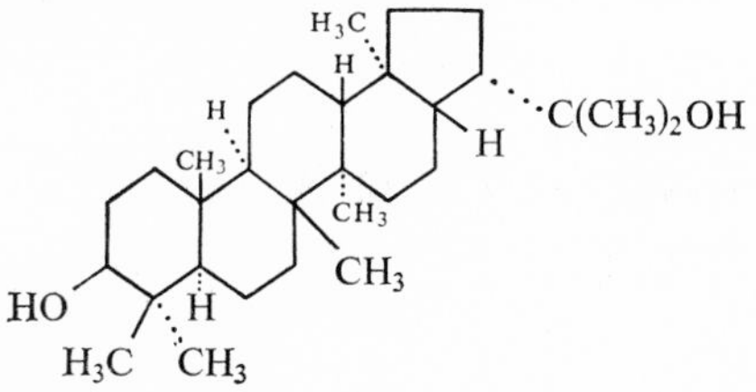

$C_{30}H_{52}O_2$ MW 444
Cryst. from $CHCl_3$–MeOH. M.p. 284–5°. $[\alpha]_D^{20}$ 53° (c, 0·72 in $CHCl_3$).
3-Ac: $C_{32}H_{54}O_3$. MW 486. Constituent of Dammer resin. Cryst. from $CHCl_3$–MeOH. M.p. 231–2°. $[\alpha]_D^{20}$ 39° (c, 0·86 in $CHCl_3$).

Černý, Vystrčil, Huneck, *Chem. Ber.*, 1963, **96**, 3021.

4 : 7 - Dihydroxy - 2 - hydroxymethyl - 5 - methoxyanthra - quinone. *See* Questinol.

2 : 3 - Dihydroxy - 4 - (3′ - hydroxyphenyl)quinoline. *See* Viridicatol.

1 : 5 - Dihydroxy - *S* - indacene - 2 : 3 : 4 : 6 : 7 : 8 - hexa - carboxylic Acid

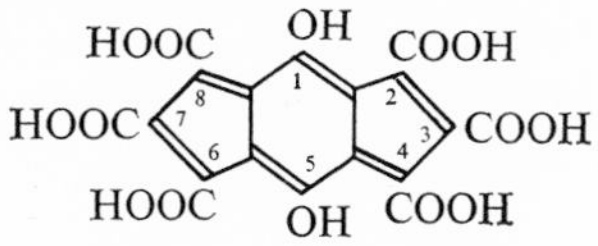

$C_{18}H_8O_{14}$ MW 448
Free acid not known.
Hexa-Me ester: $C_{24}H_{20}O_{14}$. MW 532. Deep red-green cryst. M.p. 257–9°. *Trinitrofluorenone adduct*: m.p. 239–41°.

Le Goff, La Count, *Tetrahedron Letters*, 1964, 1161.

5 : 6-Dihydroxyindole.★

N-Me ether: needles from heptane. M.p. 134–6°.

Harley-Mason, *J. Chem. Soc.*, 1950, 1276.
Mattok, Hencock, *Can. J. Chem.*, 1964, **42**, 484.

3 : 16-Dihydroxyisopimar-7-ene-2 : 15-dione. *See* Araucarolone.

1α : 19-Dihydroxy-16α-kauran-17-oic Acid

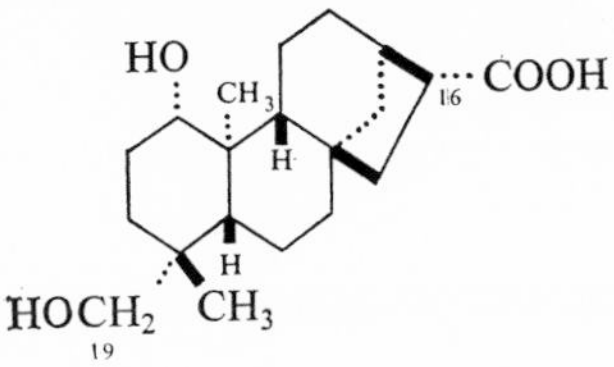

$C_{20}H_{32}O_4$ MW 336
(−)-.
Constituent of *Ricinocarpus stylosus*. M.p. 259–60°. $[\alpha]_D$ $-56°$ (EtOH).
Di-Ac: m.p. 147–9°. $[\alpha]_D$ $-40°$ ($CHCl_3$).

Henrick, Jefferies, *Tetrahedron Letters*, 1964, 1507.

3 : 5-Dihydroxy-6-methoxyaporphine

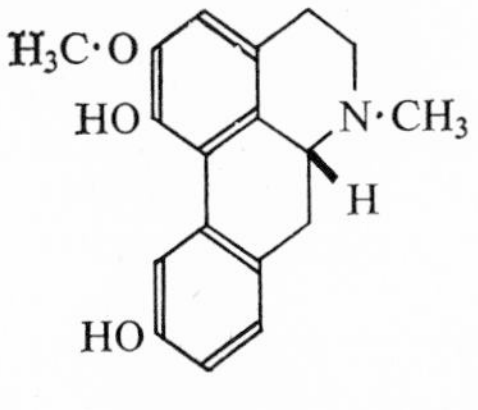

$C_{18}H_{19}O_3N$ MW 297
(R) (−)-.
Alkaloid present in the leaves of *Ocotea glaziovii*. Monohydrate: colourless cryst. M.p. 149–52° decomp. $[\alpha]_D^{26}$ $-35°$ (c, 0·2 in $CHCl_3$).
B,HCl: m.p. >300° decomp.
B,CH$_3$I: m.p. 251–3°.
B,CH$_3$Cl: hydrate, m.p. 226–9°.
O-*Me*, *(B,CH$_3$)$_2$SO$_4$*: cryst. from Me$_2$CO–hexane, m.p. 189–202° decomp.

Gilbert *et al.*, *J. Am. Chem. Soc.*, 1964, **86**, 694.

4 : 7-Dihydroxy-5-methoxy-2-methylanthraquinone. *See* Questin.

6 : 8-Dihydroxy-7-methoxy-3-methylisocoumarin. *See* Reticulol.

3 : 3′-Dihydroxy-6-methylbibenzyl

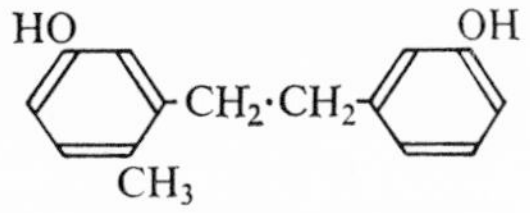

$C_{15}H_{16}O_2$ MW 228

Cryst. from C_6H_6. M.p. 127–8°.

Hooper, Massy-Westropp, *Austral. J. Chem.*, 1964, **17**, 946.

8-(2′ : 3′-Dihydroxy-3-methylbutyl)psoralen. *See* Heraclenol.

Dihydroxy-3-methyl indole. *See* Dihydroxyskatol.

3 : 4-Di(4-hydroxy-3-methylphenyl)hexane. *See* Promethestrol.★

2 : 3-Dihydroxy-3-methylvaleric Acid★

$C_6H_{12}O_4$ MW 148

(−)-.

Also present in strigosine (*q.v.*) esterified with trachelanthamidine.

Quinine salt: cryst. from EtOH–Et_2O. M.p. 203–4°. $[\alpha]_D$ −140° (c, 1·9 in MeOH).

Mattocks, *J. Chem. Soc.*, 1964, 1974.

1 : 2-Dihydroxynona-3 : 5-diyne-7-one

$CH_3{\cdot}CH_2{\cdot}CO{\cdot}C{:}C{\cdot}C{:}C{\cdot}CH(OH){\cdot}CH_2{\cdot}OH$

$C_9H_{10}O_3$ MW 166

Metabolite of *Clitocybe rhizophora* Velen. Needles from Et_2O–hexane. M.p. 34·5–35°. $[\alpha]_D^{24}$ −30° (c, 2·52 in EtOH). Light absorption: $\lambda_{max.}$ 282·5 (ε, 4300), 267 (5700), 253·5 (4200), 241 (2300), and 227·5 mμ (1400).

1 : 2-O-*Isopropylidene deriv.*: oil. $[\alpha]_D^{21}$ −65° (c, 0·35 in EtOH).

Jones, Lowe, Lowe, *J. Chem. Soc.*, 1964, 1478.

9 : 10-Dihydroxyoctadecanoic Acid.★

Swern, Scanlan, Dickel, *Organic Syntheses*, 1959, **39**, 15; Coll. Vol. **4**, 317.

16α : 20(*S*)-Dihydroxy-3-oxo-4-pregnene-18-carboxylic Acid (→20) Lactone

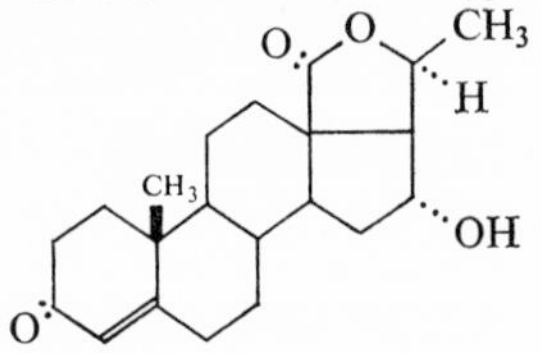

$C_{21}H_{28}O_4$ MW 344

Present in the flowers of *Paravallaris microphylla*. M.p. 242°. $[\alpha]_D^{20}$ 44° (c, 0·8 in $CHCl_3$). Light absorption: $\lambda_{max.}$ 240 mμ (ε, 15,800).

Portier, Kan, LeMen, *Tetrahedron Letters*, 1964, 1671.

11α : 15-Dihydroxy-9-oxoprost-13-enoic Acid. *See* Prostaglandin E_1.★

3 : 4-Di-*p*-hydroxyphenyl-3-hexene. *See* Diethylstilboestrol.★

7-{2-[2-(3 : 4-Dihydroxyphenyl)-2-hydroxyethylamino]-ethyl}theophylline. *See under* Akrinor.

(−)-3-(3 : 4-Dihydroxyphenyl)-2-methylalanine. *See* Presinol.★

17α : 21-Dihydroxypregna-1 : 4-diene-3 : 11 : 20-trione. *See* Prednisone.★

11 : 18-Dihydroxypregna-1 : 4-diene-3 : 20-dione-(18 → 20)-hemiketal. *See* Holadysone.

4 : 5-Dihydroxypyrimidine

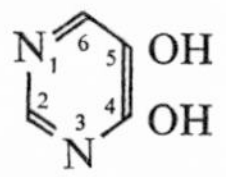

$C_4H_4O_2N_2$ MW 112

Needles from H_2O. M.p. 300° after blackening at 260°. $FeCl_3$ → deep red-purple col.

B,HBr: needles from 48% HBr. M.p. >270° decomp.

Chang, Chiang, *Sci. Sinica*, 1957, **6**, 293 (*Chem. Abstracts*, 1958, **52**, 2023).
McOmie, Turner, *J. Chem. Soc.*, 1963, 5590.

4 : 6-Dihydroxypyrimidine

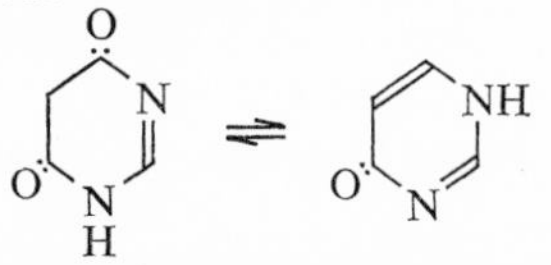

Principal tautomeric forms

$C_4H_4O_2N_2$ MW 112

Cryst. from H_2O. M.p. >230° decomp. pK_a 5·35. Light absorption: $\lambda_{max.}$ 253 mμ (ε, 8300), in 0·1*N*-HCl. $\lambda_{max.}$ 250 mμ (ε, 3600) in 0·1*N*-NaOH.

Di-O-Me ether: b.p. 85°/16 mm. n_D^{20} 1·4980.

6-O-*Me ether*: m.p. 211–12°.

Kenner *et al.*, *J. Chem. Soc.*, 1943, 388.
Davoll, Laney, *J. Chem. Soc.*, 1956, 2124.
Brown, Harper, *J. Chem. Soc.*, 1961, 1298.
Brown, Teitei, *Austral. J. Chem.*, 1964, **17**, 567.

5 : 6-Dihydroxyskatole (5 : 6-*Dihydroxy*-3-*methylindole*)

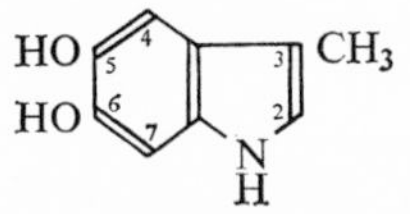

$C_9H_9O_2N$ MW 163

Colourless prisms from C_6H_6–light petroleum. M.p. 152°.

5 : 6-*Dibenzyl ether*: cryst. from C_6H_6–light petroleum. M.p. 122–3°.

Beer *et al.*, *J. Chem. Soc.*, 1949, 2061.
Heacock, Hutzinger, *Can. J. Chem.*, 1964, **42**, 514.

1 : 11-Dihydroxytetracene-5 : 12-quinone

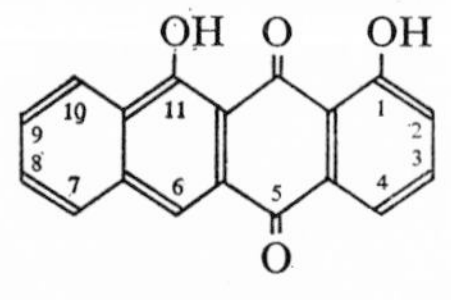

$C_{18}H_{10}O_4$ MW 290

Yellow-red fine needles. M.p. 276–8°. Light absorption $\lambda_{max.}$ 256, 300, 443 mμ in hexane. $\lambda_{max.}$ 514 mμ in MeOH–NaOH soln. $\lambda_{max.}$ 532, 569 (601) mμ in conc. H_2SO_4.

Brockmann, Brockmann, *Naturwiss.*, 1963, **50**, 519.

3′ : 5-Dihydroxy-3 : 4′ : 6 : 7-tetramethoxyflavone. *See* Casticin.

3′ : 5 - Dihydroxy - 3 : 4′ : 7 : 8 - tetramethoxyflavone (*Gossypetin tetramethyl ether*)

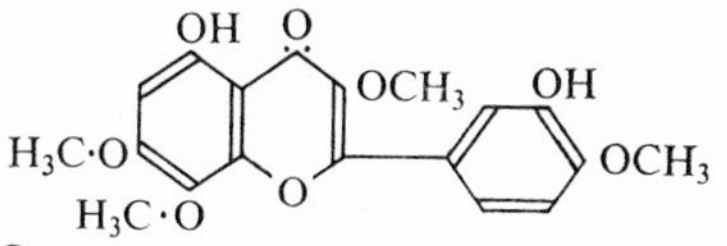

$C_{19}H_{28}O_8$　　　　　　　　　　MW 374
Constituent of *Ricinocarpus stylosus* Diels. Dimorphic needles or prisms from Me₂CO. M.p. 184–5° and 192–3°. Light absorption: $\lambda_{max.}$ 260° (log ε, 4·32), 275 (4·30), and 366 (mμ (4·20).
Di-Ac: needles from MeOH. M.p. 179–80°.
3′-*Me ether*: *see* 5-Hydroxy-3 : 3′ : 4′ : 7 : 8-pentamethoxyflavone.
Di-Me ether: *see* Gossypetin hexamethyl ether.

　　Henrick, Jefferies, *Austral. J. Chem.*, 1964, **17**, 934.

α : 3-Dihydroxytoluene★ (m-*Hydroxybenzyl alcohol*).
Metabolite of *Pencillium urticae*.

　　Rebstock, *Arch. Biochem. & Biophys.*, 1964, **104**, 156.

α : 4-Dihydroxytoluene★ (p-*Hydroxybenzyl alcohol*).
Constituent of musk melon (*Cucurbita moschata*) seedlings. Co-factor for indoleacetic acid oxidase.

　　Mumford, Stark, Smith, *Phytochemistry*, 1963, **2**, 215.

4′ : 5-Dihydroxy-3 : 7 : 8-trimethoxyflavone

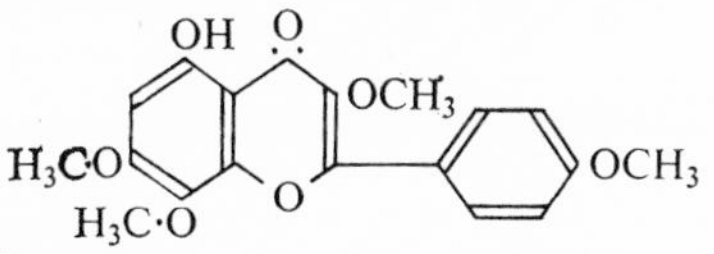

$C_{18}H_{16}O_7$　　　　　　　　　　MW 344
Constituent of *Ricinocarpus stylosus* Diels. Pale yellow needles from Me₂CO or EtOH. M.p. 266–8°.
Light absorption: $\lambda_{max.}$ 274 (log ε, 4·34), 331 (4·14), and 370 mμ (4·17).
Di-Ac: needles from MeOH. M.p. 183–5°.
4′-*Me ether*: *see* Flindulatin.★
Di-Me ether: m.p. 158°.

　　Henrick, Jefferies, *Austral. J. Chem.*, 1964, **17**, 934.

1 : 3 - Dihydroxy - 3 : 5 : 5 - trimethylcyclohexylidene - 4 - acetic Acid Lactone. *See* Loliolide.

Dihydroxyurea

(*a*)　　(HONH·)₂CO

⇅

(*b*) HONH·C(OH)ːNOH

$CH_4O_3N_2$　　　　　　　　　　MW 92
Two forms: (*a*) M.p. 102–6° decomp. (*b*) Explodes at 95° or at room temp. after several hours.

　　Boyland, Nery, *Nature*, 1964, **203**, 1379.

Di-iodobenzidine. *See* Diaminodi-iodobiphenyl.

1 : 4-Di-iodobutane.★
　　Stone, Shechter, *Organic Syntheses*, 1950, **30**, 33; Coll. Vol. **4**, 321.

Di-iodofumaronitrile (*Dicyano-di-iodoethylene*)

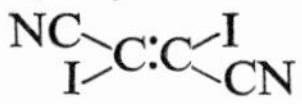

$C_4N_2I_2$　　　　　　　　　　MW 330
M.p. 188·5–189·5°.

　　Kloster-Jensen, *Acta Chem. Scand.*, 1963, **17**, 1866.

1 : 6-Di-iodohexane.★
　　Stone, Shechter, *Organic Syntheses*, Coll. Vol. **4**, 323.

3 : 6-Di-isobutyl-2-hydroxypyrazine-1-oxide. *See* Neoaspergillic Acid.

***o*-(*N*-Di-isopropylaminoethoxy)butyrophenone**

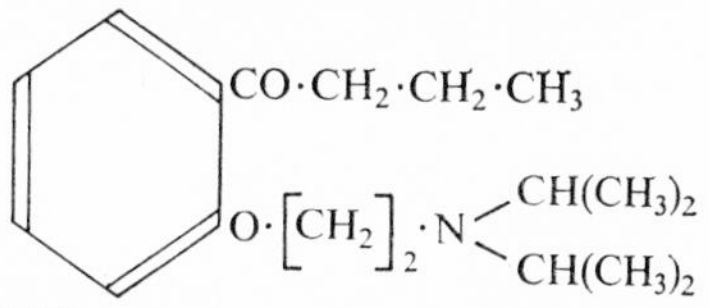

$C_{18}H_{29}O_2N$　　　　　　　　　　MW 291
Local anaesthetic. Oil. B.p. 183–5°/6–7 mm.
B,HCl: white cryst. M.p. 129–30°.

　　Da Re, Setnikar, *Experientia*, 1964, **20**, 607.

4-(*N*-Di-isopropyl-*N*-methylammonium)-2 : 2 - diphenyl-butyramide iodide. *See* Isopropamide.★

Dilactophorbic Acid. *See under* Phorbic Acid.

Dilaudid. *See* Dihydromorphinone.

Dilavase. *See under* Isoxsuprine.★

Dilinoleoyl-L-α-cephalin (*Di-*(*octadeca-9 : 12-dienoyl*)-L-α-*cephalin*)

$CH_2·O·CO·[CH_2]_7·CH{:}CH·CH_2·CH{:}CH[CH_2]_4·CH_3$
$CH·O·CO·[CH_2]_7·CH{:}CH·CH_2·CH{:}CH·[CH_2]_4·CH_3$
　　　　OH
$CH_2·O·P·O·CH_2·CH_2NH_2$
　　　　‖
　　　　O

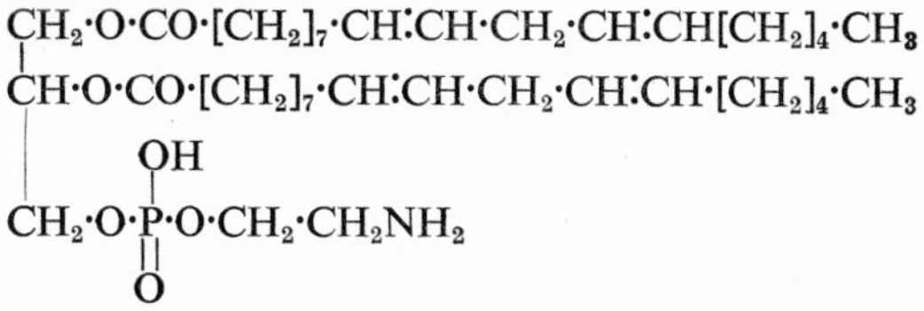

$C_{41}H_{76}O_8NP$　　　　　　　　　　MW 742
Pale yellow waxy solid. $[\alpha]_D$ +6°.

　　Dorofeeva, Tolkachev, Preobrazhenskii, *Zhur. Obshcheĭ Khim*, 1963, **33**, 2873.
　　Baer, Blackwell, *Biochemistry*, 1964, **3**, 975.

4 : 5-Dimethoxy-2-nitrobenzaldehyde★ (6-*Nitroveratraldehyde*).
See also:

　　Fetscher, *Organic Syntheses*, Coll. Vol. **4**, 735.

5 : 7-Dimethoxy-9-oxocyclopenteno[c]coumarin

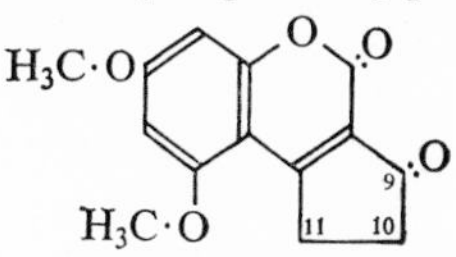

$C_{14}H_{12}O_5$　　　　　　　　　　MW 260
Cryst. M.p. 232–3°. Light absorption: $\lambda_{max.}$ 227 infl. (ε, 22,000), 238 infl. (18,300), 257 (12,800), and 355 mμ (36,800). $H_2 \rightarrow$ dihydro deriv. M.p. 182–4°.

　　Holker, Underwood, *Chemistry and Industry*, 1964, 1865.

2-(3 : 4-Dimethoxyphenyl)-5-(*N*-homoveratryl-*N*-methylamino)-2-isopropylvaleronitrile. *See* Isoptin.

3-[2-(3 : 5-Dimethyl-5-acetoxy-2-oxocyclohexyl)-2-hydroxyethyl]glutarimide.★
Ac: needles from CH_2Cl_2–Et_2O. M.p. 177–8°.
p-*Nitrobenzoyl*: plates. M.p. 167–8°.
Semicarbazone: prisms from MeOH. M.p. 214–15°.
Rao, *J. Am. Chem. Soc.*, 1960, **82**, 1129.

2-(γ : γ-Dimethylallyl)-1 : 4-naphthoquinone★ (*Deoxylapachol*).
Also present in the heartwood of *Tabebuia* sp.
Dietrichs, *Naturwiss.*, 1964, **51**, 408.

***p*-Dimethylaminobenzaldehyde.★**
Caupaigne, Archer, *Organic Syntheses*, Coll. Vol. **4**, 331.

6-Dimethylamino-4 : 4-diphenylhexan-3-one. *See* Normethadone.★

2-Dimethylaminoethyl 2-methyldiphenylmethyl Ether. *See* Orphenadrine.★

20α-Dimethylamino-3β-hydroxypregn-5-ene. *See* Irehine.

20α-Dimethylamino-3α-methylamino-5α-pregnane. *See* Pachysamine A.

(−)-6-Dimethylamino-5-methyl-4 : 4-diphenyl-3-hexanone. *See* (−)-Isomethadone.★

10-(3-Dimethylamino-2-methylpropyl)-2-methoxyphenothiazine. *See* Methotrimeprazine.★

10-(3-Dimethylamino-2-methylpropyl)phenothiazine. *See* Trimeprazine.★

5-Dimethylamino-1-naphthalene sulphonyl chloride (*Dansyl chloride*)

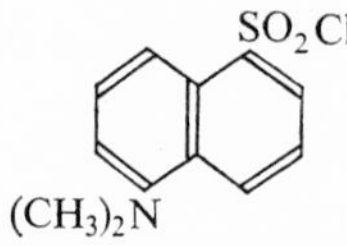

$C_{12}H_{12}O_2NSCl$ MW 269·5
Reagent which gives fluorescent derivatives with amino acids. Yellow cryst. from Me_2CO.Aq. M.p. 69°. With NH_3 → amide, m.p. 215° decomp.
Fussganger, *Ber.*, 1902, **35**, 976.
Weber, *Biochem. J.*, 1957, **51**, 155.
Hartley, Massey, *Biochim. Biophys. Acta*, 1956, **21**, 58.
Gray, Hartley, *Biochem. J.*, 1963, **89**, 59P, 379.
Seiler, Wiechmann, *Experientia*, 1964, **20**, 559.

3-Dimethylamino-1-phenyl-1-2′-pyridylpropane. *See* Pheniramine.★

5-(2-Dimethylaminopropyl)-10 : 11-dihydro-5*H*-dibenz-[*b,f*]azepine. *See* Imipramine.★

10-(2-Dimethylaminopropyl)phenothiazine. *See* Promethazine.★

10-(3-Dimethylaminopropyl)phenothiazine. *See* Promazine.★

10-(2-Dimethylaminopropyl)-2-propionylphenothiazane. *See* Propiomazine.

9-(2-Dimethylaminopropyl)-10-thia-1 : 9-diaza-anthracene. *See* Isothipendyl.★

10-(3-Dimethylaminopropyl)-10-thia-1 : 9-diaza-anthracene. *See* Prothipendyl.★

3-(3-Dimethylaminopropyl)-1 : 8 : 8-trimethyl-3-azabicyclo[3,2,1]octane

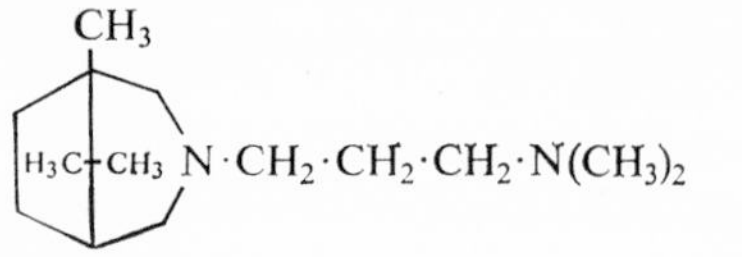

$C_{15}H_{30}N_2$ MW 238
B.p. 70–2°/0·1 mm. n_D^{25} 1·4770.
B,2HCl: m.p. 290–2°.
B,CH_3I: m.p. 237–8°.
$B,2CH_3I$: m.p. 269–71°.
$B,2(CH_3)_2SO_4$: Trimethidium methosulphate, Baratol. Ganglion blocking agent.
Rice, Grogan, *J. Org. Chem.*, 1956, **22**, 185; U.S.P. 2,786,834 (*Chem. Abstracts*, 1957, **51**, 12152).

7 : 12-Dimethylbenz[*a*]anthracene.★
Cryst. structure:
Sayre, Friedlander, *Nature*, 1960, **187**, 139.
Iball, *Nature*, 1964, **201**, 916.

***N′*-Dimethylbiguanide.** *See* Metformin.★

3 : 4-Dimethylcyclopentane-1 : 2-dione

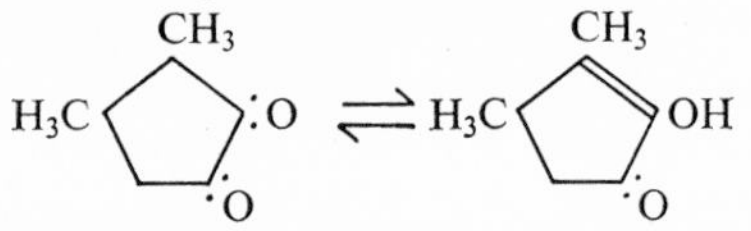

$C_7H_{10}O_2$ MW 122
Constituent of coffee. M.p. 71–2°. Light absorption: $\lambda_{max.}$ 259 mμ (log ε, 4·06).
Gianturco, Fridel, *Tetrahedron*, 1963, **19**, 2039.
Gianturco, Giammarino, Pitcher, *Tetrahedron*, 1963, **19**, 2051.

3 : 5-Dimethylcyclopentane-1 : 2-dione.
Constituent of coffee. M.p. 91–2°. Light absorption: $\lambda_{max.}$ 259 mμ (log ε, 4·07).
Me ether: 2-Methoxy-3 : 5-dimethylcyclopent-2-en-1-one. $C_8H_{12}O_2$. MW 136. Oil.
Gianturco, Fridel, *Tetrahedron*, 1963, **19**, 2039.
Gianturco, Giammarino, Pitcher, *Tetrahedron*, 1963, **19**, 2051.

Dimethyl-digol. *See* Di-Me ether *under* Di-(2-hydroxyethyl) Ether.★

2 : 4-Dimethyldocosanic Acid
$CH_3\cdot[CH_2]_{17}\cdot CH(CH_3)\cdot CH_2\cdot CH(CH_3)\cdot COOH$
$C_{24}H_{48}O_2$ MW 368
(+)-.
Constituent of the lipids of tubercle bacillus. M.p. 43–4·5°. $[\alpha]_D^{25}$ +2·2° (c, 0·72 in $CHCl_3$).
(±)-.
M.p. 50–3°.
Cason, Lange, Urscheler, *Tetrahedron*, 1964, **20**, 1955.

1α : 2β-Dimethylethylenethionosulphite

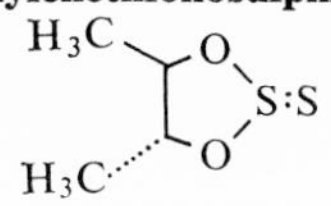

$C_4H_8O_2S_2$ MW 152

B.p. 32°/0·45 mm. n_D^{25} 1·5148. Light absorption: $\lambda_{max.}$ 257 mμ (ε, 2446).

Thompson, Crutchfield, Dietrich, *J. Am. Chem. Soc.*, 1964, **86**, 3891.

1β : 2β-Dimethylethylenethionosulphite.

B.p. 36°/0·13 mm. n_D^{25} 1·5232. Light absorption: $\lambda_{max.}$ 255 mμ (ε, 2549).

Thompson, Crutchfield, Dietrich, *J. Am. Chem. Soc.*, 1964, **86**, 3891.

3 : 3-Dimethylglutaric Acid.★

Smith, McLeod, *Organic Syntheses*, Coll. Vol. **4**, 345.

Dimethylketene.★

Acylal of dimethylmalonic acid: *see* 2-Isobutylidene-5 : 5-dimethyl-4 : 6-dioxo-*m*-dioxan.

See also:

Smith, Norton, *Organic Syntheses*, Coll. Vol. **4**, 348.

Dimethylmalonic Acid.

Dimethylketene acylal: *see* 2-Isobutylidene-5 : 5-dimethyl-4 : 6-dioxo-*m*-dioxan.

***N*: *N*-Dimethyl-2-(*o*-methyl-α-phenylbenzyloxy)ethylamine.** *See* Orphenadrine.★

5 : 5-Dimethyl-2-oxazolidinethione

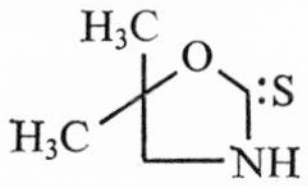

C_5H_9ONS MW 131

Produced by enzymic hydrolysis of glucoconringin. Cryst. from C_6H_6 or Et_2O. M.p. 107°.

Hopkins, *Can. J. Research*, 1938, **16B**, 341.
Kjaer, Gmelin, Jensen, *Acta Chem. Scand.*, 1956, **10**, 432.
Gmelin, Virtanen, *Acta Chem. Scand.*, 1959, **13**, 1718.

4 : 6-Dimethyl-2-oxo-2*H*-pyran-5-carboxylic Acid.★

See also:

Smith, Wiley, *Organic Syntheses*, Coll. Vol. **4**, 549.

Dimethyl peroxide

$CH_3{\cdot}O{\cdot}O{\cdot}CH_3$

$C_2H_6O_2$ MW 62

B.p. 10°. Explosive.

Rieche, Brumshagen, *Ber.*, 1928, **61**, 951.
Hanst, Calvert, *J. phys. Chem.*, 1959, **63**, 104.
Baker, Pape, Shaw, *Chemistry and Industry*, 1964, 1988.

***N*: α-Dimethyl-α-phenylsuccinimide.** *See* Methsuximide.★

***N*¹-Dimethyl-*N*²-phenyl-*N*²-(2-thienylmethyl)ethylenediamine.** *See* Methaphenilene.★

3 : 5-Dimethylpyrazole.★

Wiley, Hexner, *Organic Syntheses*, Coll. Vol. **4**, 351.

2 : 2-Dimethylpyrrolidine.★

Moffett, *Organic Syntheses*, Coll. Vol. **4**, 354.

***N'* : *N'*-Dimethyl-*N*-2-pyridyl-*N*-3-thenylethylenediamine.** *See* Thenyldiamine.★

2 : 7-Dimethylthianthrene (*Mesulphen, mitigal, sulermo*)

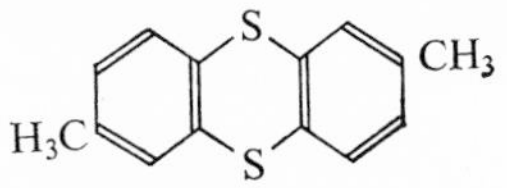

$C_{14}H_{12}S_2$ MW 244

Prisms from AcOEt. M.p. 123°. B.p. 123°/3 mm. Parasiticide and antipruritic agent.

Rame, *Dansk Tids. Farm.*, 1939, **13**, 21 (*Chem. Abstracts*, 1939, **33**, 5127).
Damanski, Kostić, *Bull. chim. Belgrade*, 1947, **12**, 243 (*Chem. Abstracts*, 1952, **46**, 5051).

6 : 7-Dimethyl-9(1'-D-threityl)isoalloxazine. *See* Threoflavin.★

5 : 8-Dimethyltocotrienol. *See* ε-Tocopherol.★

2 : 4-Dimethyltricyclo[1,1,1,0²,⁴]pentan-5-one

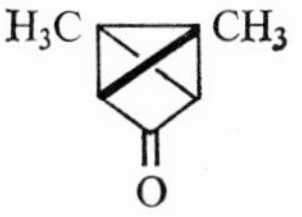

C_7H_8O MW 108

Cryst. from pentane. M.p. 57–8°.

von Doering, Pomerantz, *Tetrahedron Letters*, 1964, 961.

1 : 1-Dimethylurea.★

Kurzer, *Organic Syntheses*, 1952, **32**, 61; Coll. Vol. **4**, 361.

Dimorphone. *See* Dihydromorphinone.

Dimyristoyl-L-α-glycerylphosphoryl-L-2-amino-1-propanol. *See* Ditetradecanoyl-L-α-glycerophosphoryl-L-2-amino-1-propanol.

Dinarkon. *See under* Oxycodone.★

1 : 4-Dinitronaphthalene.★

See also:

Hodgson, Mahadevan, Ward, *Organic Syntheses*, Coll. Vol. **3**, 341.

Di-(octadeca-9 : 12-dienoyl)-L-α-cephalin. *See* Dilinoleoyl-L-α-cephalin.

Di-(octadecanoyl)-L-α-cephalin. *See* Distearoyl-L-α-cephalin.

Di-(octadec-9-enoyl)-L-α-cephalin. *See* Dioleoyl-L-α-cephalin.

Di-octadecanoyl-L-α-glycerylphosphoryl-L-2-amino-1-propanol (*Distearoyl-L-α-glycerylphosphoryl-L-2-amino-1-propanol*)

$CH_3{\cdot}[CH_2]_{16}{\cdot}CO{\cdot}O{\cdot}CH_2$
$CH_3{\cdot}[CH_2]_{16}{\cdot}CO{\cdot}O{\cdot}CH$ $\quad CH_3$
$CH_2{\cdot}O{\cdot}P(O)(OH){\cdot}O{\cdot}CH_2{\cdot}CH(NH_2)$

$C_{42}H_{84}O_8NP$ MW 761

White solid. M.p. 182–3° (with prior sintering). $[\alpha]_D^{23}$ 7° (c, 2·7 in $CHCl_3$).

Baer, Blackwell, *J. Biol. Chem.*, 1963, **238**, 3591.

Dioleoyl-L-α-cephalin (*Di-(octadec-9-enoyl)-L-α-cephalin*)

$$CH_2 \cdot O \cdot CO \cdot [CH_2]_7 \cdot CH{:}CH \cdot [CH_2]_7 \cdot CH_3$$
$$CH \cdot O \cdot CO \cdot [CH_2]_7 \cdot CH{:}CH[CH_2]_7 \cdot CH_3$$
$$OH$$
$$CH_2 \cdot O \cdot P \cdot O \cdot CH_2 \cdot CH_2 \cdot NH_2$$
$$O$$

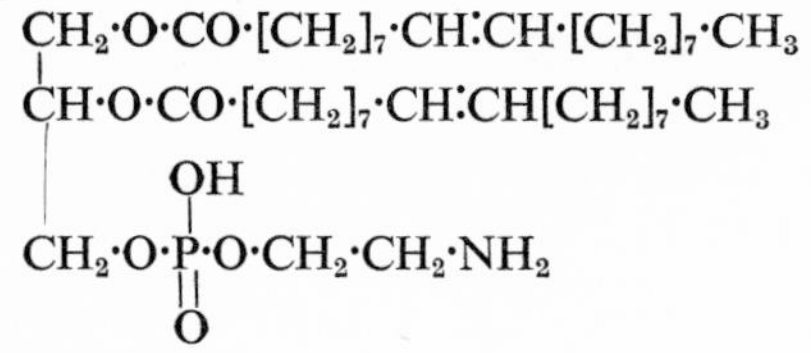

$C_{41}H_{78}O_8NP$ MW 744

White waxy solid. $[\alpha]_D$ +6° (c, 7 in CHCl₃).

Baer, Buchnea, *J. Am. Chem. Soc.*, 1959, **81**, 1758.
Baer, Blackwell, *Biochemistry*, 1964, **3**, 975.

DL-α-(Dioleoyl)-phosphatidyl-DL-serine

$$CH_2 \cdot O_2C \cdot (CH_2)_7 \cdot CH{:}CH \cdot (CH_2)_7 \cdot CH_3$$
$$CH \cdot O_2C \cdot (CH_2)_7 \cdot CH{:}CH(CH_2)_7 \cdot CH_3$$
$$O$$
$$CH_2 \cdot O \cdot P \cdot O \cdot CH_2 \cdot CH \cdot CO_2H$$
$$O \qquad NH_2$$

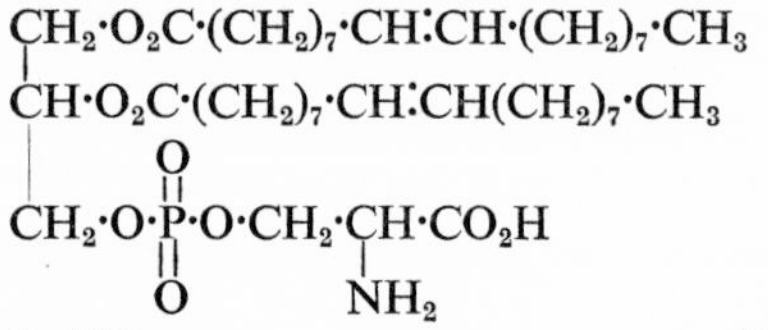

$C_{42}H_{78}O_{10}NP$ MW 787

Synthetic phosphatidyl serine with anticoagulant properties.

Turner, Silver, *Nature*, 1963, **200**, 370.

Diopal. *See under* Hyoscine.★

1 : 3-Dioxoferruginyl methyl Ether (*Compound B*)

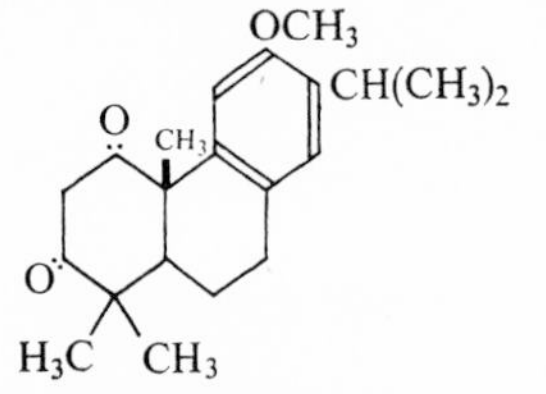

Suggested structure

$C_{21}H_{28}O_3$ MW 328

Constituent of the oleoresin of *Cupressus semper-virens*. M.p. 176–7°. $[\alpha]_D$ +22°.

Mangoni, Belardini, *Tetrahedron Letters*, 1964, 2643.

2 : 5-Dioxohexose (2 : 5-*Diketohexose*)

$$CHO$$
$$C{:}O$$
$$HO-C-H$$
$$H-C-OH$$
$$C{:}O$$
$$CH_2OH$$

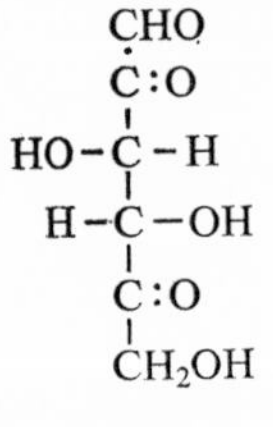

$C_6H_{10}O_6$ MW 178

Threo-D-.

Metabolite of acetic acid bacteria. Needles from AcOH–H₂O. M.p. 175–6°. $[\alpha]_D^{18}$ −81·2° → 89° (c, 4 in H₂O). Cryst. from EtOH.Aq. gave. $[\alpha]_D$ −87·5° → 89·8°.

Bis-phenylhydrazone: yellow cryst. M.p. 141°.
Bis-p-nitrophenyl hydrazone: yellow cryst. M.p. 176–7° (slow heating), 184–6° (rapid).

Terada, Suzuki, Kinoshita, *Agr. Biol. Chem.*, 1961, **25**, 871.

Weidenhagen, Bernsee, *Chem. Ber.*, 1960, **93**, 2924.
Whiting, Cogging, *Chemistry and Industry*, 1963, 1925.

1 : 3-Dioxototaryl methyl Ether (*Compound A*)

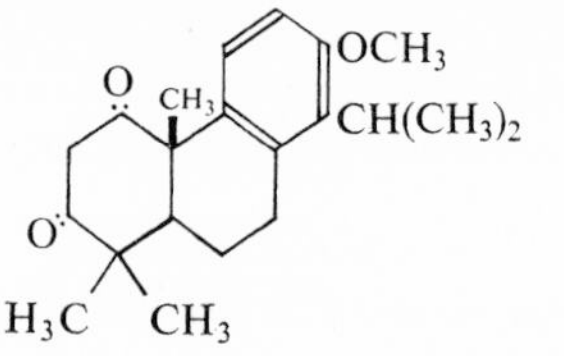

$C_{21}H_{28}O_3$ MW 328

Constituent of the oleoresin of *Cupressus semper-virens*. M.p. 191–2°. $[\alpha]_D$ +225°. Light absorption: λ_{max} 256 mμ (ε, 14,300) in acidified EtOH; λ_{max} 288 mμ (ε, 26,300) in alkaline EtOH.

1-*Me enol ether*: $C_{22}H_{30}O_3$. MW 342. M.p. 112–14°. $[\alpha]_D$ 80°.

3-*Me enol ether*: m.p. 158–9°. $[\alpha]_D$ +349°.

Mangeni, Belardini, *Tetrahedron Letters*, 1964, 2643.

Diphenylacetaldehyde.★

See also:

Rief, House, *Organic Syntheses*, 1959, **38**, 26; Coll. Vol. **4**, 375.

2 : 3-Diphenylacrylic Acid.

See also:

Buckles, Bremer, *Organic Syntheses*, Coll. Vol. **4**, 777.

2 : 6-Diphenylbiphenyl. *See* 1 : 2 : 3-Triphenylbenzene.★

3 : 4-Diphenylbiphenyl. *See* 1 : 2 : 4-Triphenylbenzene.★

3 : 5-Diphenylbiphenyl. *See* 1 : 3 : 5-Triphenylbenzene.★

3 : 4′-Diphenylbiphenyl.★

See also:

Cade, Pilbeam, *Tetrahedron*, 1964, **20**, 519.

α : β-Diphenylcinnamic Acid.★

Nitrile:

Wawzonek, Smolin, *Organic Syntheses*, 1951, **31**, 52; Coll. Vol. **4**, 387.

1 : 7-Diphenylnaphthalene

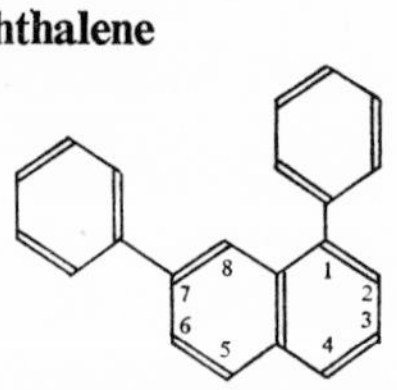

$C_{22}H_{16}$ MW 280

Needles from hexane. M.p. 93–4°. Light absorption: λ_{max} 254 (log ε, 4·74) and 300 mμ (4·11).

House, Magin, Thompson, *J. Org. Chem.*, 1963, **28**, 2403.

1 : 8-Diphenylnaphthalene.

Needles from hexane. M.p. 149·5–150·5°. Light absorption: λ_{max} 235·5 (log ε, 4·73) and 300 mμ (4·06).

House, Magin, Thompson, *J. Org. Chem.*, 1963, **28**, 2403.

1 : 2-Diphenylnaphtho[*b*]cyclobutadiene

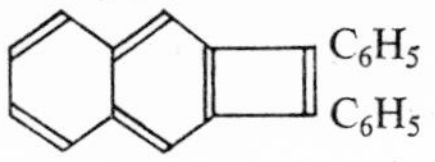

$C_{24}H_{16}$ MW 304

Scarlet needles. M.p. 137–8°.

Cava, Hwang, van Meter, *J. Am. Chem. Soc.*, 1963, **85**, 4032.

1 : 2-Diphenylphenanthro[*l*]cyclobutadiene

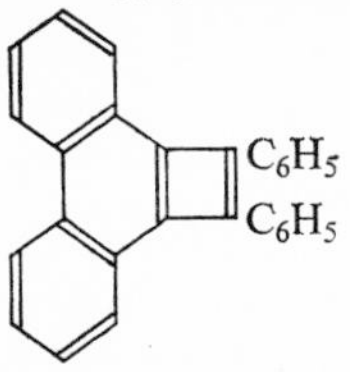

$C_{28}H_{18}$ MW 354

Unstable hydrocarbon which rapidly polymerises.

Cava, Mangold, *Tetrahedron Letters*, 1964, 1751.

1 : 2-Diphenylphenanthro[*l*]-cyclobutene

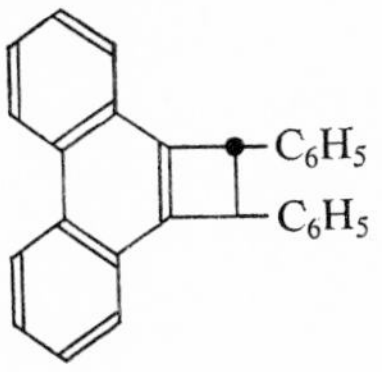

$C_{28}H_{20}$ MW 356

Trans-.

M.p. 195–7°.

Cava, Mangold, *Tetrahedron Letters*, 1964, 1751.

3′ : 2″-Diphenyl-*p*-quaterphenyl

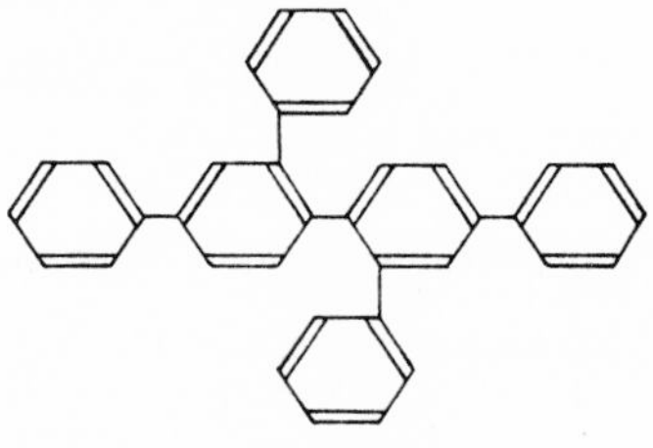

$C_{36}H_{26}$ MW 458

Sublimes at 200–300°/0·01 mm. M.p. 234·5°. Light absorption: $\lambda_{max.}$ 291 (ε, 28,600) and 253 mμ (57,000).

Cade, Pilbeam, *J. Chem. Soc.*, 1964, 114.

2 : 3-Diphenylsuccinic Acid.★

Meso-.

Dinitrile:

Davis, Ward, *Organic Syntheses*, 1954, **32**, 63; Coll. Vol. **4**, 392.

McRae, Bannard, *Organic Syntheses*, 1952, **32**, 64; Coll. Vol. **4**, 393.

1 : 7-Diphenyl-1 : 3 : 5 : 7-tetraoxoheptane

$C_6H_5·CO·CH_2·CO·CH_2·CO·CH_2·CO·C_6H_5$

$C_{19}H_{16}O_4$ MW 308

M.p. 91–2°. With $NH_2·NH_2$ → dipyrazole, m.p. 218–19°.

Miles, Harris, House, *J. Am. Chem. Soc.*, 1963, **85**, 3885.

Diprozine. *See* Promethazine.★

Dipyrido[1,2-*a* : 2′,1′-*c*]pyrazidiinium

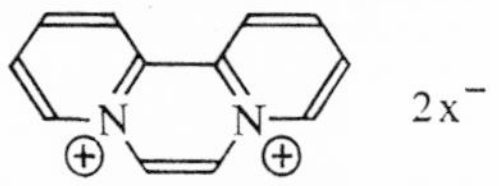

Dibromide (X = Br): cryst. + $2H_2O$ from MeOH–Et_2O. M.p. 272–3° decomp.

Dipicrate: cryst. + H_2O. M.p. 185–6°.

Corr, Glover, *Chemistry and Industry*, 1964, 2128.

Dirosine

$C_{37}H_{42}O_6N_2$ MW 610

Alkaloid from Green heart (*Ocotea rodiaei*).

B,HCl: $[\alpha]_D$ 97° (c, 1 in H_2O).

Hearst, *J. Org. Chem.*, 1964, **29**, 466.

Dissipal. *See under* Orphenadrine.★

Distamycin A

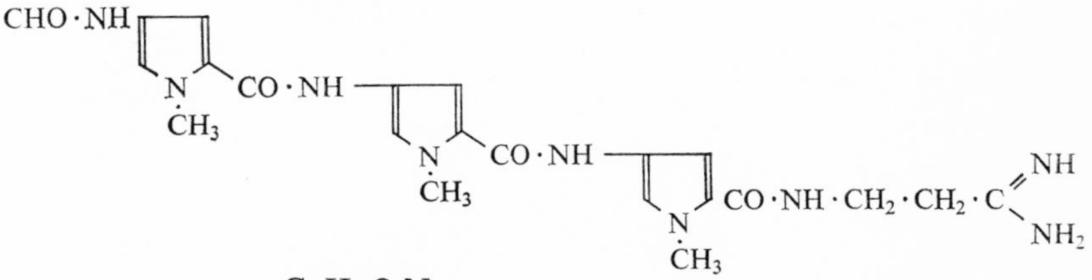

$C_{22}H_{27}O_4N_5$ MW 425

Antibiotic from *Steptomyces* sp.

B,HCl: cryst. from dil. HCl. M.p. 184–7°. Light absorption: $\lambda_{max.}$ 237 (ε, 30,000), 303 mμ (37,000).

Arcamone *et al.*, *Nature*, 1964, **203**, 1064.

Distearoyl-L-α-cephalin (*Di-octadecanoyl-L-α-cephalin*)

$CH_2·O·CO·[CH_2]_{16}·CH_3$

$CH·O·CO·[CH_2]_{16}·CH_3$

$CH_2·O·P(O)(OH)·O·CH_2·CH_2·NH_2$

$C_{41}H_{80}O_8NP$ MW 746

M.p. 180–2°.

Baer, *Can. J. Biochem. Physiol.*, 1957, **35**, 239.

Distearoyl-L-α-glycerylphosphoryl-L-2-amino-1-propanol. *See* Dioctadecanoyl-L-α-glycerylphosphoryl-L-2-amino-1-propanol.

Ditetradecanoyl-L-α-glycerylphosphoryl-L-2-amino-1-propanol (*Dimyristoyl-L-α-glycerylphosphoryl-L-2-amino-1-propanol*)

$CH_3·[CH_2]_{12}·CO·O·CH_2$

$CH_3·[CH_2]_{12}·CO·O·CH$

$CH_2·O·P(O)(OH)·O·CH_2·CH(NH_2)·CH_3$

$C_{34}H_{68}O_8NP$ MW 649

White powder. M.p. 181–2° with prior sintering. $[\alpha]_D^{24}$ +7·4° (c, 5 in $CHCl_3$).

Baer, Blackwell, *J. Biol. Chem.*, 1963, **238**, 3591.

1 : 2-Dithiacyclopenten-3-one (*Dithione*)

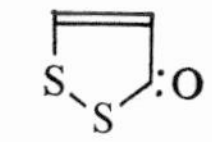

$C_3H_2OS_2$ MW 102

Colourless, oily liq. B.p. 47°/0·1 mm. M.p. 3°.

Mayer, Faust, *Chem. Ber.*, 1963, **96**, 2702.

1 : 4-Dithian.★

See also:

Gillis, Lacey, *Organic Syntheses*, 1959, **39**, 23; Coll. Vol. **4**, 396.

2 : 3-Dithiaspiro[4,5]decane

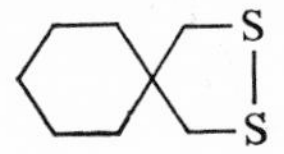

$C_8H_{14}S_2$ MW 174

Light absorption: $\lambda_{max.}$ 330 mμ.

$HgCl_2$ adduct: m.p. 91°.

Backer, Tamsma, *Rec. trav. chim.*, 1938, **57**, 1190.

Schotte, *Arkiv. Kemi*, 1950, **9**, 309.

1 : 6-Dithio-D-glucose

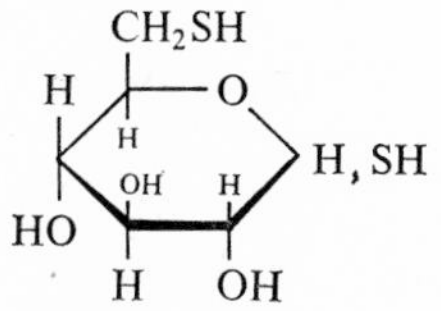

$C_6H_{12}O_4S_2$ MW 212

1 : 6-*Dibenzoyl*-2 : 3 : 4-*tri-Ac*: m.p. 130–1°. $[\alpha]_D^{20}$ −9° (c, 4 in $CHCl_3$).

Kocourek, Jiráček, *Angew. Chem., Int. Ed.*, 1964, **3**, 62.

1 : 3-Dithiolane-2-thione-4 : 5-dione

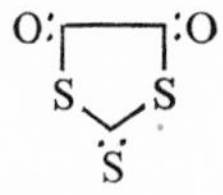

$C_3O_2S_3$ MW 164

Cryst. from hexane. M.p. 66°. B.p. 90°/2 mm. D_4^{25} 1·890.

Krebs, Gatlow, *Angew. Chem.*, 1963, **75**, 978; *Int. Ed.*, 1963, **2**, 618.

3*H*-1 : 2-Dithiole-3-thione

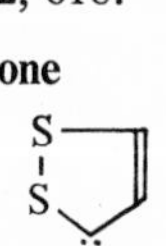

$C_3H_2S_3$ MW 134

Cryst. from C_6H_6 or MeOH. M.p. 81–2°.

Methiodide: m.p. 175°.

Challenger *et al.*, *J. Chem. Soc.*, 1953, 292.

Meyer, Kubasch, *Angew. Chem.*, 1961, **73**, 220.

Beer, Slater, *J. Chem. Soc.*, 1964, 4069.

Dithione. *See* 1 : 2-Dithiacyclopenten-3-one.

Di-α-tocopherone

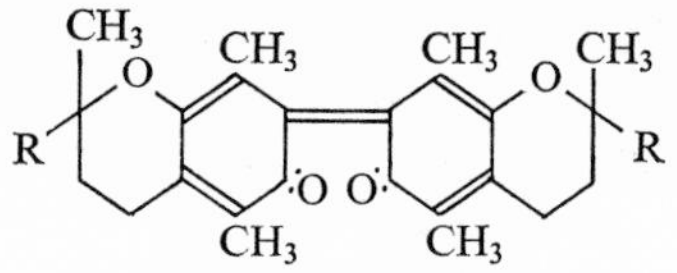

Cis-

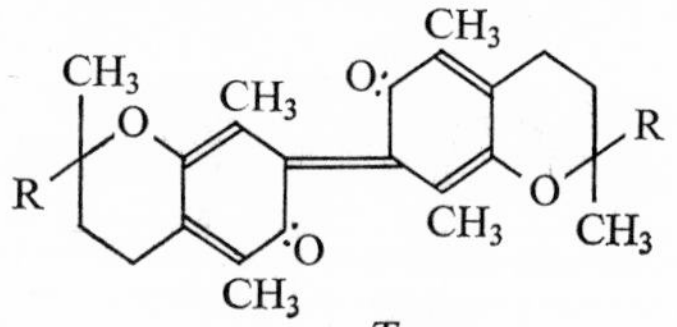

Trans-

$R = -[CH_2]_3\cdot CH(CH_3)\cdot[CH_2]_3\cdot CH(CH_3)\cdot[CH_2]_3\cdot CH(CH_3)\cdot CH_3$

$C_{56}H_{92}O_4$ MW 828

Product from ox. of α-tocopherol by $K_3Fe(CN)_6$ or rat liver.

Cis-.

Cryst. from Me_2CO at −14°. Sol. EtOH. Light absorption: $\lambda_{max.}$ 300 and 337 mμ.

Trans-.

Cryst. from Me_2CO at −7°. Insol. EtOH. Light absorption: $\lambda_{max.}$ 300 and 337 mμ.

Alaupovic *et al.*, *Am. J. Clin. Nutrition*, 1961, **9**, 76.

Csallany, Draper, *J. Biol. Chem.*, 1963, **238**, 2912; 1964, **239**, 574; *Arch. Biochem. Biophys.*, 1963, **100**, 335.

Divicine (2 : 4-*Diamino*-5 : 6-*dihydroxypyrimidine*)

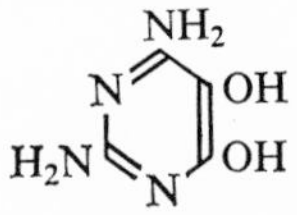

$C_4H_6O_2N_4$ MW 142

Aglycone from vetch seeds. Pale yellow microcryst. which decomp. above 300°. Light absorption: $\lambda_{max.}$ 281 mμ (log ε, 4·20) in 0·25*N*-HCl.

Di-Ac: cryst. from H_2O. M.p. 309–12° decomp.

Bendich, Clements, *Biochim. Biophys. Acta*, 1953, **12**, 462.

Davoll, Laney, *J. Chem. Soc.*, 1956, 2124.

Chesterfield *et al.*, *J. Chem. Soc.*, 1964, 1001.

Docosanedioic Acid (1 : 20-*Eicosanedicarboxylic acid, phellogenic acid*)

$HOOC\cdot[CH_2]_{20}\cdot COOH$

$C_{22}H_{42}O_4$ MW 370

Constituent of birch bark, cork, and Japan wax. M.p. 124·2–124·4°.

Mono-Me ester: $C_{23}H_{44}O_4$. MW 384. M.p. 86·4–87·4°.

Di-Me ester: $C_{24}H_{46}O_4$. MW 398. M.p. 70–70·3°.

Di-Et ester: $C_{26}H_{50}O_4$. MW 426. Cryst. from light petroleum. M.p. 61° (56°).

Di-nitrile: $C_{22}H_{40}N_2$. MW 332. Cryst. from C_6H_6. M.p. 70–1°.

Normand, Ross, Henderson, *J. Chem. Soc.*, 1926, 2633.

Ziegler, Hechelhammer, *Ann.*, 1937, **528**, 118, 138.
Drake, Carhart, Mozingo, *J. Am. Chem. Soc.*, 1941, **63**, 617.
Jensen, *Chem. Abstracts*, 1952, **46**, 8006.

2-Dodecenal

$CH_3{\cdot}[CH_2]_8{\cdot}CH{:}CH{\cdot}CHO$

$C_{12}H_{22}O$ MW 182

Trans-.

Present in citrus, ginger, carrots, etc., and in the millipede, *Rhinocricus insulatus*. B.p. 73–4°/0·5 mm., 125–8°/10 mm.

Semicarbazone: m.p. 165·5–166°.

Bedoukian, *J. Am. Chem. Soc.*, 1957, **79**, 889.
Wheeler *et al.*, *Science*, 1964, **144**, 540.

2-Dodecenoic Acid.★

Trans-.

B.p. 155–8°/3 mm., 127–30°/0·15 mm. M.p. 13–18°. n_D^{25} 1·4629. Light absorption: $\lambda_{max.}$ 210 mμ (ε, 13,650).

Allen, Kalm, *Organic Syntheses*, 1957, **37**, 27; Coll. Vol. **4**, 398.

Dolabradiene

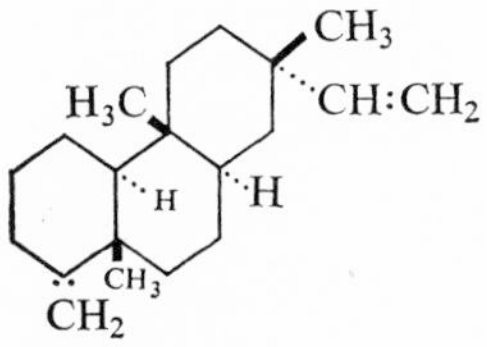

$C_{20}H_{32}$ MW 272

Constituent of the essential oil of the leaves of *Thujopsis dolabrata* Sieb. et Zucc. B.p. 169°/7 mm. n_D^{20} 1·5240. $[\alpha]_D^{25}$ −70° (neat).

Kitahara, Yoshikoshi, Oida, *Tetrahedron Letters*, 1964, 1755, 1763.

Doladene. *See* Methantheline.★

Domesticine

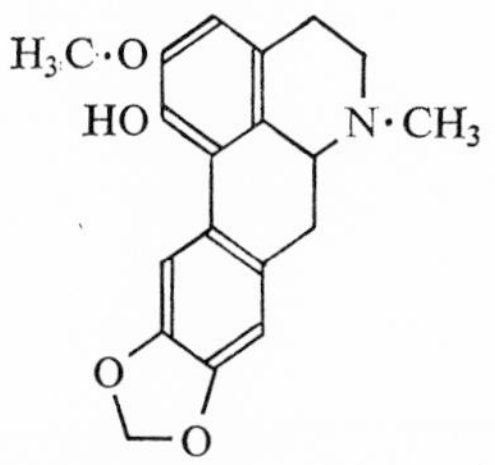

$C_{19}H_{19}O_4N$ MW 325

Alkaloid from *Nandina domestica*. Cryst. from MeOH.Aq. M.p. 115–16°. Cryst. from MeOH–C_6H_6. M.p. 84–5°. Anhydrous: m.p. 152–3° decomp. $[\alpha]_D$ +60·5°.

O-*Me*: *see* Nantensine.

Tomita, Kitamura, *J. Pharm. Soc. Japan*, 1959, **79**, 1092.
Kitamura, *J. Pharm. Soc. Japan*, 1960, **80**, 1140.

Dominal. *See* Prothipendyl.★

Dorevane. *See* Propiomazine.

Dregamine

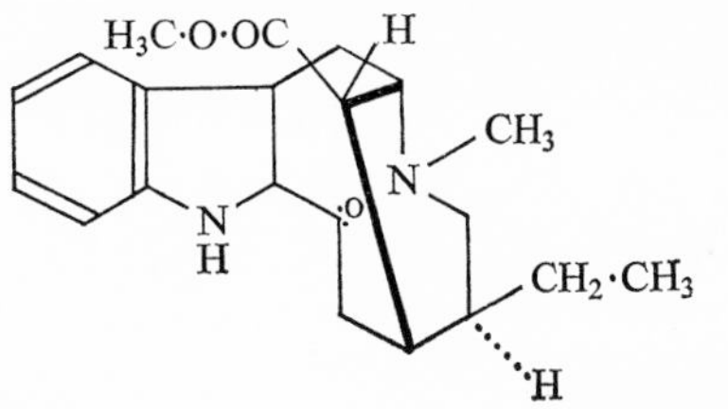

$C_{21}H_{26}O_3N_2$ MW 354

Alkaloid present in *Ervatamia coronaria* and *Voacanga dregei* E.M. Epimeric with Tabernaemontanine (*q.v.*). M.p. 180–2°.

Neuss, Cone, *Experientia*, 1959, **15**, 414.
Gorman *et al.*, *J. Am. Chem. Soc.*, 1960, **82**, 1142.
Renner, Prins, *Experientia*, 1961, **17**, 209.
Cava *et al.*, *Tetrahedron Letters*, 1963, 53.
Renner *et al.*, *Helv. Chim. Acta*, 1963, **46**, 2186.

Drimenin

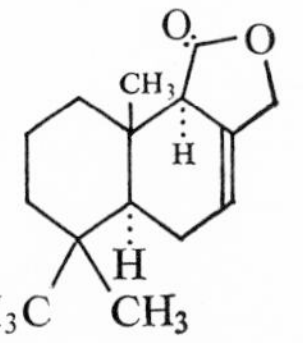

$C_{15}H_{22}O_2$ MW 234

Constituent of the bark of *Drimys winteri* Forst. Cryst. from MeOH and sublimed 110°/0·1 mm. M.p. 133°. $[\alpha]_D$ −42° (c, 0·76 in C_6H_6).

Appel *et al.*, *J. Chem. Soc.*, 1960, 4685.
Wenkert, Strike, *J. Am. Chem. Soc.*, 1964, **86**, 2044.

Drimenol.★

Synthesis:

Wenkert, Strike, *J. Am. Chem. Soc.*, 1964, **86**, 2044.

Drocode. *See* Dihydrocodeine.

Duazomycin A. *See* N-*Ac under* 6-Diazo-5-oxonorleucine.

Duazomycin B

```
CHN2            CHN2
|               |
CO              CO              COOH
|               |               |
CH2             CH2             CH·NH2
|               |               |
CH2             CH2             CH2
|               |               |
CH·NH·CO·CH·NH·CO·CH2
|
COOH
```

$C_{17}H_{23}O_8N_7$ MW 453

Cryst. antitumour substances produced by *Streptomyces ambofaciens*. Light absorption: $\lambda_{max.}$ 275 mμ ($E^{1\%}_{1\,cm.}$ 550).

Na salt: cryst. from MeOH.

Rao *et al.*, *Antibiotics Ann.*, 1959–60, p. 943; *Antimicrobial Agents and Chemotherapy*, 1962, 179.

Dubamine (α-*Piperonylquinoline*)

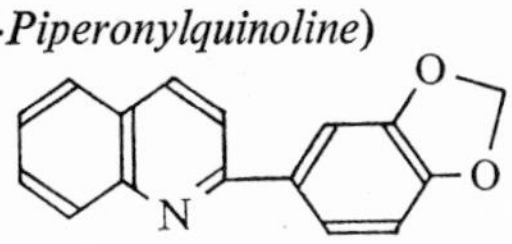

$C_{14}H_9O_2N$ MW 223

Alkaloid from *Haplophyllum dubium*. Cryst. from light petroleum or MeOH. M.p. 96–7°.

B,HCl: m.p. 201–2°.

B,HNO$_3$: m.p. 157–8°

Yunusov, *Zhur. Obshcheĭ Khim.*, 1955, **25**, 2009 (*Chem. Abstracts*, 1956, **50**, 9435).

Sidyakin, Pastukhova, Yunusov, *Uzbeksk. Khim. Zh.*, 1962, **6**, No. 3, 56 (*Chem. Abstracts*, 1963, **58**, 4608).

Dubinidine

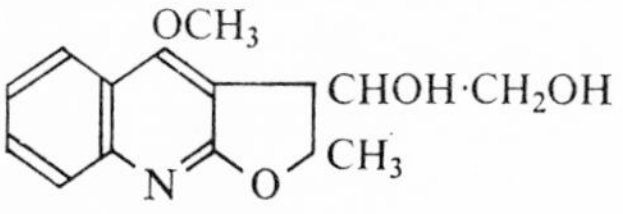

$C_{15}H_{17}O_4N$ MW 275

Alkaloid from *Haplophyllum* spp. Cryst. from Me_2CO. M.p. 132–3°. $[\alpha]_D^{26\cdot5}$ −62·95°.

B,HBr: m.p. 197–8°.

B,HCl: m.p. 195–6°. $[\alpha]_D^{18}$ −53·92°.

B,HI: m.p. 161–2°. $[\alpha]_D$ −47·32°.

B,HNO$_3$: m.p. 176–7°. $[\alpha]_D$ −52·39°.

Picrate: m.p. 155–6°.

Methiodide: m.p. 153–4°.

Mono-Ac: m.p. 186–186·5°. $[\alpha]_D$ −57·5° (c, 1·129 in EtOH).

Di-Ac: m.p. 108–9°. $[\alpha]_D^{19}$ −47·7°.

Yunusov, *Zhur. Obshcheĭ Khim.*, 1955, **25**, 2009 (*Chem. Abstracts*, 1956, **50**, 9435).

Sidyakin, Eskairov, Yunusov, *Doklady Akad. Nauk Uzbek. S.S.R.*, 1958, No. 8, 27 (*Chem. Abstracts*, 1959, **53**, 20116), *Zhur. Obshcheĭ Khim.*, 1960, **30**, 338 (*Chem. Abstracts*, 1960, **54**, 22697).

Polieutsev, *Izvest. Akad. Nauk Uzbek. S.S.R., Ser. Med.*, 1959, No. 6, 66 (*Chem. Abstracts*, 1960, **54**, 12479).

Bessonova, Sikyakin, Yunusov, *Doklady Acad. Nauk Uzbek. S.S.R.*, 1962, **19**, 50 (*Chem. Abstracts*, 1963, **58**, 4609).

Sidyakin *et al.*, *Zhur. Obshcheĭ Khim.*, 1962, **32**, 4091 (*Chem. Abstracts*, 1963, **58**, 14010).

Dubinine

$C_{16}H_{17}O_5N$ MW 303

Alkaloid from *Haplophyllum* spp. Cryst. from MeOH or EtOH. M.p. 185–6°. $[\alpha]_D$ −73·1° (Me_2CO).

B,HCl: m.p. 170–1°.

B,HNO$_3$: m.p. 148–50° decomp.

Methiodide: m.p. 211–12°.

Yunusov, *Zhur. Obshcheĭ Khim.*, 1955, **25**, 2009 (*Chem. Abstracts*, 1956, **50**, 9435).

Dulcin.★

See also:

Kurzer, *Organic Syntheses*, Coll. Vol. **4**, 52.

Duvadilan. *See* Isoxsuprine.★

E

Echinuline.★
Synthesis of hexahydro deriv.:
Casnati *et al.*, *Tetrahedron Letters*, 1964, 1597.

1 : 20-Eicosanedicarboxylic Acid. *See* Docosanedioic Acid.

Eledoisin.★
Synthesis of related peptides:
Camerino *et al.*, *Experientia*, 1963, **19**, 339.
Stürmer, Sandrin, Boissonnas, *Experientia*, 1964, **20**, 303.
Bernardi *et al.*, *Experientia*, 1964, **20**, 306.

β-Elemene.★
Present in orange oil.
Hunter, Parks, *J. Food Sci.*, 1964, **29**, 25.

Elemol

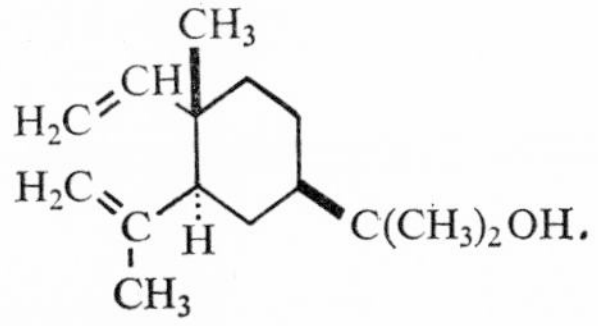

Absolute configuration:
Halsall, Theobald, Walshaw, *J. Chem. Soc.*, 1964, 1029.

Eleutherin★

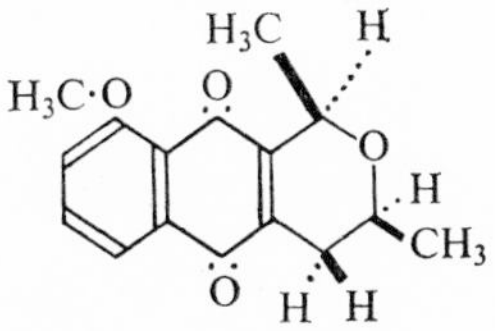

Stereochemistry:
Eisenhuth, Schmid, *Helv. Chim. Acta*, 1958, **41**, 2021.
Cameron *et al.*, *J. Chem. Soc.*, 1964, 98.

Ellagic Acid.★
3 : 3′-*Di-Me ether*: nasutin C. Constituent of the haemolymph of the termite *Nasutitermes exitiosus*. Pale cream needles from Me_2CO. M.p. 336–8° decomp.
3 : 3′ : 4-*Tri-Me ether*: nasutin B. Constituent of the haemolymph of *N. exitiosus*. Pale cream platelets from EtOH. M.p. 298° decomp.
Tetra-Me ether: m.p. 355° decomp.
Moore, *Austral. J. Chem.*, 1964, **17**, 901.

Elliotinic Acid
$C_{20}H_{30}O_2$ MW 302
Constituent of the oleoresin of slash pine (*Pinus elliotti*). Oil. $[\alpha]_D^{25}$ +40° (c, 1 in EtOH). Light absorption: $\lambda_{max.}$ 232 mμ (ε, 28,900).
Na salt: cryst. from H_2O. M.p. 387–9°. $[\alpha]_D^{25}$ +42° (c, 0·5 in EtOH).
Joye, Lawrence, *J. Org. Chem.*, 1963, **28**, 3274.
Gough, *Chemistry and Industry*, 1964, 2059.

Elliotinol
$C_{20}H_{32}O$ MW 288
Constituent of the oleoresin of slash pine. Long needles by sublimation. M.p. 14–15°. $[\alpha]_D^{25}$ +14° (c, 2 in EtOH). Light absorption: $\lambda_{max.}$ 232 mμ (ε, 20,600).
p-*Nitrobenzoyl*: cryst. from EtOH. M.p. 128–30°. $[\alpha]_D^{25}$ +74° (c, 2 in EtOH).
Tsutsui, Tsutsui, *Chem. Rev.*, 1959, **59**, 1046.
Joye, Lawrence, *J. Org. Chem.*, 1963, **28**, 3274.
Gough, *Chemistry and Industry*, 1964, 2059.

Elliptamine
$C_{24}H_{30}O_5N_2$ MW 426
Unstable alkaloid from the root bark and leaves of *Orhrosia poweri* Bailey and other *O.* spp.
Picrate: needles from MeOH.Aq. M.p. 170° decomp. Prisms from anhyd. MeOH. M.p. 215–17° decomp.
Day, Moore, *Austral. J. Chem.*, 1962, **15**, 548.
Douglas *et al.*, *Austral. J. Chem.*, 1964, **17**, 246.

Elorine. *See* Tricyclamol.★

Embichin. *See under* Mustine.★

Endo-hycodan. *See under* Dihydrocodeine.

Eneril. *See p*-Acetamidophenol.

Enmein (*Isodonin*)

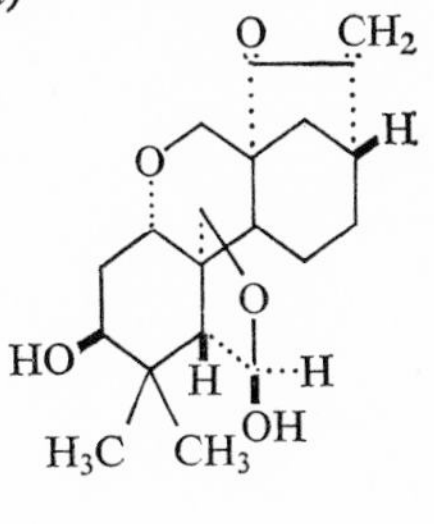

$C_{20}H_{26}O_6$ MW 362

Bitter principle from *Isodon trichocarpus* Kudo. M.p. 227–9° decomp. $[\alpha]_D^{10}$ −131·1°. $H_2 \rightarrow$ dihydro deriv. M.p. 274–5° decomp.
Di-Ac: m.p. 220–2° decomp.
Mono-Ac: m.p. 258–60° decomp.

Ikeda, Kanatomo, *Yakugaku Zasshi*, 1958, **78**, 1128 (*Chem. Abstracts*, 1959, **53**, 3389).
Kubota *et al.*, *Tetrahedron Letters*, 1964, 1243.
Iitaka, Natsume, *Tetrahedron Letters*, 1964, 1257.

Enniatin A.★
Synthesis:

Quitt, Studer, Vogler, *Helv. Chim. Acta*, 1964, **47**, 166.

Enstamine. *See* Methaphenilene.★

Entobex. *See* 4 : 7-Phenanthroline-5 : 6-dione.★

4 : 5-Epoxy-6-hydroxy-3-methoxy-*N*-methylmorphinan. *See* Dihydrocodeine.

13β : 28-Epoxy-3β-hydroxy-16-oxo-18β-oleanane. *See* Aegicerin.

Erasol. *See under* Mustine.★

7 : 22-Ergostadiene-3-one. *See* 24-Methylcholesta-7 : 22-diene-3-one.

Ergosterol peroxide

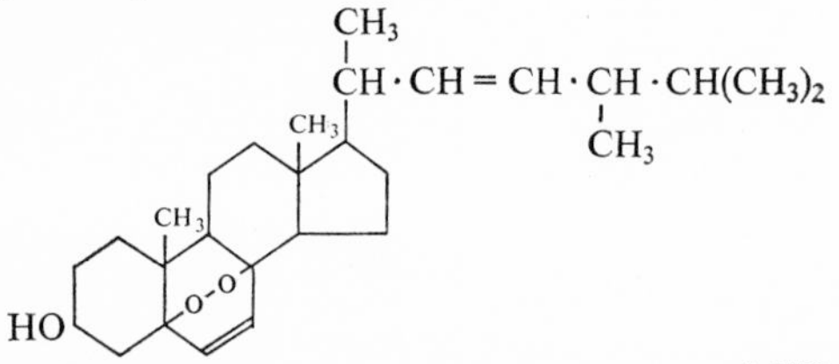

$C_{28}H_{44}O_3$ MW 428
Occurs in *Aspergillus fumigatus* and *Trichophyton schönleini*. Cryst. from MeOH. M.p. 181·5–183°. $[\alpha]_D$ −29° (c, 0·8 in $CHCl_3$). (−36°.)
Ac: cryst. from Me_2CO. M.p. 202·5–203·5°. $[\alpha]_D$ −23° (c, 0·65 in $CHCl_3$).

Windaus, Brunken, *Ann.*, 1928, **460**, 225.
Windaus, *Z. physiol. chem.*, 1942, **276**, 280.
Wieland, Prelog, *Helv. Chim. Acta*, 1947, **30**, 1028.
Bauslaugh, Just, Blank, *Nature* (Lond.), 1964, **202**, 1218.

Ergotamine★

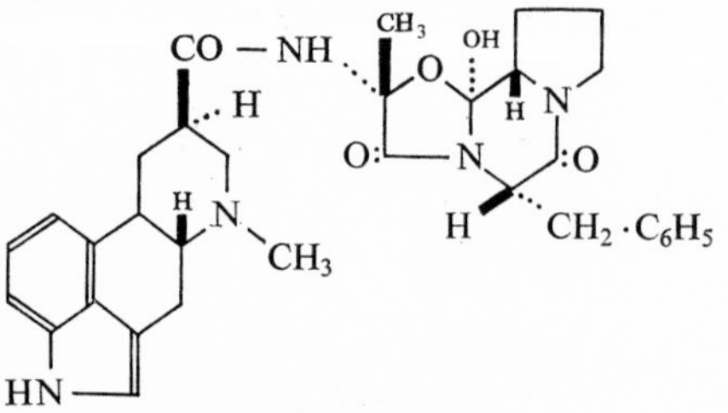

Synthesis and stereochemistry:

Hofmann *et al.*, *Helv. Chim. Acta*, 1963, **46**, 2306.

Ergothioneine.★
Is the cerebellar factor.

Crossland, Woodruff, Mitchell, *Nature*, 1964, **203**, 1388.

Erysimoside

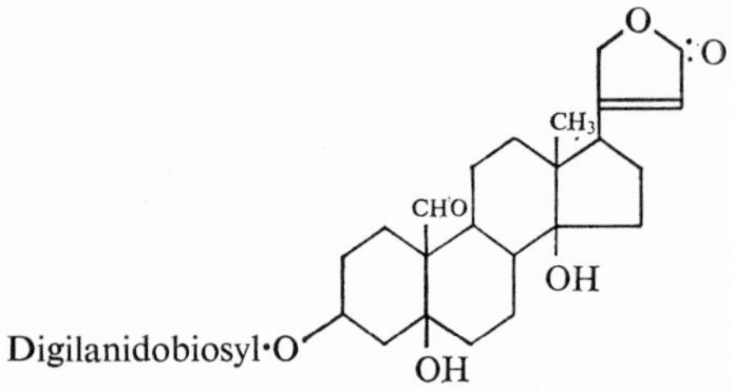

$C_{35}H_{52}O_{14}$ MW 696
Heart poison present in seeds of *Strophanthus Kombé*. M.p. 169–73°. $[\alpha]_D^{24}$ 22° (MeOH). Light absorption: $\lambda_{max.}$ 216 (log ε, 4·22) and 298–301 mμ (1·42).
Penta-Ac: cryst. from MeOH. M.p. 213–16°. $[\alpha]_D^{20}$ 34·7° (EtOH). Light absorption: $\lambda_{max.}$ 217 (log ε, 4·22) and 298–304 mμ (1·51).

Kaiser *et al.*, *Ann.*, 1961, **643**, 192.

Erysimosol

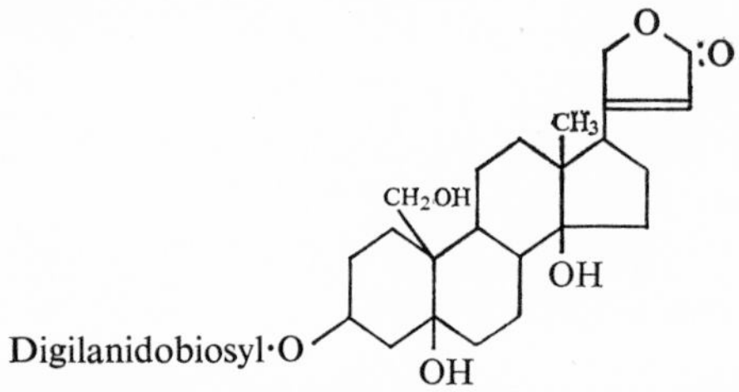

$C_{35}H_{54}O_{14}$ MW 698
Heart poison from seeds of *Strophanthus Kombé*. Amorph.
Hexa-Ac: cryst. from Py–Et_2O–cyclohexane. M.p. 146–9°. $[\alpha]_D^{20}$ 30·4°. Light absorption: $\lambda_{max.}$ 216–20 mμ (log ε, 4·22).

Kaiser *et al.*, *Ann.*, 1961, **643**, 192.

Erythritol.★
1-^{14}C-.

Kent, Wood, *J. Chem. Soc.*, 1964, 2812.

9-(1′-D-Erythrityl)-6 : 7-dimethylisoalloxazine. *See* Erythroflavin.

Erythroaphin *fb*★

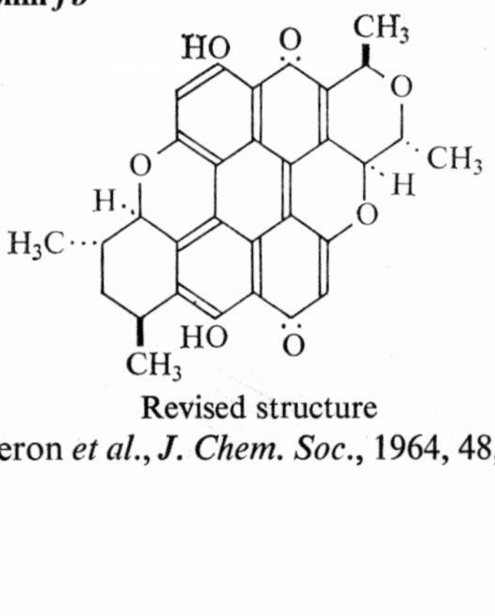

Revised structure

Cameron *et al.*, *J. Chem. Soc.*, 1964, 48, 62, 72, 90.

Erythroaphin-*sl*★

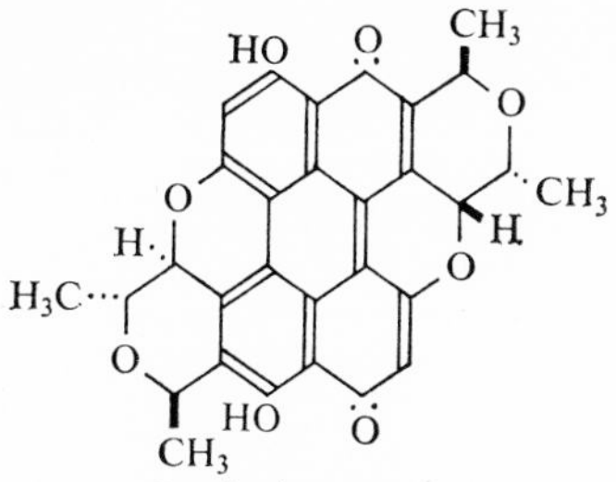

Revised structure

Cameron *et al.*, *J. Chem. Soc.*, 1964, 48, 62, 72, 90.

Erythroaphin-*tt*

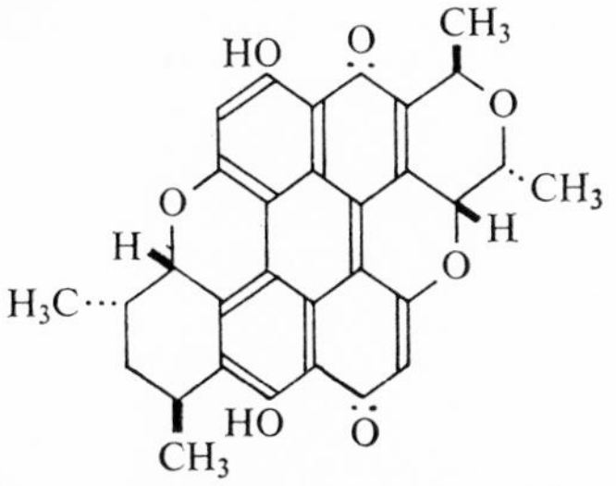

$C_{30}H_{22}O_8$ MW 510

Dark red cryst. from $CHCl_3$–EtOH. Light absorption: $\lambda_{max.}$ 253 (log ε, 4·49), 422 (4·39), 448 (4·50), 488 (3·70), 524 (4·03), 565 (4·22), and 590 mμ (3·84).

Cameron *et al.*, *J. Chem. Soc.*, 1964, 72, 90.

Erythroflavin (9-[1′-D-*Erythrityl*]-6 : 7-*dimethylisoalloxazine*)

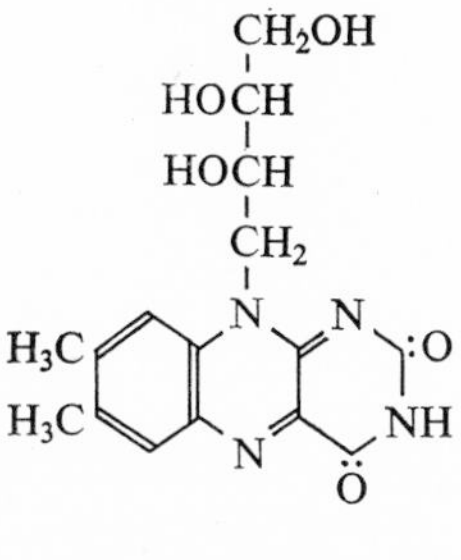

$C_{16}H_{18}O_5N_4$ MW 346

Orange plates from 6*N*-HCl. M.p. 285° decomp. $[\alpha]_D^{21}$ −106°.

4′-Phosphate: cryst. from aq.HCl. M.p. 227° decomp. $[\alpha]_D^{15}$ −18°.

Uehara, Sugeno, Mizoguchi, *J. Biochem.* (Japan), 1963, **54**, 267.

Erythrolaccin★

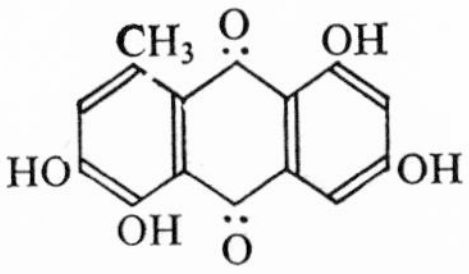

This has been shown to have the structure 1 : 3 : 5 : 6-tetrahydroxy-8-methylanthraquinone.★

Yates *et al.*, *Chemistry and Industry*, 1964, 1991.

Erythromycin★

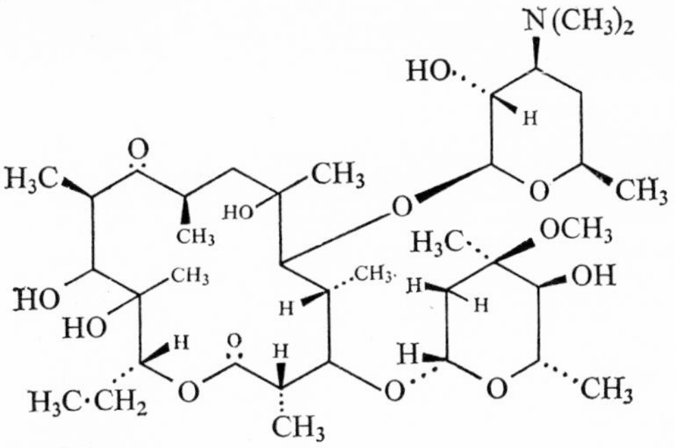

Configuration:

Hofheinz, Grisebach, *Chem. Ber.*, 1963, **96**, 2867.

Erythroskyrine★

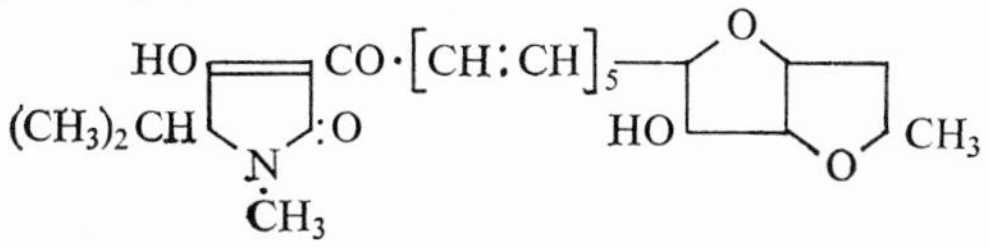

$C_{26}H_{33}O_6N$ MW 455

Metabolite of *Penicillium islandicum* Sopp. M.p. 130–3°. $[\alpha]_D$ 46·9° (c, 0·2 in EtOH). The original sample, m.p. 108–10° was impure.

Ac: m.p. 123°.

Shoji, Shibata, *Chemistry and Industry*, 1964, 419.

Erythroxydiol X

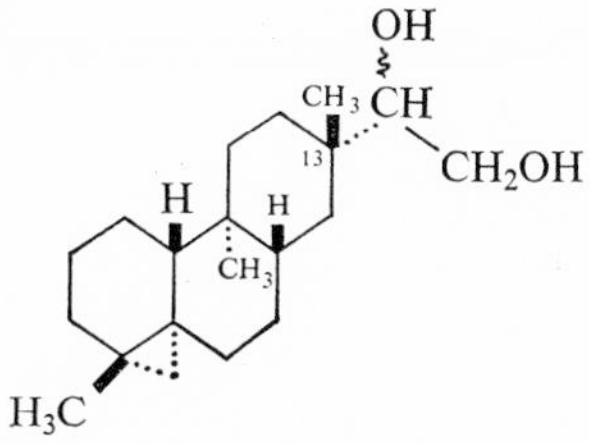

$C_{20}H_{34}O_2$ MW 306

Extractive of the trunk wood of *Erythroxylon monogynum* Roxb. M.p. 124–6°. $[\alpha]_D$ +12° ($CHCl_3$). Probably identical with Devadarool.

Acetonide: m.p. 89–90°. $[\alpha]_D$ +14° ($CHCl_3$).

Mono-Ac: m.p. 116–18°.

Di-Ac: m.p. 106–7°.

Connolly *et al.*, *Tetrahedron Letters*, 1964, 1859.

Erythroxydiol Y

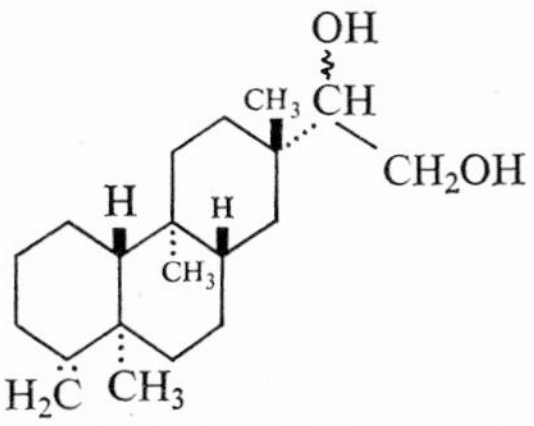

$C_{20}H_{34}O_2$ MW 306

Extractive of the trunk wood of *Erythroxylon monogynum* Roxb. M.p. 144–6°. $[\alpha]_D$ +87° ($CHCl_3$).

Acetonide: m.p. 109–10°. $[\alpha]_D$ −23° ($CHCl_3$).

Connolly *et al.*, *Tetrahedron Letters*, 1964, 1859.

Erythroxydiol Z

$C_{20}H_{34}O_2$ MW 306

Extractive of trunk wood of *Erythroxylon monogynum* Roxb. M.p. 136–8°. $[\alpha]_D$ −35° ($CHCl_3$). *Acetonide*: m.p. 108–10°. $[\alpha]_D$ −22° ($CHCl_3$).

Connolly *et al.*, *Tetrahedron Letters*, 1964, 1859.

Escigenin (*Aescigenin*)

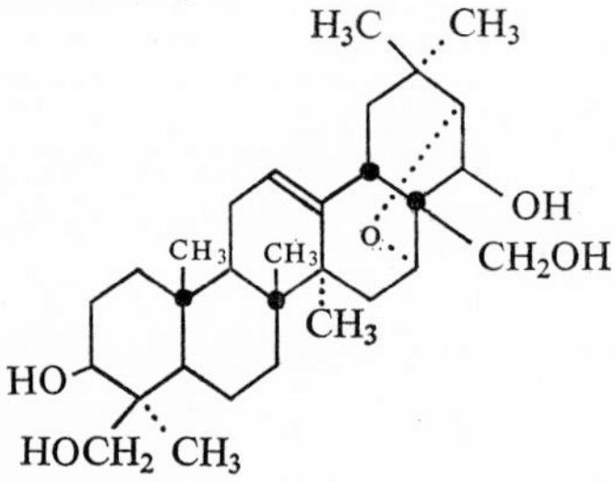

$C_{30}H_{48}O_5$ MW 488

Aglycone from Escin needles from MeOH. M.p. 307° (317–18°). $[\alpha]_D^{20}$ +33° ± 5° (c, 0·56 in EtOH). *Tetra-Ac*: m.p. 207–8°. $[\alpha]_D$ +56·7° ($CHCl_3$).

Tschesche, Axen, Snatzke, *Ann.*, 1963, **669**, 171.
Kuhn, Löw, *Ann.*, 1963, **669**, 183.

Escin (*Aescin*)

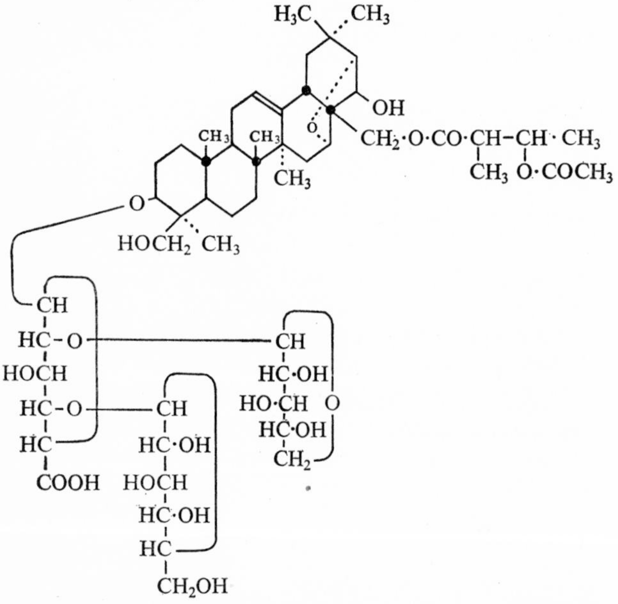

$C_{54}H_{84}O_8$ MW 1100

Saponin from horse chestnuts (*Aesculus hippocastanum* L.), with oedema inhibitory properties. Microcryst. powder. M.p. 224–5°. $[\alpha]_D^{20}$ −30° ± 5° (c, 0·58 in EtOH). Hydrol. → escigenin + xylose, glucose and glucuronic acid, etc.

Tschesche, Axen, Snatzke, *Ann.*, 1963, **669**, 171.
Kuhn, Löw, *Ann.*, 1963, **669**, 183.

Escinidin (*Äscinidin*)

$C_{30}H_{48(50)}O_5$ MW 488 (490)

Constituent of horse chestnuts (*Aesculus hippocastanum* L.). M.p. 310°. $[\alpha]_D^{20}$ 2° (Py).
Penta-Ac: m.p. 135°. $[\alpha]_D^{20}$ −5·8° ($CHCl_3$).
Tetra-Ac: m.p. 215°. $[\alpha]_D^{20}$ 17·5° ($CHCl_3$).

Kuhn, Löw, *Tetrahedron Letters*, 1964, 891.

Escorpal (*Phencarbamide, diethylaminoethyl diphenylthiocarbamate*)

$(C_6H_5)_2N{\cdot}CO{\cdot}S{\cdot}CH_2{\cdot}CH_2{\cdot}N(C_2H_5)_2$

$C_{19}H_{24}ON_2S$ MW 328

Spasmolytic drug for use in parturition. Cryst. M.p. 48–9°
B,HCl: m.p. 180–2°.

Farbenfabriken, Bayer, *Report of Therapy Congress and Pharmaceutical Exhibition*, Karlsruhe, 1963 (*Angew. Chem., Int. Ed.*, 1964, **3**, 68).

Eseramine

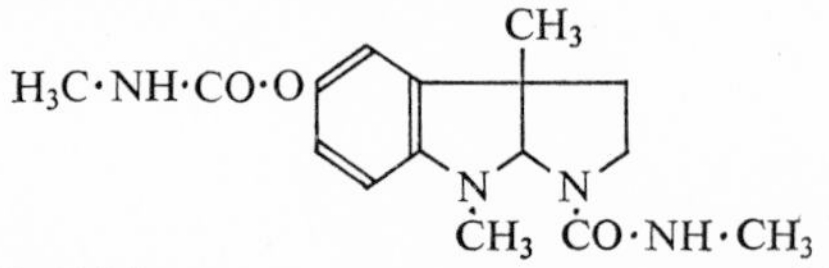

$C_{16}H_{22}O_3N_4$ MW 318

Alkaloid from *Physostigma venenosum* (Calabar beans). Needles from EtOH. M.p. 240–2° decomp. (216–18° [block]). $[\alpha]_D^{23}$ −289° (EtOH). Light absorption: $\lambda_{max.}$ 256 (ε, 13,050) and 311 mμ (2680).

Ehrenberg, *Verh. Ges. Deut. Nat. Aerzte*, 1893, **2**, 102 (*Chem. Zentr.*, 1894, II, 439).
Salway, *J. Chem. Soc.*, 1911, **99**, 2148.
Robinson, Spiteller, *Chemistry and Industry*, 1964, 459.

Esmodil. *See* *N*-(2-Methoxy-2-propenyl)trimethylammonium bromide.★

Estopen. *See under* 2-Diethylaminoethyl ester *under* Benzylpenicillinic Acid.

Ethanedithiol.★

See also:

Speziale, *Organic Syntheses*, 1950, **30**, 35; Coll. Vol. **4**, 401.

Ethiodan. *See* Iophendylate.★

Ethnine. *See* 3-(2-Morpholinoethyl)morphine.

3-Ethylcyclopentone-1 : 2-dione (*1-Ethyl-2-hydroxycyclopenten-3-one*)

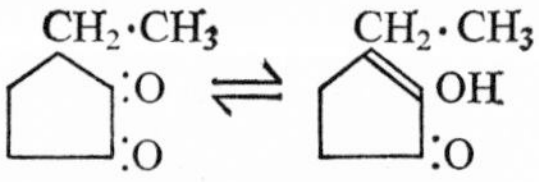

$C_7H_{10}O_2$ MW 122

Constituent of coffee. Oil. B.p. 65–8°/1 mm. which solidified *ca.* 20°. Light absorption: $\lambda_{max.}$ 259 mμ (log ε, 4·04).

Gianturco, Fridel, *Tetrahedron*, 1963, **19**, 2039.
Gianturco, Gràmmarino, Pitcher, *Tetrahedron*, 1963, **19**, 2051.

5-Ethyl-4 : 6-dimethylpyrogallol. *See* Barnol.

5-Ethylhexahydro-5-phenylpyrimidine-4 : 6-dione. *See* Primidone.★

2-Ethylhexanoic Acid.★
Nitrile: $C_8H_{15}N$. MW 125. B.p. 118–20°/100 mm., 70·5–72°/10 mm. n_D^{25} 1·4145.
Krynitsky, Carhart, *Organic Syntheses*, 1952, **32**, 65; Coll. Vol. **4**, 436.

1-Ethyl-2-hydroxycyclopenten-3-one. *See* 3-Ethylcyclopentane-1 : 2-dione.

17α-Ethyl-17-hydroxy-19-norandrost-4-en-3-one. *See* Norethandrolone.★

24-Ethylidene-4β-methyl-Δ⁷-cholesten-3β-ol. *See* Citrostadienol.

Ethyl 10-(*p*-iodophenyl)hendecanoate. *See* Iophendylate.★

Ethyl 10-*p*-iodophenylundecanoate. *See* Iophendylate.★

β-Ethyl-6-methoxy-α : α-dimethyl-2-naphthalenepropionic Acid. *See* Methallenoestril.★

3-Ethyl-3-methylglutaric Acid.★
See also:
Farmer, Rubjohn, *Organic Syntheses*, 1956, **36**, 28; Coll. Vol. **4**, 441.

4-Ethyl-2-methyl-2-octenoic Acid

$CH_3{\cdot}[CH_2]_3{\cdot}CH(CH_2{\cdot}CH_3){\cdot}CH{:}C(CH_3){\cdot}COOH$

$C_{11}H_{20}O_2$ MW 184
B.p. 141–2°/4·6 mm. n_D^{25} 1·4628.
Cason, Rinehart, *J. Org. Chem.*, 1955, **20**, 1591.
Rinehart, Perkins, *Organic Syntheses*, 1957, **37**, 37; Coll. Vol. **4**, 444.

5-Ethyl-3-methyl-5-phenylhydantoin. *See* Methoin.★

5-Ethyl-3-methyl-5-phenyl-2 : 4(3*H*,5*H*)imidazolidione. *See* Methoin.★

3-Ethyl-6-methylpyridine.★
See also:
Frank, Pilgrim, Riener, *Organic Syntheses*, 1950, **30**, 41; Coll. Vol. **4**, 451.

17α-Ethyl-19-nortestosterone. *See* Norethandrolone.★

Ethyl orthocarbonate

$C(O{\cdot}CH_2{\cdot}CH_3)_4$

$C_9H_{20}O_4$ MW 192
B.p. 158–61°. n_D^{25} 1·3905. D_4^{20} 0·9186.
Tieckelmann, Post, *J. Org. Chem.*, 1948, **13**, 265.
Smith, Delin, *Svensk Kem. Tidskr.*, 1953, **65**, 10.
Roberts, McMahon, *Organic Syntheses*, 1952, **32**, 68; Coll. Vol. **4**, 457.

4-Ethyloxazolidine-2-thione

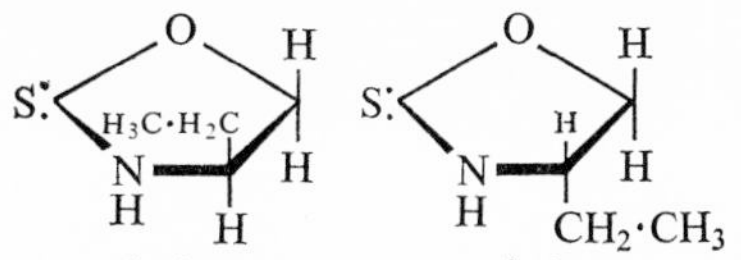

(+)- (−)-

C_5H_9ONS MW 131
(+)-. Sisaustricin.
Product of enzymic hyd. of glucosisaustricin. Prisms from Et_2O–pentane at −80°. M.p. 32–3°. $[\alpha]_D^{26}$ 46·3° (c, 1·4 in 96% EtOH).
(±)-.
M.p. 74–5°.
Rosen, *J. Am. Chem. Soc.*, 1952, **74**, 2994.
Sommerville, Andersen, *J. Org. Chem.*, 1960, **25**, 656.
Kjaer, Christensen, *Acta Chem. Scand.*, 1962, **16**, 71.

5-Ethyloxazolidine-2-thione.
(±)-.
Cryst. from AcOEt–pentane. M.p. 86·5°.
Clapp, Watjen, *J. Am. Chem. Soc.*, 1953, **75**, 1490.
Kjaer, Christensen, *Acta Chem. Scand.*, 1962, **16**, 71.

***N*-Ethyl-3-piperidyl benzilate.** *See* Pipenzolate.★

24-Ethyl-3α : 7α : 12α-trihydroxycoprostanic Acid

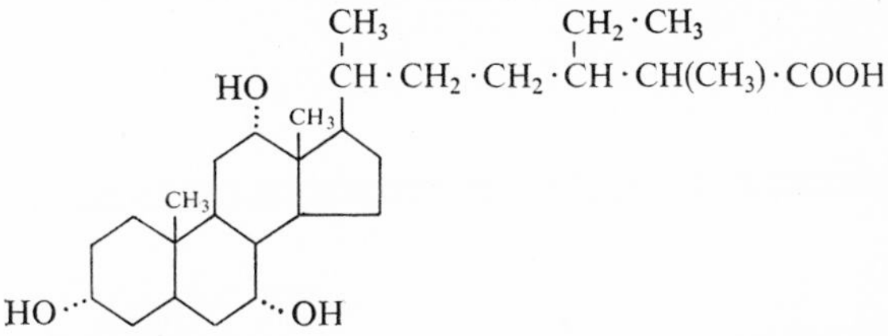

$C_{29}H_{50}O_5$ MW 478
Cryst. from AcOEt. M.p. 209–10°.
Morimoto, *J. Biochem.* (Japan), 1964, **55**, 410.

17α-Ethynyl-17β-hydroxyoestr-4-en-3-one. *See* Norethisterone.★

17α-Ethynyl-19-nortestosterone. *See* Norethisterone.★

Eucodal. *See under* Oxycodone.★

Euglycin. *See* Metahexamide.★

Euramycin. *See* Tri-Ac *under* Oleandomycin.★

Eutagen. *See under* Oxycodone.★

Eventin. *See* 1-Cyclohexyl-2-methylaminopropane.

Exogonic Acid★

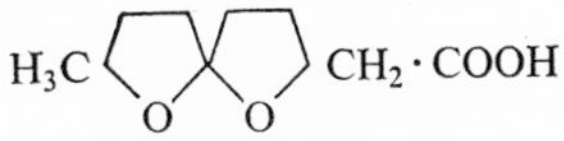

Suggested structure
Graf, Dahlke, *Naturwiss.*, 1964, **51**, 264.

F

Fabacein

$C_{34}H_{48}O_9$ MW 600

Constituent of the root of *Echinocystis fabacea*. M.p. 201–2°. $[\alpha]_D$ +36° (c, 0·515 in EtOH). Closely related to cucurbitacin B.

Tetra-Ac: amorph. $[\alpha]_D^{25}$ −2° (c, 1·76 in $CHCl_3$).

Eisenhut, Noller, *J. Org. Chem.*, 1958, **23**, 1984.
Schlegol, Noller, *Tetrahedron Letters*, 1959, No. 13, 16; *J. Org. Chem.*, 1961, **26**, 1211.

Faradiol

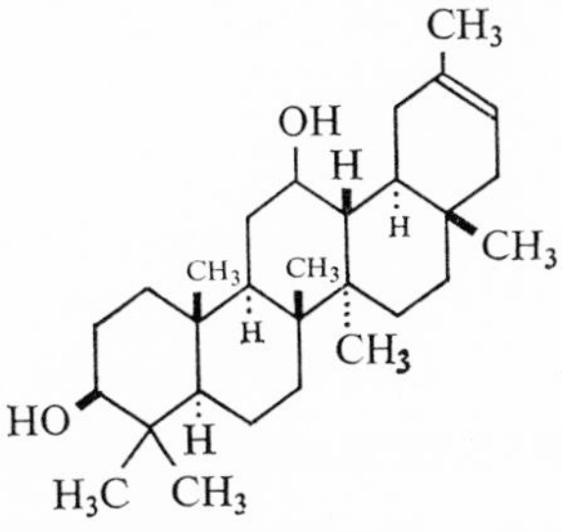

$C_{30}H_{50}O_2$ MW 442

Constituent of the blossoms of *Arnica montana* L. and *Tussilago farfara* usually associated with arnidenediol (*q.v.*). M.p. 236–7°. $[\alpha]_D$.

Di-Ac: m.p. 163–7°. $[\alpha]_D$ +54·5° ($CHCl_3$).

Zimmerman, *Helv. Chim. Acta*, 1943, **26**, 642; 1944, **27**, 332; 1946, **29**, 1455.

Fargan. *See* Promethazine.★

3-(1-Farnesyl)-4-hydroxycoumarin. *See* Ferulenol.

2-*trans-trans* Farnesyl-5-methylresorcinol. *See* Grifolin.

Favistan. *See* Methimazole.★

Fawcettidine

$C_{16}H_{23}ON$ MW 247

Present in *Lycopodium fawcettii*. Amorph. $[\alpha]_D$ 161° (c, 0·6 in EtOH). pK_a 6·2 (50% MeOH).

Methiodide: cryst. from MeOH–Me_2CO. M.p. 223–5°.

Burnell *et al.*, *Can. J. Chem.*, 1963, **41**, 3091.

Febrilix. *See* *p*-Acetamidophenol.

Fendleridine

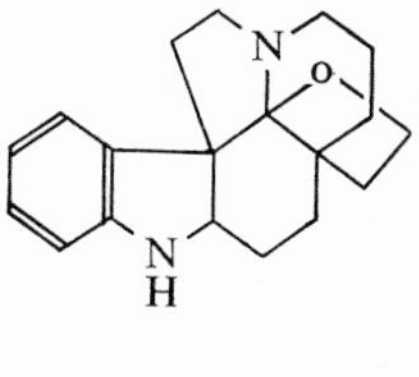

$C_{19}H_{24}ON_2$ MW 296

Minor constituent of seeds of *Aspidosperma fendleri* Woodson. M.p. 185–6°. Light absorption: $\lambda_{max.}$ 242·5° (ε, 7300) and 292·5 mμ (3050).

Burnell, Medina, Ayer, *Chemistry and Industry*, 1964, 33.

Fendlerine

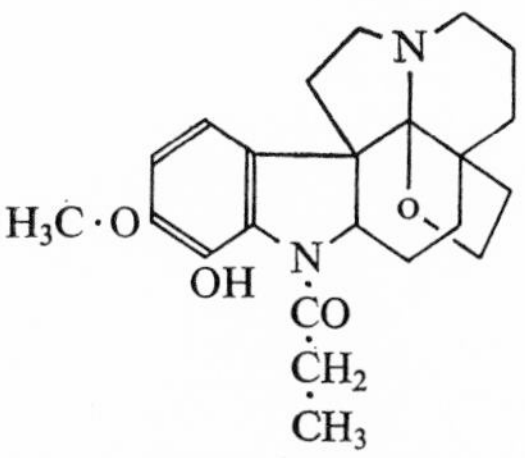

$C_{23}H_{30}O_4N_2$ MW 398

Alkaloid present in the fruit and bark of *Aspidosperma fendleri* Woodson. M.p. 179–81°. Light absorption: $\lambda_{max.}$ 225 (ε, 19,200), 258 mμ (3560).

Burnell, Medina, Ayer, *Chemistry and Industry*, 1964, 235.

Fenergan. *See* Promethazine.★

Fenidrone. *See* Oxyinchophen.★

Fentazin. *See* Perphenazine.★

Ferrichrysin

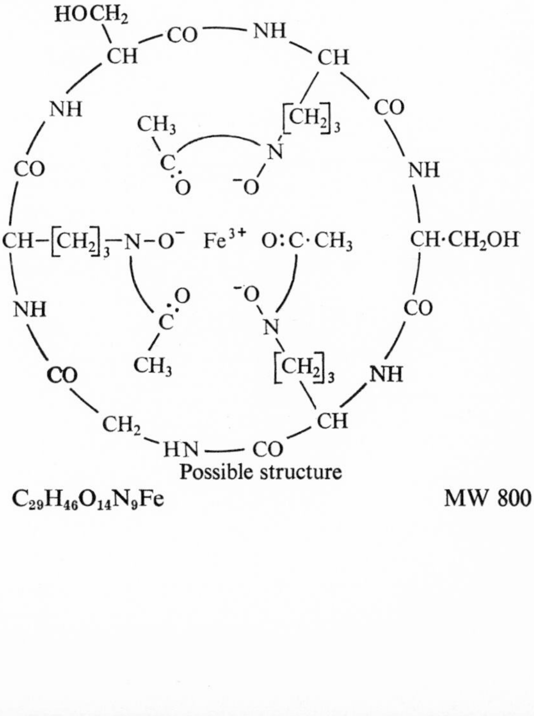

Possible structure

$C_{29}H_{46}O_{14}N_9Fe$ MW 800

Growth factor secreted by *Aspergillus* spp. Orange needles from EtOH. M.p. >260° decomp. Light absorption: $\lambda_{max.}$ 430 mμ (log ε, 3·48). HCl → glycine, ornithine, and serine.
Di-O-Ac: cryst. from EtOH–Et_2O. M.p. 223° decomp.

Keller-Schierlein, Deér, *Helv. Chim. Acta*, 1963, **46**, 1907.

Ferricrocin

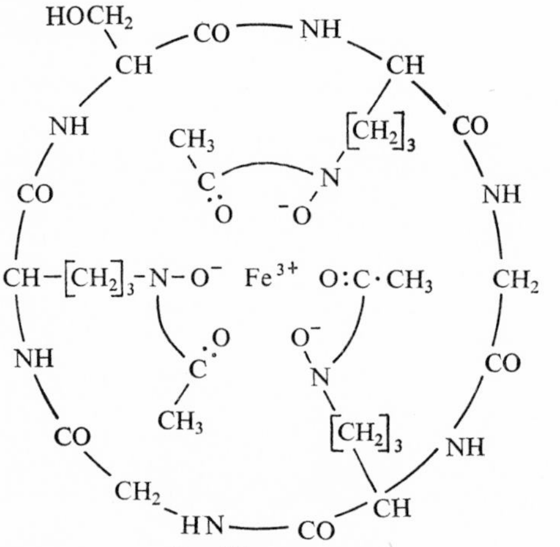

Possible structure

$C_{28}H_{44}O_{13}N_9Fe$ MW 770

Growth factor secreted by *Aspergillus* spp. Orange-brown cryst. from EtOH. M.p. >250° decomp. Light absorption: $\lambda_{max.}$ 430 mμ (log ε, 3·42).

Keller-Schierlein, *Helv. Chim. Acta*, 1963, **46**, 1907.

Ferrirhodin

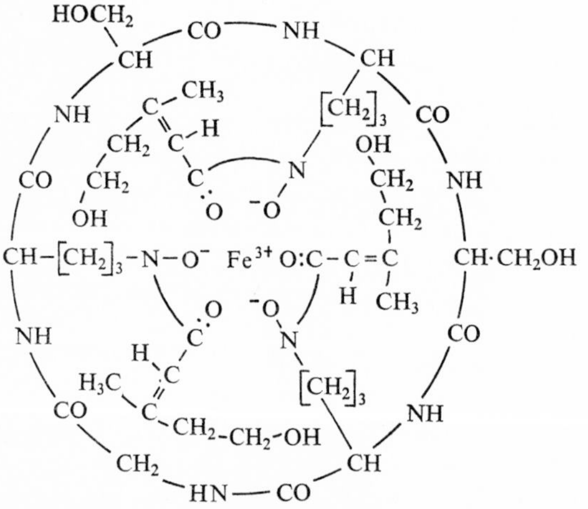

Possible structure

$C_{41}H_{64}O_{17}N_9Fe$ MW 1100

Growth factor produced by *Aspergillus* spp. Red-brown cryst. from MeOH–Et_2O. M.p. >270° decomp. Light absorption: $\lambda_{max.}$ 217 (log ε, 4·56), 252 (4·36), and 450 mμ (3·58).

Keller-Schierlein, *Helv. Chim. Acta*, 1963, **46**, 1920.

Ferrirubin

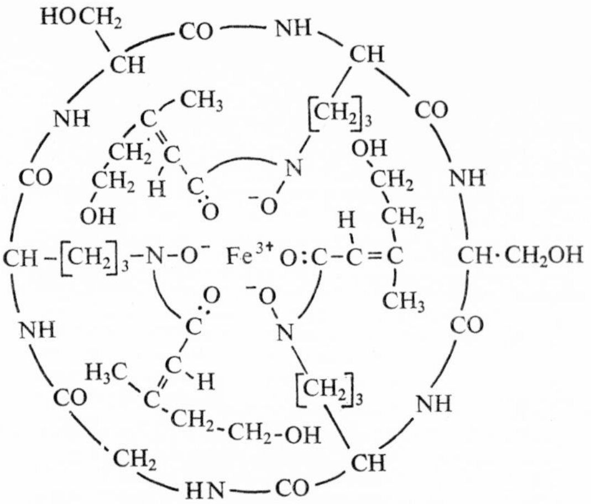

Possible structure

$C_{41}H_{64}O_{17}N_9Fe$ MW 1100

Growth factor produced by *Aspergillus* spp. Orange-red cryst. from MeOH. Light absorption: $\lambda_{max.}$ 216 (log ε, 4·58), 254 (4·34), and 450 mμ (3·53).

Keller-Schierlein, *Helv. Chim. Acta*, 1963, **46**, 1920.

Ferrocene.★

See also:

Wilkinson, *Organic Syntheses*, 1956, **36**, 31, 34; Coll. Vol. **4**, 473, 476.

Ferulenol (3-[1-*Farnesyl*)-4-*hydroxycoumarin*)

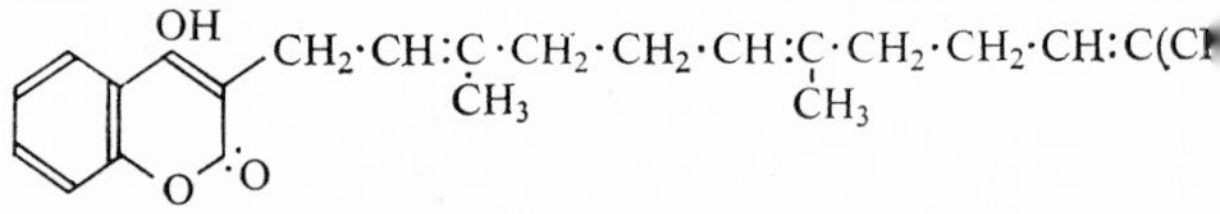

$C_{24}H_{30}O_3$ MW 366

Constituent of the latex of *Ferula communis* L. M.p. 64–5°

Carboni, Malaguzzi, Marsili, *Tetrahedron Letters*, 1964, 2783.

***o*-Ferulic Acid.** *See* 2-Hydroxy-3-methoxycinnamic Acid.

Filipin★ (14-*Deoxylagosin*)

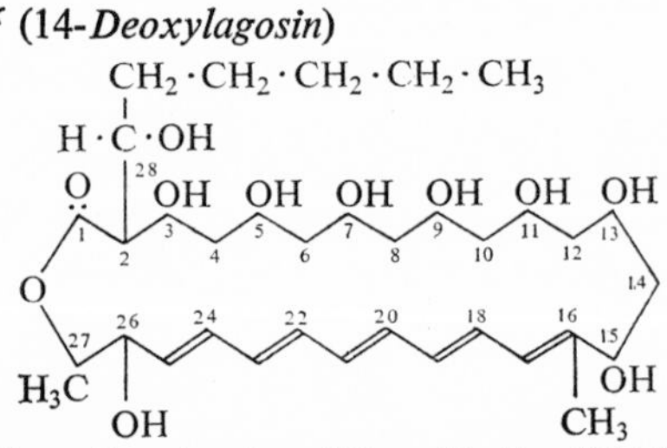

Alternative structure (Dhar, Thaller, Whiting)

$C_{35}H_{58}O_{11}$ MW 654

See also:

Cope *et al.*, *J. Am. Chem. Soc.*, 1962, **84**, 2170.
Dhar, Thaller, Whiting, *Proc. Chem. Soc.*, 1960, 310; *J. Chem. Soc.*, 1964, 842.
Ceder, Ryhage, *Acta Chem. Scand.*, 1964, **18**, 558.

Golding, Rickards, Barber, *Tetrahedron Letters*, 1964, 2615.

Flavaspidic Acid★

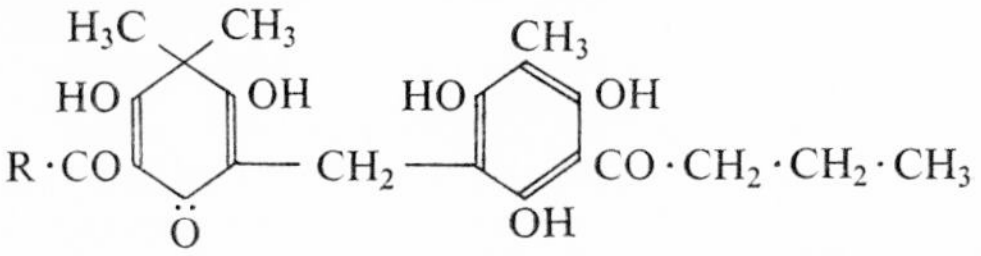

As well as the earlier known compound (R = CH_2·CH_2·CH_3), two further analogues have been found.

AB (R = CH_3)

$C_{22}H_{26}O_8$ MW 418

M.p. 210–12°.

PB (R = ·CH_2·CH_3)

$C_{23}H_{28}O_8$ MW 432

M.p. 170–1°.

Penttilä, Sundman, *Acta Chem. Scand.*, 1964, **18**, 344.

Flexin. *See* 2-Amino-5-chlorobenzoxazole.

Flexuosin A

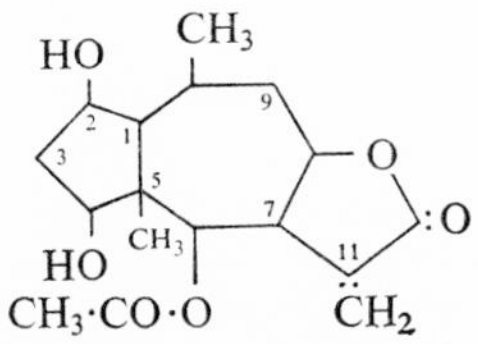

$C_{17}H_{24}O_6$ MW 336

Constituent of *Helenium flexuosum* Raf. M.p. 220–1·5°. $[\alpha]_D^{26}$ +12·4° (c, 4·93 in $CHCl_3$).

Mono-Ac: m.p. 158–60°.

Di-Ac: prisms from C_6H_6–$CHCl_3$. M.p. 129–30°. $[\alpha]_D^{24}$ −11·4° (c, 0·79 in $CHCl_3$).

Herz, Jayaraman, Watanabe, *J. Am. Chem. Soc.*, 1960, **82**, 2276.

Herz, Kishida, Lakshmikantham, *Tetrahedron*, 1964, **20**, 979.

Flexuosin B

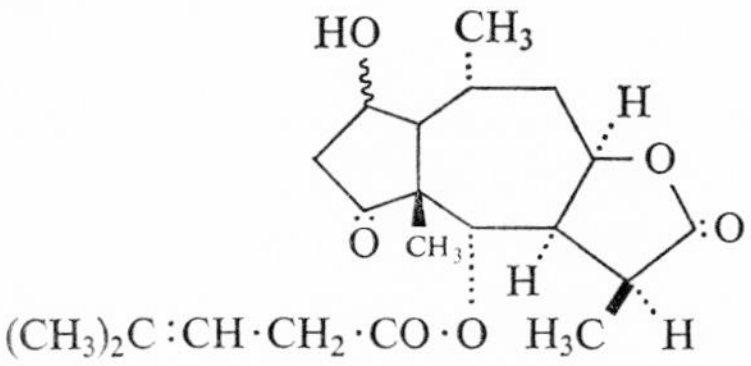

$C_{20}H_{28}O_6$ MW 364

Constituent of *Helenium flexuosum* Raf. Variable m.p. due to solvation. M.p. 132–7°, 107–10°, etc. H_2 → dihydro deriv., m.p. 85°. $[\alpha]_D^{24}$ +43·9° (c, 1·14 in $CHCl_3$).

Herz, Jayaraman, Watanabe, *J. Am. Chem. Soc.*, 1960, **82**, 2276.

Herz, Kishida, Lakshmikantham, *Tetrahedron*, 1964, **20**, 979.

Flindersiamine.★

Synthesis:

Govindachari, Prabhakar, *Indian J. Chem.*, 1963, **1**, 348.

***C*-Fluorocurine★**

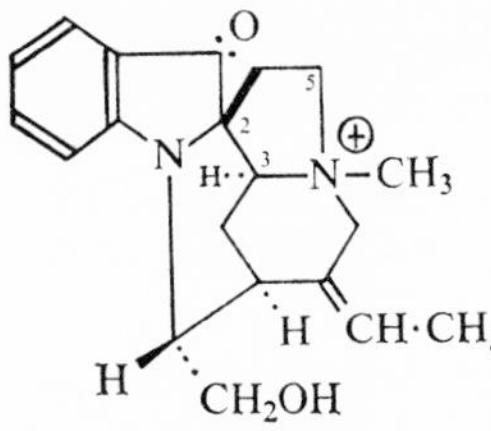

Light absorption: $\lambda_{max.}$ 235 (log ε, 4·51), 263 (3·76), 305 (2·77), and 423 mμ (3·54).

Structure:

Hesse *et al.*, *Helv. Chim. Acta*, 1964, **47**, 878.

16-Fluorohexadecanoic Acid (16-*Fluoropalmitic acid*)

F·CH_2·$[CH_2]_{14}$·COOH

$C_{16}H_{31}O_2F$ MW 288

Constituent of the seeds of *Dichapetalum toxicarium*. Cryst. from light petroleum. M.p. 71–3°.

Ward, Hall, Peters, *Nature*, 1964, **201**, 611.

1-Fluorohexane.★

B.p. 91–2°. n_D^{20} 1·375. n_D^{25} 1·372–1·373. D_4^{20} 0·8011.

Vogel, Leicester, Macey, *Organic Syntheses*, 1956, **36**, 40; Coll. Vol. **4**, 525.

16-Fluoropalmitic Acid. *See* 16-Fluorohexadecanoic Acid.

9α-Fluoro-11β : 16α : 17α : 21-tetrahydroxypregna-1 : 4-diene-3 : 20-dione *Adcortyl*, *Aristocort*, (9α-*Fluoro*-16α-*hydroxyprednisolone*, *Ledercort*, *Triamcinolone*)

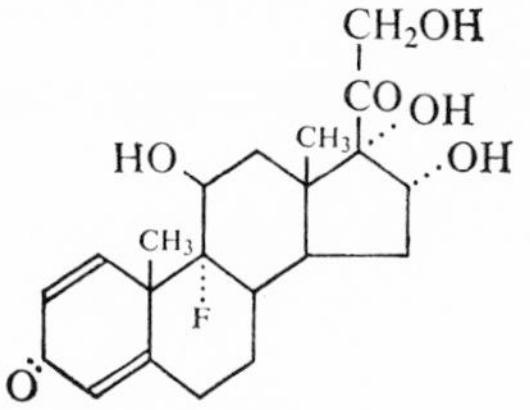

$C_{21}H_{27}O_6F$ MW 478

Used in cortisone therapy. Cryst. M.p. 269–71°. $[\alpha]_D^{25}$ +75° (Me_2CO). Light absorption: $\lambda_{max.}$ 238 mμ (ε, 15,800).

16 : 21-*Di-Ac*: solvated cryst. M.p. 186–8°. After drying. M.p. 235°. $[\alpha]_D$ +22° ($CHCl_3$).

16 : 17-*Acetonide*: cryst. M.p. 292–4°. $[\alpha]_D^{23}$ +109° ($CHCl_3$). 21-*Ac*: m.p. 266°. $[\alpha]_D^{23}$ +92° (c, 0·59 in $CHCl_3$).

Bernstein *et al.*, *J. Am. Chem. Soc.*, 1956, **78**, 5693; 1959, **81**, 1689.

Fried *et al.*, *J. Am. Chem. Soc.*, 1958, **80**, 2338.

Fluothane. *See* 2-Bromo-2-chloro-1 : 1 : 1-trifluoroethane.

Fomecin A★ (6-*Hydroxymethyl*-2 : 3 : 4-*trihydroxybenzaldehyde*)

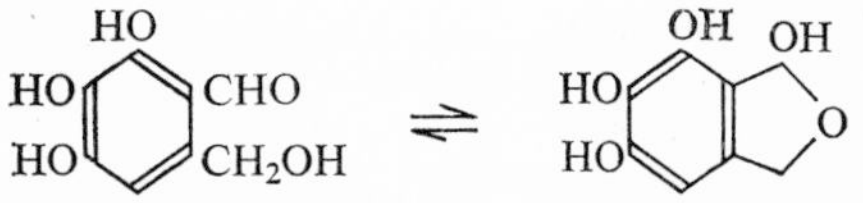

$C_8H_8O_5$ MW 184

Metabolite of *Fomes juniperinus* Schrenk. Cryst. from EtOH.Aq. Does not melt but decomp. above

160°. Light absorption: $\lambda_{max.}$ 241, 304 mμ (ε, 10,800 and 15,300).
2 : 4-*Dinitrophenylhydrazone*: cryst. from AcOEt. Decomp. without melting.
Anil: cryst. from EtOH. Decomp. without melting.
Tetra-Ac: cryst. from AcOEt–light petroleum.

McMorris, Anchel, *Can. J. Chem.*, 1964, **42**, 1595.

Fomecin B (3 : 4 : 5-*Trihydroxyphthalic aldehyde*)

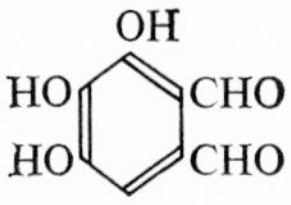

$C_8H_6O_5$ MW 182

Metabolite of *Fomes juniperinus* Schrenk. Yellow needles from AcOEt. M.p. 230° decomp. Light absorption: $\lambda_{max.}$ 263, 336 mμ (ε, 26,400 and 9200).

McMorris Anchel, *Can. J. Chem.*, 1964, **42**, 1595.

Formaldehyde.★

See also:

Walker, *Formaldehyde*, 3rd ed., Reinhold, New York, 1964, pp. 740.

Formo-onetin.★

Constituent of the heartwood of *Pterocarpus indicanus*. M.p. 265–6°.

Cooke, Rae, *Austral. J. Chem.*, 1964, **17**, 379.

Formyl chloride

H·COCl

CHOCl MW 64·5

Stable for 1 hr. at −60°.

Staab, Datta, *Angew. Chem.*, 1963, **75**, 1203; *Int. Ed.*, 1964, **3**, 132.

β-Formylcrotonic Acid (γ-*Oxoseneciosic acid*)

OHC(CH_3)·C⁚CH·COOH

$C_5H_6O_3$ MW 114

Trans-.
Me ester: $C_6H_8O_3$. MW 128. B.p. 56–7°/7 mm. n_D^{20} 1·4645. 2 : 4-*Dinitrophenylhydrazone*: m.p. 224–5°. *Semicarbazone*: m.p. 223° decomp.
Et ester: $C_7H_{80}O_3$. MW 142. B.p. 51–3°/4·5 mm. n_D^{20} 1·4597. 2 : 4-*Dinitrophenylhydrazone*: m.p. 200°. *Semicarbazone*: m.p. 208°.
Propyl ester: $C_8H_{12}O_3$. MW 156. B.p. 62·5–63°/4·7 mm. n_D^{20} 1·4600. 2 : 4-*Dinitrophenylhydrazone*: m.p. 193–193·7°. *Semicarbazone*: m.p. 193·5–194·5°.
Butyl ester: $C_9H_{14}O_3$. MW 180. B.p. 83–4°/6 mm. n_D^{20} 1·4589. 2 : 4-*Dinitrophenylhydrazone*: m.p. 166°. *Semicarbazone*: m.p. 178–9°.
3-*Methylbutyl ester*: $C_{10}H_{16}O_3$. MW 194. B.p. 82–4°/4·7 mm. n_D^{20} 1·4609. 2 : 4-*Dinitrophenylhydrazone*: m.p. 160°. *Semicarbazone*: m.p. 192–3°.
Cis-.
Cryst. from Et_2O–light petroleum. M.p. 45–6°. B.p. 110°/0·01 mm. Light absorption: $\lambda_{max.}$ 211 mμ (ε, 13,700). $C_6H_5NH_2$ → 4-anilino-3-methylbut-2-enolide, m.p. 149°.

Pommer, *Angew. Chem.*, 1960, **72**, 811.
Sisido *et al.*, *J. Am. Chem. Soc.*, 1960, **82**, 2286.
Conradie, Garbers, Steyn, *J. Chem. Soc.*, 1964, 594.

5-Formyl-4-phenanthroic Acid

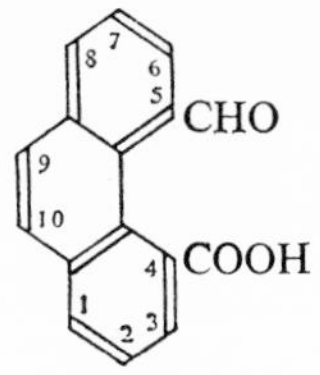

$C_{16}H_{10}O_3$ MW 250

M.p. 272–6°.

Vollmann *et al.*, *Ann.*, 1937, **531**, 65.
Dessy, Newman, *Organic Syntheses*, 1958, **38**, 32; Coll. Vol. **4**, 484.

2-Formyl-5-propynylthiophene. *See* Junipal.★

Fourneau 933. *See* Piperoxan.★

Fradiomycin. *See* Neomycin.★

Frangulin A

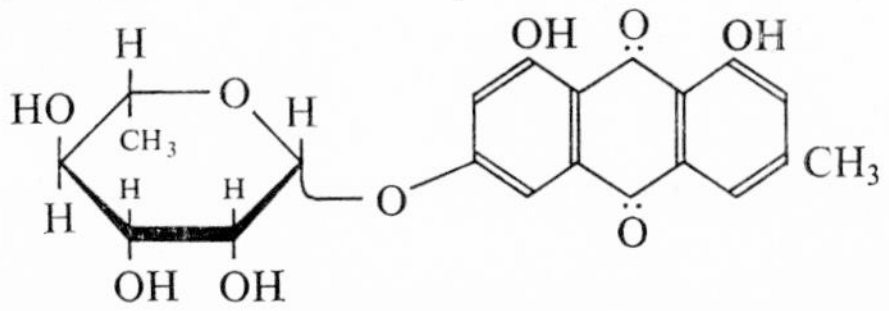

$C_{21}H_{20}O_9$ MW 416

Constituent of *Rhamnus frangula* L. M.p. 228°. Light absorption: $\lambda_{max.}$ 225 (log ε, 4·52), 264 (4·28), 282 (4·15), 300 (3·97), and 430 mμ (4·05).
Tetra-Ac: m.p. 191°. $[\alpha]_D^{20}$ −64·8° (c, 1·14 in MeOH).

Hörhammer, Bittner, Hörhammer, *Naturwiss.*, 1964, **51**, 310.

Frangulin B

$C_{21}H_{20}O_9$ MW 416

Constituent of *Rhamnus frangula* L. M.p. 196°. Light absorption as Frangulin A. Hydrol. → 3-hydroxy-1 : 8-dimethoxy-6-methylanthraquinone.
Penta-Ac: m.p. 169°. $[\alpha]_D$ −88·6° (c, 1·14 in MeOH).

Hörhammer, Bittner, Hörhammer, *Naturwiss.*, 1964, **51**, 310.

Fructose-1 : 6-diphosphate (*Harden–Young ester*)

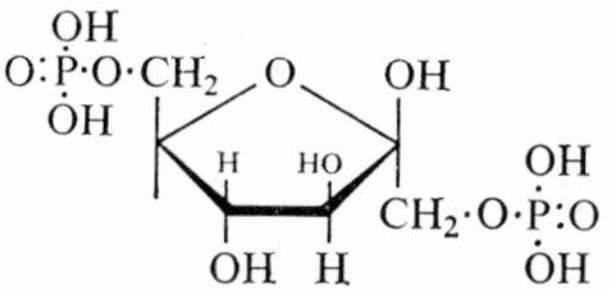

$C_6H_{14}O_{12}P_2$ MW 340

D-.
Important metabolic intermediate. $[\alpha]_D$ +4·1° (H_2O). pK_1' 1·48. pK_2' 6·29.

Harden, Young, *J. Chem. Soc.*, 1905, **21**, 189.
Young, *Biochem. J.*, 1911, **32**, 178.
Levene, Raymond, *J. Biol. Chem.*, 1928, **79**, 621.
Meyerhof, Suranyi, *Biochem. Z.*, 1936, **286**, 319.
Neuberg, Lustig, Rothenberg, *Arch. Biochem.*, 1944, **3**, 33.

Fructose-1-phosphate

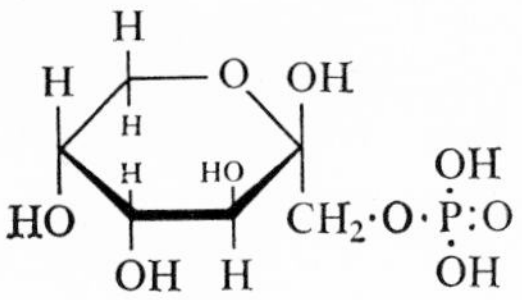

$C_6H_{13}O_9P$ MW 260

D-.
$[\alpha]_{546}^{20}$ −64·2° (H_2O).
Ba salt: $[\alpha]_{546}^{20}$ −39·6° (H_2O).
Brucine salt: $[\alpha]_{546}$ −52·1°.
Hydrazone: sinters at 96–7°. $[\alpha]_D$ −33·6° (Py : MeOH, 1 : 1).

Raymond, Levene, *J. Biol. Chem.*, 1929, **83**, 619.
Tanko, Robison, *Biochem. J.*, 1935, **29**, 961.

Fructose-2-phosphate.

D-. (Pyranose form).
Ba salt: $[\alpha]_D^{20}$ −83·3° (c, 0·36 in H_2O).
(Furanose form).
Ba salt: $[\alpha]_D^{20}$ −53·6° (c, 0·13 in H_2O).

Pontis, Fischer, *Biochem. J.*, 1963, **89**, 452.

Fructose-6-phosphate (*Neuberg ester*)

D-.
Important metabolic intermediate. pK_1' 0·97. pK_2' 6·11.
Ba salt: $[\alpha]_D$ +3·6°.

Neuberg, *Biochem. Z.*, 1918, **88**, 432.
Meyerhof, Lohmann, *Biochem. Z.*, 1927, **185**, 113.
Robison, *Biochem. J.*, 1932, **26**, 2191.
Neuberg, Lustig, Rothenberg, *Arch. Biochem.*, 1944, **3**, 33.

Frutescinol-lactone

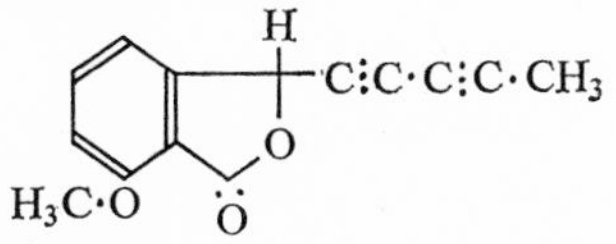

$C_{14}H_{10}O_3$ MW 226

Constituent of the root of *Chrysanthemum frutescens* L. Colourless cryst. from Et_2O-$CHCl_3$. M.p. 187–9·5°. Light absorption: $\lambda_{max.}$ 230 (ε, 7800), 291 (5300), and 297 mμ (5370).

Bohlmann, Kleine, *Chem. Ber.*, 1962, **95**, 602.
Bohlmann, Prezewowsky, *Chem. Ber.*, 1964, **97**, 1176.

Fulminene (*Benzo*[c]*picene*)

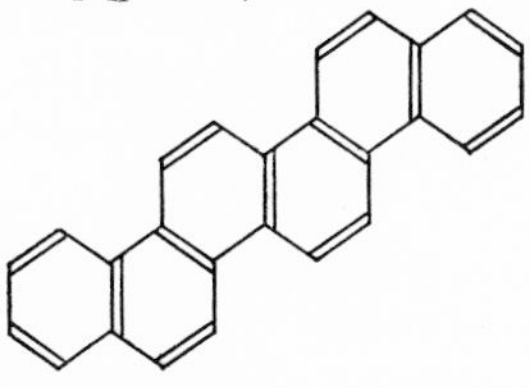

$C_{26}H_{16}$ MW 328

Constituent of coal tar. M.p. 466–7°. Light absorption: $\lambda_{max.}$ (log ε). α: 384 (3·03), 372 (2·90), 364 (3·12); *p*: 342 (4·30), 322 (4·30), 312 (4·60); β: 295 mμ (5·04) in trichlorobenzene.

Lang, Buffleb, Kalowy, *Chem. Ber.*, 1964, **97**, 494.

Fulvene

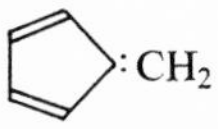

C_6H_6 MW 78

Yellow oil. B.p. 7–8°/56 mm. n_D^{20} 1·4920. Light absorption: $\lambda_{max.}$ 241 (log ε, 4·06) and 360 mμ (2·35).

Thiec, Wiemann, *Bull. soc. chim.*, 1956, 177; 1960, 1066.
Angus, McDonald Blair, Bryce-Smith, *J. Chem. Soc.*, 1960, 2003.
Meuche *et al.*, *Helv. Chim. Acta*, 1963, **47**, 1211.

Fumaric Acid.★

Di-nitrile:

Mowry, Butler, *Organic Syntheses*, 1950, **30**, 46; Coll. Vol. **4**, 486.

Fungichromin★ (*Lagosin*).

See also:

Dhar, Thaller, Whiting, *Proc. Chem. Soc.*, 1960, 310; *J. Chem. Soc.*, 1964, 842.
Golding, Rickards, Barber, *Tetrahedron Letters*, 1964, 2615.

Fungipavine (*Mecambrine*)

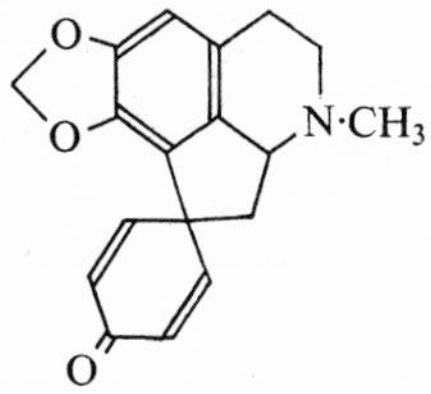

$C_{18}H_{17}O_3N$ MW 295

Alkaloid from *Papaver fugax*, *P. caucasicum* Marsch.-Bieb., and *Meconopsis cambrica*. Cryst. from Et_2O. M.p. 178·5–179·5°. $[\alpha]_D$ −116° ($CHCl_3$) (−94°).
B,HCl: m.p. 269–70°.
Picrate: m.p. 165°.
Oxime: m.p. >285°.
Semicarbazone: m.p. 237°.
2 : 4-*Dinitrophenylhydrazone*: needles. M.p. >285°.

Mnatsakanyan, Yunusov, *Doklady Akad. Nauk Uz. S.S.R.*, 1961, 36 (*Chem. Abstracts*, 1963, **58**, 1503).
Yunusov, Mnatsakanyan, Akramov, *Doklady Akad. Nauk Uz. S.S.R.*, 1961, 43 (*Chem. Abstracts*, 1963, **57**, 9900).
Slavik, Slavikova, *Coll. Czech. Chem. Commun.*, 1963, **28**, 1720.
Bick, *Experientia*, 1964, **20**, 362.
Kühn *et al.*, *Naturwiss.*, 1964, **51**, 556.

Funtuline (3β : 12β-*Dihydroxy*-5-*conanene*)

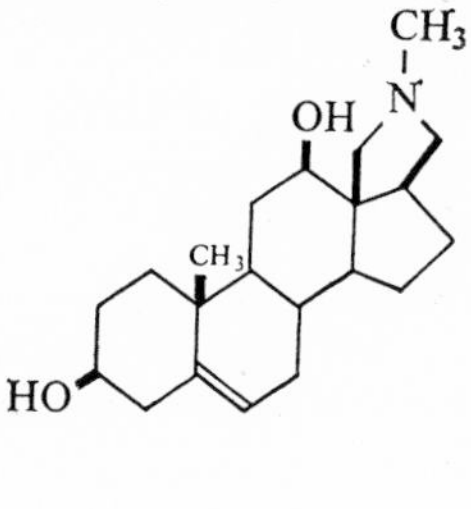

$C_{22}H_{35}O_2N$ MW 345

Constituent of *Funtumia latifolia* Stapf. Cryst. from MeOH–Et_2O. M.p. 235°. $[\alpha]_D$ −6° ($CHCl_3$: MeOH, 8 : 2).
Di-O-Ac: m.p. 237°. $[\alpha]_D$ −15° (c, 1 in $CHCl_3$).

Janot *et al.*, *Bull. soc. chim.*, 1964, 787.

Funtuphyllamine A (*20α-Amino-3β-hydroxy-5α-pregnane*)

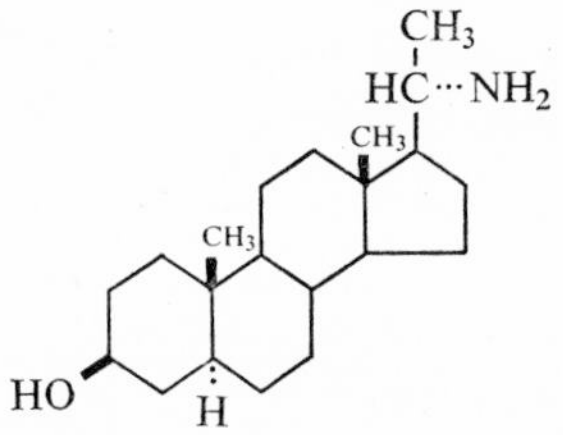

$C_{21}H_{37}ON$ MW 329
Alkaloid from *Funtumia africana.* M.p. 173°. $[\alpha]_D$ +13°.

Janot, Khoung-Huu, Goutarel, *Compt. rend.*, 1960, **250**, 2445.

Funtuphyllamine B (*3β-Hydroxy-20α-methylamino-5α-pregnane*)

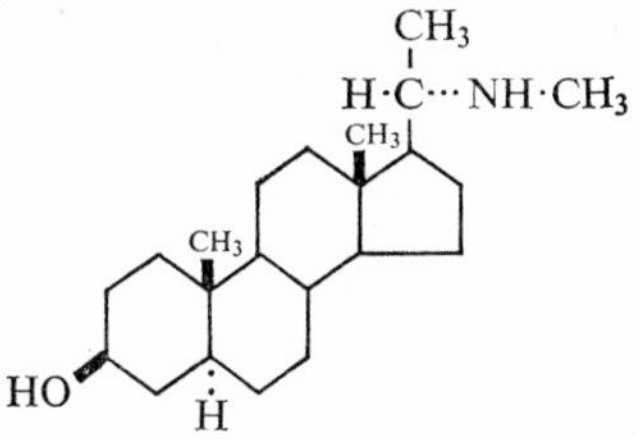

$C_{22}H_{39}ON$ MW 343
Alkaloid from *Funtumia africana* and *Malouetia bequaertiana.* M.p. 214°. $[\alpha]_D$ +24°.

Janot, Khoung-Huu, Goutarel, *Compt. rend.*, 1960, **250**, 2445.

Funtuphyllamine C (*3β-Hydroxy-20α-dimethylamino-5α-pregnane*)

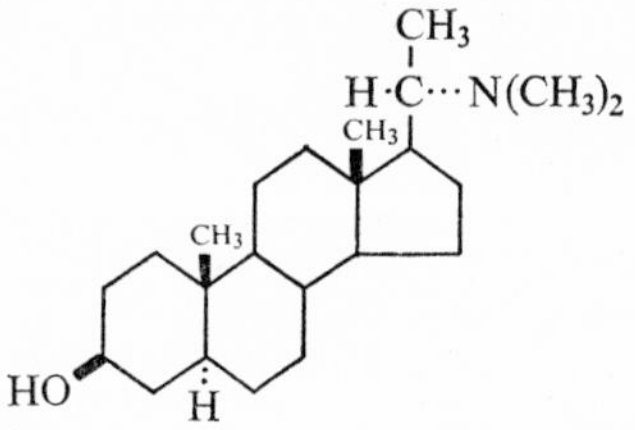

$C_{23}H_{41}ON$ MW 357
Alkaloid from *Funtumia africana.* M.p. 172°. $[\alpha]_D$ +24°.

Janot, Khoung-Huu, Goutarel, *Compt. rend.*, 1960, **250**, 2445.

Furadantin. *See* Nitrofurantoin.★

Furadonine. *See* Nitrofurantoin.★

Furan-2-carboxylic Acid.★
See also:

Harrisson, Moyle, *Organic Syntheses*, 1956, **36**, 36; Coll. Vol. **4**, 493.

3 : 4-Furandicarboxylic Acid.★
Cryst. structure:

Williams, Rundle, *J. Am. Chem. Soc.*, 1964, **86**, 1660.

2-Furanmethanethiol. *See* 2-Furfurylmercaptan.

Furfural.★
Di-acetal:

Bertz, *Organic Syntheses*, 1953, **33**, 39; Coll. Vol. **4**, 489.

2-Furfuryl Mercaptan (*2-Furanmethanethiol*)

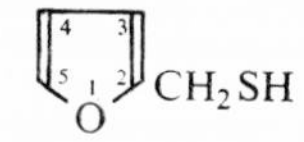

C_5H_6OS MW 114
Liq. with extremely disagreeable odour. B.p. 160°/759 mm., 84°/65 mm. n_D^{25} 1·5280. n_D^{20} 1·5330.

Kofod, *Acta Chem. Scand.*, 1953, **7**, 1302; *Organic Syntheses*, 1955, **35**, 66; Coll. Vol. **4**, 491.

***N*-(2-Furfuryl)pyrrole**

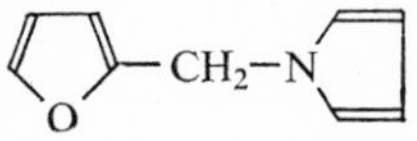

C_9H_9ON MW 147
Volatile constituent of coffee. B.p. 77–9°/1 mm. n_D^{21} 1·5317.

Reichstein, *Helv. Chim. Acta*, 1930, **13**, 349.
Gianturco, Friedel, Giammarino, *Tetrahedron*, 1964, **20**, 1763.

Furopelargone A (*Pelargone*)

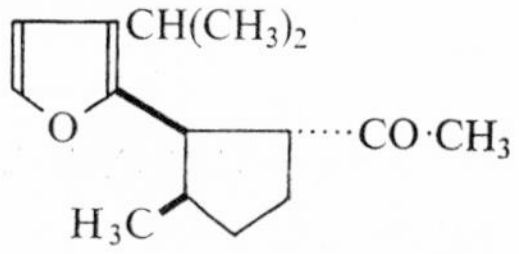

$C_{15}H_{22}O_2$ MW 234
Sesquiterpene ketone from the essential oil of *Geranium bourbon* (from *Pelargonium roseum*). B.p. 99°/2 mm., 60–2°/0·05 mm. D_4^{20} 0·986. n_D^{20} 1·4840. $[\alpha]_D^{20}$ −124·2° (neat). $[\alpha]_D^{26}$ −105° (c, 0·64 in $CHCl_3$).
Semicarbazone: cryst. from MeOH. M.p. 153–4°. $[\alpha]_D^{21}$ −170° (c, 2 in $CHCl_3$).
2 : 4-*Dinitrophenylhydrazone*: cryst. from MeOH. M.p. 101–2°. $[\alpha]_D^{20}$ −272·5° (c, 2 in $CHCl_3$).

Wolff, Nan Me Lukas, *Compt. rend.*, 1963, **252**, 1784.
Romaňuk *et al.*, *Coll. Czech. Chem. Commun.*, 1964, **29**, 1048.
Lukas *et al.*, *Tetrahedron*, 1964, **20**, 1789.

Furopelargone B

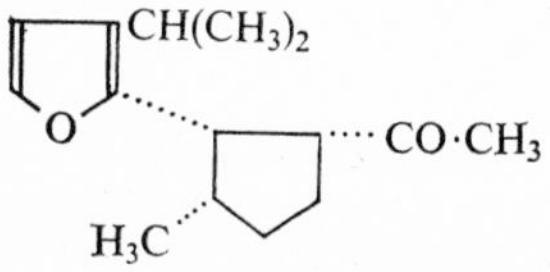

$C_{15}H_{22}O_2$ MW 234
Constituent of the essential oil of *Geranium bourbon* (from *Pelargonium roseum*). B.p. 81–3°/0·1 mm.

$[\alpha]_D^{24}$ +49° (c, 1·5 in dioxan). Light absorption: $\lambda_{max.}$ 219 mμ (ε, 8500).
Semicarbazone: m.p. 160–4°.

Lukas *et al.*, *Tetrahedron*, 1964, **20**, 1789.

β-3-Furylalanine

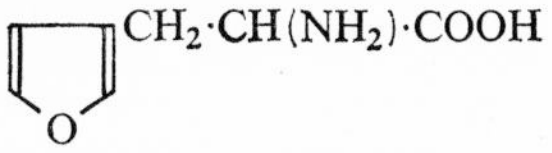

$C_7H_9O_3N$ MW 157

Antimetabolite. M.p. 255–7° decomp.
N-*Benzyloxycarbonyl*: $C_{15}H_{16}O_5N$. MW 290. M.p. 98–98·5°.

Lewis, Dunn, *Arch. Biochem. Biophys.*, 1964, **107**, 363.

Fusicoccin A

$C_{38}H_{58}O_{13}$ MW 722

Toxin produced by *Fusicoccum amygdalin* Del., causing wilting of almond tree (*Prunus amygdalus* St.). White cryst. M.p. 150–2°. $[\alpha]_D^{25}$ 73° (c, 0·6 in $CHCl_3$). H_2 → dihydro deriv. M.p. 151–3°. Hydrol. → glucose.

Ballio *et al.*, *Nature*, 1964, **203**, 297.

Fusidic Acid

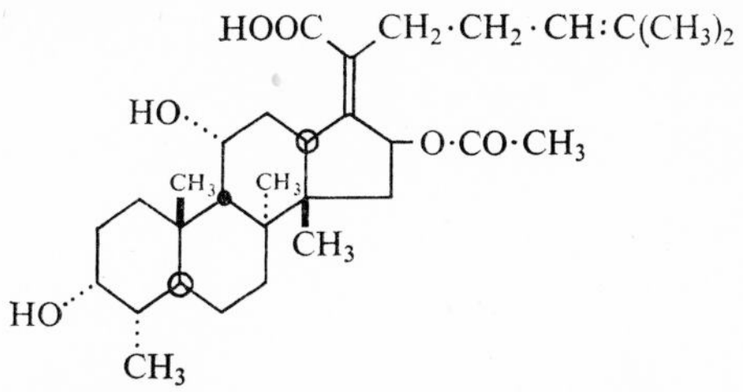

Stereochemistry:

Arigoni *et al.*, *Experientia*, 1964, **20**, 344.

See also:

Bucourt *et al.*, *Compt. rend.*, 1963, **257**, 2679.

G

6-*O*-β-D-Galactofuranosyl-D-galactose

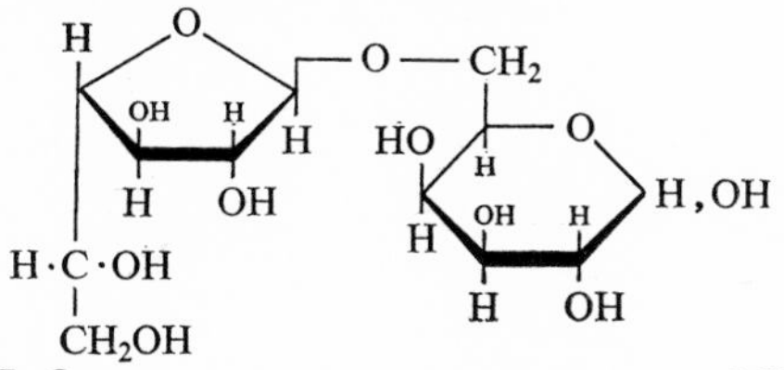

$C_{12}H_{22}O_{11}$ MW 332

Disaccharide isolated from a polysaccharide present in *Mycoplasma mycoides* var. *mycoides*. M.p. 171–4°. $[\alpha]_D^{24}$ −28·2° ± 1·3° (c, 4·5 in H_2O).

Plackett, Buttery, *Biochem. J.*, 1964, **90**, 201.

3-*O*-β-D-Galactofuranosyl-D-mannitol

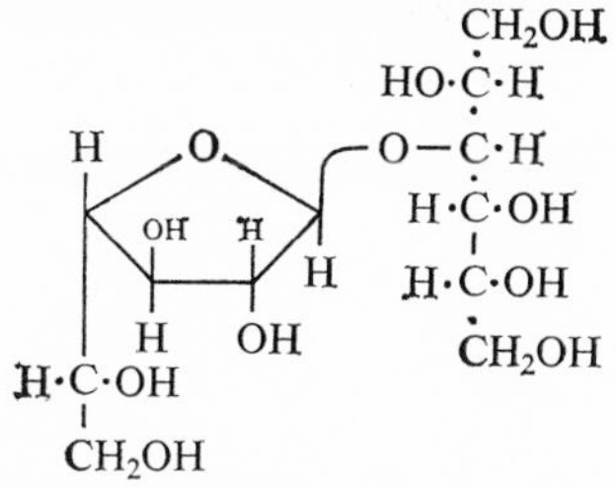

$C_{12}H_{22}O_{11}$ MW 342

Constituent of the lichen *Peltigera horizontalis* (Huds.) Baumg. Cryst. from 90% EtOH. M.p. 161–3°. $[\alpha]_D^{20}$ −61° (c, 2 in H_2O).

Pueyo, *Anneé Biol.*, 1960, **36**, 117.
Lindberg, Silvander, Wachtmeister, *Acta Chem. Scand.*, 1964, **18**, 213.

***O*-β-D-Galactopyranosyl-(1 → 4)-*O*-β-D-fructofuranose-(2 → 1)-α-D-glucopyranoside.** *See* Lactulosucrose.

α-D-Galactosamine-1-phosphate (*Chondrosamine 1-phosphate*)

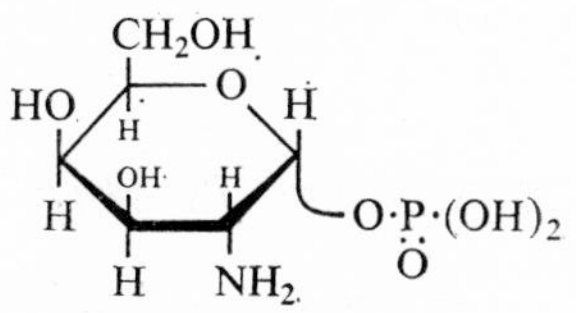

$C_6H_{14}O_8NP$ MW 259

Cryst. $[\alpha]_D^{25}$ 142·6° (c, 2 in H_2O).
N-*Ac*: $[\alpha]_D$ 112·4° (c, 2·9 in H_2O).

Carlson, Swanson, Roseman, *Biochemistry*, 1964, **3**, 402.

Galanthamine.★

B,CH₃:
Cryst. structure.

Williams, Rogers, *Proc. Chem. Soc.*, 1964, 357.

Galloflavin★

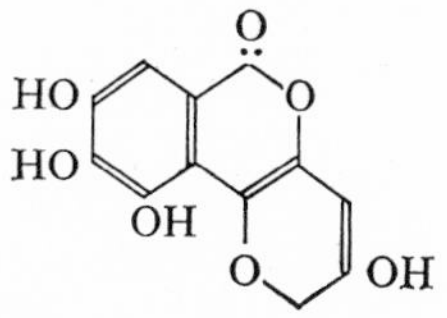

Revised structure:

Grimshaw, Haworth, Pindred, *J. Chem. Soc.*, 1955, 833.
Grimshaw, Haworth, *J. Chem. Soc.*, 1956, 418.

Garryine.★

(±)-.
Total synthesis:

Masamune, *J. Am. Chem. Soc.*, 1964, **86**, 290.
Nagato *et al.*, *J. Am. Chem. Soc.*, 1964, **86**, 929.
Valenta, Wiesner, Wong, *Tetrahedron Letters*, 1964, 2437.

Gastrin I

⌐Glu·Gly·Pro·Try·Met·Glu·Glu·Glu·Glu·Glu·Ala–
–Tyr·Gly·Try·Met·Asp·Phe·NH_2

⌐Glu = pyroglutamyl

Polypeptide hormone from antral region of hog stomach.

Gregory, Tracy, *Gut*, 1964, **5**, 103.
Gregory *et al.*, *Nature* (Lond.), 1964, **204**, 931.
Anderson *et al.*, *Nature* (Lond.), 1964, **204**, 933.

Gastrin II

SO_3H (on Tyr)

⌐Glu·Gly·Pro·Try·Met·Glu·Glu·Glu·Glu·Glu·Ala·Tyr–
–Gly·Try·Met·Asp·Phe·NH_2

Polypeptide hormone from antral region of hog stomach.

Gregory, Tracy, *Gut*, 1964, **5**, 103.
Gregory *et al.*, *Nature* (Lond.), 1964, **204**, 931.
Anderson *et al.*, *Nature* (Lond.), 1964, **204**, 933.

Gastron. *See* Methantheline.★

Gastrosedan. *See* Methantheline.★

Geijerene★

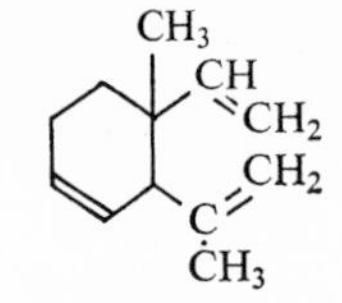

$C_{12}H_{18}$ MW 162

B.p. 75°/10 mm. 89°/20 mm., 131°/100 mm. n_D^{25} 1·4888.

2AgNO₃ adduct: m.p. 90–5° decomp.

Sutherland, *Chemistry and Industry*, 1959, 1220; *Austral. J. Chem.*, 1964, **17**, 75.
Birch *et al.*, *J. Chem. Soc.*, 1961, 2286.

Genipic Acid

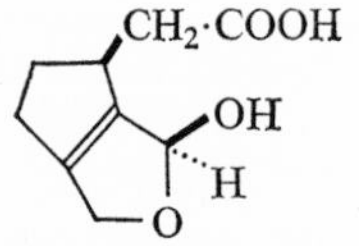

$C_9H_{12}O_4$ MW 184

Antibiotic from the jagua fruit (*Genipa americana* L.). Amorph. $[\alpha]_D^{27}$ −105° (c, 1 in EtOH). Light absorption: $\lambda_{max.}$ 203 mμ (ε, 2840).

NH_4 salt: m.p. 125–30° decomp.

Me ester: oil.

Tallent, *Tetrahedron*, 1964, **20**, 1781.

Genipinic Acid

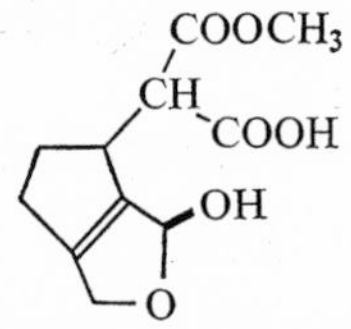

$C_{11}H_{14}O_6$ MW 242

Antibiotic from the jagua fruit (*Genipa americana* L.). Amorph. $[\alpha]_D$ −126° (c, 1 in EtOH). Light absorption: $\lambda_{max.}$ 203 mμ (ε, 3200).

Tallent, *Tetrahedron*, 1964, **20**, 1781.

Gentianine.★

Present in *Anthocleista rhizophoroides* BAK. The authors claim that, in contrast to the case with *A. procera*, the alkaloid is present in the plant and is not an artefact.

Pernet, Dupiol, Combes, *Bull. soc. chim.*, 1964, 281.

Gentisic Acid 2-β-D-glucopyranose

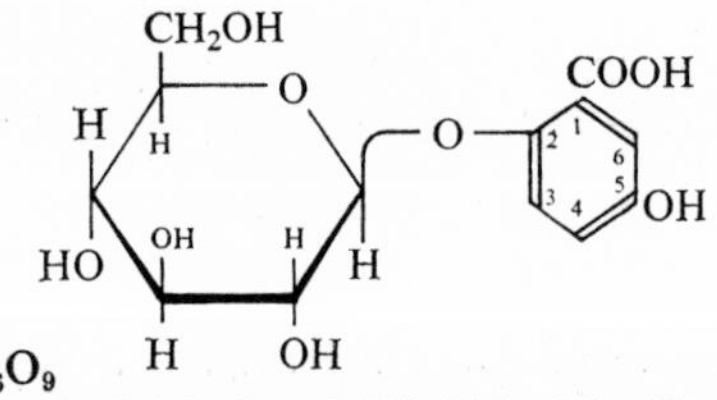

$C_{13}H_{16}O_9$ MW 316

Me ester: $C_{14}H_{18}O_9$. MW 330. Needles + H_2O. M.p. 178–80°. $[\alpha]_D$ −44° (c, 3·13 in MeOH). *Penta-Ac*: cryst. from MeOH. M.p. 135·5–136·5° (c, 5 in $CHCl_3$).

Wagner, *Arch. Pharm.*, 1958, **291**, 278.
Zane, Wender, *J. Org. Chem.*, 1964, **29**, 2078.

Gentisic Acid 5-β-D-glucopyranose.

Constituent of boron-deficient sunflower plants.

Me ester: needles from H_2O. M.p. 121–3°. $[\alpha]_D$ −25° (c, 4·1 in $CHCl_3$).

Wagner, *Arch. Pharm.*, 1958, **291**, 278.
Watanabe *et al.*, *Phytochemistry*, 1964, **3**, 391.
Zane, Wender, *J. Org. Chem.*, 1964, **29**, 2078; *Chemistry and Industry*, 1964, 1835.

Gestafortin. *See* Chloromadinone acetate.

Gewazol. *See* Metrazole.★

Ginkgetin.★

Baker *et al.* (*J. Chem. Soc.*, 1963, 1477) reports Ginkgetin has m.p. 350° decomp.

Tetra-Ac: pale yellow thick rhombic plates. M.p. 265·5–266·5°.

Tetra-Me ether, *1·5H₂O*: cryst. from EtOH.Aq. M.p. 227–8°. Cryst. from C_6H_6 as solvate, m.p. 209° (with effervescence).

Synthesis:

Nakazawa, Ito, *Chem. Pharm. Bull.* (Tokyo), 1963, **11**, 283.

Erratum p. 1511

Gitosin.★

Formula should read:

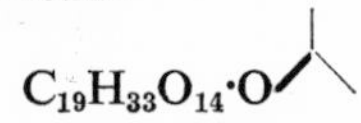

Glaucanol

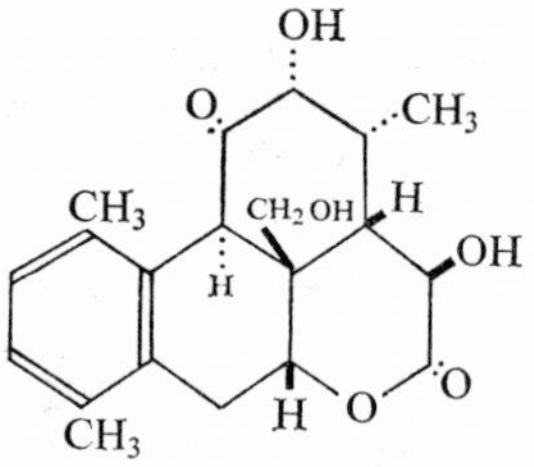

$C_{20}H_{24}O_6$ MW 360

Acid degradation product of Glaucarubol. Cryst. from Me_2CO. M.p. 228–34°. $[\alpha]_D$ +144° (c, 0·72 in MeOH).

Tri-Ac: cryst. from Et_2O. M.p. 215–20°. $[\alpha]_D$ 180° (c, 0·5 in MeOH).

Tetra-Ac: m.p. 207–9°. $[\alpha]_D$ +211° (c, 0·6 in Py).

Ham *et al.*, *J. Am. Chem. Soc.*, 1954, **76**, 6066.
Polonsky, Fouquey, Gaudemer, *Bull. soc. chim.*, 1961, 1432; 1962, 1255; 1963, 169.
Zylber, Polonsky, Mitra, *Bull. soc. chim.*, 1963, 1322.
Polonsky *et al.*, *Bull. soc. chim.*, 1964, 1818.

Glaucarubin★

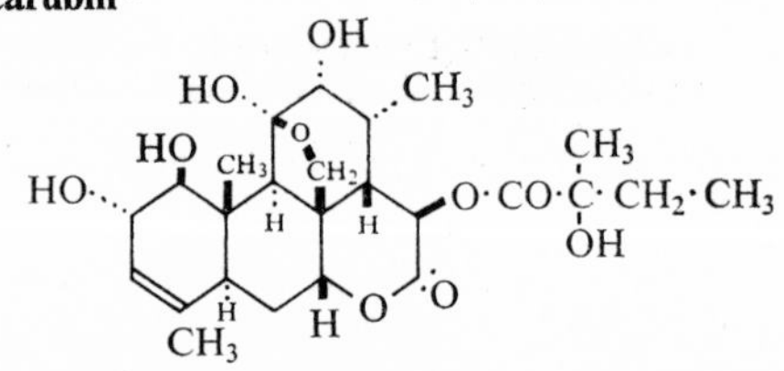

Also present in Kirondro (*Perriera madagascariensis* Courchet).

Polonsky *et al.*, *Bull. soc. chim.*, 1964, 1818, 1827.
Bourguignon, Polonsky, *Bull. soc. chim. biol.*, 1964, **46**, 1145.

Cryst. structure:

Kartha *et al.*, *Nature*, 1964, **202**, 389.
Kartha, Haas, *J. Am. Chem. Soc.*, 1964, **86**, 3630.

Glaucarubinone (*α-Kirondrine*)

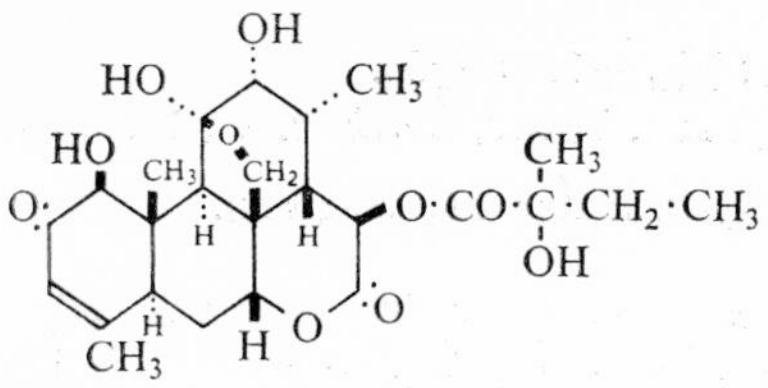

$C_{25}H_{34}O_{10}$ MW 494

Constituent of Kirondro (*Perriera madagascariensis* Courchet) and *Simaruba glauca*. Cryst. from Me_2CO. M.p. 225–8°. $[\alpha]_D$ +50° (c, 0·34 in MeOH).

Tetra-Ac: cryst. from Et_2O. M.p. 190–3°.

Bourguigon, Polonsky, *Bull. soc. chim. biol.*, 1964, **47**, 1145.

Glaucarubol★

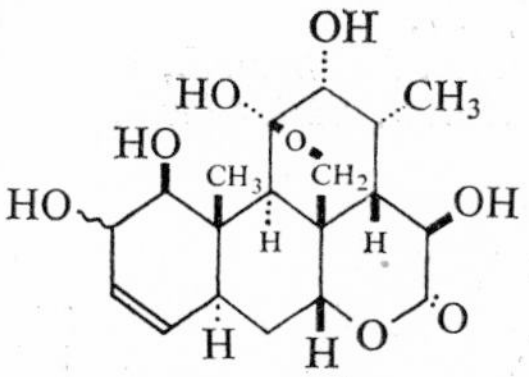

Tetra-O-Me: $C_{24}H_{36}O_8$. MW 452. Cryst. from Et_2O. M.p. 252–4°. $[\alpha]_D$ +93·5° (c, 0·6 in MeOH).

Structure:

Polonsky *et al.*, *Bull. soc. chim.*, 1964, 1827.

Glaucophanic Acid

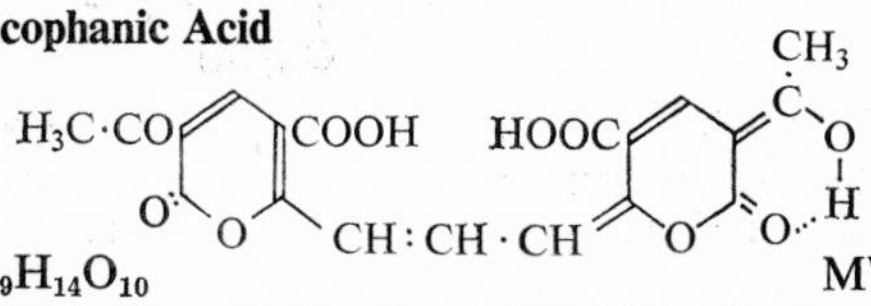

$C_{19}H_{14}O_{10}$ MW 402

Di-Me ester: $C_{21}H_{18}O_{10}$. MW 430. Dark needles. M.p. 206°.

Di-Et ester: $C_{23}H_{22}O_{10}$. MW 458. Black needles from C_6H_6. M.p. 188–9°. Light absorption: $\lambda_{max.}$ 242 (ε, 7900), 260 (6850), 290 (4400), 330 (5200), 385 (7350), 425 (6500), 515 (8400), and 672 mμ (133,500).

Claisen, *Ann.*, 1897, **297**, 1.

Crombie, Games, Knight, *Tetrahedron Letters*, 1964, 2313.

Glaziovine

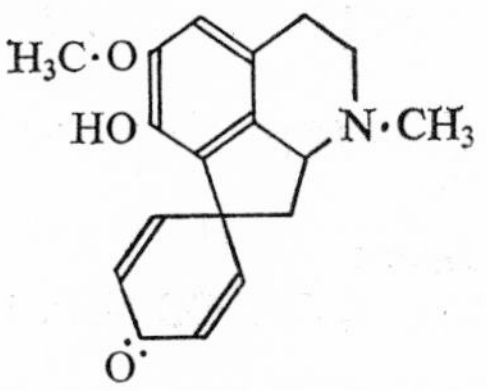

$C_{18}H_{19}O_3N$ MW 297

Alkaloid from the leaves of *Ocotea glaziovii*. Colourless needles. M.p. 235–7° decomp. $[\alpha]_D$ 7° (c, 1 in $CHCl_3$).

Picrate: cryst. from EtOH. M.p. 199–203°.

Gilbert *et al.*, *J. Am. Chem. Soc.*, 1964, **86**, 694.

Haynes *et al.*, *Proc. Chem. Soc.*, 1964, 261.

Gliotoxin.★

Shows antiviral activity.

Rightsel *et al.*, *Nature* (Lond.), 1964, **204**, 1333.

Globulol★

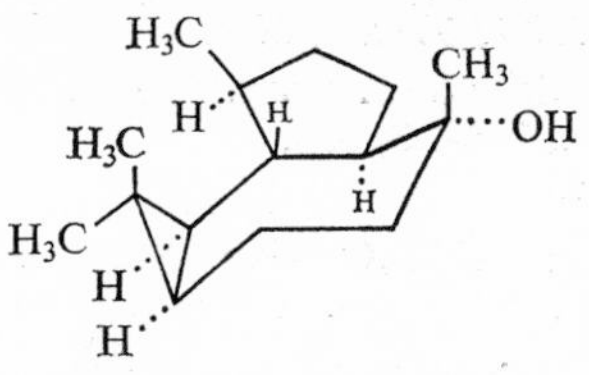

Revised structure and stereochemistry:

Büchi *et al.*, *Tetrahedron Letters*, 1959, No. 6, 14.

Glucojcaputin.★

Also present in *Dentaria pinnata* Lmk.

See also under: 2-Methylbutyl isothiocyanate.★

Delaveau, Kjaer, *Acta Chem. Scand.*, 1963, **17**, 2562.

Glucophage. *See under* Metformin.★

Glucoputranjivin.★

Present in *Dentaria pinnata* Lmk.

Delaveau, Kjaer, *Acta Chem. Scand.*, 1963, **17**, 2562.

***O*-α-D-Glucopyranosyl-(1 → 4)-2-amino-2-deoxy-α-D-glucopyranose** (*Maltosamine*)

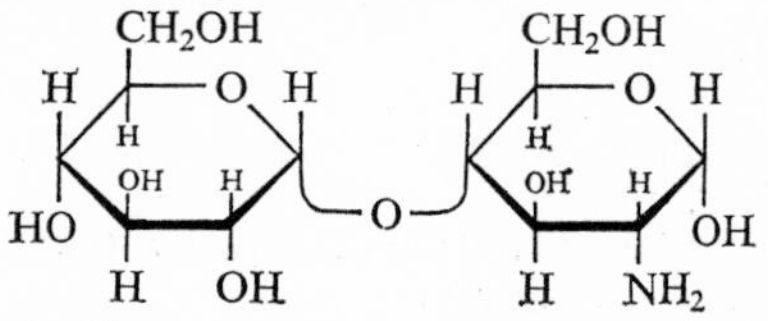

$C_{12}H_{23}O_{10}N$ MW 341

Produced by hyd. of "carboxyl-reduced" heparin.

B,HCl: cryst. M.p. 183–7° decomp. $[\alpha]_D^{20}$ 81° (c, 0·5 in H_2O).

Wolfrom, Vercellotti, Horton, *J. Org. Chem.*, 1962, **27**, 705; 1963, **28**, 278.

Wolfrom, El Khadem, Vercellotti, *Chemistry and Industry*, 1964, 545.

8-*C*-β-D-Glucopyranosylapigenin. *See* Vitexin.★

6-*C*-β-D-Glucopyranosylapigenin. *See* Isovitexin.★

3-*O*-β-D-Glucopyranosyl-D-galactopyranose. *See* Solabiose.

2β-D-Glucopyranosyl-5-hydroxybenzoic Acid Benzyl ester. *See* Trichocarpin.

6-*C*-β-D-Glucopyranosyl-luteolin. *See* Homo-orientin.

8-*C*-β-D-Glucopyranosyl-luteolin. *See* Orientin.★

9-β-D-Glucopyranosyltheophylline

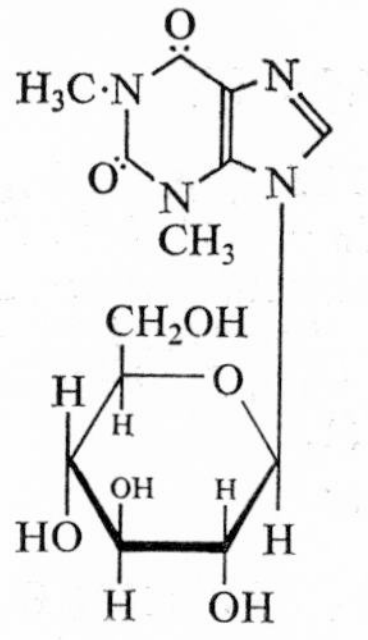

$C_{13}H_{18}O_7N_4$ MW 342

M.p. 218–20°. $[\alpha]_{578}^{25}$ −42° (H_2O). Light absorption: $\lambda_{max.}$ 238 (3·97) and 266 mμ (3·96).

Bühler, Pfleiderer, *Angew. Chem.*, 1964, **76**, 713; *Int. Ed.*, 1964, **3**, 638.

Glucosamine.★

1-*Phosphate*: $C_6H_{14}O_8NP$. MW 259. N-*Ac*: $C_8H_{16}O_9NP$. MW 300. α-*Form*: dipotassium salt. $C_8H_{14}O_9NK_2P$. MW 376. $+H_2O$. Fine needles. $[\alpha]_D^{25}$ 76·1° (c, 3·44 in H_2O). β-*Form*: disodium salt. $C_8H_{14}O_9NNa_2P$. MW 344. Cryst. $[\alpha]_D^{25}$ −1·7° (c, 2·93 in H_2O). *Penta-Ac*: α-*Form*: cryst. from $CHCl_3$–Et_2O. M.p. 132·5–133·5°. $[\alpha]_D^{25}$ 91° (c, 1·48 in $CHCl_3$).

O'Brien, *Biochim. Biophys. Acta*, 1964, **86**, 628.

N-*Ac*.
Cryst. structure:

Johnson, Phillips, *Nature*, 1964, **202**, 588.

Glucose-1-phosphate (*Cori ester*)

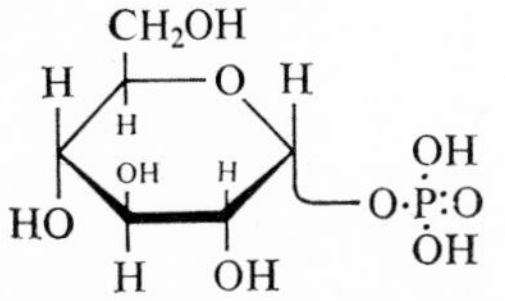

$C_6H_{13}O_9P$ MW 260

α-D-.
Important metabolic intermediate. $[\alpha]_D$ 120° (H_2O). pK_1' 1·10. pK_2' 6·13.
Di-K salt: $[\alpha]_D$ 78·5° (H_2O). $[\alpha]_{546}$ 90° (H_2O).
Ba salt: $[\alpha]_D$ 75° (H_2O).
Brucine salt: $[\alpha]_D$ +0·5° (H_2O).
β-D-.
Brucine salt: $[\alpha]_D$ −20° (H_2O).
α-L-.
Di-K salt: $[\alpha]_D$ −78·2° (H_2O).
Ba salt: $[\alpha]_D$ −73·2° (H_2O).

Cori, Colowick, Cori, *J. Biol. Chem.*, 1937, **121**, 465.
Wolfrom, Pletcher, *J. Am. Chem. Soc.*, 1941, **63**, 1050.
Potter *et al.*, *J. Am. Chem. Soc.*, 1948, **70**, 1751.
Leloir, *Fortschritte der Chemie organisher Naturstoffe*, 1951, **8**, 47.

Glucose-2-phosphate.

D-.
$[\alpha]_D$ +35° (0·1*N*-H_2SO_4).
Di-K salt: $[\alpha]_D$ +15° (H_2O).

Farrar, *J. Chem. Soc.*, 1949, 3131.

Glucose-3-phosphate.

D-.
$[\alpha]_D$ +39·5° (H_2O). $[\alpha]_{546}$ +39° (H_2O). pK_1' 0·84. pK_2' 5·67.
Ba salt: $[\alpha]_D$ +26·5° (H_2O). $[\alpha]_{546}$ +27° (H_2O).
Brucine salt: $[\alpha]_D$ −14·5° (50% Py.Aq.).

Meyerhof, Lohman, *Biochem. Z.*, 1927, **185**, 113.
Josephson, Proffe, *Ann.*, 1930, **481**, 91.
Levene, Raymond, *J. Biol. Chem.*, 1930, **89**, 479; 1931, **91**, 751.

Glucose-4-phosphate.

D-.
Brucine salt: $[\alpha]_D$ −9·8° (20% EtOH), −45·3° (Py).

Raymond, *J. Biol. Chem.*, 1936, **113**, 375.

Glucose-5-phosphate.

D-.
Ba salt: $[\alpha]_D$ +15° (H_2O).

Josephson, Potter, *Biochem. Z.*, 1933, **258**, 147.

Glucose-6-phosphate (*Robison ester*).

D-.
Important metabolic intermediate. $[\alpha]_D$ +35·1° (H_2O). $[\alpha]_{546}$ +41·4° (H_2O). pK_1' 0·94. pK_2' 6·11.
Di-K salt: $[\alpha]_D$ +21·2° (H_2O).
Ba salt: $[\alpha]_D$ +18° (H_2O). $[\alpha]_{546}$ +21·2° (H_2O).

Harden, Robison, *Proc. Chem. Soc.*, 1914, **30**, 16.
Meyerhof, Lohmann, *Biochem. Z.*, 1927, **185**, 113.
Robison, King, *Biochem. J.*, 1931, **25**, 323.
Levene, Raymond, *J. Biol. Chem.*, 1931, **91**, 751; 1931, **92**, 757.
Robison, King, *Biochem. J.*, 1931, **25**, 323.
Lardy, Fischer, *J. Biol. Chem.*, 1946, **164**, 513.

Glucosisaustricin

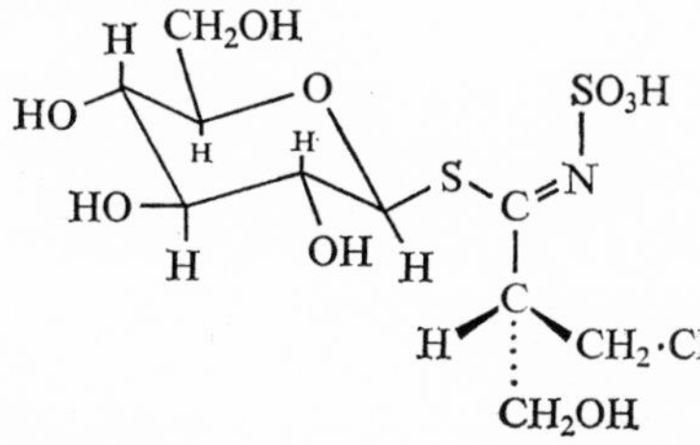

$C_{11}H_{22}O_9NS_2$ MW 376

Mustard oil precursor in the seeds of *Sisymbrium austriacum* Jacq. Hyd. → (+)-4-ethyloxazolidine-2-thione.

Kjaer, Christensen, *Acta Chem. Scand.*, 1962, **16**, 71.

Erratum p. 1530

Glutamic Acid.★

N-*Carbamoyl*: this is not ureidosuccinic acid, but ureidoglutaric acid. The m.p. should be 150° (sealed capillary).

Glutamic Acid.★

Anhydride: $C_5H_7O_3N$. MW 129. Not isolated in free state. *B,HCl*: m.p. 111° decomp. *B,HBr*: m.p. 132° decomp.

Kollonitsch, Rosegay, *Chemistry and Industry*, 1964, 1867.

γ-L-Glutamyl-L-alanine

$HOOC·CH(NH_2)·CH_2·CH_2·CO·NH·CH(CH_3)·COOH$

$C_8H_{14}O_5N$ MW 218

Present in iris leaf tissue. M.p. 194–5° decomp. $[\alpha]_D$ −28° (c, 2 in H_2O).

Morris, Thompson, Asen, *J. Biol. Chem.*, 1964, **239**, 1833.

γ-L-Glutamyl-N^{α}-amino-β-(2-methylenecyclopropyl)propionic Acid. *See* Hypoglycin B.

γ-Glutamyl-β-cyano-L-alanine.★

See also:

Tschiersch, *Tetrahedron Letters*, 1964, 747.

Biosynthesis:

Nigam, Ressler, *Biochim. Biophys. Acta*, 1964, **93**, 339.

γ-L-Glutamyl-L-cysteinyl-β-alanine (*Homoglutathione*)

OC·CH$_2$·CH$_2$·CH(NH$_2$)·COOH
|
NH
|
HS·CH$_2$·CH·CO·NH·CH$_2$·CH$_2$COOH

$C_{11}H_{19}O_6N_3S$ MW 321

Peptide present in the seeds of the mung bean (*Phaseolus aureus* Roxb.). Not obtained cryst. $[\alpha]_D^{20}$ −16·4° (c, 1·3 in H_2O) (preparation not pure). Ox. → bis-γ-L-glutamyl-L-cystinyl-bis-β-alanine (*q.v.*).

Carnegie, *Biochem. J.*, 1963, **89**, 459, 471.

α-L-Glutamyl-L-glutamic Acid

HOOC·CH$_2$·CH$_2$·CH(NH$_2$)
|
CO·NH·CH·CH$_2$·CH$_2$·COOH
|
COOH

$C_{10}H_{16}O_7N$ MW 276

M.p. 186·5–187°. $[\alpha]_D^{11}$ 19·9° (c, 1·81 in *N*-HCl).

Shiba, Imai, *J. Chem. Soc. Japan, Pure Chem. Sect.*, 1959, **80**, 497 (*Chem. Abstracts*, 1961, **55**, 8305).

γ-L-Glutamyl-L-glutamic Acid

HOOC·CH(NH$_2$)
|
CH$_2$·CH$_2$·CO·NH·CH·CH$_2$·CH$_2$·COOH (γ′)
|
COOH

$C_{10}H_{16}O_7N$ MW 276

Peptide detected in bovine brains. Colourless needles from H_2O. M.p. 191–2°. $[\alpha]_D^{16}$ +6·6° (c, 1 in 1*N*-HCl).

γ′-Amide: γ-L-glutamyl-L-glutamine. $C_{10}H_{17}O_6N_3$. MW 275. Cryst. from EtOH.Aq. M.p. 191–2°. $[\alpha]_D^{16}$ +11° (c, 1 in 1*N*-HCl).

Shiba, Imai, *J. Chem. Soc. Japan, Pure Chem. Sect.*, 1959, **80**, 497 (*Chem. Abstracts*, 1961, **55**, 8305).

Burkhart, Mitchell, *Arch. Biochem. Biophys.*, 1961, **94**, 32.

Kakimoto *et al.*, *Biochim. Biophys. Acta*, 1964, **93**, 333.

γ-L-Glutamyl-*S*-methyl-L-cysteine.★

Present in kidney beans (*Phaseolus vulgaris* L.), lima beans (*P. limensic Macted*), pinto, and black-eyed beans (*Vigna sinensis*). M.p. 107–9°.

Rinderknecht, Thomas, Aslin, *Helv. Chim. Acta*, 1958, **41**, 1.

Zacharius, Thompson, Morris, *Arch. Biochem. Biophys.*, 1958, **73**, 281; 1959, **80**, 199.

Obata, Kitasawa, *Agric. Biol. Chem.* (Japan), 1964, **28**, 624.

5β-Glutinan-3α-ol. *See* Tetrahymanol.★

Glyceric Acid.★

DL-.

3-*Phosphoryl* [1-^{14}C]:

Koorajian, Rafelson, *Biochim. Biophys. Acta*, 1964, **90**, 399.

L-α-Glycerylphosphoryl-2-amino-2-methylpropanol

HO·CH$_2$·CH(OH)·CH$_2$·O·P(=O)(O$^{\ominus}$)·O·CH$_2$·C(CH$_3$)$_2$·NH$_3^{\oplus}$

$C_7H_{18}O_6NP$ MW 243

Fine white solid. M.p. 172–4° (with light sintering at 169°). $[\alpha]_D^{28}$ −2° (c, 6 in H_2O).

Baer, Rao, *Can. J. Biochem.*, 1964, **42**, 1547.

Glycodine. *See* 3-(2-Morpholinoethyl)morphine.

***N*-Glycollyl-8-*O*-methylneuraminic Acid**

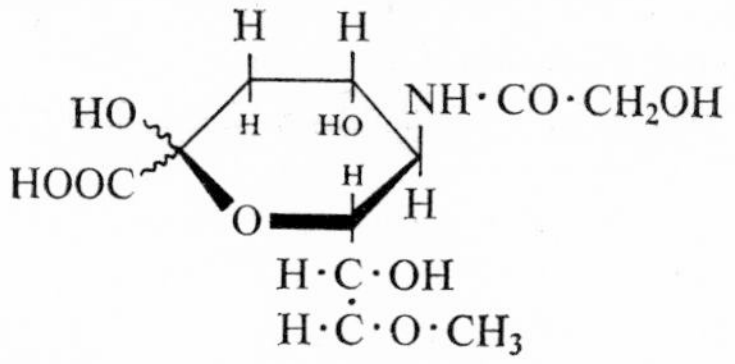

$C_{12}H_{21}O_{10}N$ MW 339

Sialic acid from the starfish *Asterias forbesi*. Amorph.

Warren, *Biochim. Biophys. Acta*, 1964, **83**, 129.

Glyoxal.★

Mono-Et hemiacetal: $C_4H_8O_3$. MW 104. B.p. 53–4°/9 mm. n_D^{25} 1·4230.

Zief, Schramm, *Chemistry and Industry*, 1964, 234.

Glyoxylic Acid.★

n-*Butyl ester*: $C_6H_{10}O_3$. MW 130. B.p. 68–74°/20 mm. D_4^{25} 1·085. n_D^{20} 1·442.

Wolf, Weijlard, *Organic Syntheses*, 1955, **35**, 18; Coll. Vol. **4**, 124.

Di-Et acetal: diethoxyacetic acid.

Moffett, *Organic Syntheses*, 1955, **35**, 59; Coll. Vol. **4**, 427.

Gomphoside★

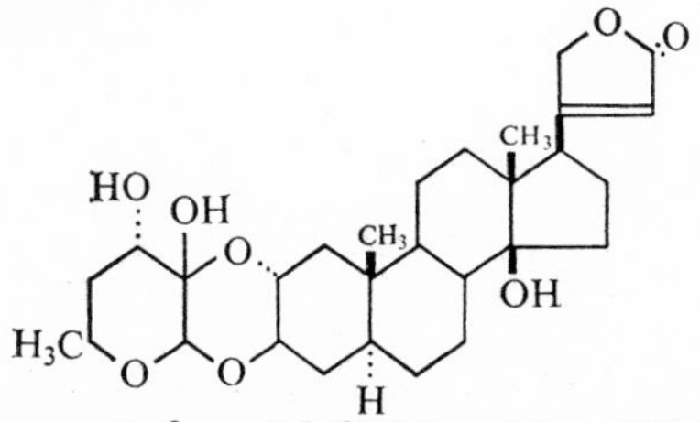

Di-Ac: cryst. from MeOH.Aq. M.p. 252–5°. $[\alpha]_D^2$ 32° (c, 0·74 in $CHCl_3$).

Coombe, Watson, *Austral. J. Chem.*, 1964, **17**, 92.

Carman, Coombe, Watson, *Austral. J. Chem.*, 1964, **17**, 573.

Gossypetin.★

3 : 4′ : 7 : 8-*Tetra-Me ether*: *see* 3′ : 5-Dihydroxy-3 : 4′ : 7 : 8-tetramethoxyflavone.

3 : 3′ : 4′ : 7 : 8 : -*Penta-Me ether*: *see* 5-Hydroxy-3 : 3′ : 4′ : 7 : 8-pentamethoxyflavone.

Hexa-Me ether: dimorphic prisms. M.p. 159–61° and 170–1°.

Henrick, Jefferies, *Austral. J. Chem.*, 1964, **17**, 934.

Gramicidin A.★
Valine Gramicidin A.
HCO–L-Val–Gly–L-Ala–D-Leu–L-Ala–D-Val–L-Val–D-Val–L-Try–D-Leu–L-Try–D-Leu–L-Try–D-Leu–L-Try–NH·CH_2·CH_2·OH
$C_{99}H_{139}O_{18}N_{19}$ MW 1881
Major constituent (82%) of Gramicidin A. Hydrol. → H·CO_2H + *seco*-Gramicidin A.
Isoleucine Gramicidin A.
HCO–L-Ileu–Gly–L-Ala–D-Leu–L-Ala–D-Val–L-Val–D-Val–L-Try–D-Leu–L-Try–D-Leu–L-Try–D-Leu–L-Try–NH·CH_2·CH_2·OH
$C_{100}H_{141}O_{18}N_{19}$ MW 1895
Minor constituent (18%) of Gramicidin A.

Ishii, Witkop, *J. Am. Chem. Soc.*, 1963, **85**, 1832; 1964, **86**, 1848.
Sarges, Witkop, *J. Am. Chem. Soc.*, 1964, **86**, 1861, 1862.

Grifolin (2-trans,trans-*Farnesyl-5-methylresorcinol*)

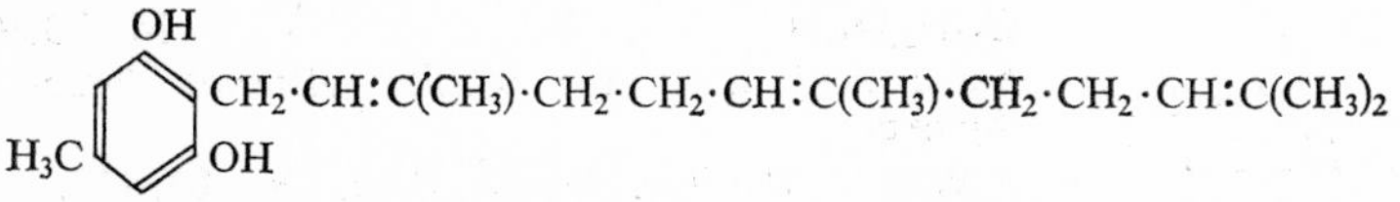

$C_{22}H_{32}O_2$ MW 328
Antibiotic from *Grifola confluens*. Colourless needles. M.p. 43°. Light absorption: $\lambda_{max.}$ 275 (ε, 935), 281 mμ (906).
Di-p-nitrobenzoyl: colourless needles from light petroleum. M.p. 62°.

Hirata, Nakanishi, *J. Biol. Chem.*, 1949, **184**, 135.
Goto, Kikisawa, Hirata, *Tetrahedron*, 1963, **19**, 135.

Griseofulvin.★
(±)-.
Total synthesis:

Stork, Tomasz, *J. Am. Chem. Soc.*, 1964, **86**, 471.

3 : 7-Guaiadiene

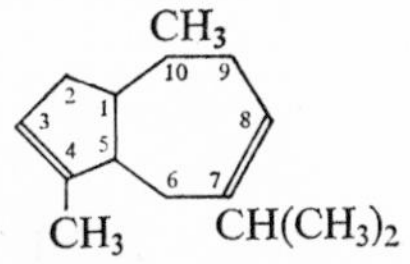

$C_{15}H_{24}$ MW 204
Constituent of the essential oil of geranium Bourbon. B.p. 110°/7 mm. D_4^{20} 0·8995. n_D^{20} 1·4951. $[\alpha]_D$ −59·2°.

Benešová *et al.*, *Coll. Czech. Chem. Commun.*, 1964, **29**, 1042.

Guanine 9β-D-arabinofuranoside (9β-D-*Arabinofuranosylguanine*)

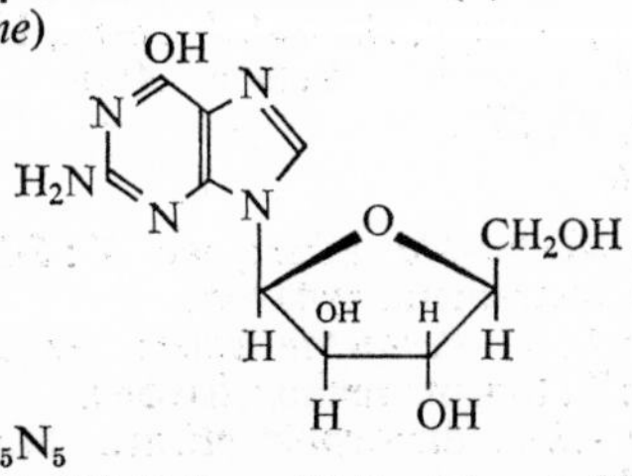

$C_{10}H_{13}O_5N_5$ MW 283
Needles + $1H_2O$ from H_2O. M.p. >300°, darkening above 265°. $[\alpha]_D^{24}$ 28° (c, 0·25 in H_2O). Light absorption: $\lambda_{max.}$ 256 mμ (ε, 12,600) at pH 1, 252 mμ (ε, 14,000) at pH 7, and 256 (ε, 11,600) and 265 mμ (ε, 11,800) at pH 13.

Reist, Goodman, *Biochemistry*, 1964, **3**, 15.

Guanosine.★
2′-O-*Me*: present in the ribonucleic acid from various plant, animal, and bacterial sources.

Smith, Dunn, *Biochim. Biophys. Acta*, 1959, **31**, 573.
Hall, *Biochim. Biophys. Acta*, 1963, **68**, 278; *Biochem. Biophys. Research. Commun.*, 1963, **12**, 429.
Morisawa, Chargaff, *Biochim. Biophys. Acta*, 1963, **68**, 147.

Guanylthiourea. *See* Amidinothiourea.

Gulonic Acid.★
D-.
γ-*Lactone*:

Karabinos, *Organic Synthesis*, 1956, **36**, 38; Coll. Vol. **4**, 506.

D-Gulosamine (2-*Amino-2-deoxygulose*

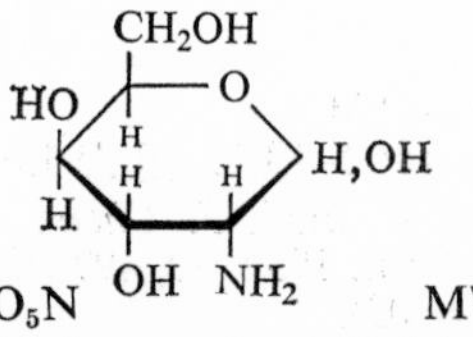

$C_6H_{13}O_5N$ MW 189
Degradation product from streptothricin and streptolin B. Ninhydrin → xylose.
B,HCl: m.p. 152–62° decomp. $[\alpha]_D^{21}$ 5·6° (5 min.) → −18·7° (final) (c, 2·9 in H_2O).
Me pyranoside: 2-*Ac*: m.p. 79–82°, $[\alpha]_D^{25}$ 72° (c, 0·74 in MeOH); O-*Benzylidene*: m.p. 111–14°, $[\alpha]_D^{25}$ 77° (c, 0·90 in MeOH). 2 : 3 : 4 : 6-*Tetra-Ac*: m.p. 119°, $[\alpha]_D^{23}$ −54° ($CHCl_3$).
2 : 3 : 4 : 6-*Tetra-Ac*: m.p. 123–4°. $[\alpha]_D^{21}$ 76° (c, 0·91 in $CHCl_3$).

van Tamelen *et al.*, *J. Am. Chem. Soc.*, 1956, **78**, 4817.
Tarasiejska, Jeanloz, *J. Am. Chem. Soc.*, 1957, **79**, 2660.
Sawden, Oftedahl, *J. Org. Chem.*, 1961, **26**, 2153.
Kuhn, Jochims, *Ann.*, 1961, **641**, 143.

Gypsogenin.
Aglycone from gypsoside. For structure *see under* Gypsoside.

Gypsoside

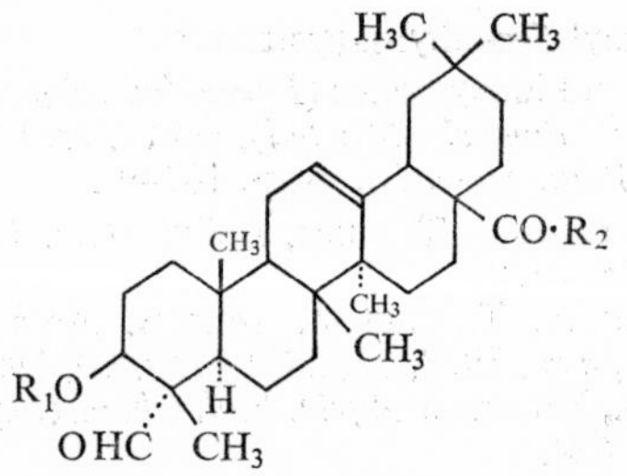

R_1 = D-Gal-1 → 4-D-Glu-1 ↘ $^4_3$D-Glur-1-
L-Ar-1 ↗
R_2 = D-Xyl-1 → 3-D-Fu-1 ↘ $^4_2$L-Rha-1-
D-Xyl-1 → 3-D-Xy-1 ↗
$C_{80}H_{126}O_{44}$ MW 1790

Present in *Gypsophila pacifica* Kom. and *G. paniculata.* Hyd. → gypsogenin lactone + galactose (1 mol.) + glucose (1 mol.) + arabinose (1 mol.) + fucose (1 mol.) + rhamnose (1 mol.) + glucuronic acid (1 mol.) + xylose (3 mol.).
Me ether: $C_{103}H_{172}O_{44}$. MW 2112. $[\alpha]_D^{20}$ 47·5° (c, 3·4 in $CHCl_3$).

Kochetkov, Khorlin, Ovodov, *Zhur. Obshcheĭ Khim, U.S.S.R.*, 1962, **32**, 782; *Tetrahedron Letters*, 1963, 477.

Gyrophoric Acid.★

Biosynthesis:

Mosbach, *Acta Chem. Scand.*, 1964, **18**, 329.

H

Halfordine

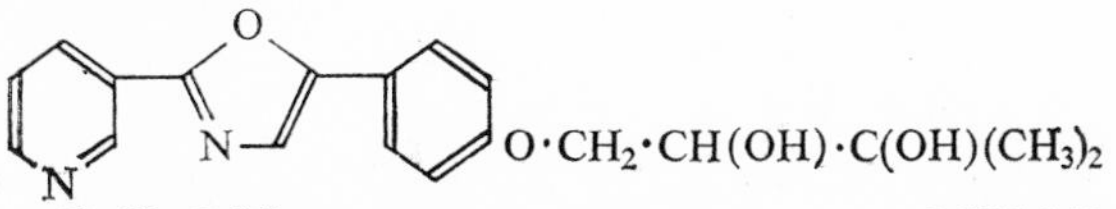

$C_{19}H_{20}O_4N_2$ MW 340

Alkaloid from bark of *Halfordia scleroxyla*. Cream needles from MeOH. M.p. 163–4°.

Ac: cryst. from Me_2CO–light petroleum. M.p. 111–12°.

N-*Me*: alkaloid isolated from *H. scleroxyla*. *B,HCl*: m.p. 235° decomp. *B,HClO₄*: m.p. 148° or 206°. *Picrate*: m.p. 143° or 198° depending on method of crystallisation.

Crow, Hodgkin, *Tetrahedron Letters*, 1963, 85; *Austral. J. Chem.*, 1964, **17**, 119.

Halfordinol

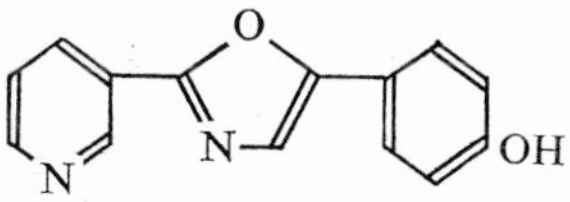

$C_{14}H_{10}O_2N_2$ MW 238

Alkaloid from *Halfordia scleroxyla*. Fine cream needles from MeOH. M.p. 255–6°.

O-*Ac*: fine cream needles. M.p. 167–80°.

O-*Me*: needles from light petroleum. M.p. 99–100°.

N-*Me*: *picrate*: orange-brown needles from Me_2CO. M.p. 316–20°. *B,HCl*: yellow-brown needles. M.p. 258°.

Crow, Hodgkin, *Austral. J. Chem.*, 1964, **17**, 119.

Halfordinone

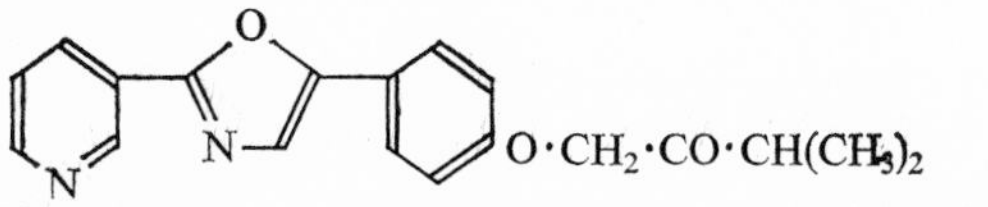

$C_{19}H_{18}O_3N_2$ MW 322

Alkaloid from *Halfordia scleroxyla*. Colourless needles from Me_2CO–light petroleum. M.p. 132–3°.

Crow, Hodgkin, *Austral. J. Chem.*, 1964, **17**, 119.

Halothane. *See* 2-Bromo-2-chloro-1 : 1 : 1-trifluoroethane.

Hamamelose.★

See also:

Foster *et al.*, *J. Chem. Soc.*, 1964, 948.

Haplocidine★

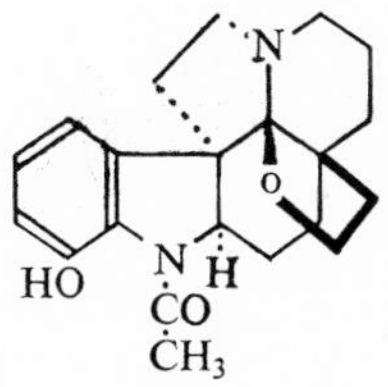

Stereochemistry:

Cava, Nomura, Talapatra, *Tetrahedron*, 1964, **20**, 581.

Haplosine★

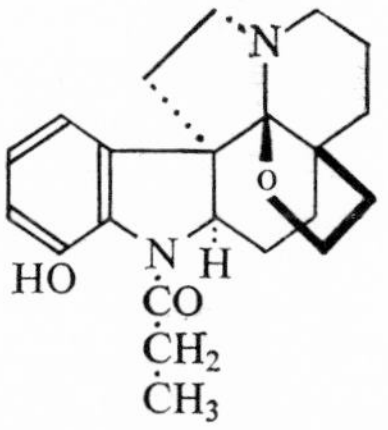

O-*Me*: $C_{23}H_{30}O_3N_2$. MW 382. M.p. 240–1°.

Stereochemistry:

Cava, Nomura, Talapatra, *Tetrahedron*, 1964, **21**, 581.

Harden–Young ester. *See* Fructose-1 : 6-diphosphate.

Harmine.★

Present in snuff used by South American Indians.

Bernauer, *Helv. Chim. Acta*, 1964, **47**, 1075.

Harongin Anthrone

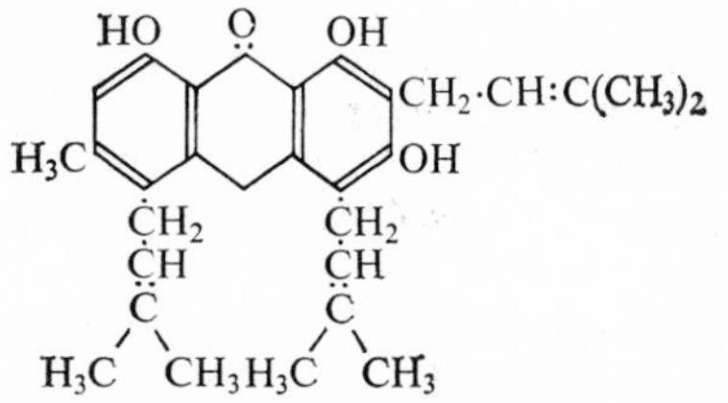

$C_{30}H_{36}O_4$ MW 460

Constituent of *Harungana madagascariensis* Poir. M.p. 208°. Ac_2O/Py → an anthracene tetra-acetate $C_{38}H_{44}O_8$. MW 628. M.p. 130°.

Ritchie, Taylor, *Tetrahedron Letters*, 1964, 1431.

Harpagoside

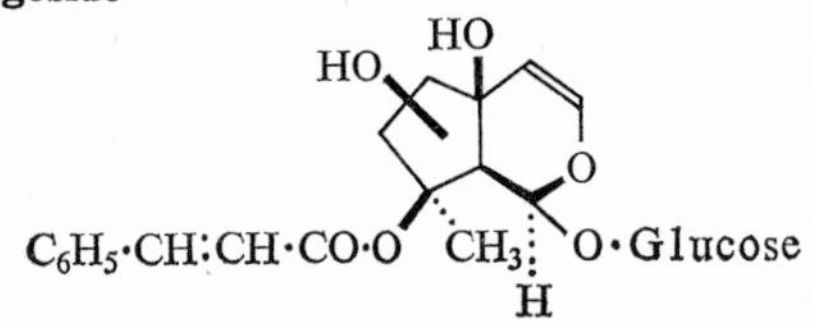

Partial structure

$C_{24}H_{30}O_{11}$ MW 494

Bitter substance from the root of *Harpagophytum procumbens* DC.

Penta-Ac: m.p. 213–14°.

Hexa-Ac: m.p. 193–4°.

Hexaphenylurethane:

Lichti, von Wartburg, *Tetrahedron Letters*, 1964, 835.

Harunganin.★

M.p. 190°. Light absorption: $\lambda_{max.}$ 242, 260, 280, 316, 334, and 411 mμ.

Mono-Me ether: m.p. 101°.

Di-Me ether: m.p. 150°.

Ritchie, Taylor, *Tetrahedron Letters*, 1964, 1431.

Hasubanonine

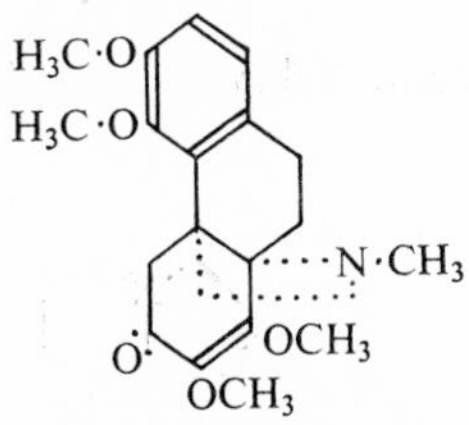

$C_{21}H_{27}O_2N$ MW 325

Alkaloid from *Stephania japonica* Miers. M.p. 116°.

Kondo *et al.*, *Ann. Rep. Itsuu Lab.*, 1951, **2**, 35; 1953, **3**, 37; 1957, **8**, 41.

Bentley, *Experientia*, 1956, **12**, 251.

Tomita *et al.*, *Tetrahedron Letters*, 1964, 2937.

Helicobasidin

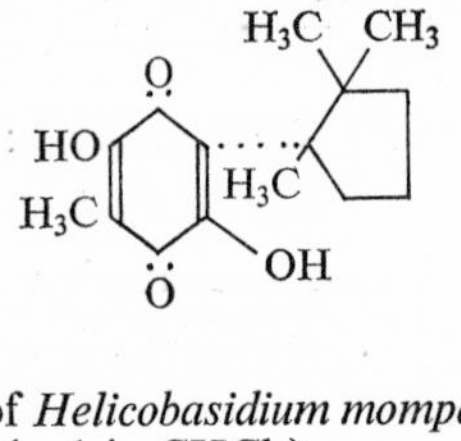

$C_{15}H_{20}O_4$ MW 264

Constituent of *Helicobasidium mompa*. M.p. 190–2°. $[\alpha]_D^{25}$ −123° (c, 1 in $CHCl_3$).

Di-Ac: m.p. 70–1°. $[\alpha]_D$ −12·4° ($CHCl_3$).

Di-O-Me: b.p. 120–30°/3 mm.

Leuco-tetra-Ac: m.p. 152–4°. $[\alpha]_D^{25}$ −9·5° ($CHCl_3$).

Natori *et al.*, *Chem. Pharm. Bull.* (Tokyo), 1963, **11**, 1343.

Hemodal. *See* 2-Methyl-1 : 4-naphthoquinone.

Hendecanedioic Acid. *See* Undecanedioic Acid.★

5-Heneicosylresorcinol

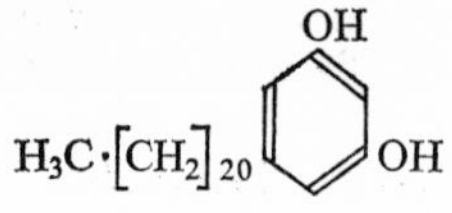

$C_{27}H_{48}O_2$ MW 404

Constituent of wheat bran. Plates from hexane. M.p. 99·5–100·5°.

Di-O-Me: needles from AcOEt. M.p. 63·5–64·5°.

Di-Ac: plates from EtOH. M.p. 72·5–73°.

Wenkert *et al.*, *J. Org. Chem.*, 1964, **29**, 435.

16-Hentriacontanol

$CH_3·[CH_6]_{14}·CH(OH)·[CH_2]_{14}·CH_3$

$C_{31}H_{64}O$ MW 452

Constituent of the lipids of *Corynebacterium diphtheriae* and *Nocardia brasiliensis* (ATCC 733). M.p. 85°.

Ac: cryst. M.p. 47–9°.

Phenylurethane: cryst. from light petroleum. M.p. 66–7°.

Pudles, Lederer, *Bull. soc. chim. biol.*, 1954, **36**, 759.

Bordet, Michel, *Bull. soc. chim. biol.*, 1964, **46**, 1101.

Hentriacont-24-en-16-one (*Palmitenone*)

$CH_3·[CH_2]_5·CH{:}CH·[CH_2]_7·CO·[CH_2]_{14}·CH_3$

$C_{31}H_{60}O$ MW 448

Produced by *Corynebacterium diphtheriae*. Cryst. M.p. 40°.

Pudles, Lederer, *Biochim. Biophys. Acta*, 1953, **11**, 602; *Bull. soc. chim. biol.*, 1954, **36**, 759.

2-*exo*-4 : 5 : 6 : 7 : 8 : 8-Heptachloro-4 : 7-methylene-4 : 4*a* : 7 : 7*a*-tetrahydroindane. *See* β-Dihydroheptachlor.

Heptafulvene

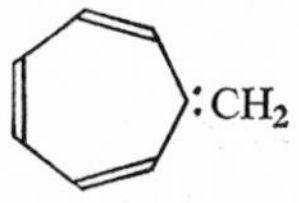

C_8H_8 MW 104

Only stable in dilute solution. Concentration → dimer: b.p. 80°/0·5 mm. Light absorption: $\lambda_{max.}$ 255, 263 mμ.

Turner *et al.*, *J. Am. Chem. Soc.*, 1957, **79**, 4127.

von Doering, Wiley, *Tetrahedron*, 1960, **11**, 183.

Heptalgin. *See* B,HCl *under* Phenadoxone.★

Heptanoic Acid.★

Amide:

Guthrie, Rabjohn, *Organic Syntheses*, 1957, **37**, 50; Coll. Vol. **4**, 513.

Heptanoylsuccinic Acid

$CH_3·[CH_2]_5·CO·CH(CH_2·COOH)·COOH$

$C_{11}H_{18}O_5$ MW 230

Di-Et ester: $C_{15}H_{26}O_5$. MW 286. B.p. 119–22°/0·7 mm. n_D^{25} 1·4395. D_{25}^{25} 0·9951. Hydrol. → 4-oxodecanoic acid.

Patrick, *J. Org. Chem.*, 1952, **17**, 1009.

Patrick, Erickson, *Organic Syntheses*, 1954, **34**, 51; Coll. Vol. **4**, 430.

Heptazone. *See* Phenadoxone.★

4-Heptenal

$CH_3·CH_2·CH{:}CH·CH_2·CH_2·CHO$

$C_7H_{12}O$ MW 112

Cis-.
Cream flavoured component of butter.
Begemann, Koster, *Nature*, 1964, **202**, 552.

Heraclenin

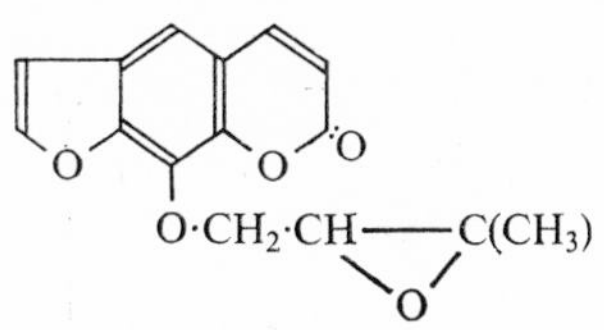

$C_{16}H_{14}O_5$ MW 286
(+)-.
Constituent of *Heracleum candicans*. Cryst. from MeOH. M.p. 111°. $[\alpha]_D^{32}$ 22° (Py). Light absorption: $\lambda_{max.}$ 250 (log ε, 4·31) and 305 mμ (4·02).
(±)-.
M.p. 114·5°.
Späth, Holzen, *Ber.*, 1935, **68**, 1123.
Sharma, Zaman, Kidwai, *Tetrahedron*, 1964, **20**, 87.

Heraclenol (8-(2′ : 3′-*Dihydroxy-3′-methylbutyl*)*psoralen*)

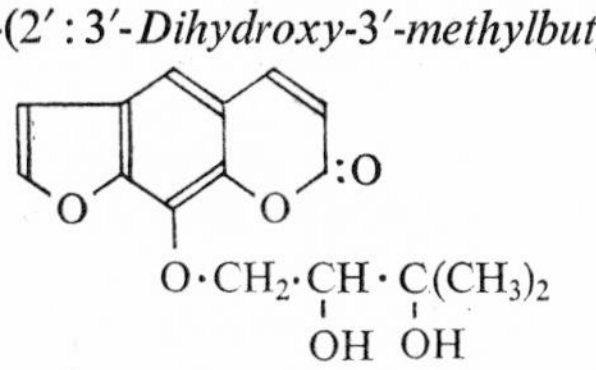

$C_{16}H_{16}O_6$ MW 304
Constituent of the root of *Heracleum candicans*. M.p. 117–18°. $[\alpha]_D^{32}$ +16·5° (Py).
Sharma *et al.*, *Naturwiss.*, 1964, **51**, 537.

1 : 2 : 3 : 4 : 5 : 7-Hexa-acetoxynaphthalene. *See* Leuco acetate *under* Spinechrome **B**.

Hexacyano-1 : 3-butadiene
$(NC)_2{\cdot}C{:}C(CN){\cdot}C(CN){:}C(CN)_2$
$C_{10}N_6$ MW 204
Colourless cryst. from dichloroethane. M.p. 253–5°. Sublime at 130°/0·3 mm. Light absorption: $\lambda_{max.}$ 302 mμ (ε, 15,300) in MeCN.
Webster, *J. Am. Chem. Soc.*, 1964, **86**, 2898.

Hexadecanal.★
1 : 2-^3H:
Weiss, *Biochemistry*, 1964, **3**, 584.

3-Hexadecenoic Acid
$CH_3{\cdot}[CH_2]_{11}{\cdot}CH{:}CH{\cdot}CH_2{\cdot}COOH$
$C_{16}H_{30}O_2$ MW 254
Trans-.
Constituent of phosphatidyl glycerol from spinach leaves (*Spinarea oleracea*) and red clover (*Trifolium pratense*). Present in the seed fat of *Helenium bigelowii* A. Gr. M.p. 53–4°.
Klenk, Knipprath, *Z. physiol. Chem.*, 1962, **327**, 283.
Hopkins, Chisholm, *Can. J. Chem.*, 1964, **42**, 2224.
Weenink, Shorland, *Biochim. Biophys. Acta*, 1964, **84**, 613.
Haverkate, de Gier, van Deenen, *Experientia*, 1964, **20**, 511.

Hexadecylmalonic Acid.★
Di-Et ester: b.p. 204–8°/2 mm. n_D^{25} 1·4433.
Floyd, Miller, *Organic Syntheses*, 1954, **34**, 13; Coll. Vol. **4**, 141.

3 : 4 : 4*a* : 5 : 6 : 7-Hexahydro-8-hydroxy-3-methyl-1-oxo-1-*H*-2-benzopyran. *See* Ramulosin.

1 : 2 : 3 : 4 : 5 : 6-Hexahydro-8-hydroxy-3 : 6 : 11-trimethyl-2 : 6-methano-3-benzazocine. *See* Metazocine.★

α-(Hexahydro-2-imino-4-pyrimidyl)glycine

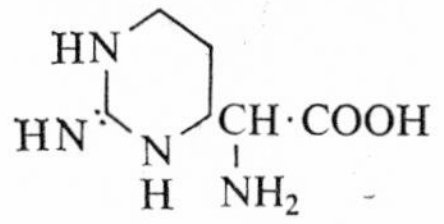

$C_6H_{12}O_2N_4$ MW 180
Amino acid component of Capreomycin. $[\alpha]_D$ +16·1° (c, 1 in H_2O). pK_a <3, 7·6, 13·8 (66% $H{\cdot}CONMe_2$.Aq.).
Herr, *Antimicrobial Agents and Chemotherapy*, 1962, 201.

1 : 2 : 3 : 4 : 6 : 7 - Hexahydro - 3 - isobutyl - 9 : 10 - dimethoxybenzo[*a*]quinolizin-2-one. *See* Tetrabenazine.★

Hexahydro-1 : 3 : 5-tripropionyl-*s*-triazine

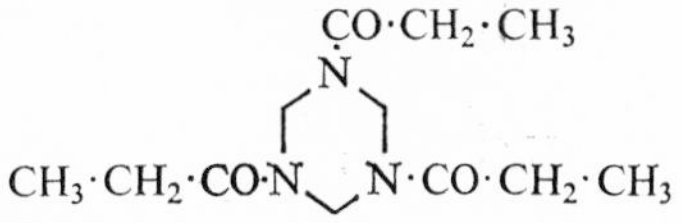

$C_{12}H_{21}O_3N_3$ MW 255
M.p. 173·2–174·1° (corr.).
Duden, Scharff, *Ann.*, 1895, **288**, 247.
Teeters, Grudsten, *Organic Syntheses*, 1950, **30**, 51; Coll. Vol. **4**, 518.

3 : 3′ : 4 : 4′ : 5′ : 7-Hexahydroxyflavan★ (*Leucorobinetidin*).
Revised absolute configuration.
(+)-2 : 3-*Trans*-3 : 4-*trans* (2R : 3S : 4R).
Drewes, Roux, *Biochem. J.*, 1964, **90**, 343.

3′ : 4′ : 5 : 6 : 7 : 8-Hexahydroxyflavone

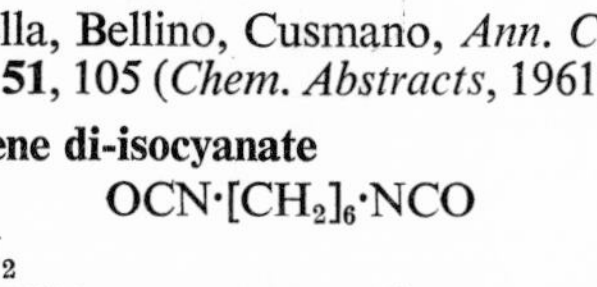

$C_{15}H_{10}O_8$ MW 318
Cryst. from EtOH. M.p. 320–2°.
3′ : 4′ : 6 : 7 : 8-*Penta-Me ether*: $C_{20}H_{20}O_8$. MW 388. M.p. 145–6°.
Hexa-Me ether: *see* Nobiletin.
Venturella, Bellino, Cusmano, *Ann. Chim.* (Italy), 1961, **51**, 105 (*Chem. Abstracts*, 1961, **55**, 19912).

Hexamethylene di-isocyanate
$OCN{\cdot}[CH_2]_6{\cdot}NCO$
$C_8H_{12}O_2N_2$ MW 168
B.p. 120–5°/10 mm., 108–11°/5 mm., 92–6°/1 mm. n_D^{20} 1·4585. D_4^{20} 1·0528.
Farlow, *Organic Syntheses*, 1951, **31**, 62; Coll. Vol. **4**, 521.

Hexa-*m*-phenylene

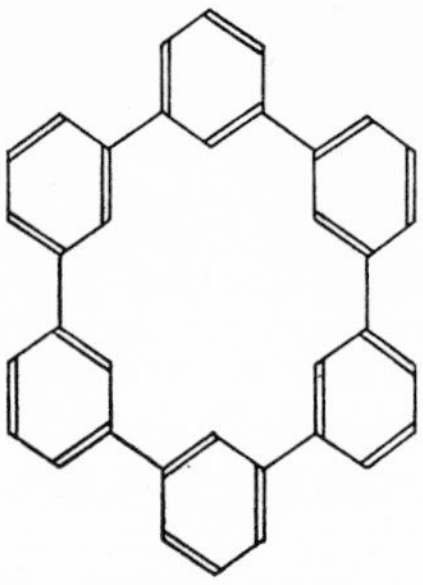

$C_{36}H_{24}$ MW 456

M.p. 509·5–511°. B.p. 650°/10^{-4} mm. Light absorption: $\lambda_{max.}$ 251·2 mμ (ε, 138,000).

Staab Binnig, *Tetrahedron Letters*, 1964, 319.

1-Hexyne.★

See also:

Campbell, Campbell, *Organic Syntheses*, Coll. Vol. **4**, 117.

Hibaene

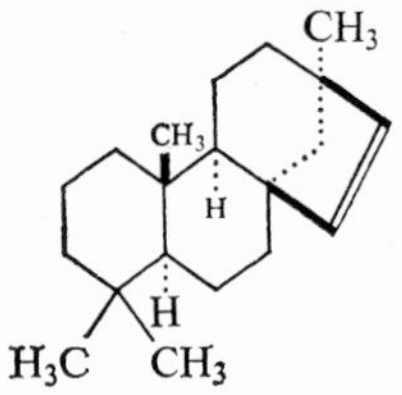

$C_{20}H_{32}$ MW 272

(−)-.

Present in the essential oil of the leaves of *Thujopsis dolabrata*, *Cupressus macrocarpa*, and *Podocarpus ferrugineus* G. Benn. M.p. 29·5–30°. $[\alpha]_D^{23}$ −49·9° (in $CHCl_3$). H_2 → dihydro deriv., m.p. 41·5–42·5°, probably identical with the saturated hydrocarbon derived from monogynol and stereoisomeric with beyerane.

(+)-.

Constituent of *Erythroxylon monogynum*. M.p. 29·5–30°. $[\alpha]_D^{28}$ +50·1° ($CHCl_3$).

$AgNO_3$ complex: m.p. 152–3·5°.

Kitahara, Yoshikashi, *Tetrahedron Letters*, 1964, 1731.

Briggs *et al.*, *Tetrahedron Letters*, 1964, 2223.

Kapadi, Dev, *Tetrahedron Letters*, 1964, 2751.

Hibaene epoxide

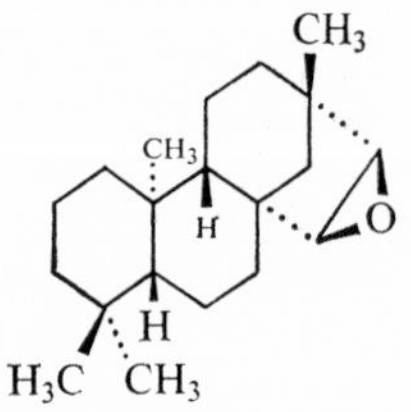

$C_{20}H_{32}O$ MW 288

(+)-.

Constituent of *Erythroxylon monogynum*. M.p. 74–5°. $[\alpha]_D$ +16·3° ($CHCl_3$).

Kapadi, Dev, *Tetrahedron Letters*, 1964, 2751.

Hiberna. *See* Promethazine.★

Erratum p. 1620

Himbaccol.★

Should read: *See* Viridiflorol.

Hinokiflavone

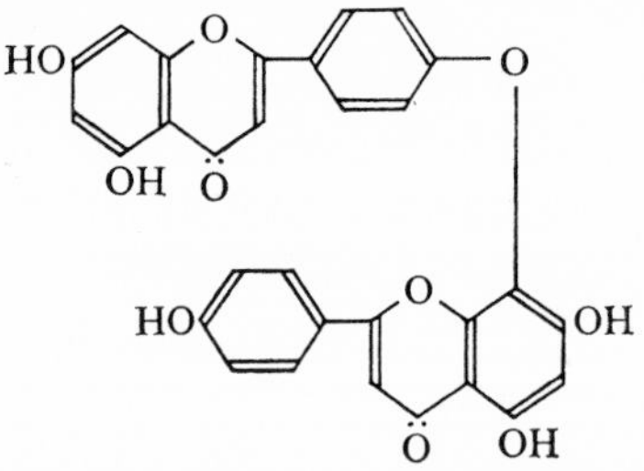

$C_{30}H_{18}O_{10}$ MW 538

From leaves of *Chamaecyparis obtusa*. Hydrate. M.p. 353–5° decomp.

Penta-Ac: m.p. 239–40° decomp.

Tri-Me ether: $C_{33}H_{24}O_{16}$. MW 580. Cryst. from MeOH. M.p. 259–60°. *Di-Ac*: m.p. 255°.

Penta-Me ether: $C_{35}H_{28}O_{10}$. MW 608. M.p. 259–60°. *Oxime*: m.p. 202–3°.

Penta-Et ether: $C_{40}H_{38}O_{10}$. MW 678. M.p. 249–50°.

Kariyone, Fukui *et al.*, *Yakugaku Zasshi*, 1960, **80**, 746, *et seq.* (*Chem. Abstracts*, 1960, **54**, 24698).

Hircinol

$C_{15}H_{14}O_3$ MW 242

Antifungal principle from *Loroglossum hiricinum* (L.) Rich. infected with *Rhizoctoria repens* Bern. Cryst. from Me_2CO–light petroleum. M.p. 162·5–164°. Light absorption: $\lambda_{max.}$ 214 (ε, 45,600), 274 (20,200), 293 (12,000), and 302 mμ (11,900).

Di-O-Ac: cryst. from Me_2CO–light petroleum. M.p. 126·5–127·5°.

Urech *et al.*, *Helv. Chim. Acta*, 1963, **46**, 2758.

Histamine.★

N$^{\alpha}$-*Cinnamoyl*: $C_{14}H_{15}ON_3$. MW 241. Alkaloid from *Acacia polystacha* and *A. argentea*. Needles from H_2O. M.p. 179–80·5°.

B,HCl: plates from Me_2CO–Et_2O. M.p. 187–9°.

Picrate: cryst. from EtOH. M.p. 165–6°. Cryst. from H_2O. M.p. 96–7°.

N$^{\alpha}$-*Cinnamoyl* N$^{\alpha}$-*Me*-N-*glucoside*: *see* Casimiroedine.

Fitzgerald, *Austral. J. Chem.*, 1964, **17**, 375.

Holadysone (11 : 18-*Dihydroxypregna*-1 : 4-*diene*-3 : 20-*dione*-(18 → 20) *hemiketal*)

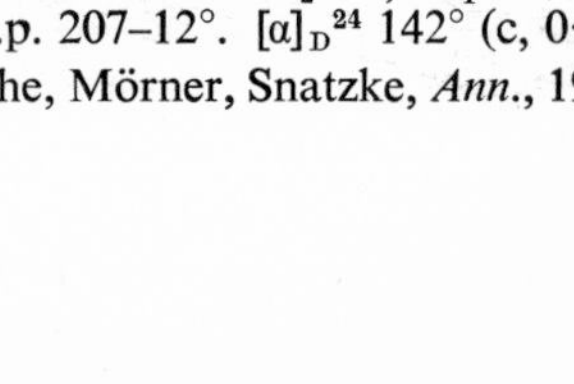

$C_{21}H_{28}O_4$ MW 344

Constituent of Kurchi (*Holarrhena antidysenterica* Wall). Needles from Me_2CO, m.p. 175·5–177·5°, or prisms, m.p. 207–12°. $[\alpha]_D^{24}$ 142° (c, 0·59 in Py).

Tschesche, Mörner, Snatzke, *Ann.*, 1963, **670**, 103.

Holafrine

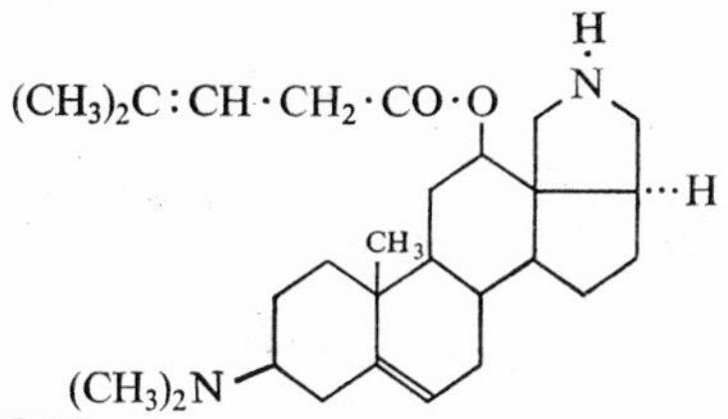

$C_{29}H_{46}O_2N_2$ MW 454

Alkaloid from *Holarrhena africana* A. DC. Plates from Me_2CO.Aq. M.p. 116–17°. $[\alpha]_D^{20}$ −19·1° (c, 0·93 in $CHCl_3$), −5·1° (c, 0·98 in EtOH). Hydrol. → 12-Hydroxyconessimine + 4-methyl-3-pentenoic acid.

B,2HClO$_4$: cryst. from MeOH–Et_2O. M.p. 180–1°.

Rostock, Seebeck, *Helv. Chim. Acta*, 1958, **41**, 11.

Holarrhetine

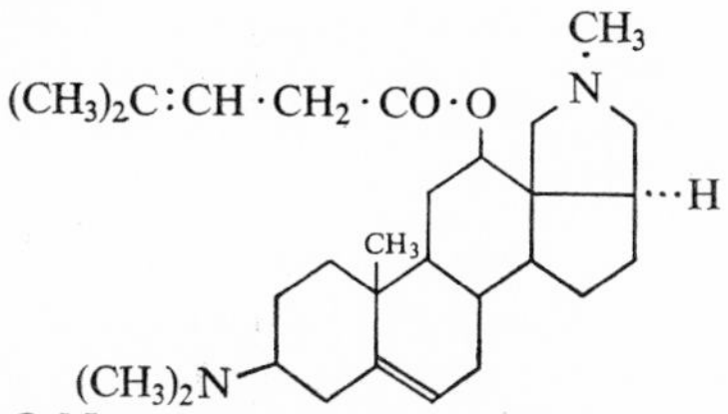

$C_{30}H_{48}O_2N_2$ MW 468

Alkaloid from *Holarrhena africana* A. DC. Cubes from Me_2CO. M.p. 74–5°. $[\alpha]_D$ −4·6° (c, 1·12 in EtOH), −14·9° (c, 1·12 in $CHCl_3$). Hydrolysis → Holarrhenine + 4-methyl-3-pentenoic acid.

B,2HCNS,0·5H$_2$O: prisms from H_2O. M.p. 148–50°.

Rostock, Seebeck, *Helv. Chim. Acta*, 1958, **41**, 11.

Homoadenosine

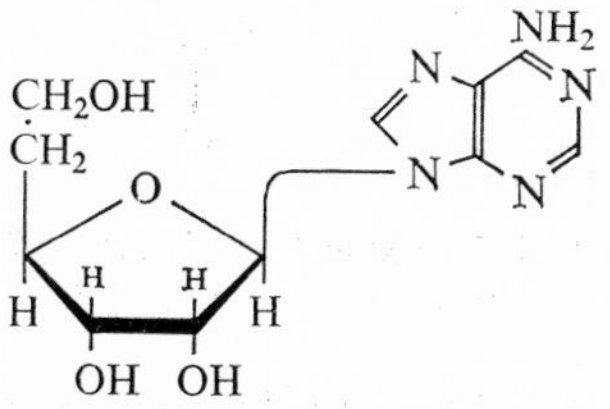

$C_{11}H_{15}O_4N_5$ MW 281

Cryst. from Me_2SO.Aq. M.p. 231·5–232·5°. $[\alpha]_D^{25}$ −16·4° (c, 0·4 in MeOH).

Ryan *et al., J. Am. Chem. Soc.*, 1964, **86**, 2503.

Homocitric Acid (3-*Carboxy*-3-*hydroxyadipic acid*)

HOOC·CH$_2$·CH$_2$·C(OH)·(COOH)·CH$_2$·COOH

$C_7H_{10}O_7$ MW 202

Intermediate in lysine biosynthesis.

Lactone: $C_7H_8O_6$. MW 188. M.p. 161–2°.

Strassman, Ceci, *Biochem. Biophys. Research Commun.*, 1964, **14**, 262.

Homocysteine.★

(L)(+)-.

$[\alpha]_D^{20}$ 77° (c, 1 in *N*-HCl).

Hope, Humphries, *J. Chem. Soc.*, 1964, 869.

Homoglutathione. *See* γ-L-Glutamyl-L-cysteinyl-β-alanine.

Homoisocitric Acid (3-*Carboxy*-2-*hydroxyadipic acid*)

HOOC·CH$_2$·CH$_2$·CH(COOH)·CH(OH)·COOH

$C_7H_{10}O_7$ MW 202

Intermediate in lysine biosynthesis. Cryst. from Me_2CO–C_6H_6. M.p. 127–9°.

Tri-Et ester: b.p. 140–1°/0·005 mm.

Tri-anilide: white cryst. from AcOH. M.p. 251° decomp.

Yamashita, *J. Org. Chem.*, 1958, **23**, 835.

Strassman, Ceci, Silverman, *Biochem. Biophys. Research Commun.*, 1964, **14**, 268.

Homolinearisine. *See* (−)*N*-Me *under* Crotonosine.

Homo-orientin★ (6-C-β-D-*Glucopyranosylluteolin*)

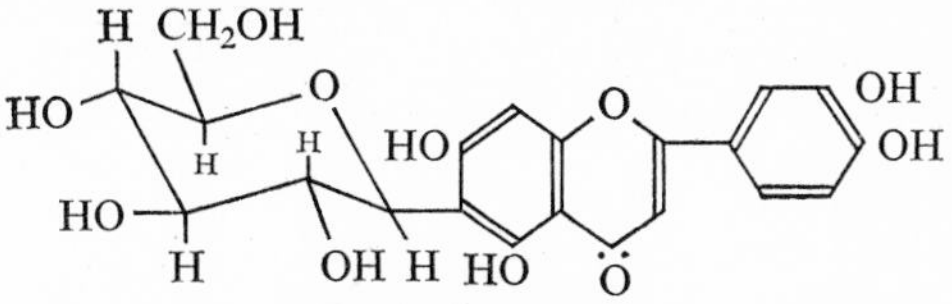

Revised structure

Koeppen, *Chemistry and Industry*, 1962, 2145.

Horowitz, Gentili, *Chemistry and Industry*, 1964, 499.

Homoribose (5-*Deoxy*-D-*allose*)

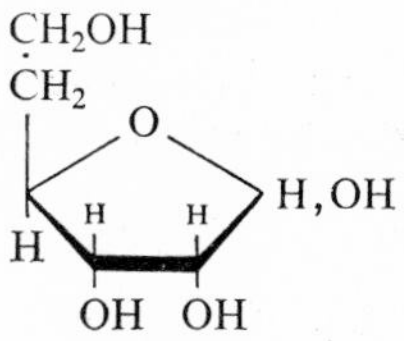

$C_6H_{12}O_5$ MW 164

Syrup. $[\alpha]_D^{23}$ +19·4° (H_2O).

Phenylosazone: cryst. from MeOH.Aq. or C_6H_6. M.p. 137–9°. $[\alpha]_D^{23}$ +17·8° (MeOH).

Ryan *et al., J. Am. Chem. Soc.*, 1964, **86**, 2503.

Homoserine★ (2-*Amino*-4-*hydroxybutyric acid*).

L-.

Present in peas and the Jack bean seeds (*Canavalia ensiformis*).

Miettinen, *Suomen Kemi*, 1953, **B26**, 26.

Homotropone (*Bicyclo*[5,1,0]*octa*-3 : 5-*dien*-2-*one*)

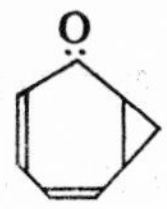

C_8H_8O MW 120

Pale yellow oil.

HSbCl$_6$ add. comp.: yellow cryst. M.p. 89–90°. Decomp. in moist air.

Iron tricarbonyl complex: yellow needles from C_6H_6–light petroleum. M.p. 131–2·5°. Ceric ammonium nitrate → homotropone.

Semicarbazone: yellow plates from EtOH.Aq. M.p. 146–7°.

Holmes, Pettit, *J Am. Chem. Soc.*, 1963, **85**, 2531.

Hop-17(21)en-3α-ol

$C_{30}H_{50}O$ MW 426

Cryst. from EtOH. M.p. 187–90°. $[\alpha]_D$ +36·6° (c, 0·4 in $CHCl_3$).

Arthur *et al., Austral. J. Chem.*, 1964, **17**, 697.

Hop-17(21)-en-3β-ol

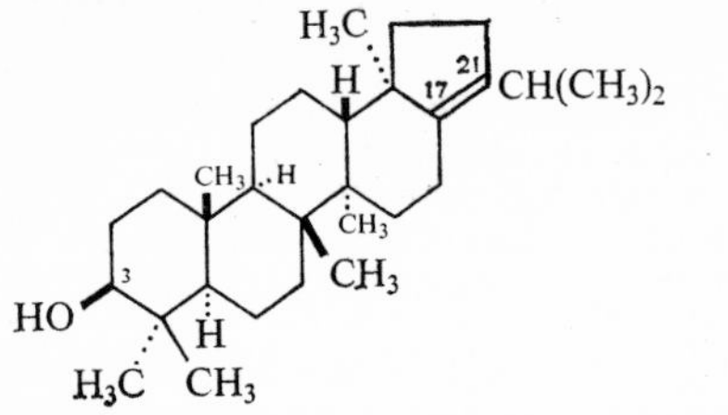

$C_{30}H_{50}O$ MW 426

Constituent of the leaves of *Quercus championi*. Hexagonal plates from EtOH. M.p. 228–9°. $[\alpha]_D$ +45·3° (c, 0·78 in $CHCl_3$).

Ac: constituent of *Q. championi*. Cryst. from EtOH. M.p. 258–62°. $[\alpha]_D$ +55·4° (c, 1·08 in $CHCl_3$).

Benzoyl: m.p. 235–7°. $[\alpha]_D$ +65·6° (c, 0·87 in $CHCl_3$).

Arthur *et al.*, *Austral. J. Chem.*, 1964, **17**, 697.

Hulupinic Acid

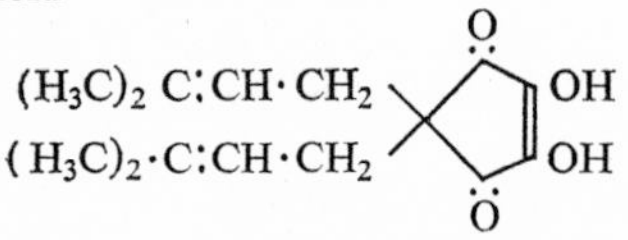

$C_{15}H_{20}O_4$ MW 264

Constituent of hops (*Humulus lupulus* L.). Needles from Et_2O–light petroleum or MeOH.Aq. M.p. 167–8°. Light absorption: $\lambda_{max.}$ 301 mμ (log ε, 4·01) in acidic EtOH. $\lambda_{max.}$ 261 (log ε, 4·16), 393 mμ (4·09) in alkaline EtOH.

Di-Me ether: b.p. 115–20°/8 × 10^{-4} mm. Light absorption: $\lambda_{max.}$ 293 mμ (log ε, 3·92).

Burton, Stevens, Elvidge, *J. Chem. Soc.*, 1964, 952.

Humbertiol

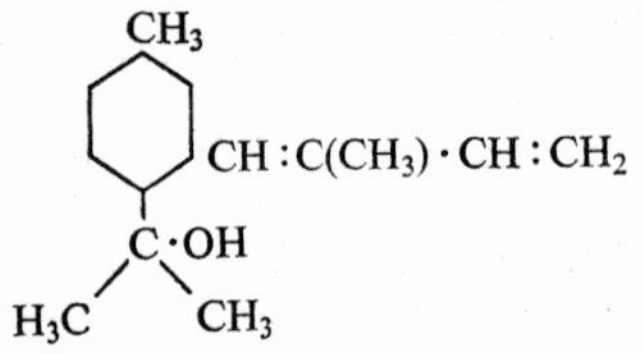

$C_{15}H_{26}O$ MW 222

Constituent of the heartwood of *Humbertia madagascariensis*.

Roulais, *Compt. rend.*, 1963, **256**, 3369.

Humulene★

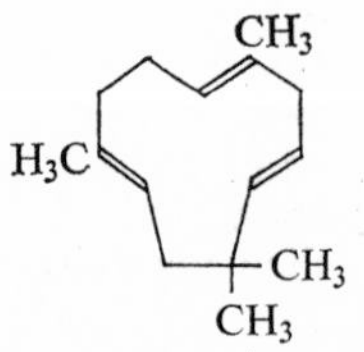

α-.

Shown to have all-*trans* configuration by X-ray crystallography of silver nitrate adduct.

McPhail, Reed, Sim, *Chemistry and Industry*, 1964, 976.

Hartsuck, Paul, *Chemistry and Industry*, 1964, 977.

Humulene epoxide I

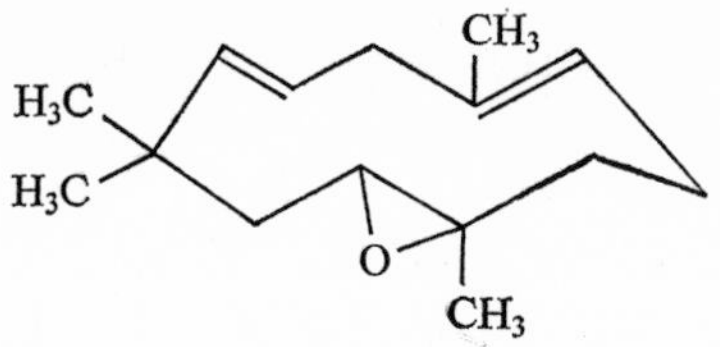

$C_{15}H_{24}O$ MW 220

Constituent of the essential oils of *Zingibar zerumbet* and hops. B.p. 104–5°/1·5 mm. n_D^{30}. D_4^{30} 0·9541. $[\alpha]_D^{30}$ −22·8° (c, 3·6 in $CHCl_3$).

Ramaswami, Bhattacharyya, *Tetrahedron*, 1962, **18**, 575.

Roberts, *J. Inst. Brewing*, 1963, **69**, 343.

Damodaran, Dev, *Tetrahedron Letters*, 1963, 1941.

Humulene epoxide II

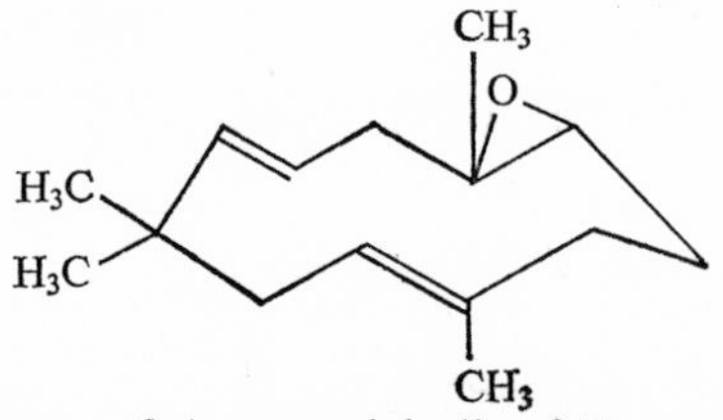

Constituent of the essential oils of *Z. zerumbet* and hops. B.p. 105–6°/1·5 mm. n_D^{30} 1·4962. D_4^{20} 0·477. $[\alpha]_D^{30}$ −31·2° (c, 4·2 in $CHCl_3$).

Damodaran, Dev, *Tetrahedron Letters*, 1963, 1941.

Humulenol

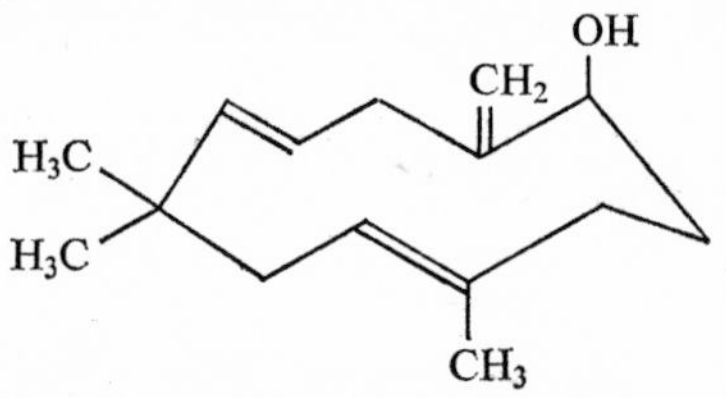

$C_{15}H_{24}O$ MW 220

Constituent of the essential oil of *Zingiber zerumbet*. B.p. 115–16°/1 mm. n_D^{30} 1·5127. $[\alpha]_D^{30}$ +30° (c, 3·6 in $CHCl_3$).

Damodaran, Dev, *Tetrahedron Letters*, 1963, 1941.

Humulinic Acid

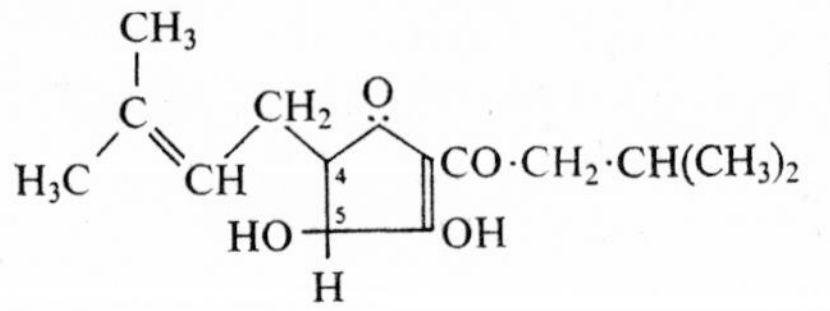

$C_{15}H_{22}O_4$ MW 266

4 : 5-*Trans*-. Humulinic Acid A.

Hydrolysis product of humulone. Cryst. from cyclohexane. M.p. 93°. Light absorption: $\lambda_{max.}$ 225·5 (ε, 9630) and 266 mμ (9620) in acidic EtOH. $\lambda_{max.}$ 250 (ε, 20,600) and 265 sh. mμ (16,420) in basic EtOH.

Oxime: cryst. from MeOH. M.p. 152–3°.

4 : 5-*Cis*-. Humulinic Acid B.

Cryst. from cyclohexane. M.p. 72–3°.

Wöllmer, *Ber.*, 1916, **49**, 780.

Wieland, *Ber.*, 1925, **58**, 102.

Harris, Howard, Pollock, *J. Chem. Soc.*, 1952, 1906.
Anteunis *et al.*, *Bull. soc. chim. Belg.*, 1962, **71**, 623.
Burton, Elvidge, Stevens, *J. Chem. Soc.*, 1964, 3816.
Alderweireldt, Anteunis, *Bull. soc. chim. Belg.*, 1964, **73**, 285.

Humulinic Acid C

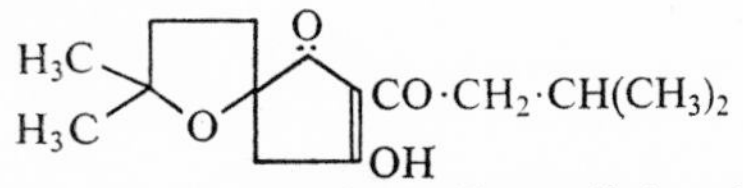

Acid isomerisation product of humulinic acid A. Oil. B.p. 125–30°/4 × 10^{-4} mm. Light absorption: $\lambda_{max.}$ 225 (ε, 14,200) and 265 mμ (10,050) in acidic EtOH. $\lambda_{max.}$ 250 (18,100) and 269 mμ (15,300) in basic EtOH.

Anteunis *et al.*, *Bull. soc. chim. Belge.*, 1962, **71**, 623; 1964, **73**, 910.
Burton, Elvidge, Stevens, *Proc. Chem. Soc.*, 1964, 220.

Humulinic Acid D

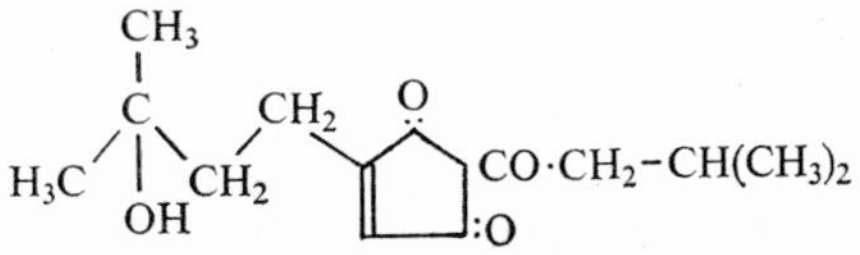

Acid isomerisation product of humulinic acid A. Oil. pK 5·55 (66% MeOH). Light absorption: $\lambda_{max.}$ 235 (ε, 16,900) and 266 mμ (ε, 17,400) in 0·1*N*-HCl. $\lambda_{max.}$ 235 (ε, 16,900), 275 (21,000), and 405 mμ (765) in basic MeOH.
Me ether: $C_{16}H_{24}O_4$. MW 280. Yellow cryst. M.p. 56·5–57°. pK 5·99 (80% MeO·CH$_2$·CH$_2$OH). Light absorption: $\lambda_{max.}$ 240 (ε, 17,700) and 268 mμ (18,500) in acidic MeOH. $\lambda_{max.}$ 238 (18,300), 278 (25,000), and 404 mμ (750) in basic MeOH.

Anteunis *et al.*, *Bull. soc. chim. Belg.*, 1962, **71**, 623; 1964, **73**, 910.

Hydrangenol (3 : 4-*Dihydro*-8-*hydroxy*-3-(4-*hydroxyphenyl)isocoumarin*)

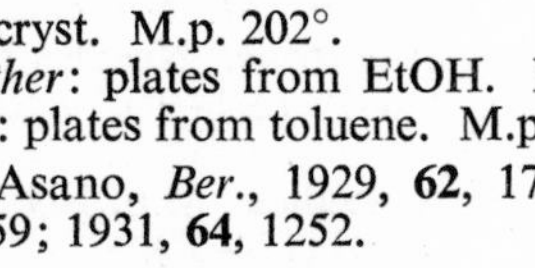

$C_{15}H_{12}O_4$ MW 256
Sweet principle in the leaves of *Hydrangea macrophylla* Seringe var. *Thumbergii* Makino ("Amacha"). Colourless plates from EtOH. M.p. 181°.
Di-Ac: colourless plates with pearly lustre. M.p. 181–2°.
Di-benzoyl: cryst. M.p. 202°.
Mono-Me ether: plates from EtOH. M.p. 122–3°.
Di-Me ether: plates from toluene. M.p. 151°.

Asahina, Asano, *Ber.*, 1929, **62**, 171; 1930, **63**, 429, 2059; 1931, **64**, 1252.

Hydrocodin. *See* Dihydrocodeine.

Hydrocodone. *See* Dihydrocodeinone.

Hydrokon. *See under* Dihydrocodeinone.

Hydromorphone. *See* Dihydromorphinone.

Hydronootkatinol

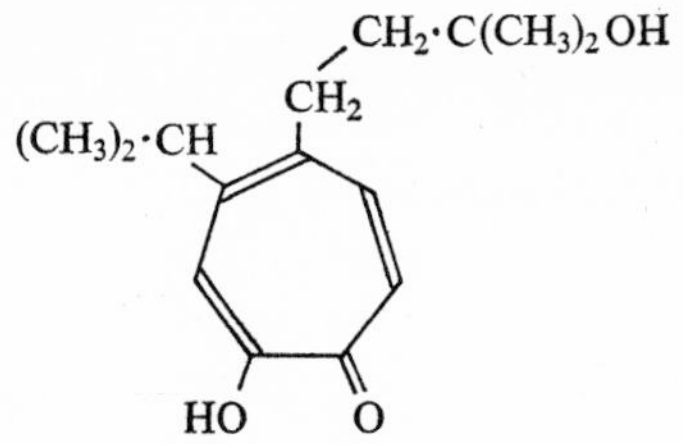

$C_{15}H_{22}O_3$ MW 250
Constituent of the heartwood of *Cupressus lindleyi* Klotsch. Pale-yellow needles. M.p. 107–8°. Light absorption: $\lambda_{max.}$ 240 (log ε, 4·47) 322 mμ (3·87).
Cu chelate: cryst. from $CHCl_3$–CCl_4. M.p. 237·5–241°.

Bicho, Zavarin, Bhacca, *J. Org. Chem.*, 1963, **28**, 2927.

11-Hydroxy(−)actinidine. *See* Tecostidine.

17α-Hydroxyandrost-4-en-3-one★ (epi-*Testosterone*).
Present in human urine:

Korenman, Wilson, Lipsett, *J. Biol. Chem.*, 1964, **239**, 1004.
Schubert, Wehrberger, Frankenberg, *Naturwiss.*, 1964, **51**, 638.

17β-Hydroxyandrost-4-en-3-one★ (*Testosterone*).
19-^{14}*C*:

Rao, Axelrod, *Chemistry and Industry*, 1963, 1838.

γ-Hydroxyarginine.★
See also:

Bell, Tirimanna, *Biochem. J.*, 1964, **91**, 356.

***m*-Hydroxybenzyl Alcohol.** *See* α : 3-Dihydroxytoluene.

***p*-Hydroxybenzyl Alcohol.** *See* α : 4-Dihydroxytoluene.

4-Hydroxy-1-butanesulphonic Acid Sultone

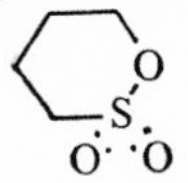

$C_4H_8O_3S$ MW 136
B.p. 134–6°/4 mm. M.p. 12·5–14·5°. n_D^{25} 1·4620. D^{25} 1·3347.

Helberger, Lantermann, *Ann.*, 1954, **586**, 158.
Snoddy, *Organic Syntheses*, 1957, **37**, 55; Coll. Vol. **4**, 529.

5-(4-Hydroxy-1-butynyl)-2-2′-bithienyl

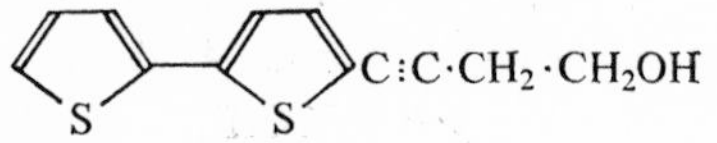

$C_{12}H_{10}OS_2$ MW 234
Constituent of the roots of *Tagetes minuta* L. M.p. 67°. Light absorption: $\lambda_{max.}$ 242 (log ε, 3·82), 328 (4·34), and 334 mμ (4·35).

Bohlmann, Herbst, *Chem. Ber.*, 1962, **95**, 2945.
Atkinson, Curtis, Phillips, *Tetrahedron Letters*, 1964, 3159; *Chemistry and Industry*, 1964, 2101.

3-Hydroxycinchophen. *See* Oxycinchophen.★

***p*-Hydroxycinnamoylquinic Acid.** *See p*-Coumaroylquinic Acid.

***p*-Hydroxycinnamoyl Alcohol.★**
4-O-*Me ether*: *see p*-Methoxycinnamoyl Alcohol.

12β-Hydroxyconessimine

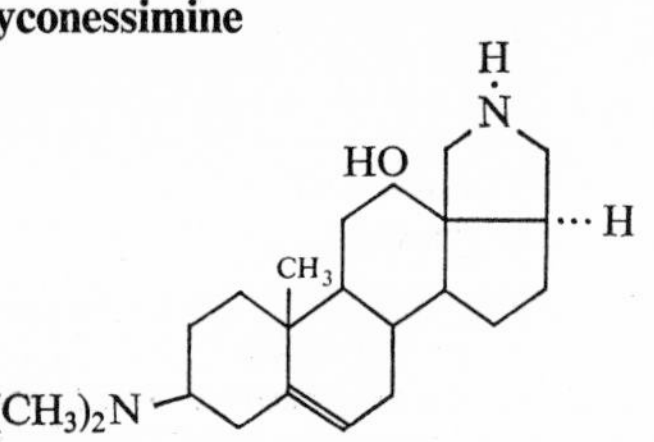

$C_{23}H_{38}ON_2$ MW 358
Needles from Me_2CO. M.p. 197–8°. $[\alpha]_D^2$ +13° (c, 1·08 in EtOH).
Di-Ac: prisms from light petroleum. M.p. 122–4°.
N-*Me*: *see* Holarrhenine.
4-*Methyl*-3-*pentenoyl ester*: *see* Holafrine.

Rostock, Seebeck, *Helv. Chim. Acta*, 1958, **41**, 11.

α-Hydroxyconessine

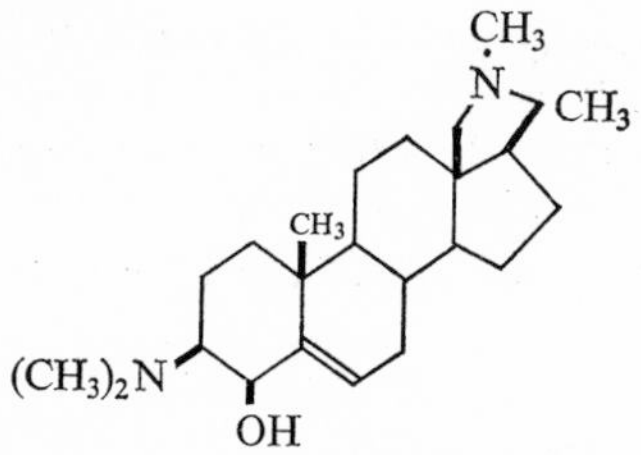

$C_{24}H_{40}ON_2$ MW 372
M.p. 157°. $[\alpha]_D$ +20° (c, 0·8 in EtOH–$CHCl_3$, 1 : 1).
O-*Ac*: m.p. 127°. $[\alpha]_D$ −75° (c, 1·1 in $CHCl_3$).

Bertho, *Ann.*, 1947, **557**, 220; 1950, **561**, 1; 1958, **619**, 96.
Haworth, Micheal, *J. Chem. Soc.*, 1957, 4973.
Goutarel, Conreur, Parello, *Bull. soc. chim.*, 1963, 2401.

2-Hydroxycyclodecanone (*Sebacoin*)

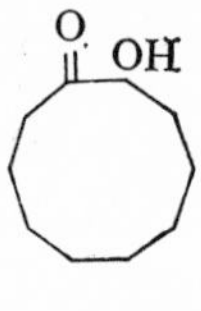

$C_{10}H_{18}O_2$ MW 170
B.p. 134–8°/14 mm., 124–8°/9 mm. Cryst. from pentane. M.p. 38–9°.

Stoll, Rouvé, *Helv. Chim. Acta*, 1947, **30**, 1822.
Allinger, *Organic Syntheses*, 1956, **36**, 79; Coll. Vol. **4**, 840.

2-Hydroxycycloheptanecarboxylic Acid

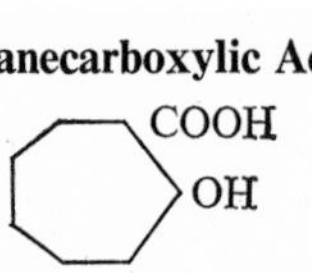

$C_8H_{14}O_3$ MW 158
Cis-.
Prisms. M.p. 71–2°.
Me ester: $C_9H_{16}O_3$. MW 172. B.p. 134–5°/22 mm. n_D^{25} 1·4720. D_{25}^{25} 1·0905. p-*Nitrobenzoyl*: m.p. 84–5°.
Trans-.
Plates. M.p. 87–8°.
Me ester: b.p. 135–6°/17 mm. n_D^{25} 1·4689. D_{25}^{25} 1·0846. p-*Nitrobenzoyl*: m.p. 34–6°.

Palau, Pascual, Rafols, *Bull. soc. chim.*, 1964, 269.

(−) - 3 - Hydroxydecanoyl - L - leucylglycylserylvalyl - threonyl-L-leucine. *See* Viscosin.★

9-Hydroxydec-2-enoic Acid.★
Trans-.
A pheromone stabilising honey-bee swarms.

Butler, Callow, Chapman, *Nature*, 1964, **201**, 733.

10-Hydroxy-2-decynoic Acid
HO·CH_2·$(CH_2)_6$·C⋮C·COOH
$C_{10}H_{16}O_3$ MW 184
Cryst. from Et_2O–light petroleum. M.p. 72–3°.
Me ether: b.p. 137°/0·2 mm. n_D^{22} 1·4700. S-*Benzylthiouronium salt*: m.p. 170–1°.

Fray *et al.*, *Tetrahedron*, 1961, **15**, 18.
Barker *et al.*, *Tetrahedron*, 1962, **18**, 177.

2-Hydroxy-3 : 6-di-isobutylpyrazine-1-oxide. *See* Neoaspergillic Acid.

4 - Hydroxy - 3 : 5 - dimethoxybenzaldehyde★ (*Syringic aldehyde*).
See also:

Allen, Leubner, *Organic Syntheses*, 1951, **31**, 92; Coll. Vol. **4**, 866.

2′-Hydroxy-4′ : 6′-dimethoxychalcone

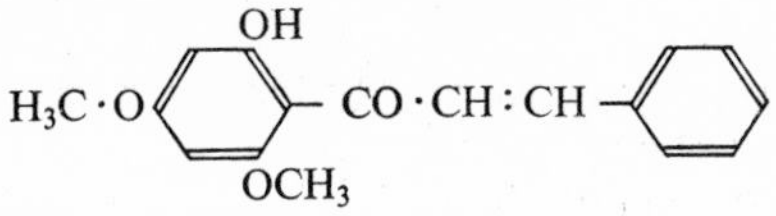

$C_{17}H_{16}O_4$ MW 284
Constituent of Kawa rhizome (*Piper methystirum*). Cryst. from MeOH.Aq. M.p. 91°. Light absorption: $\lambda_{max.}$ 340 mμ (log ε, 4·55). $\lambda_{min.}$ 268 mμ.
Ac: m.p. 131–2°.

Haensel, Ranft, Baehr, *Z. Naturforsch*, 1963, **18b**, 370.

5-Hydroxy-4′ : 7-dimethoxy-6 : 8-dimethylflavone. *See* Eucalyptin.★

7 - Hydroxy - 4′ : 6 - dimethoxyisoflavone (*Afromosin, Afrormosin*)

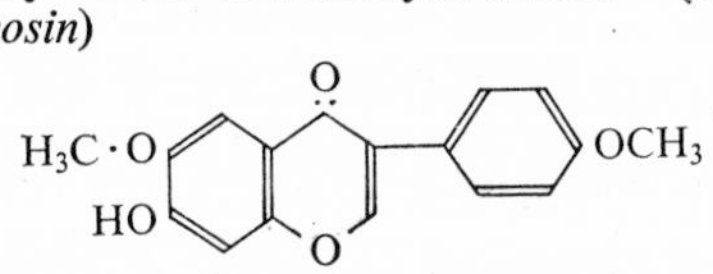

$C_{17}H_{14}O_5$ MW 298
Constituent of *Afrormosia elata* Harms, *Myrocarpus fastigratus* Fr. Allen, *M. balsamum* (L.) Harms, *Castanospermum australe*. Needles from MeOH or EtOH. M.p. 236–7° (228–9°). $\lambda_{max.}$ 258, 320 mμ (log ε, 4·37, 4).
O-*Ac*: colourless needles. M.p. 165–7°.
O-*Me*: m.p. 179–80° (174–5°).

McMurry, Theng, *J. Chem. Soc.*, 1960, 1491.
Harbourne, Gottlieb, Magalhães, *J. Org. Chem.*, 1963, **28**, 881.
Eade, Hinterberger, Simes, *Austral. J. Chem.*, 1963, **16**, 188.

5-Hydroxy-4′ : 7-dimethoxy-6-methylflavone

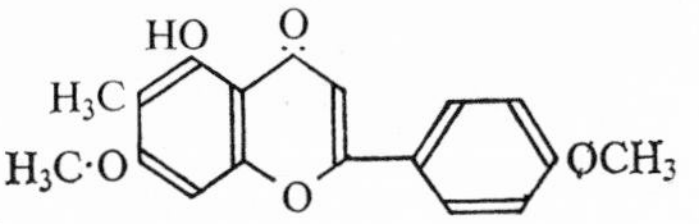

$C_{18}H_{16}O_5$ MW 312

Constituent of the leaf wax of *Eucalyptus torelliana* F. Muell and *E. urnigera* Hook. Faintly cream cryst. M.p. 187–8°. Light absorption: $\lambda_{max.}$ 213 (log ε, 4·60), 276 (4·37), and 327 mμ (4·42).

Lamberton, *Austral. J. Chem.*, 1964, **17**, 692.

3β - Hydroxy - 20α - dimethylamino - 5α - pregnane. *See* Funtuphyllamine C.

8-Hydroxy-3 : 4-dimethylisocoumarin. *See* Oospolactone.★

2′-Hydroxy-5 : 9-dimethyl-2-phenethyl-6 : 7-benzomorphan. *See* Phenazocine.★

4-Hydroxy-3 : 6-dimethyl-2-pyrone (*Methyltriacetic Lactone*)

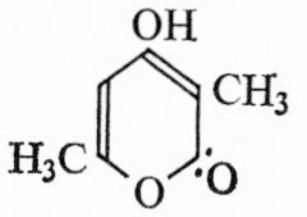

$C_7H_8O_3$ MW 140

Metabolite of *Penicillium stipitatum.* Cryst. from Me_2CO–light petroleum. M.p. 212–14°. pK 5·05. Light absorption: $\lambda_{max.}$ 288 mμ (ε, 8300).

Me ether: m.p. 83–4°.

Ac: m.p. 83–4°.

Brenneisen, Acker, Tanenbaum, *J. Am. Chem. Soc.*, 1964, **86**, 1264.

4-Hydroxydodeca-5 : 6-diene-8 : 10-diynoic Acid. *See* Odyssic Acid.★

15α-Hydroxyeburicoic Acid. *See* Sulphurenic Acid.

Hydroxyferrocene

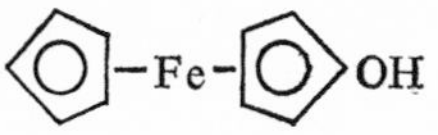

$C_{10}H_{10}OFe$ MW 202

M.p. 166–70°.

O-*Me*: m.p. 39·5–40·5°.

Ac: m.p. 64·5–66°.

Propionyl: m.p. 30–1°.

Benzoyl: m.p. 108·5–109·5°.

Nesmeyanov, Sazonova, Drozd, *Tetrahedron Letters*, 1959, No. 17, 13.

γ-Hydroxyglutamine

$NH_2{\cdot}CO{\cdot}CH(OH){\cdot}CH_2{\cdot}CH(NH_2){\cdot}COOH$

$C_5H_{10}O_4N_2$ MW 162

L-.

Amino acid present in *Phlox decussata*. Cryst. from H_2O, EtOH, or Me_2CO. M.p. 163–4°.

Brander, Virtanen, *Acta Chem. Scand.*, 1963, **17**, 2563.

3-Hydroxyhexadecanoic Acid.★

D-.

Present in extracellular glycolipids of *Rhodotorula* spp. Cryst. from Me_2CO. M.p. 78–9°. $[\alpha]_D$ −12·9° (c, 1·3 in $CHCl_3$).

Me ester: cryst. from Me_2CO. M.p. 48–9°. $[\alpha]_D$ −13·8° (c, 5·6 in $CHCl_3$), +2·1° (c, 6·8 in MeOH).

Tulloch, Spencer, *Can. J. Chem.*, 1964, **42**, 830.

van Ammers *et al.*, *Rec. trav. chim.*, 1964, **83**, 708.

5-Hydroxy-3 : 3′ : 4′ : 6 : 7 : 8-hexamethoxyflavone. *See under* Limocitrol.

γ-Hydroxyhomoarginine.★

See also:

Bell, *Biochem. J.*, 1964, **91**, 358.

4-Hydroxyhydratropic Acid. *See* 2-*p*-Hydroxyphenylpropionic Acid.

2-Hydroxy-6-(1-hydroxy-2-methylpropyl)-3-isobutyl-pyrazine-1-oxide. *See* Neohydroxyaspergillic Acid.

2-Hydroxy-6-hydroxymethyl-4*H*-pyran-4-one. *See* Isokojic Acid.★

2-Hydroxy-6-hydroxymethyl-γ-pyrone. *See* Isokojic Acid.

5′-Hydroxy-jasmonic Acid Lactone (2-(5-*Hydroxy*-cis-*pent*-2-*enyl*)-3-*oxocyclopentylacetic acid lactone*)

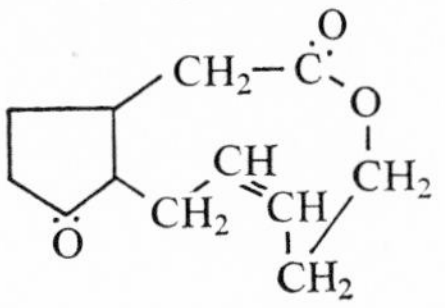

$C_{12}H_{16}O_3$ MW 208

Constituent of jasmin essence (*Jasminum grandiflorum* L.). Small needles. M.p. 104°. $[\alpha]_D^{20}$ −260° (c, 3·05 in EtOH).

Semicarbazone: m.p. 250°.

2 : 4-*Dinitrophenylhydrazone*: m.p. 165°.

Naves, Grampoloff, *Helv. Chim. Acta*, 1942, **25**, 1500.

Demole, Willhalm, Stoll, *Helv. Chim. Acta*, 1964, **47**, 1152.

19-Hydroxy-16α-kauran-17-oic Acid

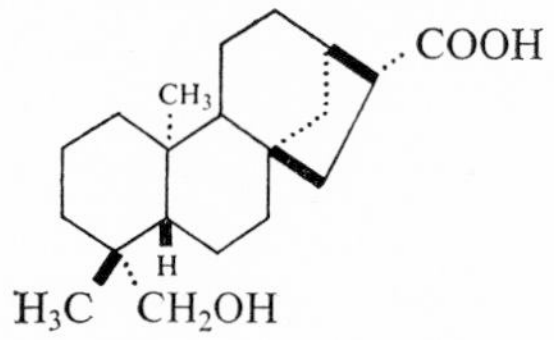

$C_{20}H_{32}O_3$ MW 320

(−)-.

Resin acid from *Ricinocarpus stylosus* Diels. Solvated prisms from AcOEt. M.p. 207° (sealed tube). $[\alpha]_D$ −66° (c, 3·2 in EtOH).

Me ester: $C_{21}H_{34}O_3$. MW 334. Needles from light petroleum as MeOH.Aq. M.p. 108–10° and 125–6°. $[\alpha]_D$ −66° (c, 4·4 in $CHCl_3$). *Ac*: needles from MeOH.Aq. M.p. 95°. $[\alpha]_D$ −69° (c, 3 in $CHCl_3$).

Henrick, Jefferies, *Chemistry and Industry*, 1963, 1801; *Austral. J. Chem.*, 1964, **17**, 915.

3-Hydroxykynurenine-*O*-sulphate. *See* Rhoditrin.★

3β-Hydroxylanosta-8 : 24-diene-21-oic Acid. *See* Trametenolic Acid.★

3β-Hydroxylanosta-8 : 24-dien-21-oic Acid

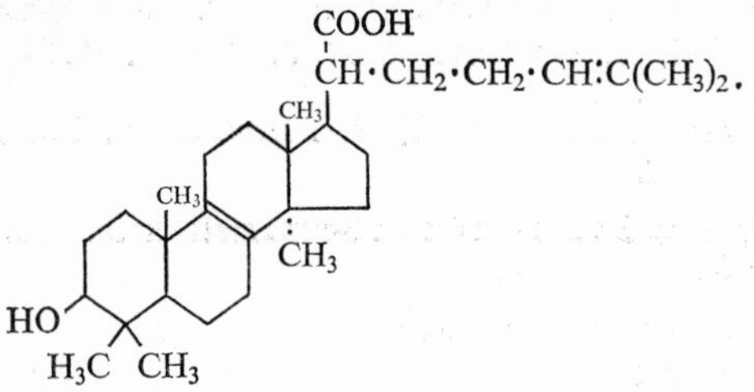

$C_{30}H_{48}O_3$ MW 456

Metabolite of the fungii *Trametes odorata* (Wulf.) Fr. and *Inonotus obliquus*. M.p. 262–7°. $[\alpha]_D^{18}$ 46° (c, 0·5 in Py).

Ac: needles from Me_2CO.Aq. M.p. 240–4° decomp. (sublime 225°).

Me ester: m.p. 129–31°. $[\alpha]_D^{18\cdot5}$ 51° (c, 0·5 in $CHCl_3$). *Ac*: m.p. 147–9°. $[\alpha]_D$ 63° (c, 0·98 in $CHCl_3$).

Halsall, Hodges, Sayer, *J. Chem. Soc.*, 1959, 2036.
Kempska, Ludwiczak, Wrzeciono, *Roczniki Chem.*, 1962, **36**, 1453 (*Chem. Abstracts*, 1963, **59**, 11602).

3β-Hydroxylup-20(29)en-27 : 28-dioic Acid. *See* Melaleucic Acid.

2-Hydroxymachaerinic Acid Lactone (*Saponin F*)

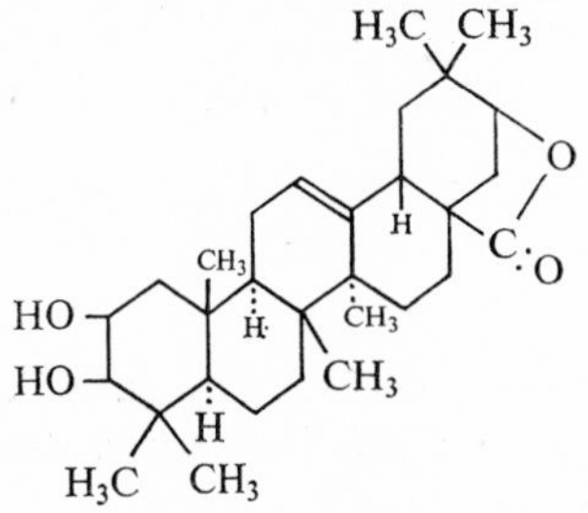

$C_{30}H_{46}O_4$ MW 470

Saponin from bean pods of *Stryphnodendron coriaceum*. Cryst. from EtOH–light petroleum. M.p. 265–7°. $[\alpha]_D$ +5°.

Di-Ac: cryst. from $CHCl_3$–MeOH. M.p. 222–6°. $[\alpha]_D$ −48°.

Tursch *et al.*, *J. Org. Chem.*, 1963, **28**, 2390.

2-Hydroxy-1-methoxyaporphine

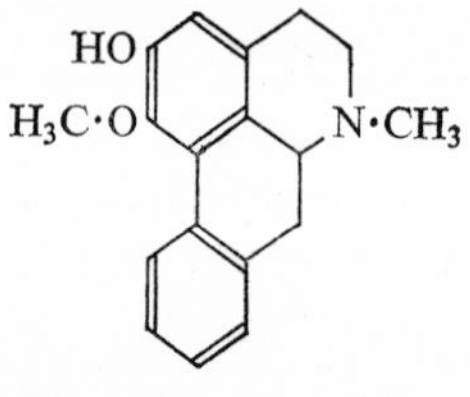

$C_{18}H_{19}O_2N$ MW 281

Alkaloid from *Nelumbo nucifera*. M.p. 195–6°. $[\alpha]_D$ −265° ($CHCl_3$).

O-*Me*: *see* Nuciferine.★

Note. This alkaloid was originally called nornuciferine, but this name is now given to the *des-N*-Me alkaloid.

Tomita, Watanabe, Furokawa, *J. Pharm. Soc. Japan*, 1961, **81**, 469, 492, 1644.

2-Hydroxy-3-methoxycinnamic Acid (o-*Ferulic acid*)

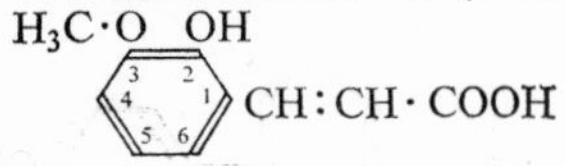

$C_{10}H_{10}O_4$ MW 194

Present in wheat shoots. M.p. 183–4°.

El-Basyouni, Towers, *Can. J. Biochem.*, 1964, **42**, 493.

2-Hydroxy-4-methoxycinnamic Acid.

See also 4-*O*-Me ether *under* Umbellic Acid.★

Cis-.

2-*Glucosyl*: present in *Lavandula* spp.

Trans-.

2-*Glucosyl*: cryst. from H_2O. M.p. 194–6°.

Brown, *Phytochemistry*, 1963, **2**, 137.

6-Hydroxy-5-methoxyisophthalaldehydic Acid. *See* 5-Carboxyvanillin.

5-Hydroxy-6-methoxynoraporphine. *See* Caaverin.

2-Hydroxy-3-*o*-methoxyphenoxypropylcarbamate. *See* Methocarbamol.★

1-*m*-Hydroxy-2-methylaminoethanol. *See* Phenylephrine.★

3β-Hydroxy-20α-methylamino-5α-pregnane. *See* Funtuphyllamine B.

3β-Hydroxy-20α-methylaminopregn-5-ene. *See* Irehamine.

17β-Hydroxy-17α-methylandrosta-1 : 4-dien-3-one (*Methandienone, dianabol, methandrostenolone*)

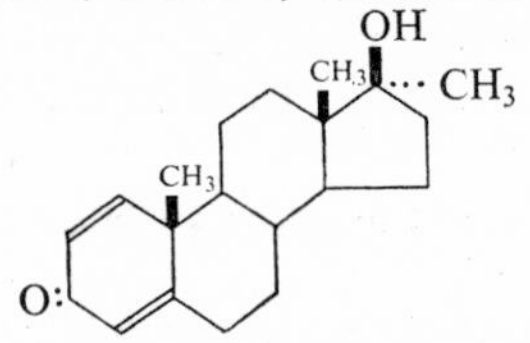

$C_{20}H_{28}O_2$ MW 300

Cryst. from Me_2CO–Et_2O. M.p. 163–4°. $[\alpha]_D^{26}$ 0° (c, 1·150 in $CHCl_3$). Light absorption: $\lambda_{max.}$ 245 mμ (ε, 15,600). Anabolic steroid for correction of negative nitrogen balance in humans.

Vischer, Meystre, Wettstein, *Helv. Chim. Acta*, 1955, **38**, 1502.
Meystre *et al.*, *Helv. Chim. Acta*, 1956, **39**, 734.
Wettstein *et al.*, U.S.P. 2,900,398 (*Chem. Abstracts*, 1960, **54**, 652).

17β-Hydroxy-17-methyl-5α-androstan-3-one (*Mestanolone, androstalone*)

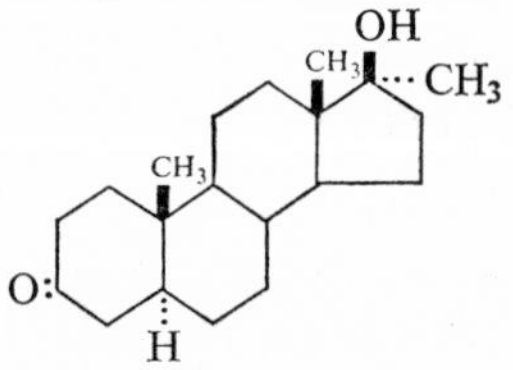

$C_{20}H_{32}O_2$ MW 304

Cryst. from AcOEt. M.p. 192–3°. Sol. Me_2CO, EtOH, Et_2O. Spar. sol. AcOEt. Used as anti-oestrogenic agent.

Semicarbazone: m.p. 235–6°.

Ruzicka, Goldberg, Rosenberg, *Helv. Chim. Acta*, 1935, **18**, 1487.

3-*C*-Hydroxymethyl-D-*glycero*tetrose. *See* Apiose.★

4-Hydroxy-4-methyl-2-pentanone★ (*Diacetone alcohol*). Hypnotic constituent of sleepy grass (*Stipa vaseyi*).

Epstein, Gerber, Karler, *Experientia*, 1964, **20**, 390.

(−)-7-[2-(β-Hydroxy-α-methyl-β-phenethylamino)-ethyl]theophylline. *See under* Akrinor.

3-Hydroxy-3-methylphthalide. *See* Acetophenone-*o*-carboxylic Acid.

17α-Hydroxy-6-methylpregna-4 : 6-diene-3 : 20-dione (*Megestrol*)

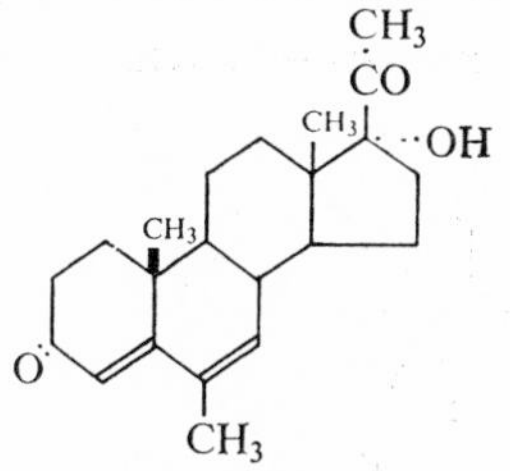

$C_{22}H_{30}O_3$ MW 342

M.p. 203–4°. $[\alpha]_D^{20}$ +42·6° (c, 1·08 in $CHCl_3$). Light absorption: $\lambda_{max.}$ 291 mμ.

Ac: Megestrol acetate. $C_{24}H_{32}O_4$. MW 384. Oral contraceptive. Cryst. from MeOH.Aq. M.p. 214–16°. $[\alpha]_D^{24}$ +5° (c, 0·43 in $CHCl_3$). Light absorption: $\lambda_{max.}$ 287·5 mμ (log ε, 4·4).

Propionyl: $C_{25}H_{34}O_4$. MW 398. Needles from MeOH. M.p. 134–5°. $[\alpha]_D^{21}$ +9° (c, 0·35 in $CHCl_3$).

Butyryl: $C_{26}H_{38}O_4$. MW 412. Needles from hexane. M.p. 102–4°. $[\alpha]_D^{21}$ −21° (c, 0·95 in $CHCl_3$).

Yü-Ch'ün Ch'ên, Huang Minlon, *Chem. Abstracts*, 1960, **54**, 19762.
Ringold *et al.*, *J. Am. Chem. Soc.*, 1959, **81**, 3712.
Ruggieri, Ferrani, Gandolfi, *Ann. Chim.* (Italy), 1959, **49**, 1371.
Ellis *et al.*, *J. Chem. Soc.*, 1960, 2828.
Burn *et al.*, *Chemistry and Industry*, 1962, 1907.
Huang-Minlon, Kuang-Tien Han, Wei-Shan Chou, *Chem. Abstracts*, 1963, **59**, 12868.

17-*Ac*-6-*Methyl*-^{14}C:

Cooley, Kellie, *Biochem. J.*, 1964, **93**, 6C.

17-*Ac*-1 : 2-$^3H_2$:

Cooley, Kellie, *Biochem. J.*, 1964, **93**, 8C.

17α-Hydroxy-6α-methylpregn-4-ene-3 : 20-dione (*Medroxyprogesterone*)

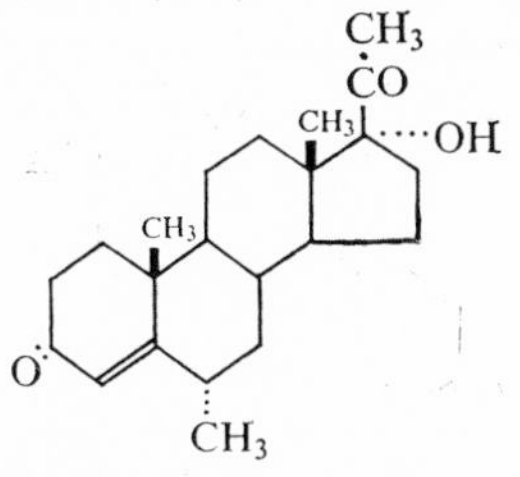

$C_{22}H_{32}O_3$ MW 344

Very active progestational agent. M.p. 220–3·5°. $[\alpha]_D$ +75° ($CHCl_3$). Light absorption: $\lambda_{max.}$ 241 mμ (ε, 16,150).

Ac: medroxyprogesterone acetate. $C_{24}H_{34}O_4$. MW 386. Cryst. from Me_2CO–light petroleum. M.p. 205–8°. [α] +56° ($CHCl_3$). Light absorption: $\lambda_{max.}$ 240 mμ (ε, 15,950).

Propionyl: $C_{25}H_{36}O_4$. MW 400. M.p. 155–7°. $[\alpha]_D$ +45° (EtOH).

Hexanoyl: $C_{28}H_{42}O_4$. MW 442. M.p. 105–7°. $[\alpha]_D$ +46° ($CHCl_3$).

Phenylacetyl: m.p. 164–6°. $[\alpha]_D$ +62° (EtOH).

β-*Cyclopentylpropionate*: m.p. 135–7°. $[\alpha]_D$ +44°.

Babcock *et al.*, *J. Am. Chem. Soc.*, 1958, **80**, 2904.

17-*Ac*-1 : 2-$^3H_2$:

Cooley, Kellie, *Biochem. J.*, 1964, **93**, 8C.

4-Hydroxymethylproline★

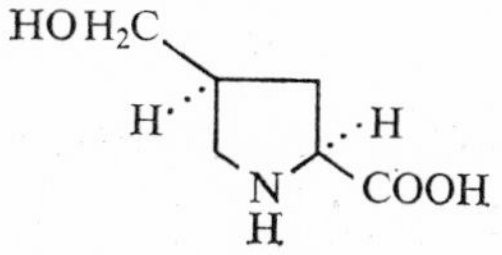

Cis-.

L- (*cis*).

Constituent of apples.

N-*Carbobenzoyloxy deriv.*: m.p. 115·5–116·5°. $[\alpha]_D^{23}$ −48·5°. *Lactone*: m.p. 94·5–95·5°.

L- (*trans*).

M.p. 227·5–229°. $[\alpha]_{590}$ −48° (H_2O).

N-*Carbenzoyloxy deriv.*: oil.

Unteh, Gibbon, *Tetrahedron Letters*, 1964, 3259.

See also:

Biemann, Deffner, Steward, *Nature*, 1961, **191**, 380.
Abraham *et al.*, *Nature*, 1961, **192**, 1150.

4-Hydroxy-*N*-methyl-L-proline (4-*Hydroxyhygric acid*)

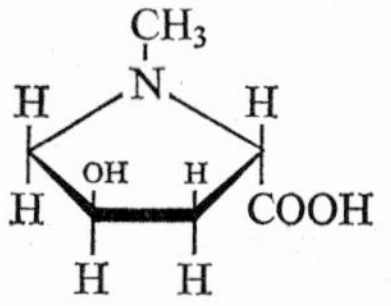

$C_6H_{11}O_3N$ MW 145

Present in bark of *Croton gubougia* and heartwood of *Afrormosia elata*. Cryst. from MeOH. M.p. 238–40° decomp. $[\alpha]_D$ −86·6° (c, 1·5 in H_2O).

B,HCl: m.p. 181–3°. $[\alpha]_D$ −55° (c, 2·3 in MeOH).

Ac: cryst. from AcOEt. M.p. 160·5–162°. $[\alpha]_D$ 67° (c, 2 in MeOH). *B,HCl*: needles from MeOH–Me_2CO. M.p. 207–9°. $[\alpha]_D$ 44° (c, 1·5 in MeOH).

Goodson, Clewer, *J. Chem. Soc.*, 1919, 923.
Morgan, *Chemistry and Industry*, 1964, 542.

3-Hydroxy-2-methylpropionic Acid.★

(R) (−)-.

$[\alpha]_{578}^{20}$ −7·6° (c, 11·95 in EtOH).

Hydrazide: m.p. 132–3°. $[\alpha]_{578}^{20}$ −28·7° (c, 8·28 in H_2O).

(S) (D)-.

N-*Phenylcarbamate*: m.p. 108–10°. $[\alpha]_D^{28}$ −17° (c, 3·1 in MeOH).

Retey, Lynen, *Biochem. Biophys. Research Commun.*, 1964, **16**, 358.
Sprecher, Clark, Sprinson, *Biochem. Biophys. Research Commun.*, 1964, **15**, 581.

***N*-(α-[Hydroxymethyl]propyl)-D-lysergamide.** *See* Methylergometrine.★

3-Hydroxymethylpyridine. *See* 3-Pyridylmethanol.★

6-Hydroxymethyl-2 : 3 : 4-trihydroxybenzaldehyde. *See* Fomecin A.

β-Hydroxy-β-methyl-δ-valerolactone. *See under* Mevalonic Acid.

Hydroxymonogynol

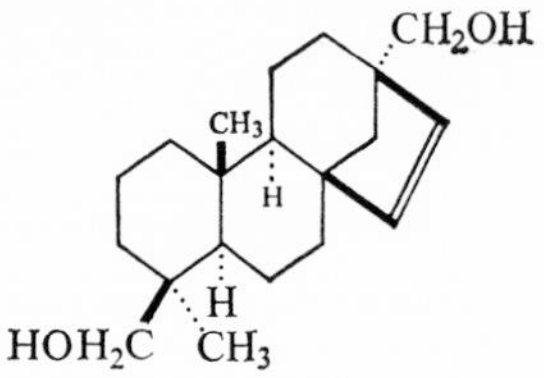

$C_{20}H_{32}O_2$ MW 304

Constituent of the wood of *Erythroxylon monogynum* Roxb. M.p. 178–9°. $[\alpha]_D^{28}$ 55·39° ($CHCl_3$).

Kapadi, Dev, *Tetrahedron Letters*, 1964, 1171, 1902, 2751.

Erratum p. 1751

2-Hydroxy-1-naphthylacetic Lactone.★

Should read: *See* Naphtho[2,1-*b*]furan-2-one.

5-Hydroxynonanoic Acid

$CH_3{\cdot}[CH_2]_3{\cdot}CH(OH){\cdot}[CH_2]_3{\cdot}COOH$

$C_9H_{18}O_3$ MW 174

Lactone: $C_9H_{16}O_2$. MW 156. B.p. 137–8°/11 mm.

Rosemund, Bach, *Chem. Ber.*, 1961, **94**, 2401, 2406.

4-Hydroxy-2-non-1-enylquinoline

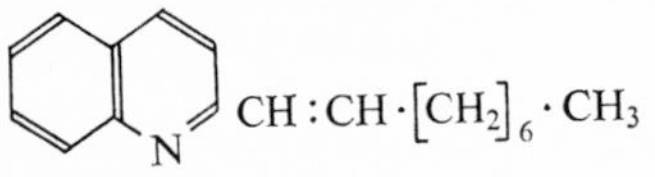

$C_{18}H_{23}ON$ MW 269

Produced by *Pseudomonas aeruginosa*. Cryst. M.p. 153°.

Wells, *J. Biol. Chem.*, 1952, **196**, 331.

***m*-Hydroxynorephedrine.** *See* Metaraminol.★

4-Hydroxy-2-nonylquinoline

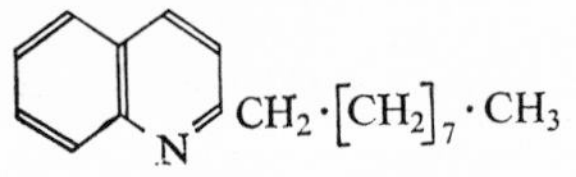

$C_{18}H_{25}ON$ MW 271

Produced by *Pseudomonas aeruginosa*. Cryst. M.p. 139°.

N-*Oxide*: leaflets. M.p. 148°.

Wells, *J. Biol. Chem.*, 1952, **196**, 331.
Cornforth, James, *Biochem. J.*, 1956, **63**, 124.

17β-Hydroxy-12-norpregn-4-en-20-yn-3-one. *See* Norethisterone.★

3-Hydroxyoctadecanoic Acid.★

D-.

Present in extracellular lipid of *Rhodotorula* spp. Cryst. from Me_2CO. M.p. 83–5°. $[\alpha]_D$ −12·2° (c, 1·4 in $CHCl_3$).

Me ester: cryst. from light petroleum. M.p. 56·5–57·5°. $[\alpha]_D$ −12·9° (c, 4·1 in $CHCl_3$).

Tulloch, Spencer, *Can. J. Chem.*, 1964, **42**, 830.

3 - Hydroxyoestra - 1 : 3 : 5(10) : 7 - tetraen - 17 - one★ (*Equilin*).

Synthesis:

Bagli *et al.*, *Tetrahedron Letters*, 1964, 387.

3β-Hydroxyolean-12-en-27 : 28-dioic Acid. *See* Cincholic Acid.

γ-Hydroxyornithine

$H_2N{\cdot}CH_2{\cdot}CH(OH){\cdot}CH_2{\cdot}CH(NH_2){\cdot}COOH$

$C_5H_{12}O_3N_2$ MW 148

Amino acid present in *Vicia* spp.

Bell, Tirimanna, *Biochem. J.*, 1964, **91**, 358.

19-Hydroxy-3-oxo-16α-(−)-kauran-17-oic Acid

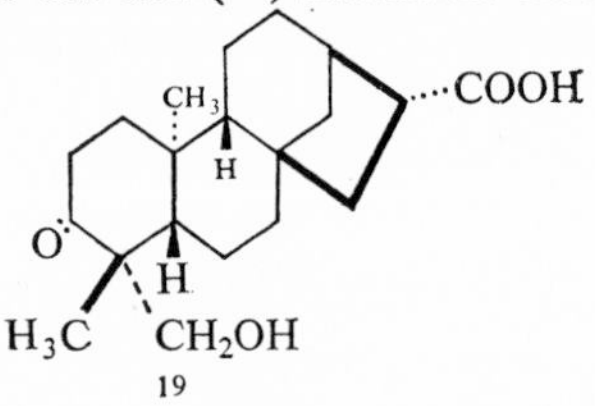

$C_{20}H_{30}O_4$ MW 334

Constituent of a *Beyeria* sp. Prisms from Me_2CO. M.p. 193–4°. $[\alpha]_D$ −115° (c, 0·92 in $CHCl_3$).

19-O-*Ac*: $C_{22}H_{32}O_5$. MW 376. Constituent of *B.* sp. Prisms from C_6H_6. M.p. 186·5–188°. $[\alpha]_D$ −47° (c, 0·85 in $CHCl_3$). *Me ester*: needles from light petroleum. M.p. 121·5–122·5°. $[\alpha]_D$ −47° (c, 1·40 in $CHCl_3$).

Baddeley *et al.*, *Austral. J. Chem.*, 1964, **17**, 578.

20(*S*)-Hydroxy-3-oxo-4 : 6-pregnadiene-18-carboxylic Acid (→ 20) Lactone

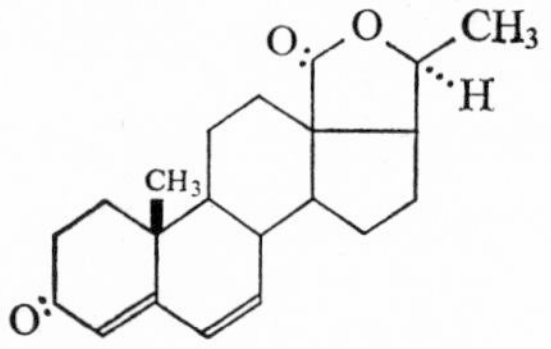

$C_{21}H_{26}O_3$ MW 326

Present in the flowers of *Paravallaris microphylla*. M.p. 238°. $[\alpha]_D^{20}$ 32° (c, 0·5 in $CHCl_3$). Light absorption: $\lambda_{max.}$ 286 mμ (ε, 28,000).

Potier, Kan, Le Men, *Tetrahedron Letters*, 1964, 1671.

20(*S*)-Hydroxy-3-oxo-4-pregnene-18-carboxylic Acid (→ 20) Lactone

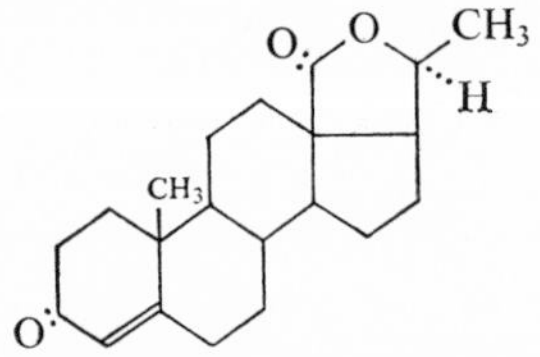

$C_{21}H_{28}O_3$ MW 328

Present in the flowers of *Paravallaris microphylla*. M.p. 198°. $[\alpha]_D^{20}$ 92° (c, 0·8 in $CHCl_3$). Light absorption: $\lambda_{max.}$ 240 mμ (ε, 16,200).

Le Men, *Bull. soc. chim.*, 1960, 860.
Potier, Kan, Le Men, *Tetrahedron Letters*, 1964, 1671.

15-Hydroxypentadecanoic Acid.★
Lactone: exaltolide.
Synthesis:
McCrae, *Tetrahedron*, 1964, **20**, 1773.

5 - Hydroxy - 3 : 3′ : 4′ : 7 : 8 - pentamethoxyflavone (*Gossypetin pentamethyl ether*)

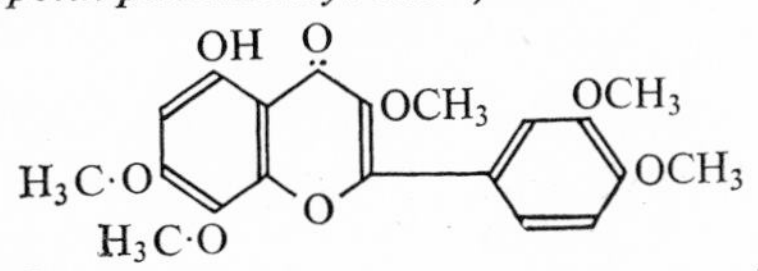

$C_{20}H_{20}O_8$ MW 388
Constituent of *Ricinocarpus stylosus* Diels. Yellow needles from EtOH. M.p. 161–2°. Light absorption: $\lambda_{max.}$ 258 (log ε, 4·26), 276 (4·28), 340 sh. (4·15), and 364 mμ (4·16).
Ac: needles from MeOH. M.p. 162–3°, with new needles m.p. 164–5°.
Me ether: gossypetin hexamethyl ether. Dimorphic prisms: (i) m.p. 159–61° and (ii) 170–1°.
Henrick, Jefferies, *Austral. J. Chem.*, 1964, **17**, 934.
See also under Gossypetin.★

2-(5-Hydroxy-*cis*-pent-2-enyl)-3-oxo-cyclopentylacetic Acid Lactone. *See* 5′-Hydroxyjasmonic Acid Lactone.

3-Hydroxy-3-phenylazetidine

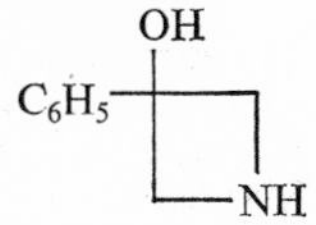

$C_9H_{11}ON$ MW 149
Cryst. from Et_2O–AcOEt. M.p. 160–2°.
B_2,$(COOH)_2$: cryst. from EtOH–MeOH. M.p. 190–2° decomp.
Testa, Fontanella, *Ann.*, 1964, **671**, 106.

3-Hydroxy-2-phenylcinchonic Acid. *See* Oxycinchophen.★

2-(4-Hydroxyphenyl)ethanol.★
1-β-D-*Glucopyranoside*: *see* Salidroside.

1-*p*-Hydroxyphenyl-2-(1-methyl-2-phenoxyethamino)-1-propanol. *See* Isoxsuprine.★

2-*p*-Hydroxyphenylpropionic Acid★ (4-p-*Hydroxyhydratropic acid*)
$C_9H_{10}O_3$ MW 166
(−)-.
Constituent of the heartwood of *Pterocarpus indicus*. M.p. 141–2°. $[\alpha]_D$ −36° (c, 1·5 in $CHCl_3$).
Me ether: m.p. 53–4°.
Cooke, Rae, *Austral. J. Chem.*, 1964, **17**, 379.

2-Hydroxy-2-phenylpropionic Acid.★
See also:
Eliel, Freeman, *Organic Syntheses*, Coll. Vol. **4**, 58.

3-Hydroxy-2-phenylpropionic Acid★ (*Tropic acid*).
S (−)-.
Absolute configuration:
Fodor, Csepreghy, *Tetrahedron Letters*, 1959, No. 7, 16.

3-Hydroxy-2-phenylquinoline-4-carboxylic Acid. *See* Oxycinchophen.★

2-[*N*-(*m*-Hydroxyphenyl)-*p*-toluidinomethyl]imidazoline. *See* Phentolamine.★

4 - Hydroxypipecolic Acid (4 - *Hydroxypiperidine* - 2 - *carboxylic acid*)

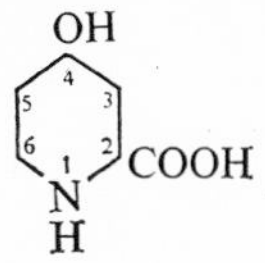

$C_6H_{11}O_2N$ MW 129
Trans L-(−)-.
Present in acacia leaves. Colourless prisms from EtOH.Aq. M.p. 294° decomp. $[\alpha]_D^{20}$ −13° (c, 1 in H_2O), +2·7° (c, 1 in 5*N*-HCl), −18·5° (c, 1 in *N*-NaOH).
B,HCl: cryst. from EtOH.Aq. M.p. 161–3°.
N-2 : 4-*Dinitrophenyl deriv.*: orange prisms from EtOH.Aq. M.p. 183°.
Benzoyl: needles from EtOH.Aq. M.p. 174°. $[\alpha]_D^{15}$ −54° (c, 1 in EtOH).
p-*Toluenesulphonyl*: prisms from AcOEt–C_6H_6. M.p. 162°. $[\alpha]_D^{19}$ −16° (c, 1 in EtOH).
1-*Phenylcarbamoyl*: m.p. 181–97°. $[\alpha]_D^{26}$ −24·5° (c, 1 in EtOH) → *Hydantoin*: prisms. M.p. 204–5°. $[\alpha]_D^{23}$ −53° (c, 1 in EtOH).
Cu salt: blue prisms from H_2O. M.p. 229° decomp.
DL-.
B,HCl: m.p. 161–3°.
Cis (−)-.
Hydrate from EtOH.Aq. M.p. 265° decomp. $[\alpha]_D^{23}$ −17° (c, 1·1 in H_2O).
N-*Benzoyl*: two forms: (i) m.p. 104°, $[\alpha]_D^{23}$ −39·5° (c, 1 in EtOH), and (ii) m.p. 191°, $[\alpha]_D^{26}$ −38·5° (c, 1 in EtOH).
N-2 : 4-*Dinitrophenyl deriv.*: yellow prisms from EtOH.Aq. M.p. 134°.
Cu salt: deep blue plates. M.p. 245° decomp.
Virtanen, Kari, *Acta Chem. Scand.*, 1955, **9**, 170.
Fowden, *Biochem. J.*, 1958, **70**, 629.
Clark-Lewis, Mortimer, *Nature*, 1959, **184**, 1234; *J. Chem. Soc.*, 1961, 189.
Fujita, Irreverre, Witkop, *J. Am. Chem. Soc.*, 1964, **86**, 1844.

5 - Hydroxypipecolic Acid (5 - *Hydroxypiperidine* - 2 - *carboxylic acid*).
Trans L-.
Amino acid present in dates, Rhodesian teak, *Rhapis excelsa*, and *Acacia* sp. M.p. 210–15° decomp. $[\alpha]_D^{20}$ −10·9° (c, 0·92 in H_2O).
N-*Carbobenzyloxy*: cryst. from Me_2CO–light petroleum. M.p. 150–2°. $[\alpha]_D^{20}$ −17·9° (c, 1 in Me_2CO).
DL-.
B,HCl: cryst. from EtOH. M.p. 192–4°.
Allo-.
Slim needles from EtOH.Aq. M.p. 255–8° decomp. (sublimes 220–40°). $[\alpha]_D$ −31·1° (c, 0·8 in H_2O).
B,HBr: m.p. 205–7°.
Lactone, B,HBr: platelets. M.p. 228–31°.
King, King, Warwick, *J. Chem. Soc.*, 1950, 3590.
Virtanen, Kari, *Acta Chem. Scand.*, 1954, **8**, 1290.
Grobbelaar, Pollard, Steward, *Nature*, 1955, **175**, 703.
Witkop, Foltz, *J. Am. Chem. Soc.*, 1957, **79**, 197.

Fujita, Irreverre, Witkop, *J. Am. Chem. Soc.*, 1964, **86**, 1844.

Hydroxypiperidine-2-carboxylic Acid. *See* Hydroxypipecolic Acid.

6-Hydroxypyridine-3-carboxylic Acid.★
See also:
Boyer, Schoen, *Organic Syntheses*, 1956, **36**, 44; Coll. Vol. **4**, 532.

12β-Hydroxysandaracopimaric Acid

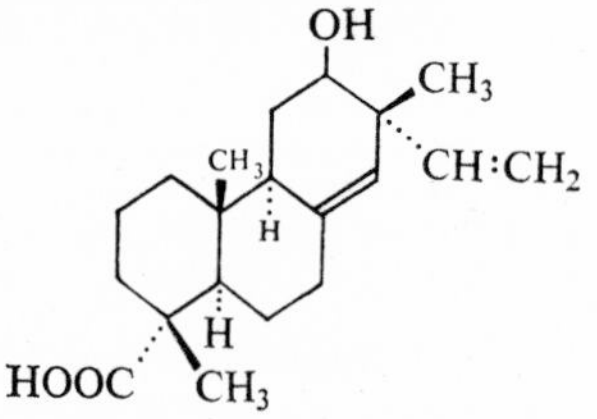

$C_{20}H_{30}O_3$ MW 318
Plates from MeOH.Aq. M.p. 270°. $[\alpha]_D$ 11° (c, 0·8 in EtOH).
12β-*Ac*: $C_{22}H_{32}O_4$. MW 360. Constituent of N. African sandarac (*Tetraclinis articulata*). Three forms: M.p. 140·5–141·5°, 156–8·5°, and 170°. $[\alpha]_D$ −50° (EtOH).

Edwards, Nicolson, Rodger, *Can. J. Chem.*, 1960, **38**, 663.
ApSimon, Edwards, *Can. J. Chem.*, 1961, **39**, 2543.
Gough, *Chemistry and Industry*, 1964, 2059.

17-Hydroxystachene

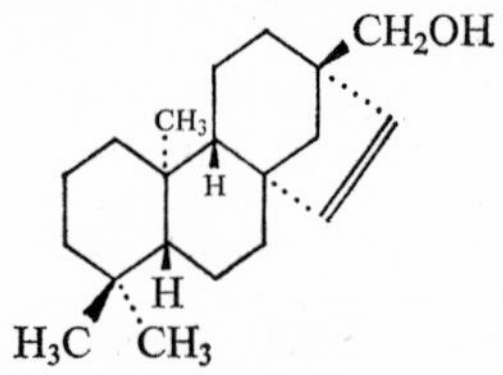

$C_{20}H_{32}O$ MW 288
Present in the trunk wood of *Erythroxylon monogynum* Roxb. M.p. 121·5–123°. $[\alpha]_D$ 67° ($CHCl_3$).
Ac: m.p. 56–7°. $[\alpha]_D$ 54° ($CHCl_3$).
p-*Toluenesulphonyl*: m.p. 128–9°. $LiAlH_4 \rightarrow$ stachene.

Murray, McCrindle, *Chemistry and Industry*, 1964, 500.

19-Hydroxystachene

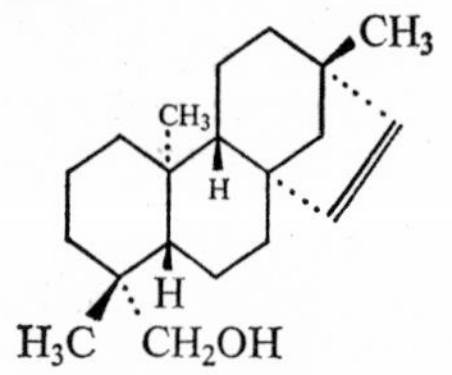

$C_{20}H_{32}O$ MW 288
Present in the trunk wood of *Erythroxylon monogynum* Roxb. M.p. 119–20°. $[\alpha]_D$ 39° ($CHCl_3$).
Ac: m.p. 72–72·5°. $[\alpha]_D$ 34° ($CHCl_3$).
p-*Toluenesulphonyl*: m.p. 105–8°.

Gupta, Muthana, *J. Ind. Inst. Sci.*, 1954, **36A**, 76, 122.
Murray, McCrindle, *Chemistry and Industry*, 1964, 500.

3-Hydroxytetracycloxide

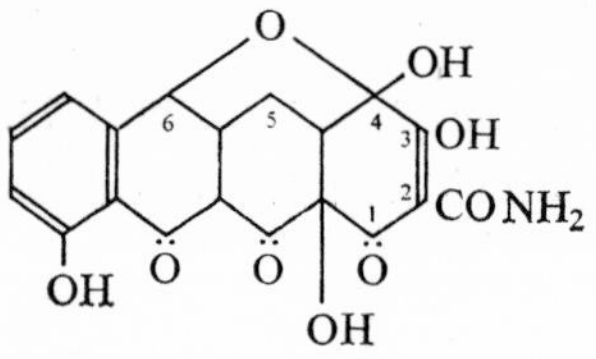

$C_{19}H_{15}O_9N$ MW 401
Light absorption: $\lambda_{max.}$ 258 (log ε, 4·64) and 338 mμ (3·67) in methanolic 0·1*N*-HCl.

Esse *et al.*, *J. Am. Chem. Soc.*, 1964, **86**, 3874.

6-Hydroxytetradecanoic Acid

$CH_3\cdot[CH_2]_7\cdot CH(OH)\cdot[CH_2]_4\cdot COOH$

$C_{14}H_{28}O_3$ MW 244
(−)-Butolic Acid.
Constituent of lac. M.p. 58–9°. $[\alpha]_D$ −1·3° ($CHCl_3$).
Me ester: $C_{15}H_{30}O_3$. MW 258. M.p. 26–7°. $[\alpha]_D$ −2·2° ($CHCl_3$). $[\alpha]_D^{30}$ 1·4488.

Khurana *et al.*, *Tetrahedron Letters*, 1964, 1537.

2′-Hydroxy-4 : 4′ : 6-trimethoxychalcone

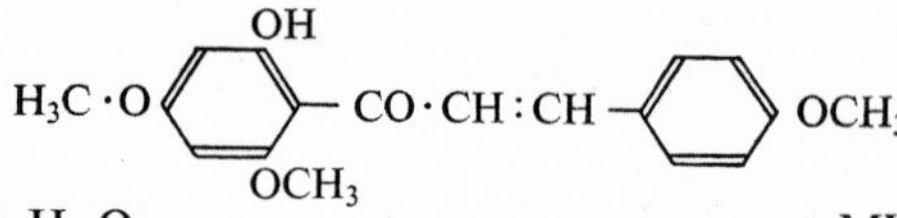

$C_{18}H_{18}O_5$ MW 314
Constituent of Kava rhizome (*Piper methysticum*). Cryst. from MeOH.Aq. M.p. 114–15°. Light absorption: $\lambda_{max.}$ 364 mμ (log ε, 4·55). $\lambda_{min.}$ 268 mμ.
Ac: two forms: (i) by fast cryst. from MeOH.Aq., m.p. 108–9°, (ii) by slow cryst., m.p. 120–1°.

Haensel, Runft, Baehr, *Z. Naturforsch.*, 1963, **18b**, 370.

2′-Hydroxy-2 : 5 : 9-trimethyl-6 : 7-benzomorphan. *See* Metazocine.★

4-Hydroxytutin. *See* Mellitoxin.

4-Hydroxyundeca-5 : 6-dien-8 : 10-diynoic Acid. *See* Nemotinic Acid.★

4-Hydroxy-2-*n*-undecylquinoline

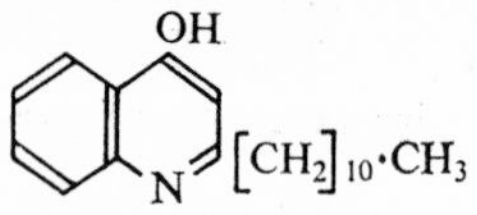

$C_{20}H_{29}ON$ MW 299
N-*Oxide*: $C_{20}H_{29}O_2N$. MW 315. Metabolite of *Pseudomonas pyocyanea*, an antagonist of dihydrostreptomycin. Colourless leaflets. M.p. 148·5–149·5°.

Cornforth, James, *Biochem. J.*, 1956, **63**, 124.

3β-Hydroxyurs-12-en-23-oic Acid. *See* Commic Acid B.

15-Hydroxyvaleranone. *See* Kanokonol.

α-Hydroxy-*o*-xylene.★
See also:
Brasen, Hauser, *Organic Syntheses*, Coll. Vol. **4**, 582.

Hymorphan. *See* Dihydromorphinone.

Hyosamine. *See* Mono-*N*-Me *under* 2-Deoxystreptamine.

Hyperin.★

Present in the flowers of *Acacia melanoxylon*. $[\alpha]_D$ −83° (c, 0·2 in Py). Light absorption: $\lambda_{max.}$ 259 (log ε, 4·31) and 364 mμ (4·39).

Falco, de Vries, *Naturwiss.*, 1964, **51**, 462.

Hypoglycin B (γ-L-*Glutamyl*-N$^\alpha$-*amino*-β-*(2-methylenecyclopropyl)glutamic acid*)

$$H_2N \cdot CH \cdot CH_2 \cdot CH_2 \cdot CO \cdot NH \cdot CH \cdot CH_2 \cdot \triangle : CH_2$$
$$\qquad COOH \qquad\qquad\qquad COOH$$

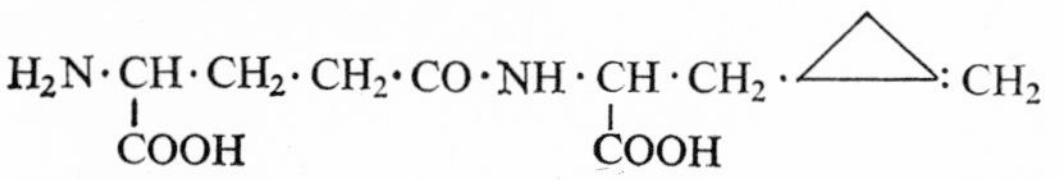

$C_{12}H_{18}O_5N_2$ MW 270

Biologically active component of *Blighia sapida*. Colourless needles from Me$_2$CO.Aq. Double m.p. (i) 194–5° and (ii) 200–7°. $[\alpha]_D^{32}$ +9·6° (c, 1·12 in H_2O). pK_2' 3·75, pK_3' 9·36.
Dinitrophenyl deriv.: cryst. from AcOEt–CHCl$_3$. M.p. 170–2°.
Phenylthiohydantoin deriv.: needles from EtOH.Aq. M.p. 186–8°.

Hassall, Reyle, *Biochem. J.*, 1955, **60**, 334.
v. Holt *et al.*, *Naturwiss.*, 1956, **43**, 279.

Jöhl, Stoll, *Helv. Chim. Acta*, 1959, **42**, 156.
Hassall, John, *Tetrahedron Letters*, 1959, No. 3, 7; *J. Chem. Soc.*, 1960, 4112.

Hypophyllanthin

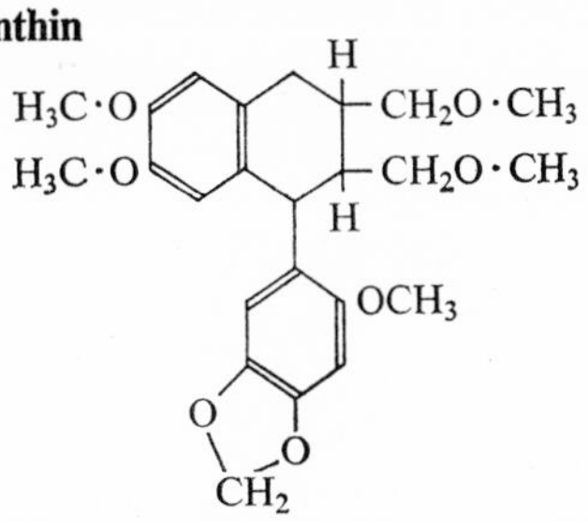

$C_{24}H_{30}O_7$ MW 430

Constituent of the leaves of *Phyllanthus niruri* L. Long needles from light petroleum. M.p. 128°. $[\alpha]_D$ 3·9° (CHCl$_3$). Light absorption: $\lambda_{max.}$ 230·5 and 280 mμ (log ε, 4·56 and 2·23).

Row *et al.*, *Tetrahedron Letters*, 1964, 1557.

Hypoxanthine.★

Improved synthesis:

Taylor, Cheng, *Tetrahedron Letters*, 1959, No. 12, 9.

I

Ibogaine.★

See also:

Sallay, *Tetrahedron Letters*, 1964, 2443.

Erratum p. 1830

Icaritin.★

Alternative name should read: (3 : 5 : 7-*Trihydroxy*-8-[3-*hydroxy*-3-*methylbutyl*]-4′-*methoxyflavone*).

Ichthynone★

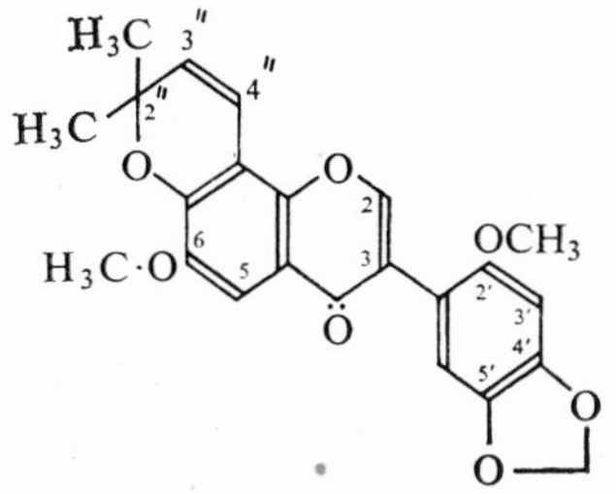

Fish poison from the root bark of the Jamaican Dogwood (*Piscidia erythrina* L.). (According to *Index Kewensis* the name *Ichthyomethia piscipula* L. given in the main work is incorrect.) Light absorption: $\lambda_{max.}$ 232 (ε, 33,600), 262 (24,300), 309 (14,100), 331 (11,000), and 345 mμ (9400).

The *Tetrahydro deriv.* reported in the main work is in fact a *Dihydro deriv.*: m.p. 236–8°. The *Hydrazone* and *Phenylhydrazone* reported in the main work have been shown to be pyrazole derivatives.

Schwarz *et al.*, *Tetrahedron*, 1964, **20**, 1317.
Dyke *et al.*, *Tetrahedron*, 1964, **20**, 1331.

Ileu$_8$-oxytocin. *See* Mesotocin.

Imidazolidine-2 : 4 : 5-trione.★

See also:

Murray, *Organic Syntheses*, 1957, **37**, 71; Coll. Vol. **4**, 744.

***s*-Indacene**

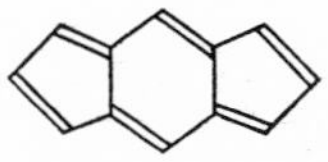

$C_{12}H_8$ MW 152

Unstable red oil.

Brown, *J. Chem. Soc.*, 1951, 2391.
Hafner, *Angew. Chem.*, 1963, **75**, 1041; *Int. Ed.*, 1963, **2**, 133.

Indazole.★

See also:

Ainsworth, *Organic Syntheses*, 1959, **39**, 27; Coll. Vol. **4**, 536.
Buu-Hoï *et al.*, *Bull. soc. chim.*, 1964, 2019.

Indicaxanthin

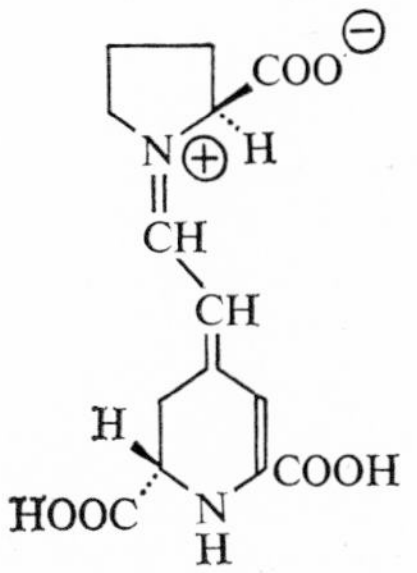

$C_{14}H_{16}O_6N_2$ MW 308

Constituent of the fruits of *Opuntia ficus-indica*. Cryst. from H_2O which decomp. 160–2°. $[\alpha]_D^{20}$ +394° (c, 1 in 0·1*M*-phosphate buffer; pH 7). pK_a 3·3. Light absorption: $\lambda_{max.}$ 260 (log ε, 3·73), 305 (3·19), and 485 mμ (4·63) in H_2O.

Piattelli, Minale, Prota, *Tetrahedron*, 1964, **20**, 2325.

Indigoidin. *See* 5 : 5′-Diamino-4 : 4′-dihydroxy-3 : 3′-diazadipheno-2 : 2′-quinone.

Indole 3-aldehyde.★

See also:

James, Snyder, *Organic Syntheses*, 1959, **39**, 30; Coll. Vol. **4**, 539.

3 : 3′-Indolylacrylic Acid.★

Configuration:
Trans-.

Rappe, *Acta Chem. Scand.*, 1964, **18**, 818.

β-5-Indolyl-α-alanine (*Isotryptophan*)

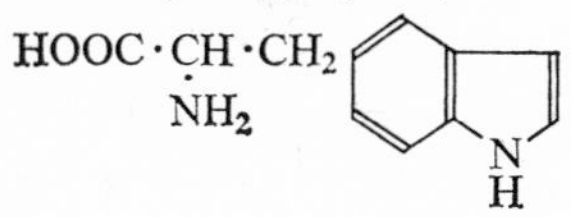

$C_{11}H_{12}O_2N_2$ MW 204

Cryst. from MeOH.Aq. M.p. 213–15°.
N-*Benzoyl*: cryst. from MeOH.Aq. M.p. 184–6°.

Behringer, Duesberg, *Chem. Ber.*, 1963, **96**, 377.

Indorm. *See* Propiomazine.

Inositol.
Myo-.
Biogenesis:
Kindl, Hoffmann-Ostenhof, *Biochem. Z.*, 1964, **339**, 374.

Insulin.★
Synthesis of A chain (sheep):
Katsoyannis, Tometsko, Fukuda, *J. Am. Chem. Soc.*, 1963, **85**, 2863.
Synthesis of B chain (sheep):
Katsoyannis *et al.*, *J. Am. Chem. Soc.*, 1964, **86**, 930.

Insulton. *See* Methoin.★

Intensatin (3-[β-*Diethylaminoethyl*]-7-*ethoxycarbonylmethoxy*-4-*methyl*-2-*oxo*-1 : 2-*chromene*)

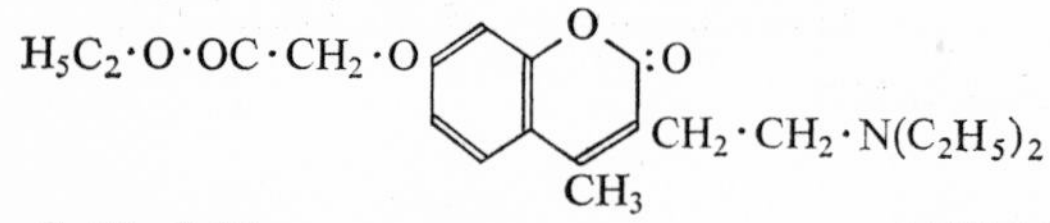

$C_{20}H_{25}O_5N$ MW 361
Coronary dilatant drug.
B,HCl: m.p. 159–60°.
Cassella-Riedel Pharma G.m.b.H., *Report of Therapy Congress and Pharmaceutical Exhibition*, Karlsruhe, 1963 (*Angew. Chem., Int. Ed.*, 1964, **3**, 68).

Iodinin.★
Present in *Pseudomonas iodina* (*Chromobacterium iodium*), *Brevibacterium crystalloiodinum*, and *Waksmania* spp.
Yoshioka, Kidani, *J. Pharm. Soc. Japan*, 1952, **72**, 1301.
Sneath, *J. Gen. Microbiol.*, 1956, **15**, 70.
Irie, Kurosawa, Nagaoka, *Bull. Chem. Soc. Japan*, 1960, **33**, 1057.
Gerber, Lechavalier, *Biochemistry*, 1964, **3**, 598.

4-Iodo-1 : 2-dimethoxybenzene★ (4-*Iodoveratrole*).
See also:
Janssen, Wilson, *Organic Syntheses*, 1956, **36**, 46; Coll. Vol. **4**, 547.

***o*-Iodosobenzoic Acid.** *See* 1 : 3-Dihydro-1-hydroxy-3-oxo-1 : 2-benziodoxole.

Irehamine (3β-*Hydroxy*-20α-*methylaminopregn*-5-*ene*)

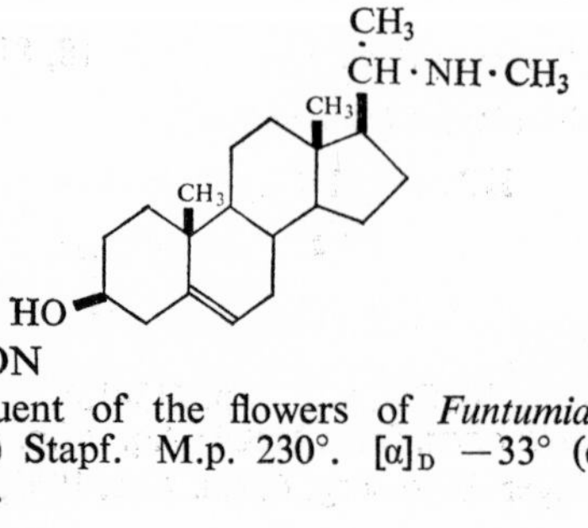

$C_{22}H_{37}ON$ MW 331
Constituent of the flowers of *Funtumia elastica* (Preuss) Stapf. M.p. 230°. $[\alpha]_D$ −33° (c, 0·9 in $CHCl_3$).
Di-Ac: cryst. from AcOEt. M.p. 224°. $[\alpha]_D$ −60° (c, 0·9 in $CHCl_3$).
N-*Ac*: cryst. from EtOH. M.p. 237°. $[\alpha]_D$ −47° (c, 1 in $CHCl_3$).
Truong-Ho *et al.*, *Bull. soc. chim.*, 1963, 2332.

Irehine (20α - *Dimethylamino* - 3β - *hydroxypregn* - 5 - *ene*)

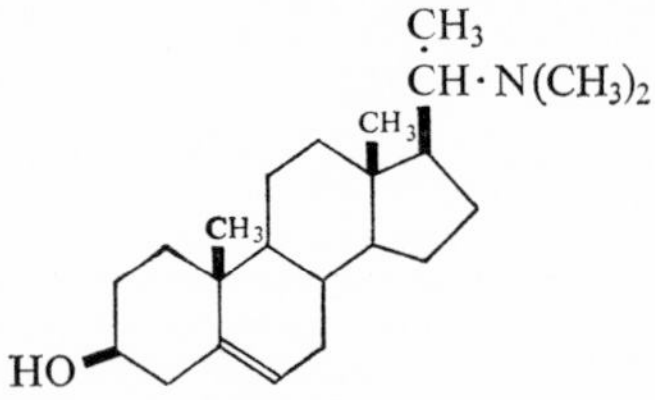

$C_{23}H_{39}ON$ MW 345
Constituent of the flowers of *Funtumia elastica* (Preuss) Stapf. M.p. 174°. $[\alpha]_D$ −46°.
Truong-Ho, Khuong-Huu, Goutarel, *Bull. soc. chim.*, 1963, 544.
Truong-Ho *et al.*, *Bull. soc. chim.*, 1963, 2332.

Irehline★ (*Concurchine*).
Concurchine★ is identical with Irehline.
Janot *et al.*, *Compt. rend.*, 1964, **258**, 2089.

Ismine.★
Alternative synthesis:
Hill, Carlson, *Tetrahedron Letters*, 1964, 1157.

Isoarborinol
$C_{30}H_{48}O$ MW 424
Constituent of the leaves of *Glyrosmis arborea*. Epimeric with arborinol. Cryst. from $CHCl_3$–MeOH. M.p. 294–294·5°. $[\alpha]_D$ +47° (c, 0·53 in $CHCl_3$).
Ac: cryst. from hexane. M.p. 287–8°. $[\alpha]_D$ +56° (c, 0·81 in $CHCl_3$).
Vorbrüggen, Pakrashi, Djerassi, *Ann.*, 1963, **668**, 57.

Isoartocarpin. *See* Cycloartocarpin.

Isobetanidin
$C_{18}H_{16}O_8N_2$ MW 388
Aglycone from betanin. Stereoisomeric at C_{15} with betanidin (*q.v.*).
Wyler, Dreiding, *Helv. Chim. Acta*, 1959, **42**, 1699.
Wyler, Mabry, Dreiding, *Helv. Chim. Acta*, 1963, **46**, 1745.

Isoboldine

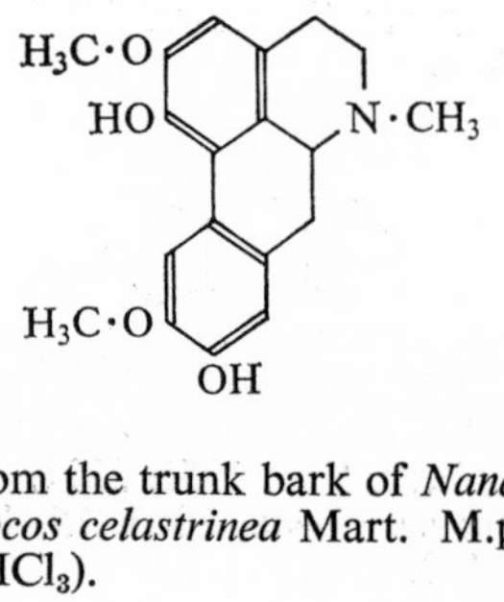

$C_{19}H_{21}O_4N$ MW 327
Alkaloid from the trunk bark of *Nandina domestica* and *Symplocos celastrinea* Mart. M.p. 128°. $[\alpha]_D^{13}$ +65·3° ($CHCl_3$).

Chikamatsu, Tomita, *J. Chem. Soc. Japan*, 1961, **82**, 1708, 17110.
Tomita, Fujie, *J. Pharm. Soc. Japan*, 1962, **82**, 1457.
Tschesche *et al.*, *Tetrahedron*, 1964, **20**, 1435.

2-Isobutylidene-5 : 5-dimethyl-4 : 6-dioxo-*m*-dioxan (*Dimethylketene acylal of dimethyl malonic acid*)

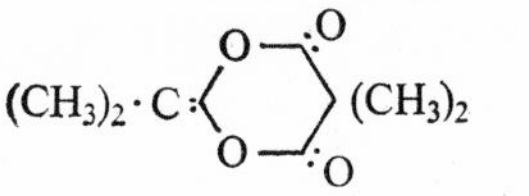

$C_9H_{12}O_4$ MW 184
Stable intermediate for the preparation of dimethylketene.★ Cryst. from light petroleum. M.p. 80°.
Staudinger, *Helv. Chim. Acta*, 1925, **8**, 306.
Bestian, Günthe, *Angew. Chem.*, 1963, **75**, 841; *Int. Ed.*, 1963, **2**, 618.

Isochlorogenic Acid.★
This acid has been shown to be a mixture of 3 : 4-, 3 : 5-, and 4 : 5-dicaffeoylquinic acids (*q.v.*).
Scarpati, Guiso, *Annali di Chimica*, 1963, **53**, 1315; *Tetrahedron Letters*, 1964, 2851.

Isodesmosine

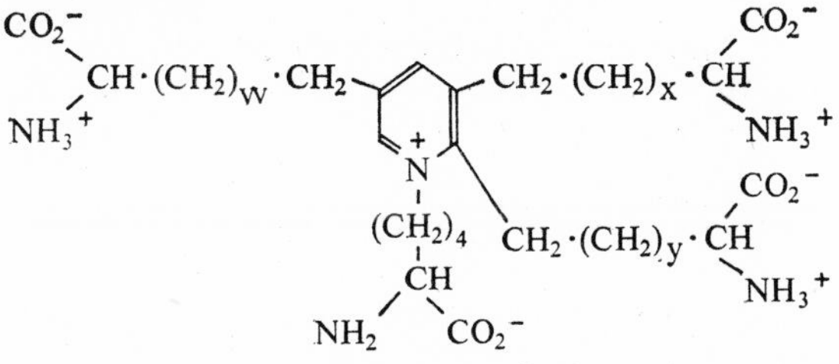

w + x + y = 4

$C_{24}H_{39}O_8N_5$ MW 525
Degradation product of elastin.
Partridge, Elsden, Thomas, *Nature*, 1963, **197**, 1297; 1963, **200**, 651.

Isodextropimaric Acid. *See* Isopimaric Acid.

Isodonin. *See* Enmein.

Isodrimenin

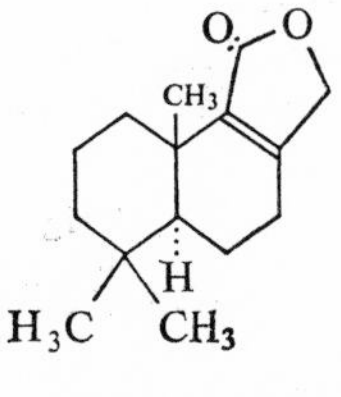

$C_{15}H_{22}O_2$ MW 234
From the bark of *Drimys winteri* Forst. Cryst. from hexane and by sublimation at 100°/0·1 mm. M.p. 131–2°. $[\alpha]_D$ 87° (c, 2·02 in $CHCl_3$), 78° (c, 0·80 in C_6H_6).
Apell *et al.*, *J. Chem. Soc.*, 1960, 4685.
Wenkert, Strike, *J. Am. Chem. Soc.*, 1964, **86**, 2044.

Isoeburnamine.★
pK_a' 7·8. Light absorption: $\lambda_{max.}$ 229 (ε, 34,600) and 282 mμ (7900).
See also:
Bartlett *et al.*, *J. Org. Chem.*, 1963, **28**, 2197.

Isoechinochrome. *See* Spinochrome C.

Isoelemicin (3 : 4 : 5-*Trimethoxy*-1-*propenylbenzene*)

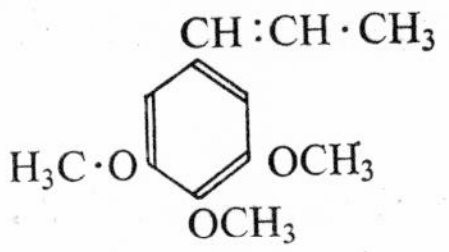

$C_{12}H_{16}O_3$ MW 208
Constituent of oil of nutmeg. B.p. 153–6°/10 mm. D^{20} 1·077. n_D^{20} 1·547. $Br_2 \rightarrow$ dibromo deriv., m.p. 89–90°.
Semmler, *Ber.*, 1908, **41**, 2183.
Shulgin, Kerlinger, *Naturwiss.*, 1964, **51**, 360.
See also Elemicin.★

Isoeleutherin.★

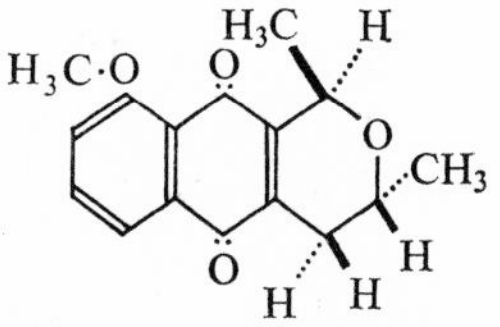

Stereochemistry:
Eisenhuth, Schmid, *Helv. Chim. Acta*, 1958, **41**, 2021.
Cameron *et al.*, *J. Chem. Soc.*, 1964, 98.

Isofungipavine. *See* Mecambroline.

Isohibaene

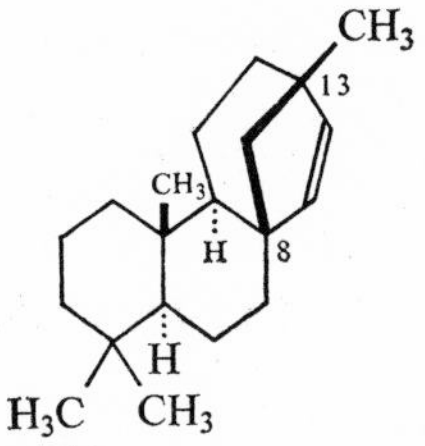

$C_{20}H_{32}$ MW 272
Plates from EtOH. M.p. 73–5°. $[\alpha]_D$ +8° (c, 0·016 in MeOH).
Wenkert, Jeffs, Mahajan, *J. Am. Chem. Soc.*, 1964, **86**, 2218.

Isojervine★

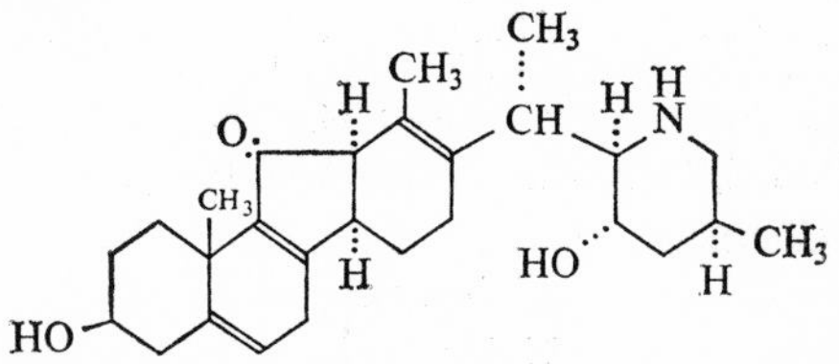

$C_{27}H_{39}O_3N$ MW 425
Forms solvates with $CHCl_3$, m.p. 140–9°, and Me_2CO, m.p. 105–12°.
N-*Ac*: m.p. 207–10°. $[\alpha]_D^{25}$ 15° (c, 0·93 in $CHCl_3$).
Tri-Ac: m.p. 187–90°. $[\alpha]_D^{25}$ 29° (c, 0·988 in $CHCl_3$).

N-*Me*: rods from MeOH–AcOEt. M.p. 220–4° decomp. $[\alpha]_D$ 0°.

Wintersteiner, Moore, *Tetrahedron Letters*, 1962, 795; *J. Org. Chem.*, 1964, **29**, 262.
Masamune *et al.*, *Bull. Chem. Soc. Japan*, 1962, **35**, 1749.
Dauben *et al.*, *J. Org. Chem.*, 1963, **28**, 293.

Mass spectrum:

Budzikiewicz, *Tetrahedron*, 1964, **20**, 2267.

Isoleurosine

$C_{46}H_{60}O_9N_4$ MW 812

Alkaloid from *Vinca rosea* L. M.p. 202–6° decomp. $[\alpha]_D^{26}$ +61·2°. pK_a' 4·8, 7·3 (66% H·CONMe$_2$). Light absorption: $\lambda_{max.}$ 214, 261, 287 mμ.

Svoboda *et al.*, *J. Pharm. Sci.*, 1961, **50**, 409.

Isoliensinine

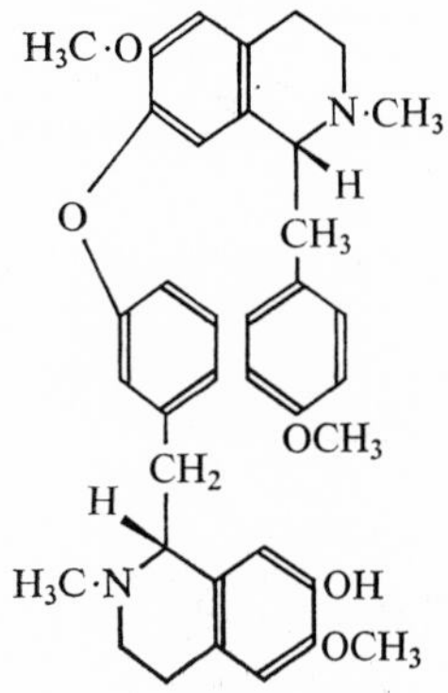

$C_{37}H_{42}O_6N_2$ MW 610

From the embryo of the lotus seed (*Nelumbo nucifera* Gaertn.). Oil. $[\alpha]_D^{29}$ −43·3° ($CHCl_3$), +49·3° (Me_2CO).
B,2HClO$_4$·H$_2$O: m.p. 200–3°. $[\alpha]_D^{22}$ −70° (Me_2CO).
B,2HCl·4H$_2$O: m.p. 185–6°.
Di-O-Me ether: $C_{39}H_{46}O_6N_2$. MW 638. *Styphnate*: m.p. 133–5°. $[\alpha]_D^{27}$ −81·5° (Me_2CO).

Tomita *et al.*, *Tetrahedron Letters*, 1964, 2637.

Isolimocitrol (3 : 3′ : 5 : 7-*Tetrahydroxy*-4′ : 6 : 8-*trimethoxyflavone*)

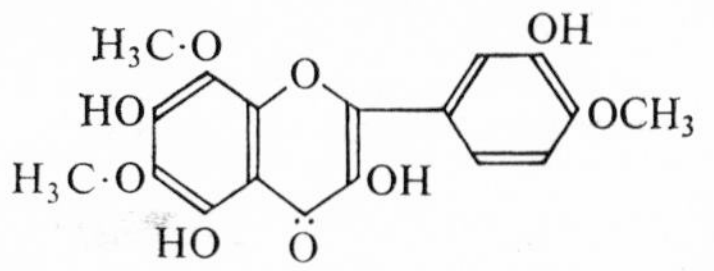

$C_{15}H_{16}O_9$ MW 378

Yellow needles. M.p. 236–8°. Light absorption: $\lambda_{max.}$ 260, 276, *ca.* 350, and 375 mμ in EtOH.
3β-D-*Glucosyl*: $C_{24}H_{26}O_{14}$. MW 538. Constituent of *Citrus limon*. Cryst. from MeOH.Aq. M.p. 220–5°.

Gentili, Horowitz, *Tetrahedron*, 1964, **20**, 2313.

Isolongifolene

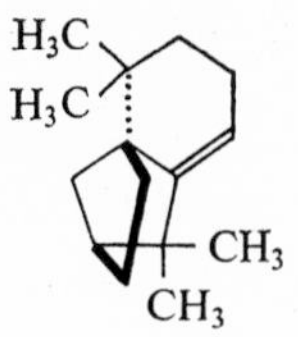

$C_{15}H_{24}$ MW 204

Acid catalysed re-arrangement product of longifolene. Colourless liquid. B.p. 82–3°/0·4 mm. $D_4^{26·5}$ 0·9292. $n_D^{26·5}$ 1·4980. α_D −82·2° (homogeneous). $[\alpha]_D$ −78·1° (c, 5·5 in EtOH). $H_2 \rightarrow$ isolongifolane (b.p. 84°/0·4 mm. $D_4^{26·5}$ 0·9272. $n_D^{26·5}$ 1·4930. α_D 4° (homogeneous)).

Nayak, Dev, *Tetrahedron*, 1960, **8**, 42.
Prahlad *et al.*, *Tetrahedron Letters*, 1964, 417.

Iso-octanoic Acid. *See* 6-Methylheptanoic Acid.★

Isophorone oxide. *See* 2 : 3-Epoxy-3 : 5 : 5-trimethylcyclohexanone.

Isopimaric Acid (*Isodextropimaric acid, miropinic acid*)

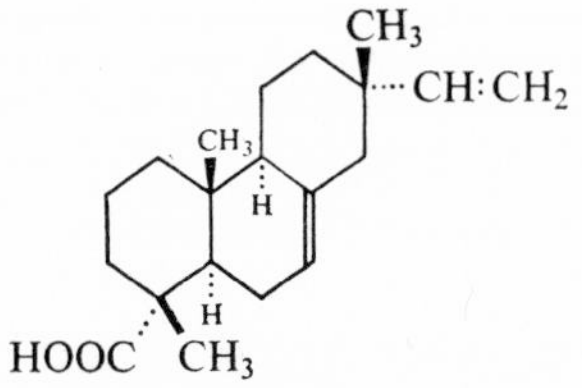

$C_{20}H_{30}O_4$ MW 334

From the oleoresin of *Pinus palustris*. M.p. 162–4°. $[\alpha]_D^{24}$ ±0°. $H_2 \rightarrow$ dihydro acid, m.p. 173–5°.
Me ester: $C_{21}H_{32}O_4$. MW 348. M.p. 61·5–62°.
2-*Amino*-2-*methylpropan*-1-*ol salt*: m.p. 194–6°.

Harris, Sanderson, *J. Am. Chem. Soc.*, 1948, **70**, 2081.
Edwards, Howe, *Can. J. Chem.*, 1959, **37**, 760; *Chemistry and Industry*, 1959, 537.
Wenkert, Camberlin, *J. Am. Chem. Soc.*, 1959, **81**, 537.
Bruun, Fischmeister, Stenhagen, *Acta Chem. Scand.*, 1959, **13**, 379.
Briggs, Cambie, *Tetrahedron*, 1960, **8**, 356.
Antkowiak, ApSimon, Edwards, *J. Org. Chem.*, 1962, **27**, 1930.
Ireland, Newbould, *J. Org. Chem.*, 1962, **27**, 1931; 1963, **28**, 23.

Isopinastric Acid

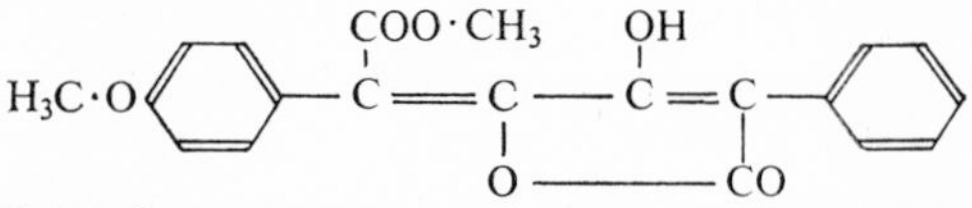

$C_{20}H_{16}O_6$ MW 352

Fine needles from C_6H_6. M.p. 120–1°.
Ac: yellow thin rectangular plates. M.p. 159–61°.
Me ether: $C_{21}H_{18}O_6$. MW 366. Yellow rectangular prisms. M.p. 129–31°.

Grover, Seshadri, *Tetrahedron*, 1958, **4**, 105.
Agarwal, Seshadri, *Tetrahedron*, 1963, **19**, 1965.

6-Isopropenylfulvene

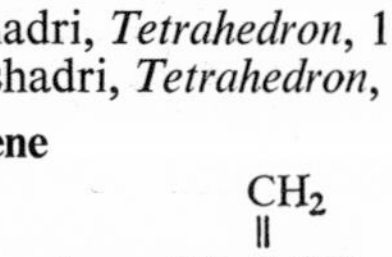

C_9H_{10} MW 118

Cryst. from light petroleum. M.p. −13·8° to −12·9°. D_4^{18} 0·919. Light absorption: $\lambda_{max.}$ 277 (log ε, 4·31), 288 (4·48), 293 (4·49), 298 (4·50), 307 (4·25), and 395 mμ (2·31).

Neuenschwander, Meuche, Schaltegger, *Helv. Chim. Acta*, 1964, **47**, 1022.

1-Isopropenyl-4-methylcyclohexane.★
Cis-.
B.p. 68–82°/80 mm. n_D^{20} 1·4594. D_4^{20} 0·8320. $[\alpha]_D^{22}$ −55° (c, 1 in $CHCl_3$).
Trans-.
B.p. 68–82°/80 mm. n_D^{20} 1·4502. D_4^{20} 0·8140. $[\alpha]_D^{22}$ −55° (c, 1 in $CHCl_3$). Has orange odour of limonene.

Thomas, Stoll, *Helv. Chim. Acta*, 1964, **47**, 413.

3-Isopropylidene-2 : 2-dimethylcyclopropyl propionate.★
Synthesis: The synthetic ester had no sex attractant activity towards the American cockroach. It was proposed that the sex attractant had the structure 2 : 2 : 4-tetramethylbicyclo[1,1,0]butyl propionate.

Day, Whiting, *Proc. Chem. Soc.*, 1964, 368.

6-Isopropyl-5-(3-methyl-2-butenyl)tropolone. *See* Nootkakin.★

2-Isopropyl-5-methyl-1 : 3-cyclohexadiene★ (2 : 4-p-*Menthadiene*)
$C_{10}H_{16}$ MW 136
Constituent of Valencia orange oil. B.p. 56°/25 mm. n_D^{23} 1·4660. Light absorption: $\lambda_{max.}$ 260 mμ.

Hunter, Brogden, *J. Org. Chem.*, 1964, **29**, 498.

2-Isopropylthiamorpholin-3-one-5-carboxylic Acid

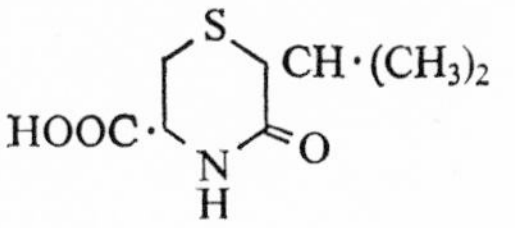

$C_8H_{13}O_3NS$ MW 203
Needles from Et_2O. M.p. 140°. $[\alpha]_D^{25}$ 4·1° (EtOH). Light absorption: $\lambda_{max.}$ 202·8° mμ (ε, 13,000).

Mizuhara *et al.*, *Nature*, 1963, **200**, 678.

Isoptin (2-[3 : 4-*Dimethoxyphenyl*]-5-[N-*homoveratryl*-N-*methylamino*]-2-*isopropylvaleronitrile*)

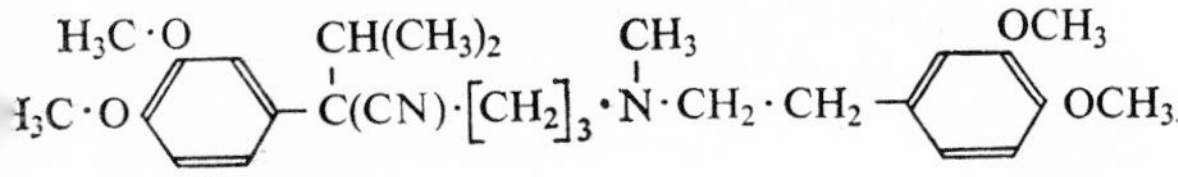

$C_{27}H_{38}O_4N_2$ MW 454
Coronary dilatant drug. Pale yellow oil. B.p. 243–6°/0·01 mm. n_D^{25} 1·5448.
B,HCl: m.p. 138·5–140·5°.

Knoll A.G., *Report of Therapy Congress and Pharmaceutical Exhibition*, Karlsruhe, 1963 (*Angew. Chem., Int. Ed.*, 1964, **3**, 68).

Isoquinuclidine. *See* 2-Azabicyclo[2,2,2]octane.

Isorenieratene. *See* Leprotene.

Isorhodeosamine. *See* 2-Amino-2 : 6-dideoxy-D-glucose.

Isorosenolic Acid

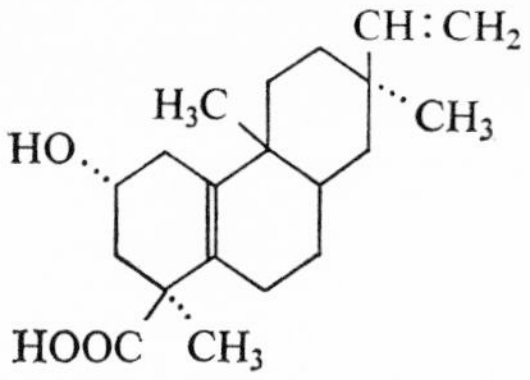

$C_{20}H_{30}O_3$ MW 318
Minor metabolite of *Trichothecium roseum* Link. M.p. 193°. Light absorption: $\lambda_{max.}$ 203 mμ (ε, 6000). H_2 → dihydro deriv. m.p. 184° and tetrahydro deriv. m.p. 230°.

Scott *et al.*, *Tetrahedron Letters*, 1964, 849.

Isotryptophan. *See* β-5-Indolyl-α-alanine.

Isovalthine.★
L-.
Present in urine. M.p. 186° decomp. $[\alpha]_D^{17}$ −52·4° (in 2*N*-HCl). Heat → 2-Isopropylthiamorpholin-3-one-5-carboxylic acid.
Allo-L-.
M.p. 185° decomp. $[\alpha]_D^{17}$ 82° (in 2*N*-HCl).

Ohmori *et al.*, *Nature*, 1963, **200**, 678; *Arch. Biochem. & Biophys.*, 1964, **104**, 509.

Isovenenatine (*Alstovenine*)

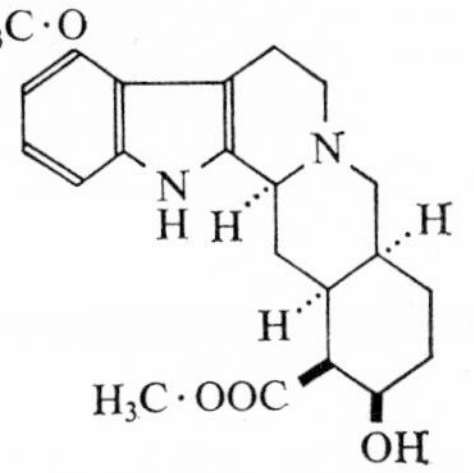

$C_{32}H_{28}O_4N_2$ MW 384
Alkaloid from the bark of *Alstonia venenata* R. Br. M.p. 169–71°. $[\alpha]_D^{24}$ 9·42°.

Ray, Chatterjee, *J. Ind. Chem. Soc.*, 1963, **40**, 1043.

Govindachi *et al.*, *Tetrahedron Letters*, 1964, 901.

Itaconitin

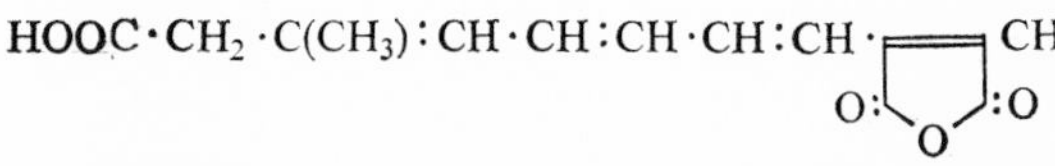

$C_{14}H_{14}O_5$ MW 262
Colouring matter in *Aspergillus itaconicus* Kinoshita. M.p. 168°.

Kinoshita, Nakajima, *Chem. Pharm. Bull.* (Tokyo), 1958, **6**, 31.

Nakajima, Kinoshita, Shibata, *Chemistry and Industry*, 1964, 805.

J

Jacareubin

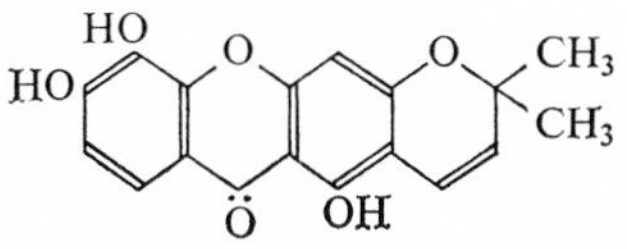

$C_{18}H_{14}O_6$ MW 326

Constituent of the heartwood of *Calophyllum brasiliense* (Guttiferae). Bright yellow prisms from MeOH. M.p. 256–7° decomp. Light absorption: $\lambda_{max.}$ 240 (ε, 12,200), 279 (40,200), 334 mμ (18,200).

Tri-Ac: feather needles from MeOH. M.p. 212–13°.

Di-Me ether: plates from MeOH. M.p. 191–2°.

Tri-Me ether: needles from MeOH. M.p. 182–3°.

King, King, Manning, *J. Chem. Soc.*, 1953, 3932.
Bhak, Venkataraman, *Tetrahedron*, 1963, **19**, 77.
Burling, Jefferson, Scheinmann, *Tetrahedron Letters*, 1964, 599, 1289.

Jaceidin (4′ : 5 : 7 - *Trihydroxy* - 3 : 3′ : 6 - *trimethoxy* - *flavone*)

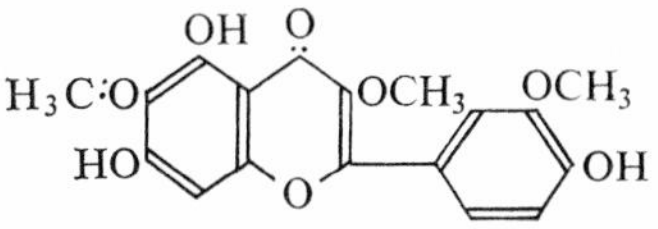

$C_{18}H_{16}O_8$ MW 360

Aglycone from Jacein. M.p. 127–33°. Light absorption: $\lambda_{max.}$ 255 (log ε, 4·23), 350 mμ (4·32).

4′ : 5 : 7-*Tri-Me ether*: *see* Quercetagetin hexa-Me ether.

4′ : 5 : 7-*Tri-Et ether*: colourless needles from Et_2O–hexane. M.p. 118°.

Farkas *et al.*, *Chem. Ber.*, 1964, **97**, 610.

Jacein

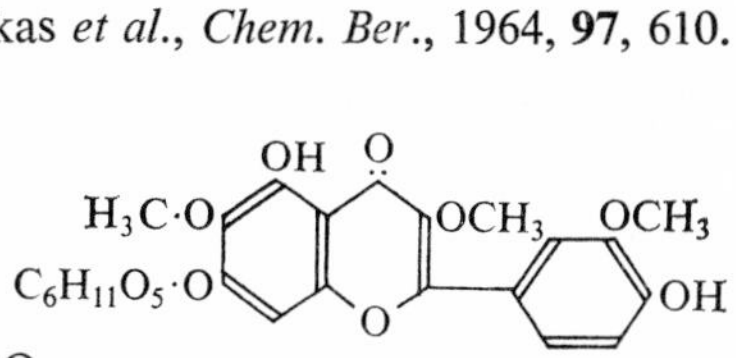

$C_{24}H_{26}O_{13}$ MW 522

Glucoside present in *Centaurea jacea* L. Cryst. from EtOH. M.p. 205–7°. $[\alpha]_D$ −73·1° (c, 1·48 in MeOH). Light absorption: $\lambda_{max.}$ 258 (log ε, 4·30), 354 mμ (4·32). $FeCl_3$ → green col. Hydrol. → jaceidin.

Hexa-Ac: cryst. from isobutyl methyl ketone. M.p. 200–1°.

Farkas *et al.*, *Chem. Ber.*, 1964, **97**, 610.

Jacoline

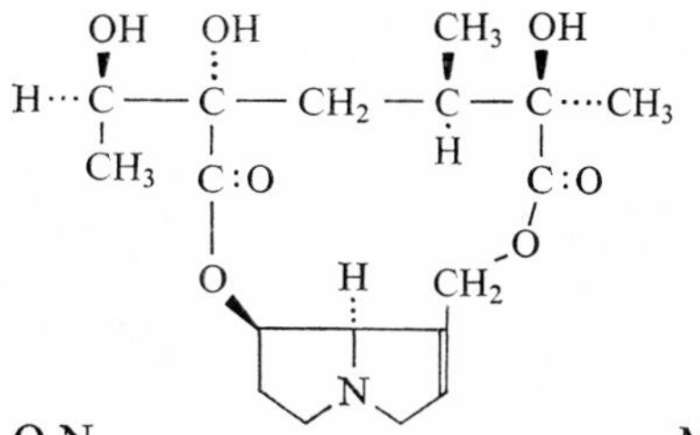

$C_{18}H_{27}O_7N$ MW 333

Alkaloid from *Senecio jacobaea* L. M.p. 221°. $[\alpha]_D$ 48° ($CHCl_3$).

Bradbury, Culvenor, *Chemistry and Industry*, 1954, 1021; *Austral. J. Chem.*, 1954, **7**, 378.
Bradbury, Willis, *Austral. J. Chem.*, 1956, **9**, 258.
Geissman, *Austral. J. Chem.*, 1959, **12**, 247.

Jacozine

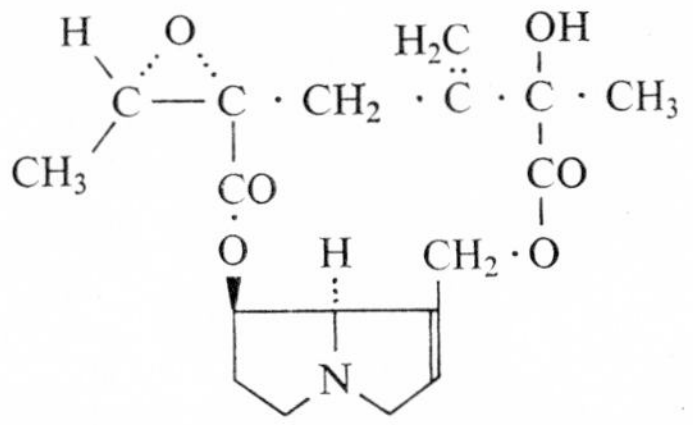

$C_{18}H_{23}O_6N$ MW 349

Alkaloid from *Senecio jacobaea* L. M.p. 228°. $[\alpha]_D$ −140° ($CHCl_3$). Light absorption: $\lambda_{max.}$ 233 mμ (ε, 1731).

Bradbury, Culvenor, *Chemistry and Industry*, 1954, 1021; *Austral. J. Chem.*, 1954, **7**, 378.
Bradbury, Willis, *Austral. J. Chem.*, 1956, **9**, 258.
Culvenor, *Austral. J. Chem.*, 1964, **17**, 233.

Jamaicin

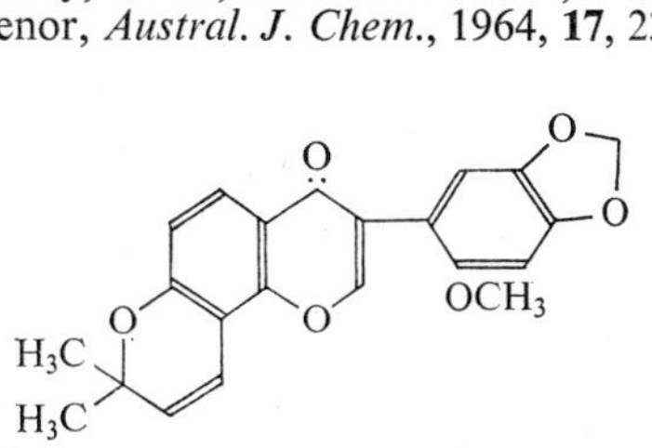

$C_{22}H_{18}O_6$ MW 378

From the root bark of *Piscidia erythrina* L. Two forms: (i) prisms from MeOH, m.p. 193–4°; (ii) m.p. 160–3°.

Moore, Eng, *J. Am. Chem. Soc.*, 1956, **78**, 395.
Stamm, Schmid, Büchi, *Helv. Chim. Acta*, 1958, **41**, 2006.

Jamine

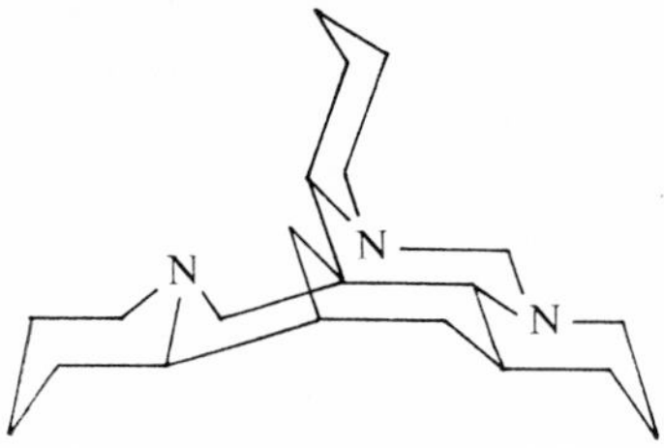

$C_{21}H_{35}N_3$ MW 329

(±)-.
Alkaloid present in the seeds of *Ormosia panamensis* and *O. jamaicensis*. M.p. 153–4°.
(+)-.
$[\alpha]_{589}$ +7·9°. $[\alpha]_{436}$ +13°.
(−)-.
$[\alpha]_{589}$ −3·8°. $[\alpha]_{420}$ −7°.

Karle, Karle, *Tetrahedron Letters*, 1964, 2065.
Naegeli, Wildman, Lloyd, *Tetrahedron Letters*, 1964, 2069, 2075.

Jasmolin II

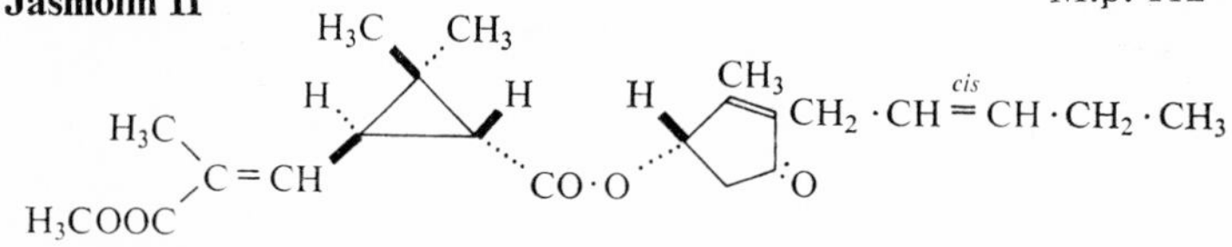

$C_{22}H_{30}O_5$ MW 374

Minor constituent of the flowers of *Chrysanthemum cinerariaefolium* (pyrethrum extract). Light absorption: $\lambda_{max.}$ 229 mμ (ε, 22,900).

Godin *et al.*, *Chemistry and Industry*, 1964, 371.

Jervine.★

Mass spectrum:
Budzikiewicz, *Tetrahedron*, 1964, **20**, 2267.

Junipal.★

Synthesis:
Schulte, Reisch, Horner, *Chem. Ber.*, 1962, **95**, 1943.
Atkinson, Curtis, Phillips, *Chemistry and Industry*, 1964, 2101.

Juniperol (*Kuromatsuol*, *Longiborneol*, *Macrocarpol*)

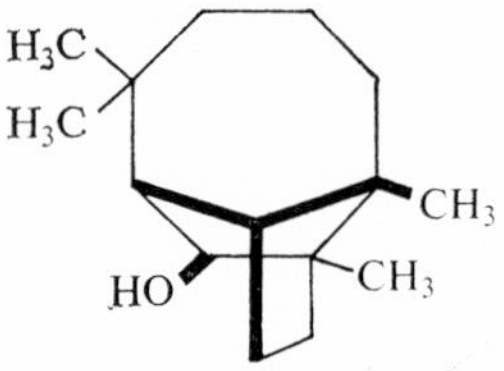

$C_{15}H_{26}O$ MW 222

Constituent of *Juniperus communis* L., *Pinus thunbergii*, Parlatore (kuromatsuol), *Cupressus macrocarpa* (macrocarpol), and *Dacrydium cupressinum*. M.p. 112° (107°). $[\alpha]_D$ 25·4° (EtOH), 16° ($CHCl_3$).

Mattson, *Bidr. Finl. Nat. Folk*, 1913, **H72**, 1.
Briggs, Sutherland, *J. Org. Chem.*, 1942, **7**, 397.
Brandt, Thomas, *N.Z. J. Sci. Tech.*, 1951, **B33**, 30.
Erdtman, Thomas, *Chemistry and Industry*, 1955, 384.
Naffa, Ourisson, *Bull. soc. chim.*, 1954, 1410.
Akiyoshi, Erdtman, Kubota, *Tetrahedron*, 1960, **9**, 237.

K

Kallidin.★

Review:

Schröder, Hempel, *Experientia*, 1964, **20**, 529.

Kanokonol (15-*Hydroxyvaleranone*)

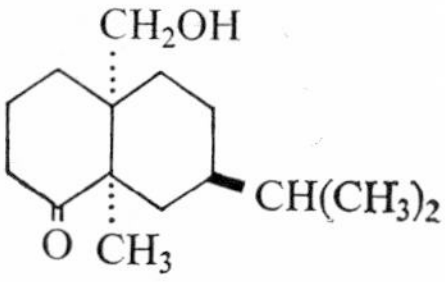

$C_{15}H_{26}O_2$ MW 238

Constituent of valerian root oil (*Valeriana wallichi*). M.p. 53–4°. $[\alpha]_D$ −72° (c, 5·8 in $CHCl_3$). Light absorption: $\lambda_{max.}$ 290 mμ (ε, 50).

Ac: constituent of valerian roots. B.p. 180–5° (bath)/ 0·3 mm. D_4^{25} 1·050. n_D^{25} 1·490. $[\alpha]_D$ −55·5° (c, 1·18 in $CHCl_3$).

Semicarbazone: m.p. 192–3°.

Hikino, Hikino, Takemoto, *Chem. Pharm. Bull.* (Tokyo), 1963, **11**, 1210.

Kulkarni, Paknikar, Bhattacharyya, *Tetrahedron*, 1964, **20**, 1289.

Kappaxin. *See* 2-Methyl-1 : 4-naphthoquinone.

16α-Kaurane-17 : 19-dioic Acid

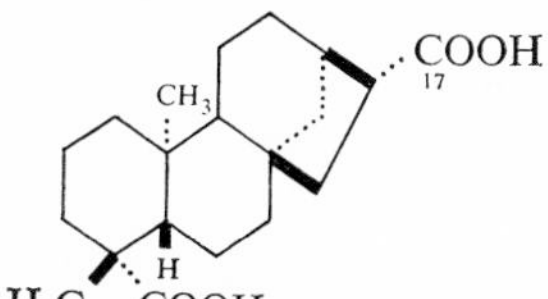

$C_{20}H_{30}O_4$ MW 334

(−)-.

Resin acid from *Ricinocarpus stylosus* Diels. Solvated prisms from Me_2CO or needles from MeOH. M.p. 271–2°. $[\alpha]_D$ −108° (c, 4 in EtOH).

Di-Me ester: $C_{22}H_{34}O_4$. MW 262. Needles from MeOH.Aq. M.p. 108–9°. $[\alpha]_D$ −105° (c, 3·9 in $CHCl_3$).

17-*Mono-Me ester*: $C_{21}H_{32}O_4$. MW 248. Prisms from light petroleum. M.p. 188–90°. $[\alpha]_D$ −110° (c, 3·1 in $CHCl_3$).

19-*Mono-Me ester*: needles from light petroleum. M.p. 190–2°. $[\alpha]_D$ −110° (c, 3·5 in $CHCl_3$).

Henrick, Jefferies, *Chemistry and Industry*, 1963, 1801; *Austral. J. Chem.*, 1964, **17**, 915.

16α-(−)-Kaurane-3α : 17 : 19-triol

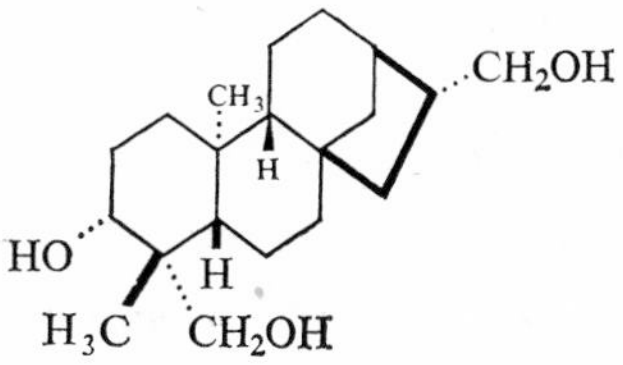

$C_{20}H_{34}O_3$ MW 322

Constituent of a *Beyeria* sp. Cryst. from MeOH. M.p. 249–50°. $[\alpha]_D$ −39° (c, 1·35 in Py).

Tri-Ac: platelets from light petroleum. M.p. 126–126·5°. $[\alpha]_D$ −56° (c, 0·79 in $CHCl_3$).

Baddeley *et al.*, *Austral. J. Chem.*, 1964, **17**, 578.

16β-Kaurane-16α : 17 : 19-triol

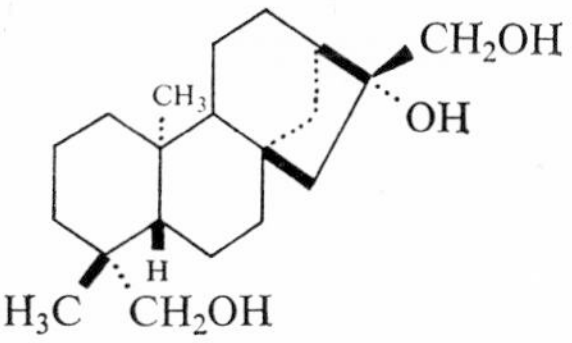

$C_{30}H_{34}O_3$ MW 324

(−)-.

Minor constituent of *Ricinocarpus stylosus* Diels. Needles from AcOEt. M.p. 224–6°. $[\alpha]_D$ −38° (c, 3 in EtOH).

Di-Ac: two forms: (i) m.p. 141–3°, and (ii) 151–2°. $[\alpha]_D$ −39° (c, 2·2 in $CHCl_3$).

Tri-Ac: needles from light petroleum. M.p. 149–50°. $[\alpha]$ −63° (c, 1·1 in $CHCl_3$).

Henrick, Jefferies, *Chemistry and Industry*, 1963, 1802; *Austral. J. Chem.*, 1964, **17**, 915.

Kaurene.★

Total synthesis:

Masamune, *J. Am. Chem. Soc.*, 1964, **86**, 290.

16-Kaurene-3α : 19-diol

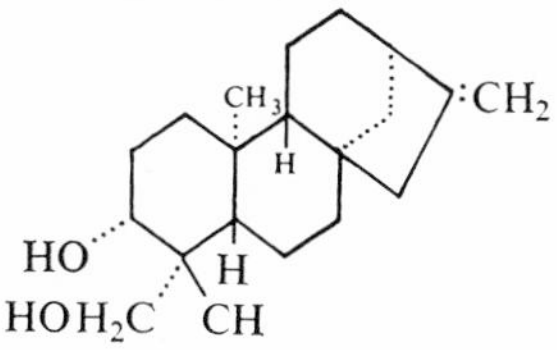

$C_{20}H_{32}O_2$ MW 304

(−)-.
Constituents of *Beyeria leschenaultii* (DC.) Bail. Prisms from AcOEt. M.p. 184–5°. $[\alpha]_D$ −66° (c, (1·66 in $CHCl_3$).
Di-Ac: plates from MeOH.Aq. M.p. 113–14°. $[\alpha]_D$ −66° (c, 1·95 in $CHCl_3$).

Baddeley, Jefferies, Retallack, *Tetrahedron*, 1964, **20**, 1983.

Kaur-16-en-18-oic Acid. *See* Kaurenic Acid.★

Kaur-16-en-19-oic Acid

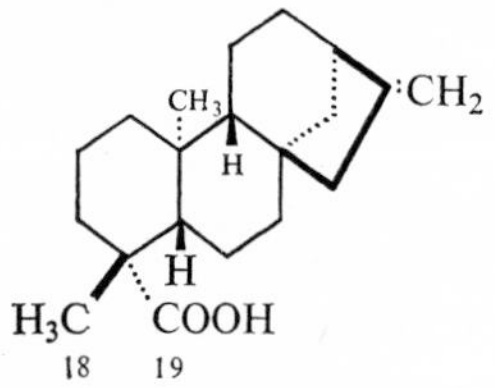

$C_{20}H_{30}O_2$ MW 302

(−)-.
Constituent of *Ricinocarpus stylosus* Diels. Prisms from MeOH. M.p. 179–81°. Needles from MeOH.Aq. M.p. 169–71°. $[\alpha]_D$ −110° (c, 3 in $CHCl_3$).
Me ester: $C_{21}H_{32}O_2$. MW 316. Plates from MeOH.Aq. M.p. 88–9°. $[\alpha]_D$ −107° (c, 3·2 in $CHCl_3$)

Henrick, Jefferies, *Chemistry and Industry*, 1963, 1802; *Austral. J. Chem.*, 1964, **17**, 915.
Galt, Hanson, *Chemistry and Industry*, 1964, 837.

Kemadrin. *See* B,HCl *under* Procyclidine.

Ketsucrose. *See* β-D-Fructofuranosyl-α-D-ribohexopyranoside-3-ulose.

α-Kirondrine. *See* Glaucarubinone.

Kisantoside

$C_{36}H_{56}O_{15}$ MW 728

Cardenolide from *Strophanthus vanderijstii* Staner. Small prisms from H_2O. M.p. 175–85°. $[\alpha]_D$ +27·7° (c, 0·65 in MeOH).

Brenneisen *et al.*, *Helv. Chim. Acta*, 1964, **47**, 799, 814.

Konakion. *See* Vitamin K_1.★

Kurcholessin

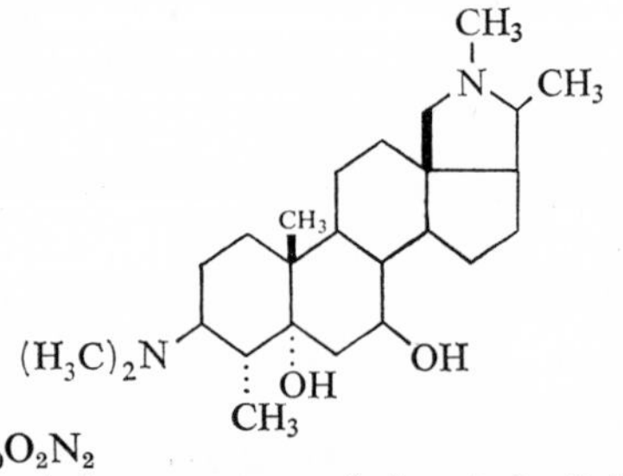

$C_{24}H_{40}O_2N_2$ MW 404

Produced from extract of the rind of *Holarrhena antidysenterica* Wall by methylation. M.p. 218·5–221·5°. $[\alpha]_D$ −4° ($CHCl_3$).
B,HCl: m.p. 255–65° decomp.

Tschesche, Otto, *Chem. Ber.*, 1962, **95**, 1144.
Tschesche, Meise, Snatzke, *Tetrahedron Letters*, 1964, 1659.

Kuromatsuol. *See* Juniperol.

L

Laballenic Acid (2 : 3-*Methyleneheptadeca*-4 : 5-*dienoic acid*)

$CH_3\cdot[CH_2]_{10}\cdot CH{:}C{:}CH\cdot CH$——$CH\cdot COOH$
$\quad\quad\quad\quad\quad\quad\quad\quad\quad\quad\quad\quad\quad \diagdown CH_2 \diagup$

Suggested structure

$C_{18}H_{30}O_2$ MW 278

Constituent of the seed oil of *Leonotis nepetaefolia.*

Me ester: $C_{19}H_{32}O_2$. MW 292. Oil. $[\alpha]_D^{26}$ $-47{\cdot}3°$ (c, 1·8 in EtOH). Light absorption: $\lambda_{max.}$ 181·5 mμ (ε, 19,930).

Bagby, Smith, Wolff, *Chemistry and Industry*, 1964, 1861.

Lactulosucrose (O-β-D-*Galactopyranosyl*-(1 → 4)-O-β-D-*fructofuranosyl*-(2 → 1)-α-D-*glucopyranoside*)

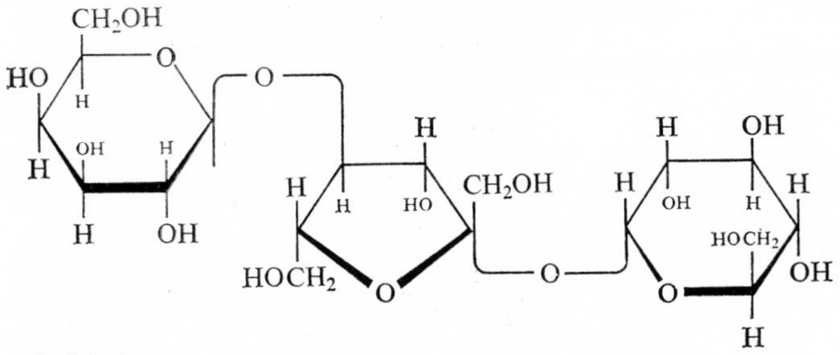

$C_{18}H_{32}O_{16}$ MW 504

Metabolite of *Leuconostoc mesenteroides* Strain K. Cryst. $[\alpha]_D^{24}$ 44·1° (c, 2).

Suzuki, Hehre, *Arch. Biochem. & Biophys.*, 1964, **105**, 339.

Lacumin. *See* Pecazine.★

β-Lagodesoxycholic Acid. *See* 3α : 12α-Dihydroxy-5α-cholanic Acid.

Lagosin (*A* 246)

$C_{35}H_{58}O_{12}$ MW 670

Antibiotic from *Streptomyces* spp. May be identical with Fungichromin (*q.v.*). Needles from MeOH.Aq. M.p. 230–40° decomp. $[\alpha]_D$ $-146°$ (c, 0·369 in MeOH). H_2 → perhydro deriv. M.p. 160–2°. $[\alpha]_D$ 3·5° (c, 1·08 in MeOH).

Dhar, Thaller, Whiting, *Proc. Chem. Soc.*, 1958, 148; *J. Chem. Soc.*, 1964, 842.

Berry, Whiting, *J. Chem. Soc.*, 1964, 862.

Laksholic Acid

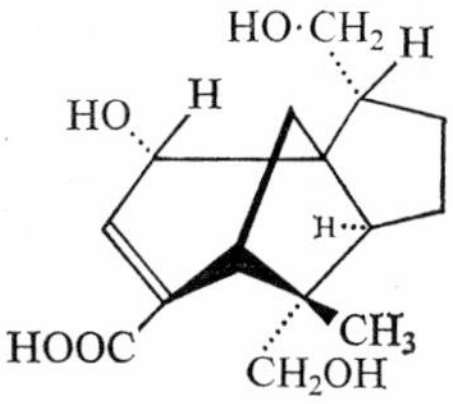

$C_{15}H_{22}O_5$ MW 282

Constituent of lac. Cryst. from $CHCl_3$–EtOH. M.p. 181–3°. $[\alpha]_D$ 49·4° ($CHCl_3$).

Khurana *et al.*, *Tetrahedron Letters*, 1964, 1537.

***epi*-Laksholic Acid**

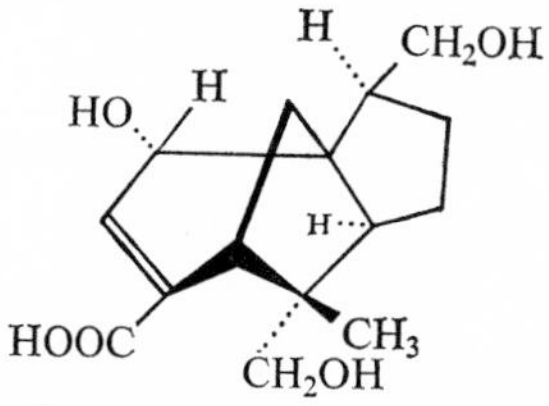

$C_{15}H_{22}O_5$ MW 282

Constituent of lac. Cryst. from $CHCl_3$–EtOH. M.p. 201–3°. $[\alpha]_D$ 63·7° ($CHCl_3$).

Khurana *et al.*, *Tetrahedron Letters* 1964, 1537.

Lankamycin

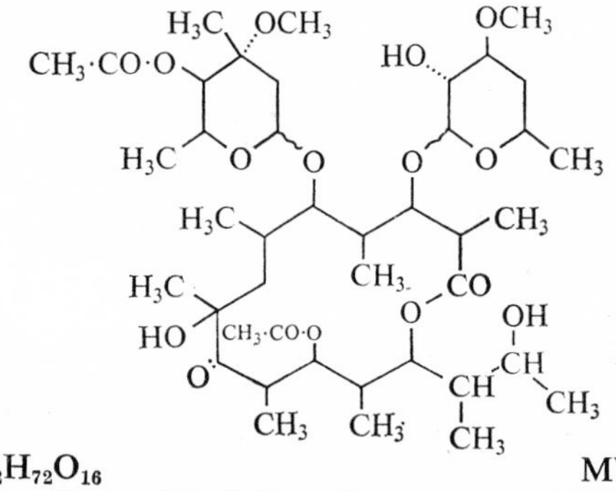

$C_{42}H_{72}O_{16}$ MW 832

Macrolide antibiotic from *Streptomyces violaceoniger* Waksman and Curtis. Colourless cryst. from Et_2O. M.p. 146–7°. $[\alpha]_D$ $-94°$ (c, 1·23 in light petroleum). Light absorption: $\lambda_{max.}$ 289 mμ (log ε, 1·50).

Gaumann *et al.*, *Helv. Chim. Acta*, 1960, **43**, 601.
Keller-Schierlein, Roncari, *Helv. Chim. Acta*, 1962, **45**, 138; 1964, **47**, 78.

Lanceol★

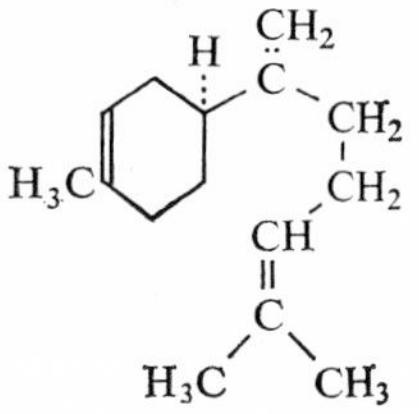

Stereochemistry:
Manjarrez, Ríos, Guzmán, *Tetrahedron*, 1964, **20**, 333.

5α-Lanosta-9(11) : 24-dien-3β-ol. *See* Parkeol.

Lappaconine.★
Mono-Ac: m.p. 150–2°. *B,HClO₄*: m.p. 146° decomp.
Tri-Ac: m.p. 184–5°.
Khaimova *et al.*, *Tetrahedron Letters*, 1964, 2711.

Lappaconitine.★
Di-Ac: m.p. 125–7°.
Khaimova *et al.*, *Tetrahedron Letters*, 1964, 2711.

Largon. *See* Propiomazine.

Laserolide

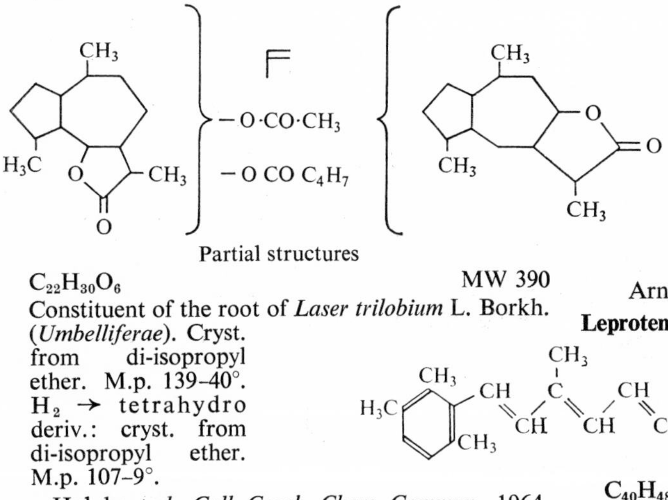

Partial structures

$C_{22}H_{30}O_6$ MW 390

Constituent of the root of *Laser trilobium* L. Borkh. (*Umbelliferae*). Cryst. from di-isopropyl ether. M.p. 139–40°. $H_2 \rightarrow$ tetrahydro deriv.: cryst. from di-isopropyl ether. M.p. 107–9°.
Holub *et al.*, *Coll. Czech. Chem. Commun.*, 1964, **29**, 938.

Lathyrine.★
Synthesis:
Shvachkin, Berestenko, *Zhur. Obshcheĭ Khim.*, 1964, **34**, 3506.
See also:
Ramachandran, Rao, *Biochim. Biophys. Acta*, 1964, **86**, 264.

Landicon. *See* Dihydromorphinone.

Laurifoline

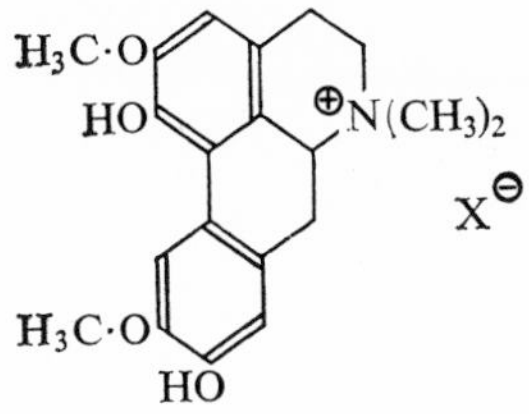

(+)-.
Quaternary alkaloid from *Cocculus laurifolus*.
Chloride (X = Cl): $C_{20}H_{24}O_4NCl$. MW 377·5. M.p. 253° decomp. $[\alpha]_D^{24}$ +26·3° (H_2O).
(±)-.
Chloride: m.p. 238° decomp.
Tomita, Kusuda, *Chem. Pharm. Bull.* (Tokyo), 1953, **1**, 1, 5.
Albonico, Kuck, Deulofeu, *Chemistry and Industry*, 1964, 1580.

Laurolitsine

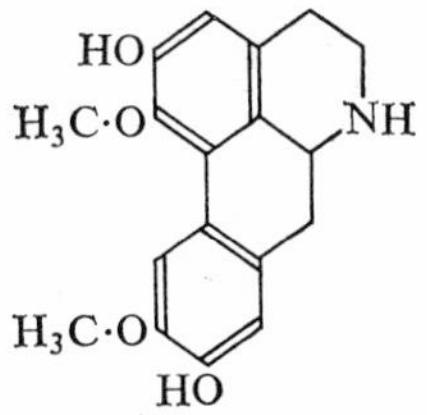

$C_{18}H_{19}O_4N$ MW 313

Amorph. alkaloid from *Neolitsea sericea* and *Litsea japonica*. M.p. 138–40° with swelling at 115–18°. $[\alpha]_D^{11}$ +102·5° (EtOH).
Picrate: m.p. 212° decomp.
Picrolonate: m.p. 239° decomp.
N-*Me*: *see* Boldine.
Nakasato, Nomura, *Chem. Pharm. Bull.* (Tokyo), 1959, **7**, 780.
Kozuka, *J. Pharm. Soc. Japan*, 1962, **82**, 1567.

Laurotetanine.★
N-*Me*: also present in *Phylica rogersii* Pillans. O-*Et*, *B,CH₃I*: cryst. from Me_2CO–MeOH. M.p. 206–7°. $[\alpha]_D$ 61° (c, 0·7 in EtOH).
Arndt, Baarschers, *J. Chem. Soc.*, 1964, 2244.

Leprotene (*Isorenieratene*)

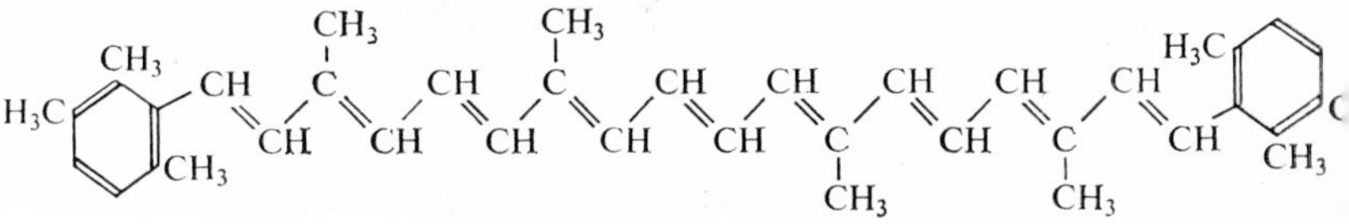

$C_{40}H_{48}$ MW 528

Constituent of various *Mycobacterium* spp., and the marine sponge *Reniera japonica*. M.p. 198–200°. Light absorption: $\lambda_{max.}$ (440), 465, and 495 mμ in C_6H_6; (460), 484, and 515 mμ in CS_2.
Grundmann, Takeda, *Naturwiss.*, 1937, **25**, 27.
Goodwin, Jamikorn, *Biochem. J.*, 1956, **62**, 269, 275.
Yamaguchi, *Bull. Chem. Soc.* (Japan), 1957, **30**, 111; 1958, **31**, 51.
Jensen, Weedon, *Naturwiss.*, 1964, **51**, 482.
Jensen, *Acta Chem. Scand.*, 1964, **18**, 1562.

Leptazole. *See* Metrazole.★

Leptospermone.★
See also:
Murin *et al., Chem. Ber.*, 1959, **92**, 2033.

Lergine. *See* Tricyclamol.★

Lerigan. *See* Promethazine.★

Leucocyanidin Gallate

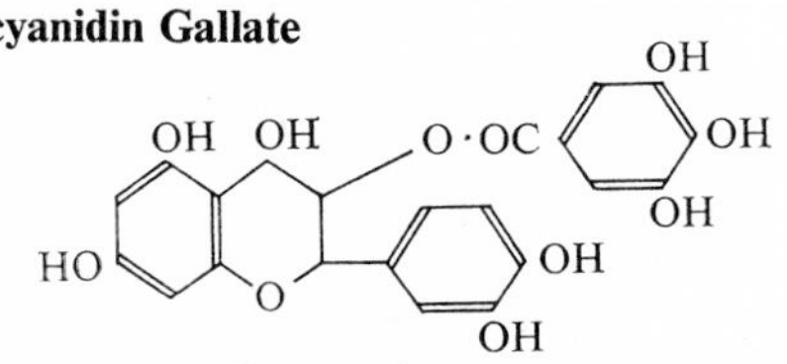

Suggested structure

$C_{22}H_{18}O_{11}$ MW 458

(+)-.
Extractive of Babul (*Acacia arabica*) bark. White powder which darken at 250° but does not melt below 350°. $[\alpha]_D^{30}$ +23·4° (c, 0·8 in Me_2CO).
Octa-Ac: cryst. from EtOH. M.p. 158°.
Hepta-Me ether: cryst. from AcOEt–light petroleum. M.p. 158°. *Ac*: cryst. from hexane. M.p. 170°.

Bhanu, Rajadurai, Nayudamma, *Austral. J. Chem.*, 1964, **17**, 803.

Leukerin. *See* 6-Mercaptopurine.★

Leurocristine.★ *See* Vincristine.

Levomepromazine. *See* Methotrimeprazine.★

Levopimaric Acid ($\Delta^{12,14}$-*Abietadienoic acid*)

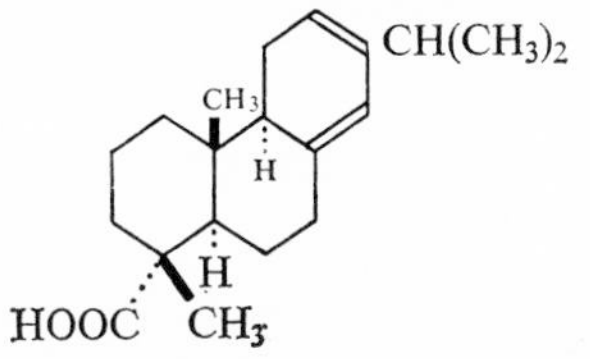

$C_{20}H_{30}O_2$ MW 302

Constituent of the oleoresin of *Pinus palustris*. M.p. 150–2°. $[\alpha]_D$ −276° (c, 1 in EtOH). Light absorption: $\lambda_{max.}$ 272 ($E_{1\,cm.}^{1\%}$ 192) mμ.
2-*Amino*-2-*methylpropanol salt*: $[\alpha]_D$ −218° (c, 1 in EtOH).

Ruzicka, Kaufman, *Helv. Chim. Acta*, 1940, **23**, 1346.
Harris, Sanderson, *J. Am. Chem. Soc.*, 1948, **70**, 334.
Loeblich *et al., J. Am. Chem. Soc.*, 1955, **77**, 6311.
Wenkert *et al., J. Am. Chem. Soc.*, 1964, **86**, 2038.

Liensinine

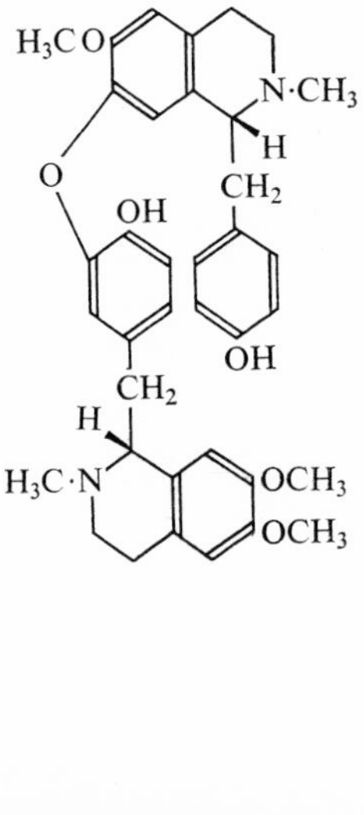

$C_{37}H_{42}O_6N_2$ MW 610

From the embryo of the lotus seed (*Nelumbo nucifera* Gaertn.). M.p. 95–9°. $[\alpha]_D^{30\cdot6}$ +15·85° (c, 0·88 in Me_2CO).
B,HClO₄: m.p. 212–14°.
Di-Ac: m.p. 124°.
Di-Me ether: m.p. 105–10°. *B,CH₃Br*: m.p. 203° from MeOH.

Chao Tse-yuan (Yuan Chih Chao) *et al., Sci. Sinica* (Peking), 1962, **11**, 215 (*Chem. Abstracts*, 1962, **57**, 7384).
Pan Pei-chuan (Pe-ch'uan P'an) *et al., Sci. Sinica* (Peking), 1962, **11**, 321 (*Chem. Abstracts*, 1963, **58**, 3467).

***N*-Lignoceryl-1-D-shignosyl-β-lactoside.** *See* Cytolipin H.

Ligustilide

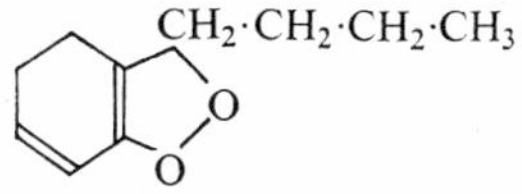

$C_{12}H_{14}O_2$ MW 190

Constituent of the roots of *Ligusticum acutilobum* Sieb. et Zucc. and senkyu (*Cnidium officinale* Makino). B.p. 168–9°/6 mm. n_D^{25} 1·5649.

Mitsuhashi, Nagai, Murumatsu, *Chem. Pharm. Bull. Japan*, 1960, **8**, 243; 1961, **9**, 115.
Mitsuhashi, Nagai, *Tetrahedron*, 1963, **19**, 1277.
Mitsuhashi, Muramatsu, *Tetrahedron*, 1964, **20**, 1971.

Limaspermine.★
See also:
Cava, Nomura, Talapatra, *Tetrahedron*, 1964, **20**, 581.

Limocitrin.★
3β-D-*Glucosyl*: $C_{23}H_{24}O_{14}$. MW 524. Constituent of *Citrus limon*. Cryst. from H_2O. M.p. 150° followed by resolidification and m.p. 240–5°. *Hepta-Ac*: needles from EtOH. M.p. 167–8°.

Gentili, Horowitz, *Tetrahedron*, 1964, **20**, 2313.

Limocitrol (3 : 4′ : 5 : 7 - *Tetrahydroxy* - 3′ : 6 : 8 - *trimethoxyflavone*)

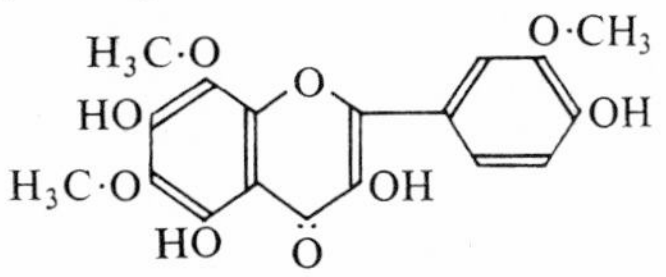

$C_{18}H_{16}O_9$ MW 376

Fine yellow needles from MeOH. M.p. 210–11° or from EtOH. M.p. 221–2°. $FeCl_3$ → green col.
Tetra-Ac: needles from AcOEt–Et_2O. M.p. 203–4°.
3 : 4′ : 7-*Tri-Me ether*: $C_{21}H_{22}O_4$. MW 418. Cryst. from MeOH. M.p. 110–11° (122–3°).
Tetra-Me ether: $C_{22}H_{24}O_9$. MW 432. Needles from MeOH. M.p. 128–128·5°.
3-β-*Glucosyl*: $C_{24}H_{26}O_{14}$. MW 502. Constituent of lemon (*Citrus limon*). Yellow prisms from H_2O. M.p. 163° resolidify then m.p. 203–4°. *Hepta-Ac*: needles from EtOH. M.p. 159·5–160·5°.

Gentili, Horowitz, *Tetrahedron*, 1964, **20**, 2313.

Lincomycin (*Lincocin*)

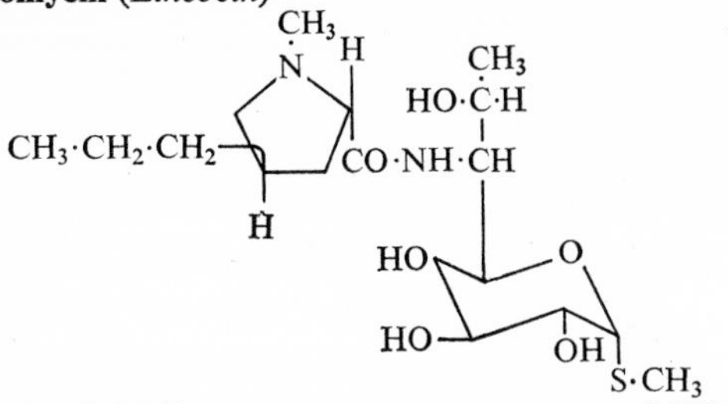

$C_{18}H_{34}O_6N_2S$ MW 406

Antibiotic produced by *Streptomyces lincolnensis* var. *lincolnensis* n. sp. pK_a' 7·5.

B,HCl: cryst. $[\alpha]_D$ +137° (c, 1 in H_2O).

Mason *et al.*, *Antimicrobial Agents and Chemotherapy*, 1962, 554, 560, 565, 570.
Hoeksema *et al.*, *J. Am. Chem. Soc.*, 1964, **86**, 4223.

Linderane

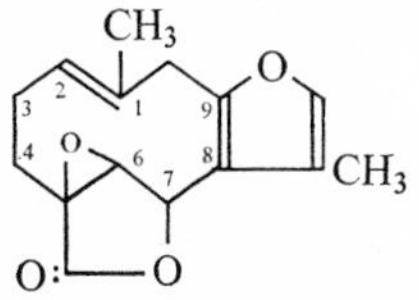

$C_{15}H_{16}O_4$ MW 260

Constituent of the root of *Lindera strychnifolia* Vill. Needles from Me_2CO. M.p. 190–1° decomp. [α] 180·3° (c, 1·043 in dioxane).

Takeda, Minato, Horibe, *Tetrahedron*, 1963, **19**, 2307.

Linearisine (*Dihydrocrotonosine*)

$C_{17}H_{19}O_3N$ MW 285

Alkaloid from *Croton linearis* Jacq. Anisotropic rods from EtOH. M.p. 219–22° decomp. Light absorption: $\lambda_{max.}$ 228 (log ε, 4·30), 282 (3·19), and 288 mμ (3·22). The structure is that of the dihydro deriv. of crotonosine (*q.v.*).

B,HCl: rods from EtOH. M.p. >300°.

Hayes, Stuart, *J. Chem. Soc.*, 1963, 1784, 1789.
Hayes *et al.*, *Proc. Chem. Soc.*, 1964, 261.

Lipotropic Hormone. *See* Lipotropin.

Lipotropin (*LPH, lipotropic hormone*).

A pituitary hormone consisting of a polypeptide containing 59 amino-acid residues with glutamic acid as the NH_2-terminal amino-acid and lysine at the ·COOH· terminus. Molecular weight 6900. The hormone effects the mobilisation of fat *in vivo*.

Birk, Li, *J. Biol. Chem.*, 1964, **239**, 1048.
Li, *Nature*, 1964, **201**, 924.

Liriodenine.★

This is identical with Spermatheridine (*q.v.*).

Buchanan, Dickey, *J. Org. Chem.*, 1960, **25**, 1389.

Lithospermic Acid

$C_{16}H_{14}O_7$ MW 318

Extractive from the roots of *Lithospermum ruderale*. M.p. 130–1°. $[\alpha]_D^{23}$ 122° (c, 0·2 in H_2O).

Tetra-Ac: m.p. 94–8°.

Me ester: m.p. 102–4°. *Tetra-Ac*: cryst. from EtOH. M.p. 76–8°.

Penta-O-Me: cryst. from MeOH.Aq. M.p. 67–9°.

Johnson *et al.*, *Phytochemistry*, 1963, **2**, 145.

Lobinaline★

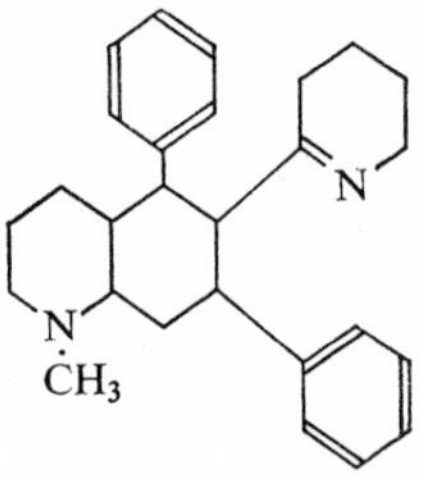

$C_{27}H_{34}N_2$ MW 386

Alkaloid from *Lobelia cardinalis* L. Cryst. from hexane. M.p. 108–10°. $[\alpha]_D^{20}$ 38° ($CHCl_3$).

Note. Manske gave this alkaloid the formula $C_{28}H_{38}ON_2$, but his isolate was shown to be a hydrate.

Robison *et al.*, *Tetrahedron Letters*, 1964, 1513.

Lochnericine★

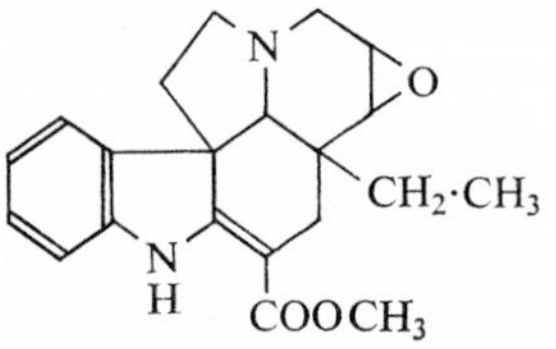

Suggested structure

Moza *et al.*, *Tetrahedron Letters*, 1964, 2561.

Lochneridine

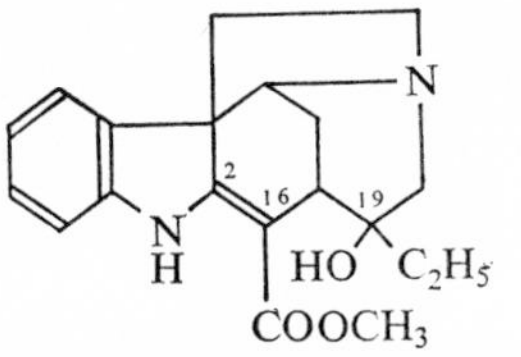

$C_{20}H_{24}O_3N_2$ MW 340

Alkaloid from *Vinca rosea* L. Prisms from MeOH. M.p. 211–14° decomp. pK_a 5·5 (66% H·CONMe₂).

Light absorption: $\lambda_{max.}$ 230, 293, 328 mμ.

Ac_2O/Py → akuammicine.

Svoboda *et al.*, *J. Pharm. Sci.*, 1961, **50**, 409.
Nakagawa *et al.*, *Chemistry and Industry*, 1962, 1986.

Lochnerinine★

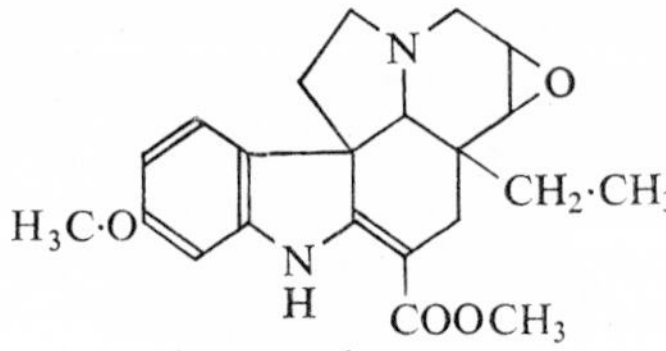

Suggested structure

Moza *et al.*, *Tetrahedron Letters*, 1964, 2561.

α-Lofoline★

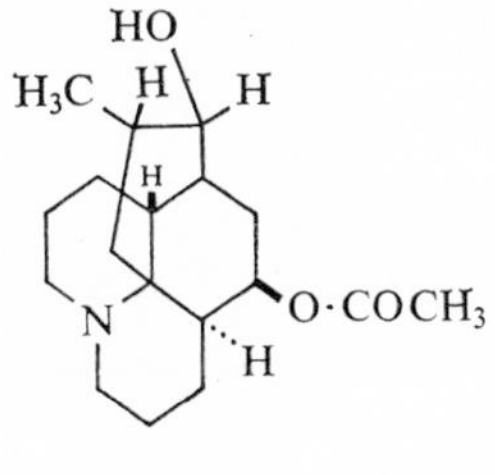

Epimeric with Fawcettine.
O-*Ac*: $C_{20}H_{31}O_4N$. MW 349. Component of lycopodium alkaloid L.9 (Manske, Marion). Oil. *B,HClO₄*: cryst. from $Me_2CO–Et_2O$. M.p. 272–3° decomp.

Manske, Marion, *Can. J. Res.*, 1943, **21B**, 92.
Anet, *Tetrahedron Letters*, 1960, No. 20, 13.
Ayer, Hogg, Soper, *Can. J. Chem.*, 1964, **42**, 949.

Loliolide (1 : 3-*Dihydroxy*-3 : 5 : 5-*trimethylcyclohexylidene*-4-*acetic acid lactone*)

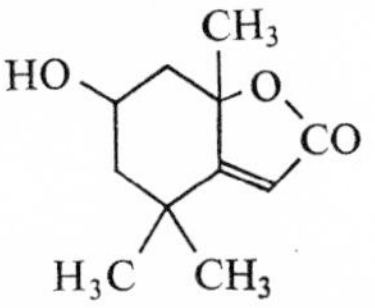

$C_{11}H_{16}O_3$ MW 196
Constituent of perennial ryegrass (*Lolium perenne*). Plates from CCl_4. M.p. 148–9°. $[\alpha]_D$ −92° (c, 1·1 in $CHCl_3$).
1-*Ac*: prisms from light petroleum–$CHCl_3$. M.p. 86–7°.

White, *New Zealand J. Agric. Res.*, 1958, **1**, 859.
Hodges, Porte, *Tetrahedron*, 1964, **20**, 1463.

Lonchocarpic Acid

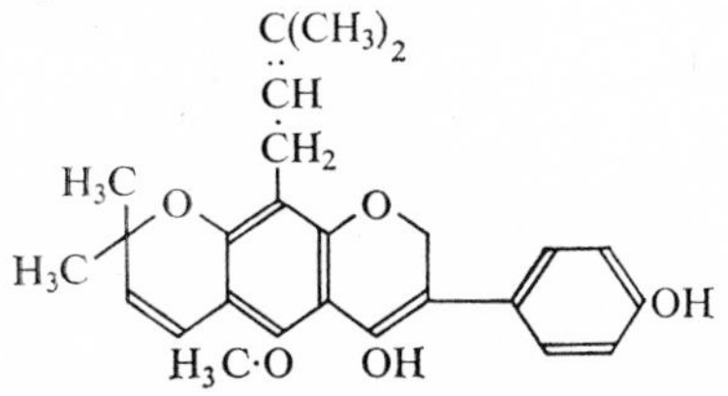

$C_{26}H_{26}O_6$ MW 434
Constituent of *Lonchocarpus* and *Derris* spp. Prisms from MeOH which sintered 200–5° and then had m.p. 223°. Cryst. from AcOEt had m.p. 204°. $H_2 \rightarrow$ tetrahydro deriv.: m.p. 239–40°.
Di-Ac: cryst. from EtOH. M.p. 154°.
Mono-Me ether: $C_{27}H_{28}O_6$. MW 448. Cryst. from EtOH. M.p. 210–12°.
Di-Me ether: $C_{28}H_{30}O_6$. MW 462. Cryst. from MeOH. M.p. 150–1°.

Jones, *J. Am. Chem. Soc.*, 1934, **56**, 1247.
Jones, Haller, *J. Org. Chem.*, 1943, **8**, 493.
Clarke, *J. Org. Chem.*, 1943, **8**, 489.
Murti, Rao, Seshadri, *Proc. Ind. Acad. Sci.*, 1948, **27A**, 111.
Pelter, Johnson, *Tetrahedron Letters*, 1964, 2817.

Longiborneol. *See* Juniperol.

Longihomocamphenylone

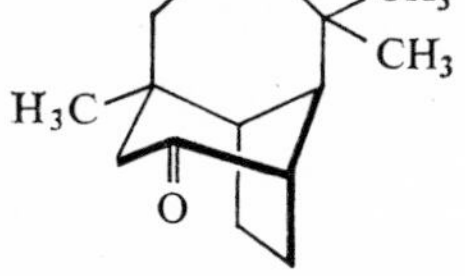

$C_{15}H_{24}O$ MW 220
Oxidation product of longifolene. M.p. 55–7°.

Naffa, Ourisson, *Bull. soc. chim.*, 1954, 1115.
Munavalli, Ourisson, *Bull. soc. chim.*, 1964, 729.

α-Longipinene

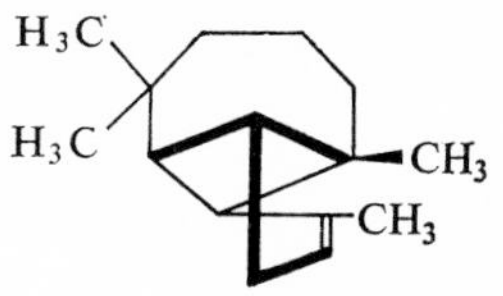

$C_{15}H_{24}$ MW 204
Constituent of the wood of Scots pine (*Pinus silvestris*). B.p. 102–6°/10 mm. D_4^{22} 0·9122. n_D^{22} 1·4924. $[\alpha]_D^{22}$ +36·9° (c, 2·2 in $CHCl_3$).

Erdtman, Westfelt, *Acta Chem. Scand.*, 1963, **17**, 2351.

Longispinogenin (3β : 16β : 28-*Trihydroxy*-18β-*olean*-12-*ene*)

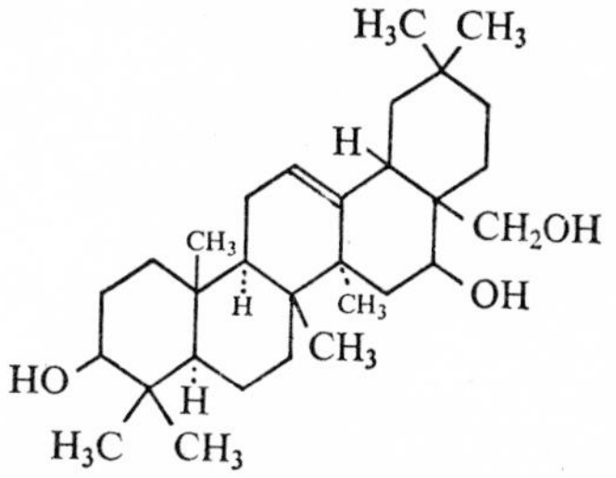

$C_{30}H_{50}O_3$ MW 458
Constituent of the cactus, *Lemaireocereus longispinus*. Needles from Me_2CO. M.p. 247–9°. $[\alpha]_D^{25}$ 53°.
Tri-Ac: needles from MeOH. M.p. 219–21°. $[\alpha]_D^{25}$ +73°.

Djerassi, McDonald, Lemin, *J. Am. Chem. Soc.*, 1953, **75**, 5940.
Djerassi, Geller, Lemin, *Chemistry and Industry*, 1954, 161.

Lophocerine (1 : 2 : 3 : 4-*Tetrahydro*-7-*hydroxy*-1-*iso*-*butyl*-6-*methoxy*-2-*methylisoquinoline*)

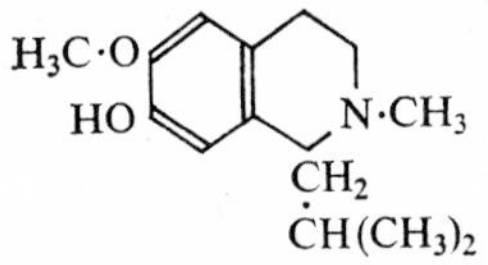

$C_{15}H_{23}O_2N$ MW 249
Alkaloid from the cactus *Lophocereus schottii*. Oil.
Me ether: $C_{16}H_{25}O_2N$. MW 263. *Picrate*: m.p. 180–2°. *Styphnate*: m.p. 210–12°.
Et ether: $C_{17}H_{27}O_2N$. MW 277. *Picrate*: m.p. 150–3°. *Styphnate*: m.p. 182–3°.
Picrate: m.p. 191·5–193°.
Styphnate: cryst. from EtOH. M.p. 171–2°.

Bobbitt, Chou, *J. Org. Chem.*, 1959, **24**, 1106.

LPH. *See* Lipotropin.

Luminol (5-*Amino*-2 : 3-*dihydro*-1 : 4-*phthalazinedione*)

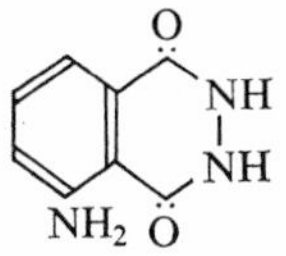

$C_8H_7O_2N_3$ MW 177
Strongly chemiluminescent. Yellow needles. M.p. 329–32°.

Curtius, Semper, *Ber.*, 1913, **46**, 1170.
Albrecht, *Z. physik. Chem.* (Leipzig), 1928, **136**, 321.
Huntress, Stanley, Packer, *J. Am. Chem. Soc.*, 1934, **56**, 241.
White *et al.*, *J. Am. Chem. Soc.*, 1964, **86**, 940, 941.

Lunidine

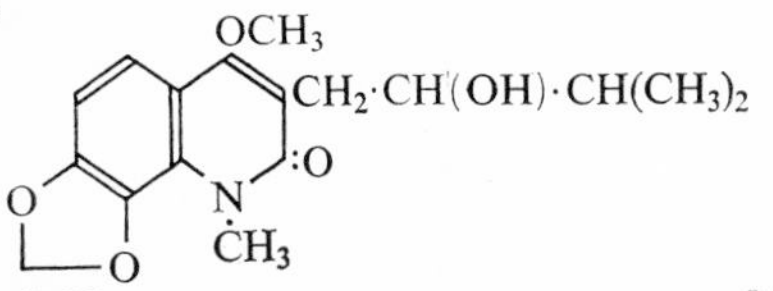

$C_{17}H_{21}O_5N$ MW 319

Alkaloid from *Lunasia amara* Blanco var. *repanda* (Lauterb. et K. Schum.) Lauterb. Cryst. from di-isopropyl ether. M.p. 65–6·5°. $[\alpha]_D^{20}$ 28° (c, 0·4 in EtOH). Light absorption: $\lambda_{max.}$ 216 sh. (log ε, 4·32), 226 (4·42), 236 sh. (4·35), 259 sh. (4·31), 266 (4·35), 317 (3·93), and 331 mμ (3·81); $\lambda_{min.}$ 248 and 279 mμ.
Ac: cryst. from hexane–Et·CO·Me. M.p. 111–12°. $[\alpha]_D^{20}$ 85° (c, 0·4 in EtOH).

Rüegger, Stauffacher, *Helv. Chim. Acta*, 1963, **46**, 2329.

Lunidonine

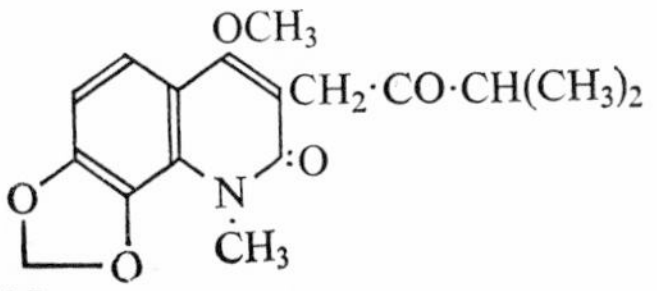

$C_{17}H_{19}O_5N$ MW 317

Alkaloid from *Lunasia amara* Blanco var. *repanda* (Lauterb. et K. Schum.) Lauterb. Cryst. from MeOH. M.p. 118–19°. Light absorption: $\lambda_{max.}$ 216 (sh., log ε, 4·33), 226 (4·41), 236 (sh., 4·37), 259 (sh., 4·30), 266 (4·35), 312 (3·93), and 331 mμ (3·78); $\lambda_{min.}$ 248 and 279 mμ.
Semicarbazone: cryst. from AcOEt. M.p. 209–11°.

Rüegger, Stauffacher, *Helv. Chim. Acta*, 1963, **46**, 2329.

Lupanine.★
See also:

Clemo, Raper, Seaton, *J. Chem. Soc.*, 1956, 3390.
van Tamelen, Baran, *J. Am. Chem. Soc.*, 1956, **78**, 2913.

Lup-20-en-3β : 16β-diol

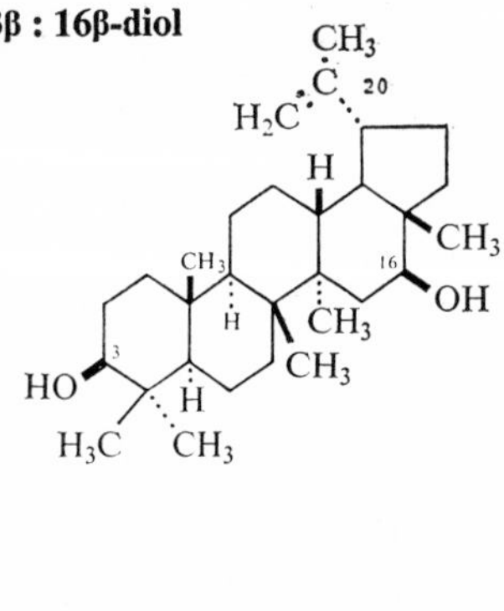

$C_{30}H_{50}O_2$ MW 442

Constituent of *Beyeria leschenaultii* (DC.) Bail. Needles from Me_2CO. M.p. 218–19°. $[\alpha]_D$ +23° (c, 1·18 in $CHCl_3$).
Di-Ac: plates from EtOH. M.p. 200–1°. $[\alpha]_D$ +42° (c, 1·14 in $CHCl_3$).

Baddeley *et al.*, *Austral. J. Chem.*, 1964, **17**, 908.

Lycocernuine (*Alkaloid L*33)

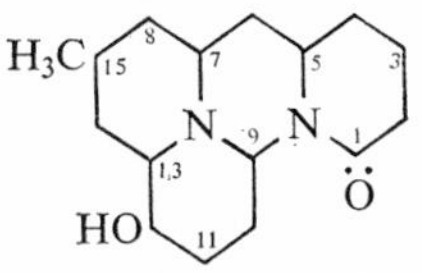

$C_{16}H_{26}O_2N_2$ MW 278

Alkaloid from *Lycopodium cernuum*. M.p. 230°. pK 6·4 (50% MeOH).
O-Ac: $C_{18}H_{28}O_3N_2$. MW 320. Oil.

Marion, Manske, *Can. J. Research*, 1948, **26B**, 1.
Ayer *et al.*, *Tetrahedron Letters*, 1964, 2201.

Lyconnotine

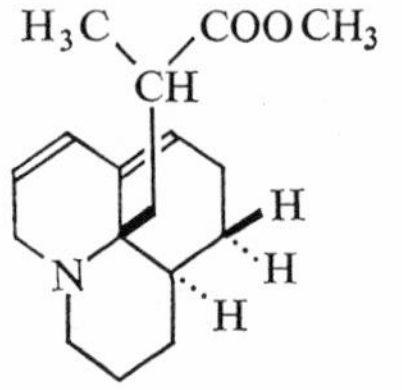

$C_{17}H_{25}O_3N$ MW 291

Minor alkaloid from *Lycopodium annotinum* L. M.p. 123°. $[\alpha]_D^{20}$ +125°. pK_a 7·5 (80% MeO·CH_2–CH_2OH). Light absorption: $\lambda_{max.}$ 235 mμ (log ε, 4·3).
Picrolonate: m.p. 230–1°.

Anet *et al.*, *Tetrahedron Letters*, 1964, 751.
Valenta *et al.*, *J. Am. Chem. Soc.*, 1964, **86**, 2533.

Lycopodine.★
Transformation into annofoline:

Ayer, Law, Piers, *Tetrahedron Letters*, 1964, 2959.

Lycorine.★
Biosynthesis:

Battersby *et al.*, *J. Chem. Soc.*, 1964, 1595.

Lysine.★
6-N-*Me*; *B,HCl*: cryst. $[\alpha]_D$ +9·9° (c, 2 in H_2O) +23·1° (c, 1 in 6*N*-HCl).
6-N-*Et*; *B,HCl*: cryst. $[\alpha]_D$ +3·4° (in 6*N*-HCl).

Benoiton, *Can. J. Chem.*, 1964, **42**, 2043.

8-Lysine-3-phenylalanyloxytocin. *See* Vasopressin.★

Lysinoalanine. *See* N^{ϵ}-(DL-2-Amino-2-carboxyethyl)-L-lysine.

Lyteca. *See p*-Acetamidophenol.

Lytensium. *See* Pentamethonium Bromide.★

M

Maaliol

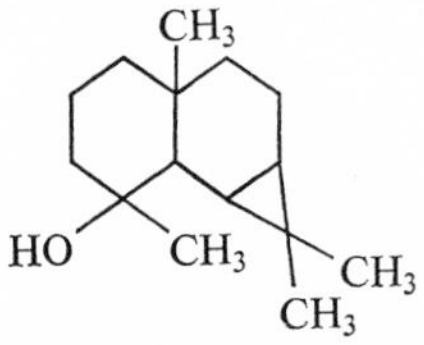

$C_{15}H_{26}O$ MW 222

Occurs in Chinese Spikenard oil (from *Nardostachys jatamansi* DC.), in roots of *Valeriana officinalis* L., in the resin of *Canarium samoense* Engl., and in the essential oils of *Eriostemon myoporoides*, and *Prostanthera prunellioides*. Cryst. from EtOH. M.p. 103·5–105°. $[\alpha]_D$ 18·35° (c, 1·1 in EtOH).

Hellyer, *Austral. J. Chem.*, 1962, **15**, 157.
Stoll, Seebeck, Stauffacher, *Helv. Chim. Acta*, 1957, **40**, 1205.
Naves, *Helv. Chim. Acta*, 1963, **46**, 2139.
Büchi *et al.*, *J. Am. Chem. Soc.*, 1951, **81**, 1968.

Machaerinic Acid

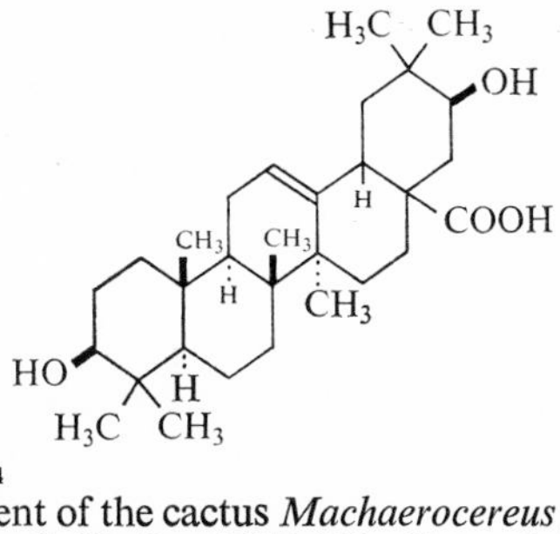

$C_{30}H_{48}O_4$ MW 472

Constituent of the cactus *Machaerocereus gummosus*. *Me ester*: $C_{31}H_{50}O_4$. MW 486. Cryst. from MeOH, Me_2CO–hexane, or Et_2O. M.p. 232–4°. $[\alpha]_D^{31}$ +76° ($CHCl_3$). *Di-Ac*: m.p. 278–80°. $[\alpha]_D$ +86° ($CHCl_3$). *Lactone*: $C_{30}H_{46}O_3$. MW 454. Saponin from bean pods of *Stryphnodendron coriaceum*. M.p. 240–3°. $[\alpha]_D$ −16° (c, 1 in $CHCl_3$).

Djerassi, Lippmann, *J. Am. Chem. Soc.*, 1955, **77**, 1825.
Djerassi, Mills, *J. Am. Chem. Soc.*, 1958, **80**, 1236.
Tursch *et al.*, *J. Org. Chem.*, 1963, **28**, 2390.

Macranthin

$C_{16}H_{19}O_5N$ MW 305

Alkaloid from *Crinum macrantherum* Engl. Colourless needles from EtOH. M.p. 238–40° decomp. $[\alpha]_D^{22}$ −19° (c, 0·235 in $CHCl_3$), +49° (c, 0·229 in EtOH). pK_{MCS}* 7·23. Light absorption: $\lambda_{max.}$ 235·5 (log ε, 3·53) and 292 mμ (3·67).
O-*Ac*: $C_{18}H_{21}O_6N$. MW 347. Alkaloid from *C. macrantherum*. Fine needles in Me_2CO. M.p. 222–4°. $[\alpha]_D$ −26° (c, 0·213 in $CHCl_3$), +18° (c, 0·213 in EtOH). pK_{MCS}* 6·74.
Di-O-Ac: $C_{20}H_{23}O_2N$. MW 389. Alkaloid from *C. macrantherum*. Fine needles from Me_2CO–Et_2O. M.p. 219–21°. $[\alpha]_D^{22}$ +44° (c, 0·284 in $CHCl_3$), +38° (c, 0·203 in EtOH). pK_{MCS}* 6·47.
Tri-Ac: colourless prisms from C_6H_6–Et_2O. M.p. 188–91°. $[\alpha]_D^{22}$ −2° (c, 0·22 in $CHCl_3$).

Hauth, Stauffacher, *Helv. Chim. Acta*, 1964, **47**, 185.

Macrocarpol. *See* Juniperol.

Macronin

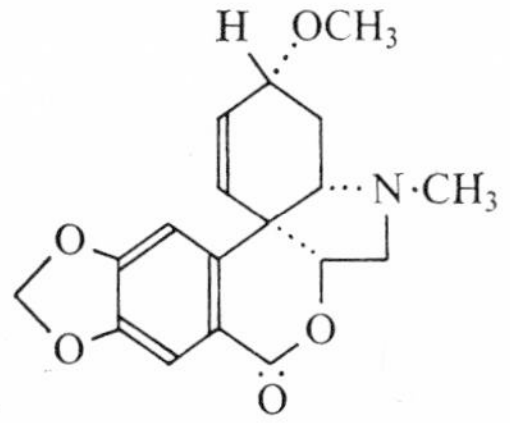

$C_{18}H_{19}O_5N$ MW 329

Alkaloid from *Crinum macrantherum* Engl. Prisms from Me_2CO. M.p. 203–5°. $[\alpha]_D^{22}$ +413° (c, 0·228 in $CHCl_3$), +380° (c, 0·225 in EtOH). Light absorption: $\lambda_{max.}$ 228·5 (log ε, 4·49), 268 (3·74), and 308 mμ (3·78). pK_{MCS}* 6·31.

Hauth, Stauffacher, *Helv. Chim. Acta*, 1964, **47**, 185.
Murphy, Wildman, *Tetrahedron Letters*, 1964, 3857.

Maculosidine

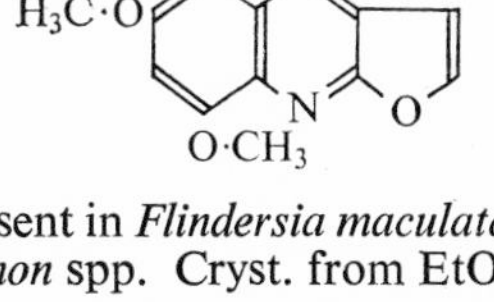

$C_{14}H_{13}O_4N$ MW 259

Alkaloid present in *Flindersia maculata* (*F. maculosa*) and *Eriostemon* spp. Cryst. from EtOH. M.p. 185–6°.

Brown *et al.*, *Austral. J. Chem.*, 1954, **7**, 181.
Duffield, Jefferies, Lucich, *Austral. J. Chem.*, 1962, **15**, 812; 1963, **16**, 123.
Duffield *et al.*, *Tetrahedron*, 1963, **19**, 593.
Govindachari, Prabhakar, *Ind. J. Chem.*, 1963, **1**, 17.

Madagascin

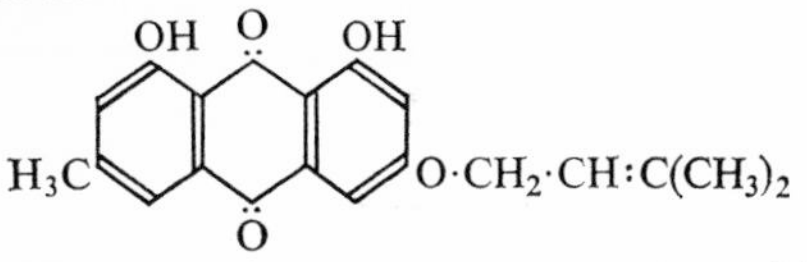

$C_{20}H_{18}O_5$ MW 338

Constituent of *Harungana madagascariensis* Poir. M.p. 156–7°.

Ritchie, Taylor, *Tetrahedron Letters*, 1964, 1431.

Madagascin Anthrone

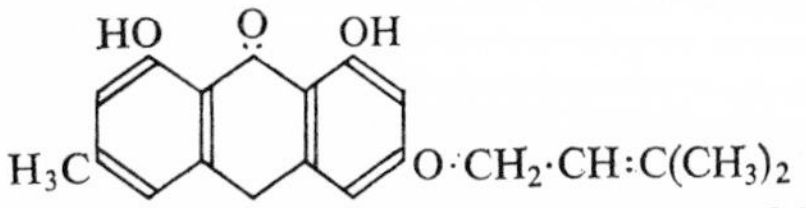

$C_{20}H_{20}O_4$ MW 324

Constituent of *Harungana madagascariensis* Poir. Buff-coloured pigment. M.p. 168°. Light absorption: $\lambda_{max.}$ 220, 254, 272, 306, 357 mμ.

Ritchie, Taylor, *Tetrahedron Letters*, 1964, 1431.

Magnoflorine (*Corytuberine methiodide, Thalictrine*)

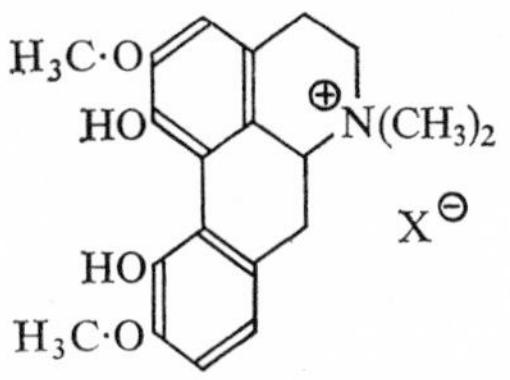

(+)-.

Quaternary alkaloid from *Magnolia*, *Aquilegia*, *Michelia*, and other spp.

Iodide (X = I): $C_{20}H_{24}O_4NI$. MW 469. M.p. 248–9° decomp. $[\alpha]_D^{15}$ +200·1° (MeOH).

(±)-.

Iodide, **B**,1·5H_2O. M.p. 243° decomp.

Nakano, *Chem. Pharm. Bull.* (Tokyo), 1954, **2**, 329.

Tomita, Kikkawa, *J. Pharm. Soc. Japan*, 1957, **77**, 195.

Gopinath *et al.*, *J. Sci. Ind. Res.* (India), 1959, **18B**, 444.

Ishii, Harada, *J. Pharm. Soc. Japan*, 1961, **81**, 238.

Yang, Lu, Hsiao, *J. Pharm. Soc. Japan*, 1962, **82**, 794, 816; 1963, **83**, 216.

Maleic Hydrazide.★

See also:

Ohashi, Mashima, Kubo, *Can. J. Chem.*, 1964, **42**, 970.

Malignolipin.

Phospholipid present in human malignant tumours. Hydrol. → choline + spermine + phosphoric acid + a fatty acid.

Picrate: m.p. 269° decomp.

Kôsaki *et al.*, *Science*, 1958, **127**, 1176.

Sax *et al.*, *J. Biol. Chem.*, 1963, **238**, 3817.

Malonic Acid.★

tert-*Bu, Et ester*: *see tert*-Butyl ethyl malonate.

Di-tert *Bu ester*: *see* Di-*tert*-butyl malonate.

Malouetine★

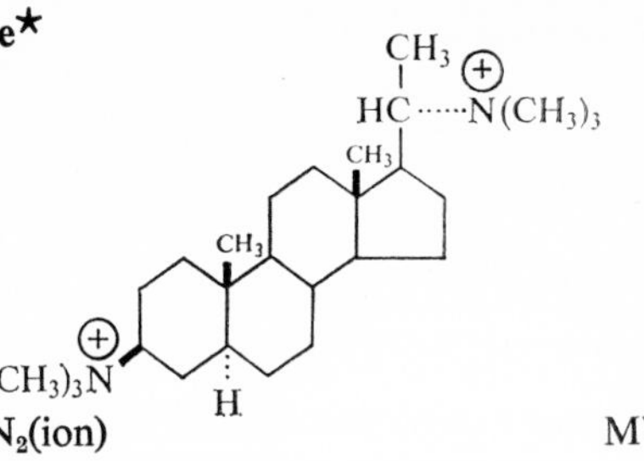

$C_{27}H_{52}N_2$(ion) MW 404

Structure:

Janot, Lainé, Goutarel, *Ann. Pharm. Fr.*, 1960, **18**, 673.

Maltobiouronic Acid (4-O-[α-D-*Glucopyranosyluronic acid*]-D-*glucose*)

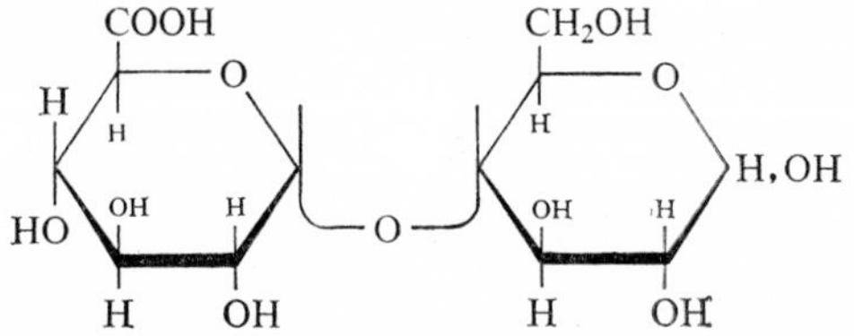

$C_{12}H_{20}O_{12}$ MW 356

Monohydrate cryst. $[\alpha]_D$ 116° (c, 2·52 in H_2O).

Me ester-Hepta-Ac: cryst. from MeOH. M.p. 197–8°. $[\alpha]_D$ 77° (c, 0·54 in $CHCl_3$).

Dutton, Slessor, *Can. J. Chem.*, 1964, **42**, 1110.

Maltosamine. *See* *O*-α-D-Glucopyranosyl-(1 → 4)-2-amino-2-deoxy-α-D-glucopyranose.

Mammeigin

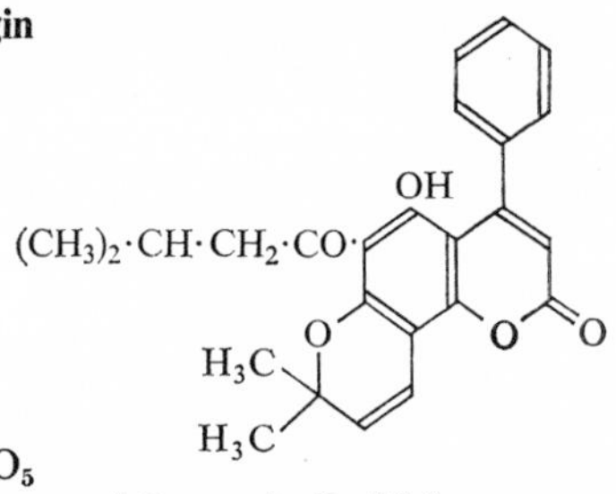

$C_{25}H_{24}O_5$ MW 404

Constituent of the seed oil of *Mammea americana* L. Cryst. from Et_2O–hexane. M.p. 144–6°. Light absorption: $\lambda_{max.}$ 234 (log ε, 4·45), 286 (4·52), and 365 mμ (4·11) in EtOH. $\lambda_{max.}$ 251 (log ε, 4·38), 312 (4·41), and 438 mμ (3·84) in alkaline EtOH.

Finnegan, Mueller, *Chemistry and Industry*, 1964, 1065.

Mammeisin. *See* **5** : 7-Dihydroxy-8-isopentenyl-6-isovaleryl-4-phenylcoumarin.★

***o*-α-D-Mannopyranosyl-(1 → 6)-*o*-α-D-mannopyranosyl-(1 → 1)-(1-*R*)*myo*inositol.★**

See also:

Ballou, Lee, *Biochemistry*, 1964, **3**, 682.

Marevan. *See under* 3-(2-Acetyl-1-phenylethyl)-4-hydroxycoumarin.

Marrubiin.★

Also present in *Leonotis leonurus* R. Br. (Wilde dagga). M.p. 160°. $[\alpha]_D$ 33·3° (c, 1 in $CHCl_3$).

Rivett, *J. Chem. Soc.*, 1964, 1857.

Matromycin. *See* Oleandamycin.★

C-Mavacurine.★

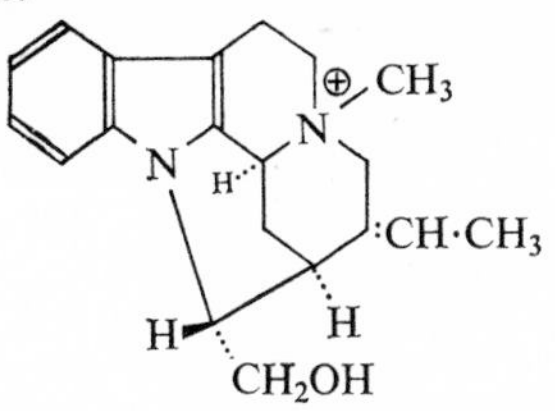

Light absorption: $\lambda_{max.}$ 223 (log ε, 4·63) and 279 mμ (3·90).
Structure:

Hesse *et al.*, *Helv. Chim. Acta*, 1964, **47**, 878.

Mayurone

$C_{15}H_{22}O$ MW 218

Constituent of the wood "Mayur pankhi" (*Thuja orientalis* or *T. compacta*). M.p. 69·5–70°. $[\alpha]_D^{30}$ 253·4°.

Chetty, Dev, *Tetrahedron Letters*, 1964, 73.

Mecambridine

$C_{19}H_{21}O_5N$ MW 343

Alkaloid from *Meconopsis cambrica*. Cryst. from EtOH–Et_2O. M.p. 179–80°. $[\alpha]_D^{24}$ −243°. pK 5·85.
B,HCl: cryst. from H_2O. M.p. 224–5° decomp.
Picrate: cryst. from EtOH.Aq. M.p. 203–4°.

Slavik, Slavikova, *Coll. Czech. Chem. Commun.*, 1963, **28**, 1720.

Mecambrine. *See* Fungipavine.

Mecambroline (*Isofungipavine*)

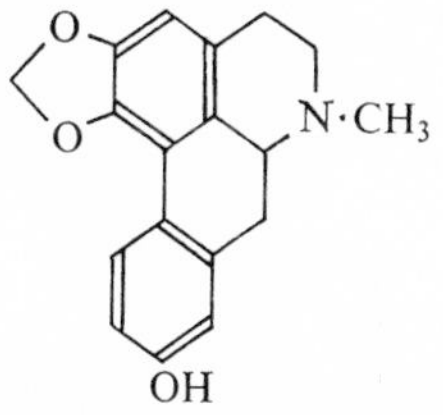

$C_{18}H_{17}O_3N$ MW 295

Alkaloid from *Meconopsis cambrica*. M.p. 145°. $[\alpha]_D^{23}$ 76°. pK 6·42.
B,HCl: cryst. from H_2O. M.p. 264–6°.
Picrate: m.p. 179–80°.

Slavik, Slavikova, *Coll. Czech. Chem. Commun.*, 1963, **28**, 1720.

Medroxyprogesterone. *See* 17α-Hydroxy-6-α-methylpregn-4-ene-3 : 20-dione.

Megestrol. *See* 17α-Hydroxy-6-methylpregna-4 : 6-diene-3 : 20-dione.

Melaleucic Acid (3β-*Hydroxylup*-20(29)-*en*-27 : 28-*dioic acid*)

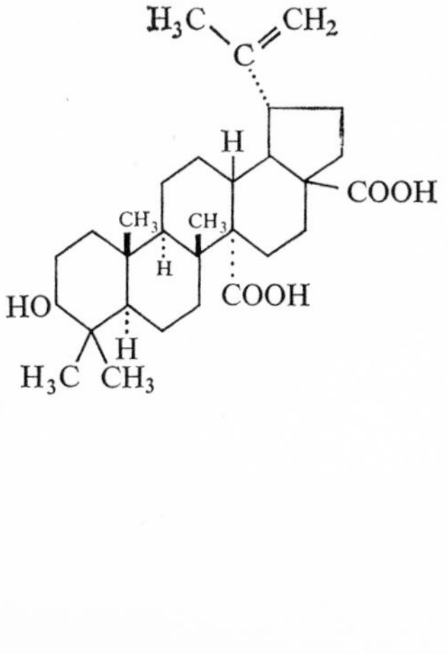

$C_{30}H_{46}O_5$ MW 486

Constituent of the bark of *Melaleuca* spp. M.p. 363–4°. Forms *Ac* and *Benzoyl* deriv.
Di-Me ester: $C_{32}H_{50}O_5$. MW 514. M.p. 204°.

Arthur *et al.*, *Chemistry and Industry*, 1956, 926.
Chopra *et al.*, *Tetrahedron Letters*, 1963, 1847.

α-Melanocyte Stimulating Hormone. *See* α-Melanotropin.

β-Melanocyte Stimulating Hormone. *See* β-Melanotropin.

α-Melanotropin (α-*MSH*, α-*Melanocyte stimulating hormone*)

CH_3·CO(N)·Ser·Tyr·Ser·Met·Glu·His·Phe·Arg–
1 2 3 4 5 6 7 8
–Try·Gly·Lys·Pro·Val·NH_2
9 10 11 12 13

$C_{75}H_{108}O_{20}N_{22}S$ MW 1720

Hormone from posterior pituitary glands of pigs, cattle, horses, and monkeys. Isoelectric point at pH 10·5–11. $[\alpha]_D^{25}$ −58·5° (c, 1 in 10% AcOH).

Lerner, Lee, *J. Am. Chem. Soc.*, 1955, **77**, 1066.
Lee, Lerner, *J. Biol. Chem.*, 1956, **221**, 943.
Harris, Lerner, *Nature* (Lond.), 1957, **179**, 1346.
Li, *Adv. Protein Chem.*, 1957, **12**, 269.
Harris, *Biochem. J.*, 1959, **71**, 451.
Dixon, Li, *J. Am. Chem. Soc.*, 1960, **82**, 4568.
Lee, Lerner, Buettner-Janusch, *J. Biol. Chem.*, 1961, **236**, 1390.
Schwyzer, Costopanagiotis, Sieber, *Helv. Chim. Acta*, 1963, **46**, 870.
Schally *et al.*, *Arch. Biochem. Biophys.*, 1964, **107**, 332.

β-Melanotropin (β-*MSH*, β-*Melanocyte stimulating hormone*).
The composition of this hormone depends on the species.

Porcine:

H·Asp·Glu·Gly·Pro·Tyr·Lys·Met·Glu·His·Phe–
1 2 3 4 5 6 7 8 9 10
–Arg·Tyr·Gly·Ser·Pro·Pro·Lys·Asp·OH
11 12 13 14 15 16 17 18

$C_{98}H_{144}O_{28}N_{28}S$ MW 2192

Hormone from pig pituitary gland.

Lee, Lerner, *J. Biol. Chem.*, 1956, **221**, 943.
Geschwind, Li, Barnafi, *J. Am. Chem. Soc.*, 1956, **78**, 620; 1957, **79**, 620.
Li, *Adv. Protein Chem.*, 1957, **12**, 269.
Harris, Roos, *Biochem. J.*, 1959, **71**, 434.

Bovine (Seryl β-MSH):

H·Asp·Ser·Gly·Pro·Tyr·Lys·Met·Glu·His·Phe–
1 2 3 4 5 6 7 8 9 10
–Arg·Try·Gly·Ser·Pro·Pro·Lys·Asp·OH
11 12 13 14 15 16 17 18

$C_{96}H_{142}O_{27}N_{28}S$ MW 2150

Hormone from ox pituitary glands. $[\alpha]_D^{25}$ −57·5° (c, 1 in 1*N*-AcOH).

Geschwind, Li, Barnafi, *J. Am. Chem. Soc.*, 1957, **79**, 6394.
Schwyzer *et al.*, *Helv. Chim. Acta*, 1963, **46**, 1975.

Melibentin (3 : 5 : 6 : 7 : 8-*Pentamethoxy*-3′ : 4′-*methylenedioxyflavone*)

$C_{21}H_{20}O_9$ MW 416

Constituent of *Melicope broadbentiana* Bail. Rhombs from EtOH.Aq. M.p. 127–9·5°.

Briggs, Cebale, *Austral. J. Chem.*, 1964, **17**, 461.

Melleril. *See* B,HCl *under* Thioridazine.★

Mellitoxin (4-*Hydroxytutin*)

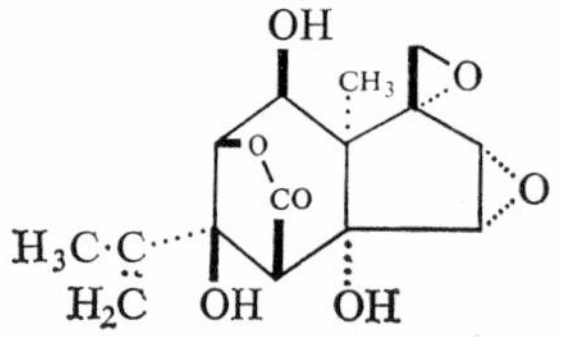

$C_{15}H_{18}O_7$ MW 130

Metabolite of *Scolypopa australis* feeding on leaves of stems of *Coriaria arborea*. Cryst. M.p. 225–40° decomp. $[\alpha]_D$ +31·9°. Br_2.Aq. → monobromo-mellitoxin. M.p. 250° decomp.

Di-Ac: m.p. 208°.

Sutherland, Palmer-Jones, *New Zealand J. Sci. Technol.*, 1947, **29A**, 107, 114, 121, 129.

Hodges, White, Shannon, *Tetrahedron Letters*, 1964, 371.

Memine. *See* 3-(2-Morpholinoethyl)morphine.

Menadione. *See* 2-Methyl-1 : 4-naphthaquinone.

Menaphthone. *See* 2-Methyl-1 : 4-naphthoquinone.

Menisperine. *See* *N*-Methylisocorydinium salts.

2 : 4-*p*-Menthadiene. *See* 2-Isopropyl-5-methyl-1 : 3-cyclohexadiene.

Mepane. *See* Promethestrol.★

Mepazine. *See* Pecazine.★

Mephenamine. *See* Orphenadrine.★

Mephyton. *See* Vitamin K_1.★

2-Mercaptobenzimidazole.★

See also:

Van Allan, Deacon, *Organic Syntheses*, 1950, **30**, 56; Coll. Vol. **4**, 569.

Mercodinone. *See under* Dihydrocodeinone.

Merthiolate. *See* Thiomersal.★

Mesitoic Acid. *See* 2 : 4 : 6-Trimethylbenzoic Acid.★

Mesotocin (*Ileu*$_8$-*oxytocin*)

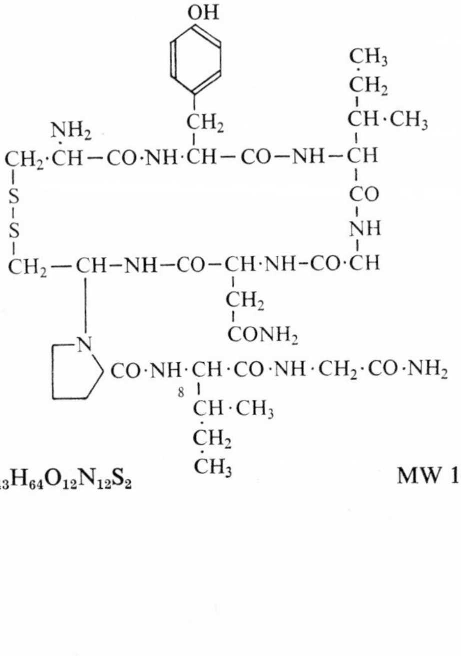

$C_{43}H_{64}O_{12}N_{12}S_2$ MW 1004

Hormone present in the frog (*Rana esculenta*).

Acher *et al.*, *Biochim. Biophys. Acta*, 1964, **90**, 613.

Metacortandracin. *See* Prednisone.★

Metacortandralone. *See* Prednisolone.★

Methanesulphonic Acid.★

Chloride:★ b.p. 64–6°/20 mm.

Hearst, Noller, *Organic Syntheses*, 1950, **30**, 58; Coll. Vol. **4**, 571.

1 : 6-Methanocyclodecapentaene

$C_{11}H_{10}$ MW 142

Colourless cryst. M.p. 28–9°. Light absorption: $\lambda_{max.}$ 256 (ε, 68,000), 259 (63,000), 298 mμ (6200).

Vogel, Roth, *Angew. Chem.*, 1964, **76**, 145; *Int. Ed.*, 1964, **3**, 228.

Methionyl-lysyl-bradykinin

H–Met–Lys–Arg–Pro–Pro–Gly–Phe–Ser–Pro–Phe–Arg–OH
1 2 3 4 5 6 7 8 9 10 11

$C_{61}H_{94}O_{13}N_{18}S$ MW 1318

Peptide producing signs of inflammatory response isolated from ox blood. Isolated as B,2AcOH,6H_2O: $[\alpha]_D^{25}$ −86·5° (c, 0·5 in H_2O).

Elliott, Lewis, Smyth, *Biochem. J.*, 1963, **87**, 21P.

Schröder, *Experientia*, 1964, **20**, 39.

Schröder, Hempel, *Experientia*, 1964, **20**, 529 (*Review*).

Methœstrol. *See* Promethestrol.★

***N*-4-Methoxybenzyl-*N′* : *N′*-dimethyl-*N*-2-pyrimidyl-ethylenediamine.** *See* Thonzylamine.★

***p*-Methoxycinnamyl Alcohol** (3-p-*Methoxyphenyl*-2-*propen*-1-*ol*)

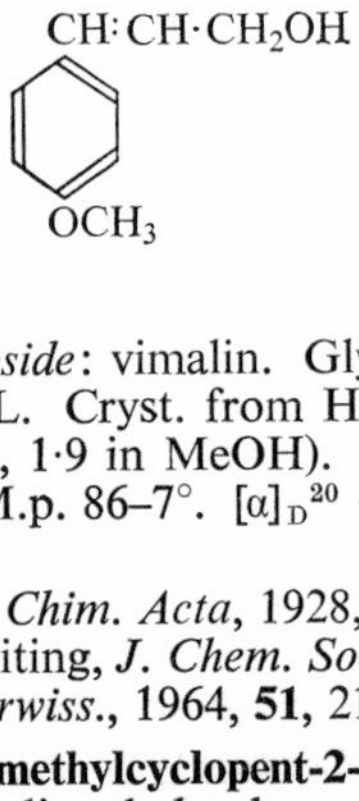

$C_{10}H_{12}O_2$ MW 164

M.p. 79–80°.

1-β-*Glucopyranoside*: vimalin. Glycoside present in *Salix viminalis* L. Cryst. from H_2O. M.p. 143–4°. $[\alpha]_D^{20}$ −60·6° (c, 1·9 in MeOH). *Tetra-Ac*: needles from MeOH. M.p. 86–7°. $[\alpha]_D^{20}$ −37·3° (c, 1·45 in $CHCl_3$).

Karrer, *Helv. Chim. Acta*, 1928, **11**, 1209.

Marshall, Whiting, *J. Chem. Soc.*, 1956, 4082.

Thieme, *Naturwiss.*, 1964, **51**, 217.

2-Methoxy-3 : 5-dimethylcyclopent-2-en-1-one. *See* Me ether *under* 3 : 5-dimethylcyclopentane-1 : 2-dione.

Methoxyeugenol. *See* 4-Allyl-2 : 6-dimethoxyphenol.

3β-Methoxy-*D* : *C-friedo*-oleana-9(11)ene. *See* Arundoin.

7-Methoxy-1 : 2-(*N*-methylaziridino)mitosene

$C_{16}H_{17}O_5N_3$ MW 331

Biologically active reduction product from mitomycin B. Does not melt but loses birefringence at 230°. $[\alpha]_D^{25}$ 36·4° (c, 0·99 in dimethyl sulphoxide).

Patrick *et al.*, *J. Am. Chem. Soc.*, 1964, **86**, 1889.

3-Methoxy-4 : 5-methylenedioxyamphetamine. *See* 1-(3-Methoxy-4 : 5-methylenedioxyphenyl)-2-propylamine.

1-(3-Methoxy-4 : 5-methylenedioxyphenyl)-2-propylamine (3-*Methoxy*-4 : 5-*methylenedioxyamphetamine*, *MMDA*)

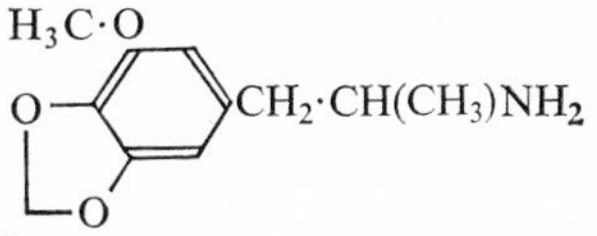

$C_{11}H_{15}O_3N$ MW 209

Psychotropic drug of greater potency than trimethoxyamphetamine and mescaline.

Shulgin, *Nature*, 1964, **201**, 1120.

3-Methoxy-4 : 5-methylenedioxypropiophenone. *See* Crocatone.

7-Methoxymitosene

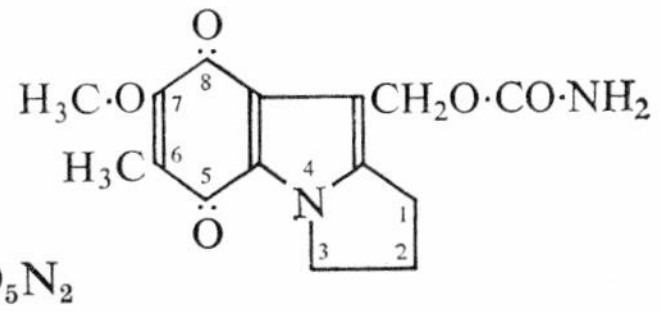

$C_{15}H_{16}O_5N_2$ MW 304

Antibacterial agent. M.p. 206–7°. Light absorption: $\lambda_{max.}$ 230 (ε, 19,200), 287 (14,600), 345 (3870), and 460 mμ (1390).

Allen, Poletto, Weiss, *J. Am. Chem. Soc.*, 1964, **86**, 3877.

***p*-Methoxyphenylacetic Acid.★**

Nitrile: *p*-Methoxyphenylacetonitrile.

Rorig *et al.*, *Organic Syntheses*, 1956, **36**, 50; Coll. Vol. **4**, 576.

3-*p*-Methoxyphenyl-2-propen-1-ol. *See* *p*-Methoxycinnamyl Alcohol.

Methyl 4-acetamido-4-deoxy-L-erythrofuranoside

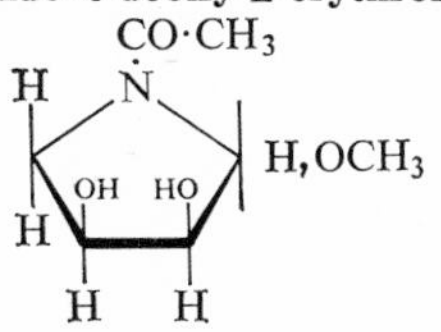

$C_7H_{13}O_4N$ MW 175

Syrup.

Di-Ac: syrup. $[\alpha]_D$ −9° (c, 3·09 in $CHCl_3$).

Szarek, Jones, *Can. J. Chem.*, 1964, **42**, 20.

3-Methyladenine

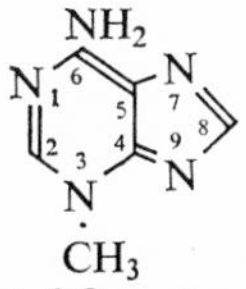

Suggested fine structure

$C_6H_7N_5$ MW 149

pK 5·7. Light absorption: $\lambda_{max.}$ 273 (at pH 4) and 272 mμ (at pH 12).

B,H₂SO₄: needles from MeOH. M.p. 268–70°.

Picrate: needles from H_2O. Sublimed above 270°.

Elion, *Ciba Foundation Symposium on the Chemistry and Biology of Purines*, Wolstenholm and O'Connor, Editors. J. A. Churchill, London, 1957, p. 39.

Brookes, Lawley, *J. Chem. Soc.*, 1960, 539.

Pal, Horton, *J. Chem. Soc.*, 1964, 400.

***p*-(2-Methylaminopropyl)phenol** (*Pholedrine*, *Veritain*, *Veritol*)

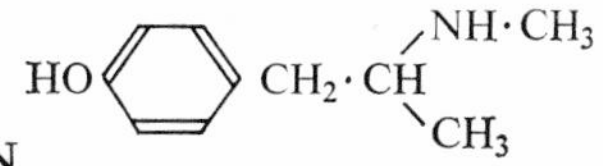

$C_{10}H_{15}ON$ MW 165

Sympathomimetic agent. M.p. 162–3°.

B₂,H₂SO₄: cryst. M.p. 320–3° decomp.

The Merck Index, 7th ed., Merck and Co., Rahway, 1960, 672.

6-α-Methyl-5α-androstane-3 : 7 : 17-trione

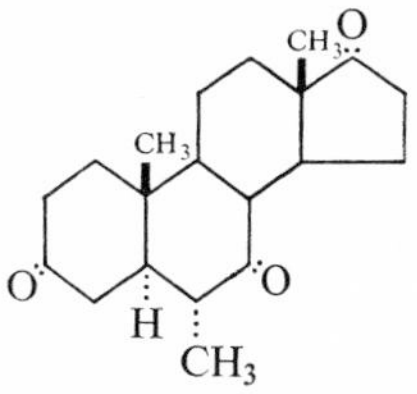

$C_{20}H_{28}O_3$ MW 316

Cryst. from methoxyethanol. M.p. 182°. $[\alpha]_D^{20}$ +43° (c, 0·1 in dioxan).

Brienne, Ouannes, Jacques, *Bull. soc. chim.*, 1964, 1773.

3-Methylbenzofuran.★

See also:

Boehme, *Organic Syntheses*, Coll. Vol. **4**, 590.

24-Methylcholesta-7 : 22-diene-3-one (7 : 22-*Ergostadiene*-3-*one*)

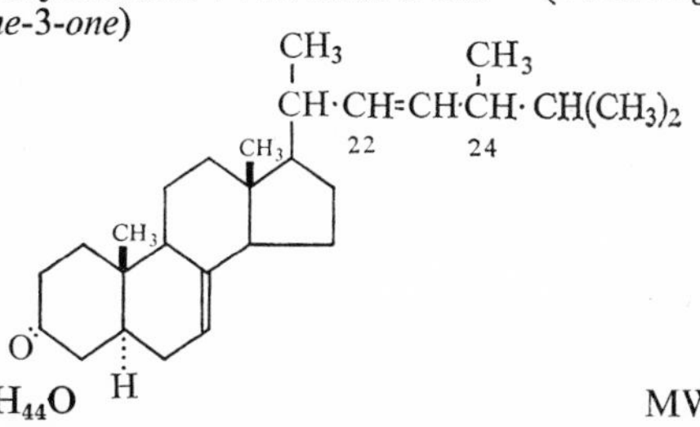

$C_{28}H_{44}O$ MW 396

Constituent of *Fomes fomentarius*. Cryst. from Me_2CO. M.p. 184–7°. $[\alpha]_D$ 6° ($CHCl_3$).

Barton, Cox, *J. Chem. Soc.*, 1948, 1354.

Arthur, Halsall, Smith, *J. Chem. Soc.*, 1958, 2603.

2-Methyl-1 : 3-cyclobutanedione

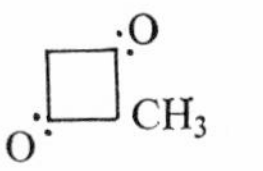

$C_5H_6O_2$ MW 98

Cryst. from AcOEt–light petroleum. M.p. 119°. Light absorption: $\lambda_{max.}$ 247 mμ (ε, 10,540). pK_a 3.

Et enol ether: $C_7H_{10}O_2$. MW 126. B.p. 110°/18 mm.

Johns, Kriegler, *Austral. J. Chem.*, 1964, **17**, 765.

3-Methylcyclobutene

C_5H_8 MW 68

B.p. 32°. n_D^{20} 1·4005.

Gil-Av, Shabtai, *J. Org. Chem.*, 1964, **29**, 257.

11-(2-Methylcyclohex-2-enyl)undec-9-enoic Acid

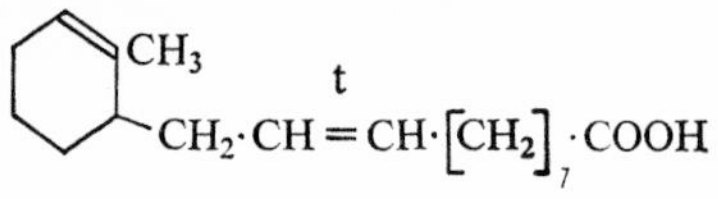

$C_{18}H_{30}O_2$ MW 278

9-*Trans*-.
Major product of heating linseed oil at 275° in the absence of air.
Et ester: $C_{20}H_{34}O_2$. MW 306. Oil.

Hutchinson, Alexander, *J. Org. Chem.*, 1963, **28**, 2522.

***S*-Methylcysteine.** *See under* Cysteine.

2-Methyl-2 : 5-decanediol

$CH_3[CH_2]_4{\cdot}CHOH{\cdot}[CH_2]_2{\cdot}C(OH)(CH_3)_2$

$C_{11}H_{24}O_2$ MW 188

B.p. 65–9°/2 mm. n_D^{25} 1·4420.

Colonge, Marey, *Organic Syntheses*, 1958, **38**, 41; Coll. Vol. **4**, 601.

***N*$_\alpha$-Methyldesoxysarpagine.** *See* Affinisine.

3-*C*-Methyl-2 : 6-dideoxy-L-*arabo*-hexose. *See* Olivomycose.

***o*-Methyldiphenhydramine.** *See* Orphenadrine.★

α-Methyldopa. *See* Presinol.★

Methylene-bis-norflavaspidic Acid

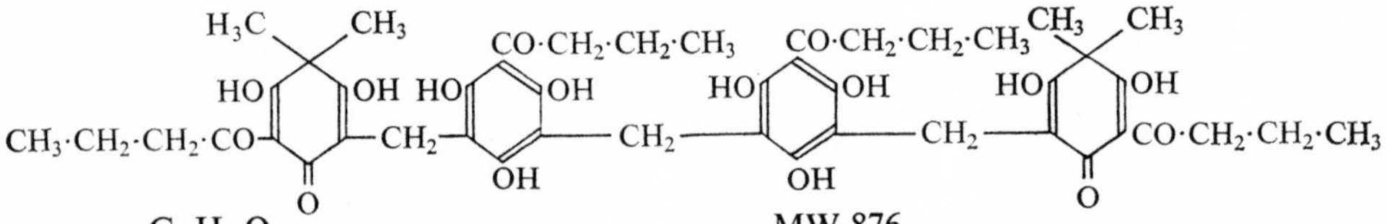

$C_{47}H_{56}O_{16}$ MW 876

Constituent of the fern *Dryopteris austriaca*. Cryst. from Me_2CO. M.p. 158–65°.

Penttilä, Sundman, *Acta Chem. Scand.*, 1963, **17**, 2370.

2-Methylenecycloheptene-1 : 3-diglycine

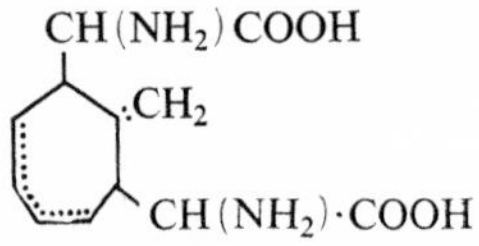

Partial structure

$C_{12}H_{18}O_4N_2$ MW 254

Amino acid from the mushroom *Lactarius helvus*. Turns yellow at 200°. Did not melt below 300°.

Casimir, Virtanen, *Acta Chem. Scand.*, 1959, **13**, 2139.

Komamine, Virtanen, *Acta Chem. Scand.*, 1959, **13**, 2141.

Honkanen *et al.*, *Acta Chem. Scand.*, 1964, **18**, 1319.

Methylenedioxybenzene.

See also:

Benn, May, *Chemistry and Industry*, 1964, 499.

And under Catechol.★

γ-Methyleneglutamic Acid.★

See also:

Blake, Fowden, *Biochem. J.*, 1964, **92**, 136.

2 : 3-Methyleneheptadeca-4 : 5-dienoic Acid. *See* Laballenic Acid.

4-Methyleneproline

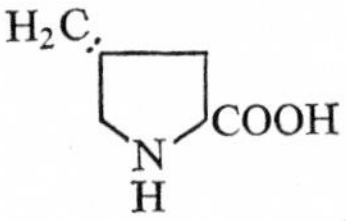

$C_6H_9O_2N$ MW 127

DL-.
Amino acid present in loquat seeds (*Eriobotrya japonica*). M.p. *ca.* 225° decomp. (243–5° decomp.).
B,HCl: fine plates from EtOH–AcOEt. M.p. 217–18°.
Benzyloxycarbonyl deriv.: *B, dicyclohexylamine.* M.p. 139°.
(−)-.
Benzyloxycarbonyl deriv.: *B, dicyclohexylamine.* M.p. 160–1°. $[\alpha]_D^{19}$ −5·5° (c, 2 in $CHCl_3$).

Gray, Fowden, *Nature*, 1962, **193**, 1285.

Bethell, Kenner, Sheppard, *Nature*, 1962, **194**, 864.

Burgstahler, Trollope, Aiman, *Nature*, 1964, **202**, 388.

6-Methyl-Δ^{8,9}-ergolene-8-carboxylic Acid

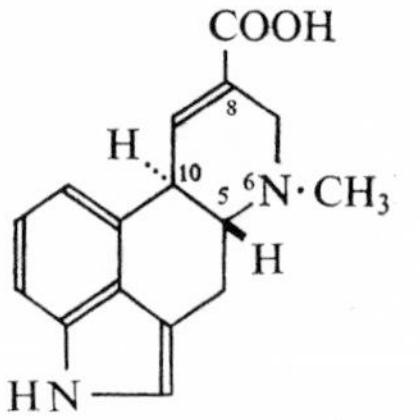

$C_{16}H_{16}O_2N_2$ MW 268

Metabolite of a strain of *Claviceps paspali* Stevens et Hall. M.p. 245–7° decomp. $[\alpha]_D$ −208° (c, 0·4 in 0·1*N*-NaOH).
B,HCl: m.p. 257–8° decomp. $[\alpha]_D$ −176° (c, 0·9 in 0·1*N*-HCl).

Kobel, Schreier, Rutschmann, *Helv. Chim. Acta*, 1964, **47**, 1052.

Methyl 22-feruloyloxydocosanoate. *See* Phellochryseine.

Methylfluorene.★

See also:

Schoen, Becker, *Organic Syntheses*, 1959, **39**, 43; Coll. Vol. **4**, 623.

3-Methylfuran.★
See also:
Burness, *Organic Syntheses*, 1959, **39**, 46; Coll. Vol. **4**, 628.

3-Methylfuran-2-carboxylic Acid.★
See also:
Burness, *Organic Syntheses*, 1959, **39**, 46, 49; Coll. Vol. **4**, 628, 649.

3-Methylglutaric Acid.★
Anhydride:
Cason, *Organic Syntheses*, 1958, **38**, 52; Coll. Vol. **4**, 630.

3-Methylhistidine

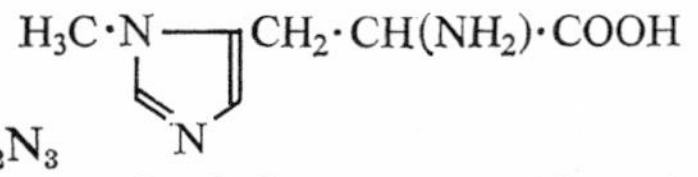

$C_7H_{11}O_2N_3$ MW 169

Constituent of whale meat. White plates from H·CONMe₂.Aq. M.p. 248–50° decomp. $[\alpha]_D^{20}$ −24·7° (c, 2·8 in H_2O).

B,HCl: white plates from $H{\cdot}CONMe_2$.Aq. M.p. 251–2° decomp. $[\alpha]_D^{22}$ 6·9° (c, 2 in H_2O), 9·4° (c, 2 in *N*-HCl).

B,2HCl: stout prisms. M.p. 258–9°. $[\alpha]_D^{20}$ 12·9° (c, 2 in *N*-HCl).

Cocks, Dennis, Nelson, *Nature*, 1964, **202**, 184.

***N*-Methylisocorydinium** (*Menisperine*)

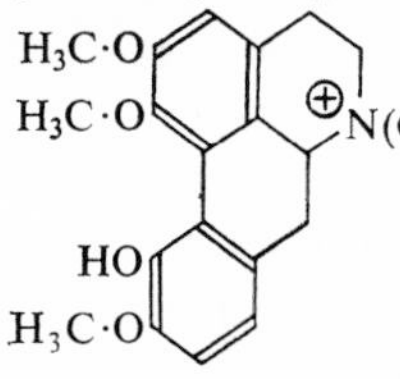

$C_{21}H_{26}O_4N$ MW 356 (ion)

Quaternary alkaloid from *Bragantia wallichi*, *Cryptocarya angulata*, *C. triplinervis*, *Fagara coco*, *Legnephora moorei*, and other spp.

Chloride (X = Cl): $C_{21}H_{26}O_4NCl$. MW 391·5. M.p. 217–21° (slow heating), 235° (rapid heating). $[\alpha]_D$ 168·6° (H_2O).

Iodide (X = I): $C_{21}H_{26}O_4NI$. MW 483. M.p. 219° (slow heating), 231–2° (rapid heating).

Comin, Deulofeu, *J. Org. Chem.*, 1954, **19**, 1774.
Cooke, Haynes, *Austral. J. Chem.*, 1954, **7**, 99.
Katritzky, Jones, Bhatnagar, *J. Chem. Soc.*, 1960, 1950.
Kikkawa, *J. Pharm. Soc. Japan*, 1958, **78**, 1006.

1-Methylisoquinoline.★
See also:
Weinstock, Boekelheide, *Organic Syntheses*, 1958, **38**, 58; Coll. Vol. **4**, 641.

Methylmalonylcoenzyme A

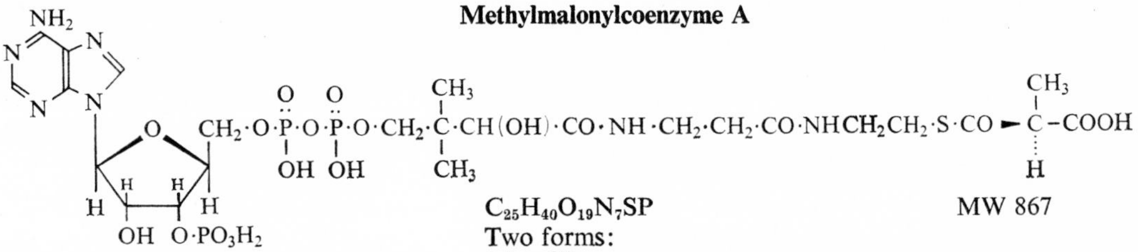

$C_{25}H_{40}O_{19}N_7SP$ MW 867

Two forms:
(*a*) D (S)-.
Product of enzymatic carboxylation of propionyl coenzyme A. Must be isomerised to the diastereoisomeric form (*b*) before it can be converted enzymatically to succinyl coenzyme A.
(*b*) L (S)-.

Beck, Flavin, Ochoa, *J. Biol. Chem.*, 1957, **229**, 997.
Mazumder *et al.*, *J. Biol. Chem.*, 1961, **236**, PC53.
Herge, Mill, Lane, *Biochim. Biophys. Acta*, 1962, **56**, 538.
Overath *et al.*, *Biochem. Z.*, 1962, **335**, 500.
Sprecher, Clark, Sprinson, *Biochem. Biophys. Research Commun.*, 1964, **15**, 581.
Ratey, Lynen, *Biochem. Biophys. Research Commun.*, 1964, **16**, 358.

2-Methyl-1 : 4-naphthoquinone (*Aquakay*, *Hemodal*, *Kappaxin*, *Menadione*, *Menaphthone*, *Synkay Thyloquinone*, *Vitamin K_3*)

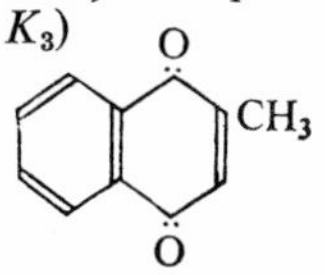

$C_{11}H_8O_2$ MW 172

Shows Vitamin K activity. Bright yellow light-sensitive cryst. M.p. 105–7°.

4-*Mono-oxime*: $C_{11}H_9O_2N$. MW 187. Platelets from EtOH. M.p. 165–70° decomp.

Fieser, *J. Biol. Chem.*, 1940, **133**, 391.
Veldstra, Wiardi, *Rec. trav. chim.*, 1943, **62**, 75.

3-Methyl-4-nitropyridine.★
1-*Oxide*:
Taylor, Crovetti, *Organic Syntheses*, 1956, **36**, 53; Coll. Vol. **4**, 654.

Methyl orthocarbonate

$C(O{\cdot}CH_3)_4$

$C_5H_{12}O_4$ MW 136

B.p. 113·5–114°. n_D^{20} 1·3858. D_4^{20} 1·020.

Tieckelmann, Post, *J. Org. Chem.*, 1948, **13**, 265.
Smith, Delin, *Svensk, Kem. Tidskr.*, 1953, **65**, 10.

3-Methyloxidole.★
Endler, Becker, *Organic Syntheses*, 1957, **37**, 60; Coll. Vol. **4**, 657.

3-Methyl-2 : 3′-pentenylcyclopenten-1-one (cis-*Jasmone*)
Synthesis:
Stork, Borch, *J. Am. Chem. Soc.*, 1964, **86**, 936.

α-Methylphenethylhydrazine (*Pheniprazine*)

$C_6H_5{\cdot}CH_2{\cdot}CH(CH_3){\cdot}NH{\cdot}NH_2$

$C_9H_{14}N_2$ MW 150

(+)-.
Used in treatment of hypertension. Liquid. B.p. 82–6°/0·5 mm. n_D^{20} 1·5401.

B,HCl: Cavodil. Cryst. M.p. 152–4°. $[\alpha]_D^{25}$ 12·8° (c, 5 in H_2O).
(±)-.
B,HCl: m.p. 122–4°.

Biel *et al., J. Am. Chem. Soc.*, 1958, **80**, 1519.

3-Methyl-3-phenylglutaric Acid.★

McElvain, Clemens, *Organic Syntheses*, 1959, **39**, 54; Coll. Vol. **4**, 664.

3-Methyl-2-phenylmorpholine. *See* Phenmetrazine.★

***N*-Methyl-2-phenylsuccinimide.** *See* Phensuximide.★

***N*-(1-Methyl-2-piperidinoethyl)propionanilide** (*Phenampromid*)

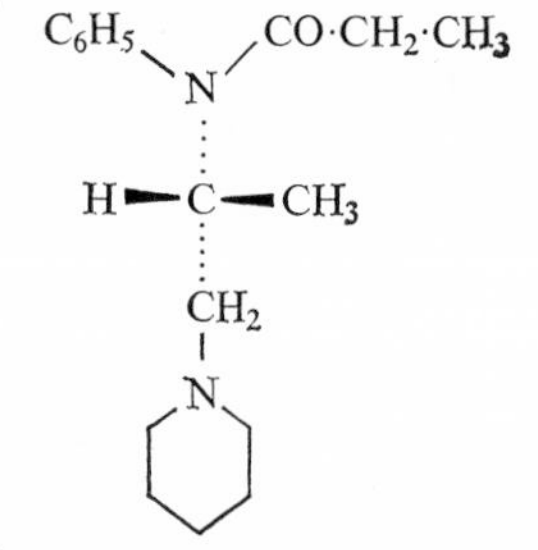

$C_{17}H_{26}ON_2$ MW 274

(−) (R)-.
Potent analgesic.
B,HCl: cryst. from Et_2O–EtOH. M.p. 202–3°. $[\alpha]_D^{25}$ −18·9° (c, 2 in H_2O).
(−)-*Malate*: cryst. from EtOH. M.p. 178·5–179·5°. $[\alpha]_D^{25}$ −16·3° (c, 2 in H_2O).
(+)-.
B,HCl: m.p. 202–3°. $[\alpha]_D^{25}$ 18·9° (c, 2 in H_2O).
(+)-*Tartrate*: cryst. from EtOH. M.p. 204·5–205·5°. $[\alpha]_D^{25}$ 23·7 (c, 2 in H_2O).
(±)-.
B.p. 124–8°/0·2 mm. n_D^{28} 1·518.
B,HCl: m.p. 201–2°.

Wright, Brabander, Hardy, *J. Am. Chem. Soc.*, 1959, **81**, 1518; *J. Org. Chem.*, 1961, **26**, 476.
Portoghese, *Chemistry and Industry*, 1964, 582.

3-(2-Methylpiperidino) propyl benzoate. *See* Piperocaine.★

10-[2-(1-Methyl-2-piperidyl)ethyl]-2-methylthiophenothiazine. *See* Thioridazine.★

Methyl sciadopate

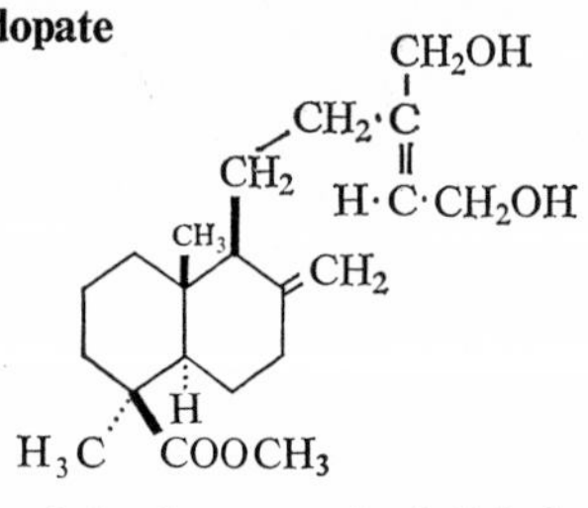

$C_{21}H_{34}O_4$ MW 350

Extractive of the heartwood of *Sciadopitys verticillata* Sieb. et Zucc. Cryst. from Me_2CO.Aq. M.p. 108·5°. KOH in ethylene glycol → parent acid as an oil.
Di-Ac: oil. B.p. 160–185°/10^{-3} mm.

Sumimoto, *Tetrahedron*, 1963, **19**, 643.
Sumimoto, Tanaka, Matsufuji, *Chemistry and Industry*, 1963, 1928; *Tetrahedron*, 1964, **20**, 1427.

3-Methylthiophene.★
See also:
Feldkamp, Tullar, *Organic Syntheses*, 1954, **34**, 73; Coll. Vol. **4**, 671.

Methyl *p*-tolyl sulphone.★
See also:
Field, Clark, *Organic Syntheses*, 1958, **38**, 62; Coll. Vol. **4**, 674.

Methyltriacetic Lactone. *See* 4-Hydroxy-3 : 6-dimethyl-2-pyrone.

6-Methyl-6-vinylfulvene

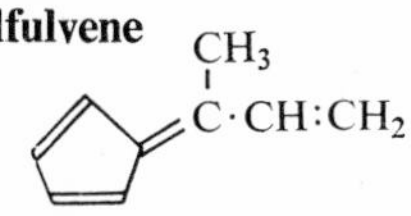

C_9H_{10} MW 118

Red needles from light petroleum. M.p. −31·2° to −30·5°. D_4^{18} 0·912. Light absorption: $\lambda_{max.}$ 285 (log ε, 4·32), 294 (4·45), 299 (4·46), 303 (4·47), 313 (4·26), and 394 mμ (2·35).

Neuenschwander, Meuche, Schaltegger, *Helv. Chim. Acta*, 1964, **47**, 1022.

Methylviologen. *See* Paraquat.★

Michelalbine. *See* Norushinsunine.

Micheline A. *See* Ushinsunine.

Michepressine

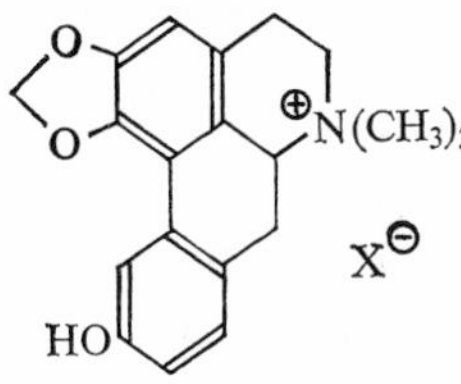

$C_{19}H_{20}O_3N$ MW 310 (ion)

Quaternary alkaloid from *Michelia compressa*.
Iodide (X = I): $C_{19}H_{20}O_3NI$. MW 437. M.p. 235–6° decomp. $[\alpha]_D^{15}$ −130·8° (MeOH). O-*Me*: *see* Laureline methiodide.

Ito, *J. Pharm. Soc. Japan*, 1961, **81**, 703.

Milontin. *See* Phensuximide.★

Miltanthin.
Unstable alkaloid from the roots of *Papaver caucasicum* Marsch.-Bieb.
B,chloroaurate: m.p. 110–15°.
Picrate: m.p. 119–23°.
Picrolonate: m.p. 159–63°.

Kühn *et al., Naturwiss.*, 1964, **51**, 556.

Miroestrol

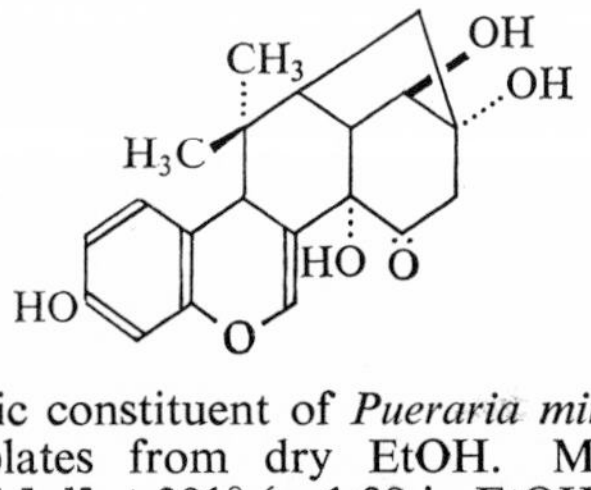

$C_{20}H_{22}O_6$ MW 358

Oestrogenic constituent of *Pueraria mirifica*. Rectangular plates from dry EtOH. M.p. 268–70° decomp. $[\alpha]_D^{17}$ +301° (c, 1·08 in EtOH).
3-*Me ether*: prisms from dioxan. M.p. 271° (slight decomp.).
3-*Ac*: plates from EtOH–AcOEt. M.p. 235–42° (slight decomp.).

3 : 18β(?)-*Di-Ac*: rods from toluene–light petroleum. M.p. 184–90°.
2-*Bromo deriv.* (used for crystallographic study): needles from MeOH. Decomp. above 237°.

Butenandt, *Naturwiss.*, 1940, **28**, 532.
Bounds, Pope, *J. Chem. Soc.*, 1960, 3696.
Taylor, Hodgkin, Rollett, *J. Chem. Soc.*, 1960, 3685.
Ohrt, Norton, *Nature*, 1964, **201**, 1210.

Miropinic Acid. *See* Isopimoric Acid.

MMDA. *See* 1-(3-Methoxy-4 : 5-methylenedioxyphenyl)-2-propylamine.

Monodral. *See* B,CH_3Br *under* Penthienate.★

Monogynol

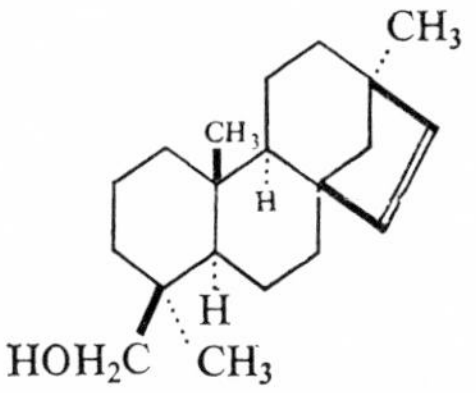

$C_{20}H_{32}O$ MW 288

Constituent of the wood of *Erythroxylon monogynum* Roxb. M.p. 119–119·5°. $[\alpha]_D^{24}$ +33·9° (c, 3·2 in $CHCl_3$). H_2 → dihydro comp. M.p. 127–8°.

Murray, McCrindle, *Chemistry and Industry*, 1964, 500.
Kapadi, Dev, *Tetrahedron Letters*, 1964, 1171, 1902, 2751.

See also:

Connolly *et al.*, *Tetrahedron Letters*, 1964, 1864 (*Footnote*).
Hanson, *Chemistry and Industry*, 1964, 1579.

Monorden. *See* Radicicol.

Monotropein★

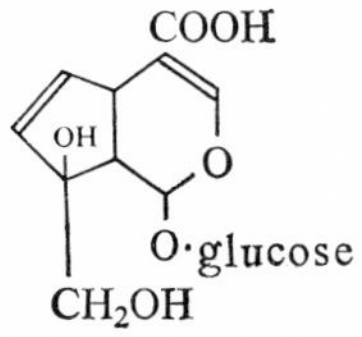

M.p. 150–2°. $[\alpha]_D^{29}$ −123·4°. Light absorption: $\lambda_{max.}$ 235 mμ (log ε, 3·83).
Modified structure:

Bobbitt, Rao, Kiely, *Chemistry and Industry*, 1964, 931.

6-Morpholino-4 : 4-diphenylheptan-3-one. *See* Phenadoxone.★

3-(2-Morpholinoethyl)morphine (*Ethnine*, *Pholcodine*, *Glycodine*, *Memine*)

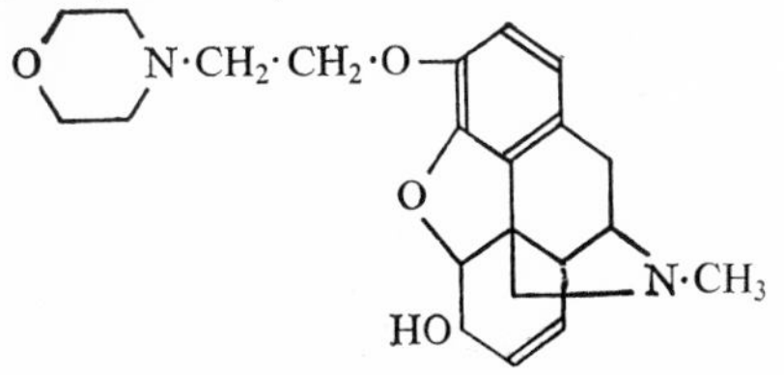

$C_{23}H_{30}O_4N$ MW 398

Antitussive. Monohydrate cryst. M.p. 98° (91°).
Di-methobromide: m.p. 290°.
Di-methiodide: m.p. 240°.

Laboratoires Dausse, B.P. 680,952 (*Chem. Abstracts*, 1954, **48**, 2788); B.P. 717,900 (*Chem. Abstracts*, 1955, **49**, 15983).

α-MSH. *See* α-Melanotropin.

β-MSH. *See* β-Melanotropin.

Mucobromic Acid.★
See also:

Taylor, *Organic Syntheses*, Coll. Vol. **4**, 688.

Mustakone

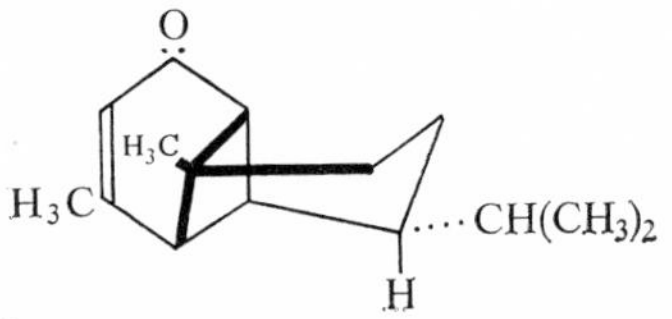

$C_{15}H_{22}O$ MW 218

Constituent of the essential oil of *Cyperus rotundus* L. B.p. 128–9°/1 mm. $[\alpha]_D$ +0·34° (c, 2·6 in $CHCl_3$).
Semicarbazone: m.p. 198–9°.

Kapadia *et al.*, *Tetrahedron Letters*, 1963, 1933.

ε-Muurolene ((+)-ε-*Cadinene*)

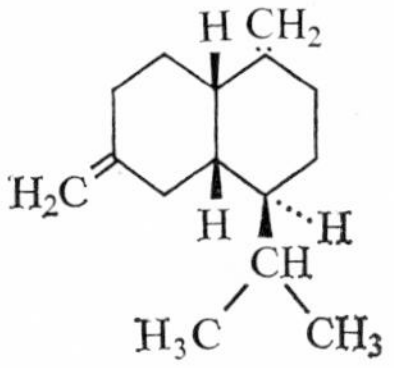

$C_{15}H_{24}$ MW 204

(+)-.
The hydrocarbon isolated from ylang ylang oil and also present in Swedish sulphate turpentine and earlier called ε-cadinene (*q.v.*) has been shown to have a *cis* fused ring system and is therefore not strictly a cadinene.

Westfelt, *Acta Chem. Scand.*, 1964, **18**, 572.

Myacin. *See* Neomycin.★

Mycarose.★
See also:

Korte, Claussen, Snatzke, *Tetrahedron*, 1964, **20**, 1477.

Mycifradin. *See* Neomycin.★

Myricetin.★
3 : 4′ : 7-*Tri-Me ether*: *see* 3′ : 5 : 5′-Trihydroxy-3 : 4′ : 7-trimethoxyflavone.
3 : 3′ : 4′ : 5′ : 7-*Penta-Me ether*: pale yellow needles from MeOH. M.p. 146–7° and 149–50°.
Hexa-Me ether: dimorphic needles from C_6H_6–light petroleum. M.p. 155–6° and 160–1°.

Henrick, Jefferies, *Austral. J. Chem.*, 1964, **17**, 934.

Mysoline. *See* Primidone.★

N

Nadeine. *See* Dihydrocodeine.

Nantenine (O-*Methyldomesticine*)

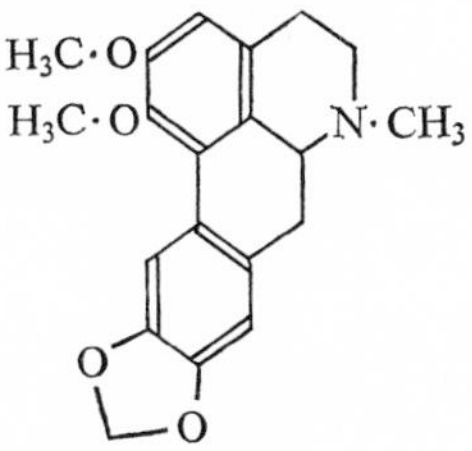

$C_{20}H_{21}O_4N$ MW 339

(+)-.
Alkaloid from the seeds of *Nandina domestica.* M.p. 138–9°. $[\alpha]_D^{18}$ +101° ($CHCl_3$).
(±)-. Thalicthuberine.
Present in the roots of *Thalictrum thunbergii.* M.p. 126–7°.

Fujita, Tomimatsu, *J. Pharm. Soc. Japan*, 1959, **79**, 1252.
Kitamura, *J. Pharm. Soc. Japan*, 1960, **80**, 219, 613.
Tomita, Kitamura, *J. Pharm. Soc. Japan*, 1959, **79**, 1092.

1-Naphthaldehyde.★
See also:
Angyal, Tetaz, Wilson, *Organic Syntheses*, 1950, **30**, 67; Coll. Vol. **4**, 690.

Naphthalene-1 : 5-disulphonic Acid.★
Dichloride:★
Caesar, *Organic Syntheses*, 1952, **32**, 88; Coll. Vol. **4**, 693.

Naphtho-[2′,1′ : 1,2]-tetracene

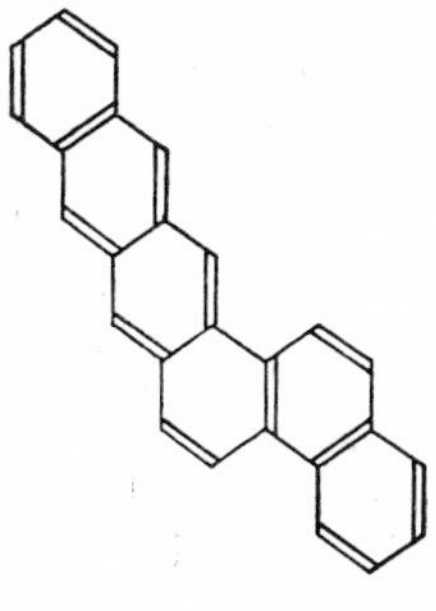

$C_{26}H_{16}$ MW 328

Orange leaflets from xylene. M.p. 370°. H_2SO_4 → brown-violet → green soln. Light absorption: $\lambda_{max.}$ 304 (log ε, 4·98), 314 (5·20), 342 (4·20), 376 (3·21), 393 (3·46), 416 (3·76), 442 (3·98), and 472 mμ (3·98).

Clar, Guye-Vuillème, Stephen, *Tetrahedron*, 1964, **20**, 2107.

Erratum p. 2410
Narcipoetine.★
Should read:
$C_{18}H_{21}O_4N$ MW 315

Narcotine★

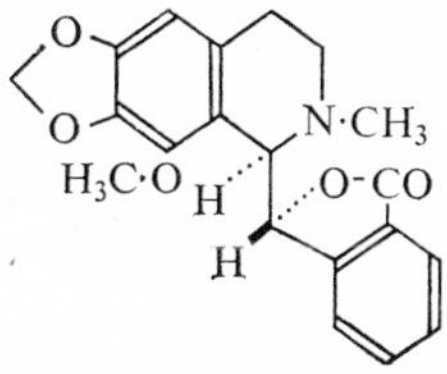

α- (1R : 9S).
Stereochemistry:
Battersby, Spencer, *Tetrahedron Letters*, 1964, 11.

Nardil. *See* B,H_2SO_4 *under* Phenethylhydrazine.★

Narphen. *See* Phenazocine.★

Narwedine

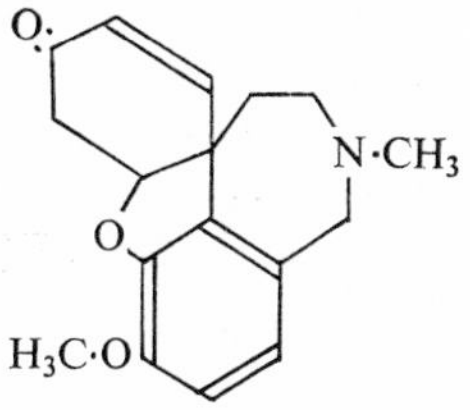

$C_{17}H_{19}O_3N$ MW 285

Amaryllidacae alkaloid. Prisms from Me_2CO. M.p. 188–90°. $[\alpha]_D^{25}$ +100° (c, 0·2 in $CHCl_3$).
Semicarbazone: prisms from MeOH. M.p. 240–1° decomp.
Picrate: cryst. M.p. 123°.
B,CH_3I: cryst. from MeOH–Me_2CO. M.p. 195–6° decomp.

Boit, Döpke, Beitner, *Chem. Ber.*, 1957, **90**, 2197.

Nasutin A★ (2 : 2′-*Dicarboxy*-4 : 4′ : 6 : 6′-*tetrahydroxybiphenyl dilactone*)

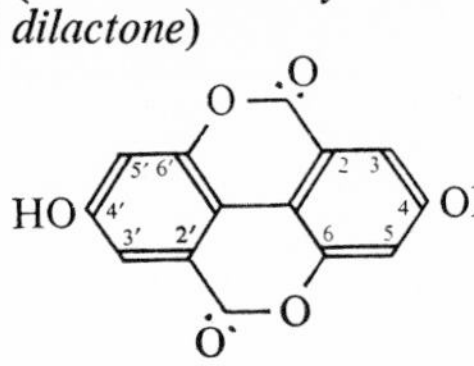

$C_{14}H_6O_6$ MW 270

Constituent of the haemolymph of the termite *Nasutitermes exitiosus* and of castoreum, the dried scent glands of the Canadian beaver. Yellow needles as platelets from Me_2CO. Sublimes with some decomp. at 300°. The original material★ was heterogeneous.

Di-Me ether: $C_{16}H_{10}O_6$. MW 298. Pale yellow platelets. M.p. >360°.

Di-Ac: colourless needles. M.p. 284–8° decomp.

Lederer, *J. Chem. Soc.*, 1949, 2115.
Moore, *Nature*, 1962, **195**, 1101; *Austral. J. Chem.*, 1964, **17**, 901.

Nasutin B. *See* 3 : 3′ : 4-Tri-Me ether *under* Ellegic Acid.

Nasutin C. *See* 3 : 3′-Di-Me ether *under* Ellegic Acid.

Neblinine (15-*Demethoxyobscurinervidine*)

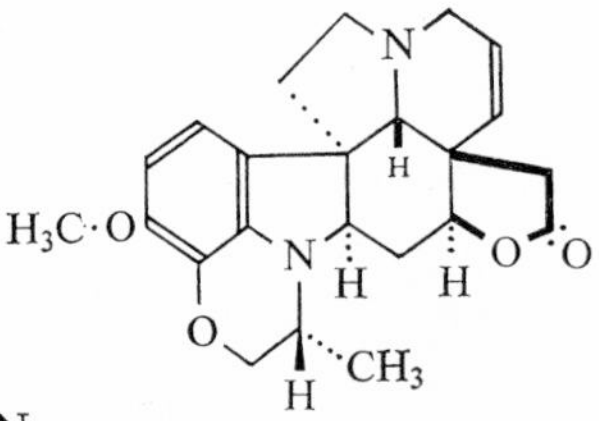

$C_{23}H_{26}O_4N_2$ MW 394

Alkaloid from *Aspidosperma neblinine* Monachino. Cryst. from hexane. M.p. 256–8° decomp. $[\alpha]_D{}^{27}$ −14° (c, 1·19 in $CHCl_3$). H_2 → dihydro comp. M.p. 230–3° decomp.

Brown, Djerassi, *J. Am. Chem. Soc.*, 1964, **86**, 2451.

Neburnamine.

Alkaloid from *Hunteria eburnea* bark. Cryst. from CH_2Cl_2. M.p. 290–2°. $[\alpha]_D$ −199° (MeOH). pK_a' 9·9, 7·7. Light absorption: $\lambda_{max.}$ 230 sh. ($E^{1\%}_{1\,cm.}$ 460) 284 sh. (130), and 293 mμ (140).

Bartlett *et al.*, *J. Org. Chem.*, 1963, **28**, 2197.

Neoaspergillic Acid (3 : 6-*Di-isobutyl*-2-*hydroxypyrazine*-1-*oxide*)

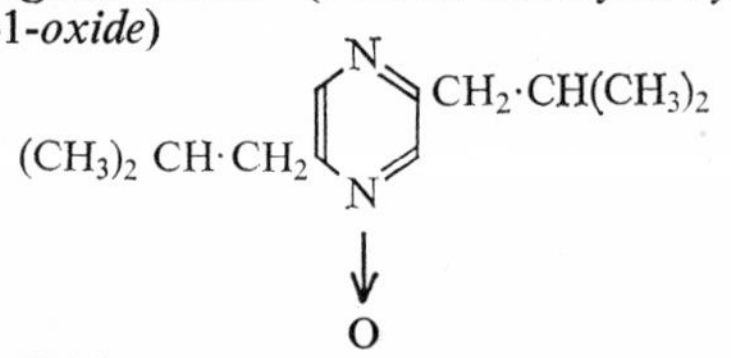

$C_{12}H_{20}O_2N_2$ MW 224

Metabolite of *Aspergillus sclerotiorum* with antibiotic activity. White powder from MeOH.Aq. M.p. 125–6°. $[\alpha]_D$ 0°. Light absorption: $\lambda_{max.}$ 236 (ε, 9150), and 328 mμ (10,500). Redn. → flavacol.

Micetich, MacDonald, *J. Chem. Soc.*, 1964, 1507.
MacDonald, Micetich, Haskins, *Can. J. Microbiol.*, 1964, **10**, 90.

Neochlorogenic Acid. *See* 5-*O*-Caffeoylquinic Acid.

Neocnidilide

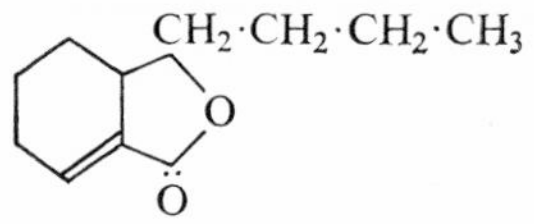

$C_{12}H_{18}O_2$ MW 194

Constituent of the roots of *Cnidium officinale* Makino and celery oil. M.p. 24–7°. B.p. 147–8°/4 mm. $n_D{}^{21}$ 1·5010. $[\alpha]_D{}^{11}$ −62·55° (c, 1·1 in $CHCl_3$). Light absorption: $\lambda_{max.}$ 216 mμ (log ε, 3·85).

Mitsuhashi, Muramatsu, *Tetrahedron*, 1964, **20**, 1971.

Neodigoxoside

$C_{47}H_{74}O_{17}$ MW 910

Glycoside from leaves of *Digitalis lanata* Ehrh. M.p. 235–9°. $[\alpha]_D$ +5·6° (Py). Light absorption: $\lambda_{max.}$ 217 mμ (log ε, 4·22). Hydrolysis → digoxigenin + digitoxose.

Kaiser, Haak, Spingler, *Naturwiss.*, 1963, **50**, 668.

Neohetramine. *See* Thonzylamine.★

Neohydroxyaspergillic Acid (2-*Hydroxy*-6-(1-*hydroxy*-2-*methylpropyl*)-3-*isobutylpyrazine*-1-*oxide*)

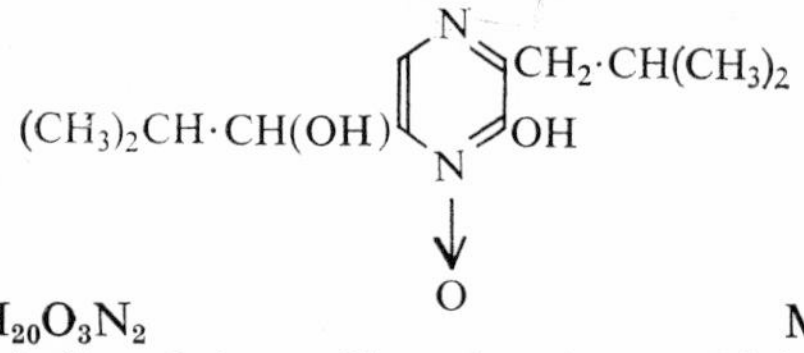

$C_{12}H_{20}O_3N_2$ MW 240

Metabolite of *Aspergillus sclerotiorum*. Light yellow needles from MeOH.Aq. M.p. 170–1°. $[\alpha]_D{}^{25}$ −57° (c, 0·64 in EtOH). Different cryst. form from hexane. Light absorption $\lambda_{max.}$ 235 (ε, 8250) and 328 mμ (8940).

Weiss *et al.*, *Arch. Biochem. & Biophys.*, 1958, **74**, 150.
Micetich, MacDonald, *J. Chem. Soc.*, 1964, 1507.

Neo-Intermedeol

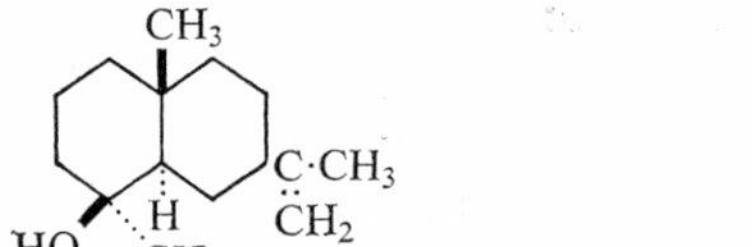

$C_{15}H_{26}O$ MW 222

Constituent of the essential oil of *Bothriochloa intermedia*. B.p. 85–7°/0·5 mm. $[\alpha]_D{}^{25}$ +7·5° (c, 2·635 in EtOH).

Zalkow, Shaligram, Zalkow, *Chemistry and Industry*, 1964, 194.

Neopterin (2-*Amino*-4-*hydroxy*-6-(D-*erythro*-1 : 2 : 3-*trihydroxypropyl*)*pteridine*)

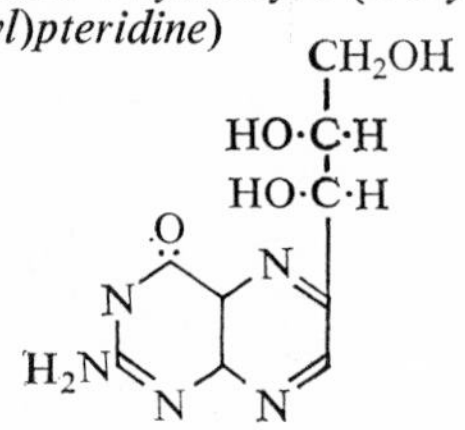

$C_9H_{10}O_4N_5$ MW 252

Present in bee pupae.
(+)-.
$[\alpha]_D^{25}$ 45° (c, 0·3 in 0·1*N*-HCl).
(−)-.
$[\alpha]_D$ −44° (c, 0·3 in 0·1*N*-HCl).

Rembold, Buschmann, *Ann.*, 1963, **662**, 72; *Chem. Ber.*, 1963, **96**, 1406.

Neophryn. *See* B,HCl *under* Phenylephrine.★

Neosamine B. *See* 2 : 6-Diamino-2 : 6-dideoxy-L-idose.

Neosynephrine. *See* B,HCl *under* Phenylephrine.★

Neothesin. *See* Piperocaine.★

Neothiobinupharidine

$C_{30}H_{42}O_2N_2S$ MW 494

Alkaloid present in the yellow water lily. M.p. 159–60°. Thought to be stereoisomer of thiobinupharidine.
B,2HClO₄: m.p. 320° decomp.
B,CH₃I: m.p. 240–2°.

Achmatowicz, Wróbel, *Tetrahedron Letters*, 1964, 129, 927.

Nepetalactone

$C_{10}H_{14}O_2$ MW 166

The essential oil of catnip (*Nepeta cataria*) consists of a mixture of the *cis–trans* (75%) and *trans–cis* (25%) lactones, of which the latter is the most potent attractant for cats. The mixture isolated from the essential oil had b.p. 71–2°/0·05 mm.
Cis–trans-.

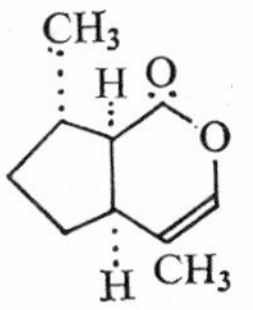

n_D^{25} 1·4878. $[\alpha]_D^{27.5}$ 11·1° ($CHCl_3$).
Acid → *cis–trans*-nepetalic acid.
Trans–cis-.

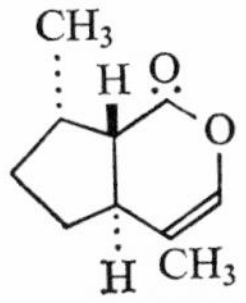

n_D^{25} 1·4878. $[\alpha]_D$ 21·9° ($CHCl_3$) (calculated).

McElvain, Bright, Johnson, *J. Am. Chem. Soc.*, 1941, **63**, 1558.
McElvain, Eisenbraun, *J. Am. Chem. Soc.*, 1955, **77**, 1599, 3383.
Bates, Eisenbraum, McElvain, *J. Am. Chem. Soc.*, 1958, **80**, 3413, 3420.
Bates, Sigel, *Experientia*, 1963, **19**, 564.
Achmad, Cavill, *Proc. Chem. Soc.*, 1963, 166.

Nepetalic Acid

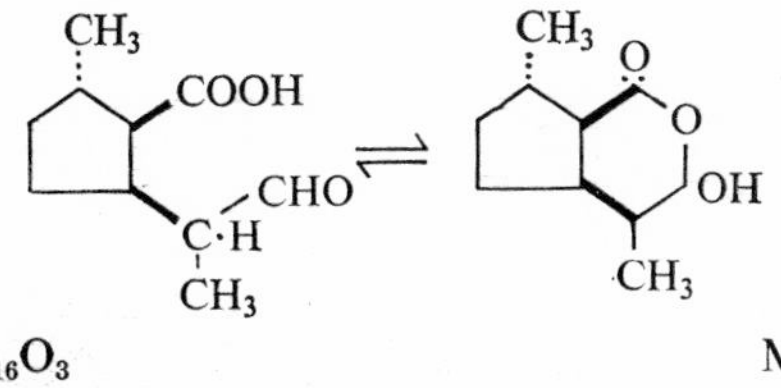

$C_{10}H_{16}O_3$ MW 184

Cis–trans-.
Cryst. from Et_2O–light petroleum. M.p. 75–6°.
Semicarbazone: m.p. 160–1°.
Me ester: $C_{11}H_{18}O_3$. MW 198. B.p. 113–15°/12 mm. n_D^{25} 1·4555. $[\alpha]_D$ 16·1°. *Semicarbazone*: cryst. from MeOH. M.p. 150–1°.
Lactone: *see* Nepetalactone.

McElvain, Bright, Johnson, *J. Am. Chem. Soc.*, 1941, **63**, 1558.
Bates, Eisenbraum, McElvain, *J. Am. Chem. Soc.*, 1958, **80**, 3420.

Nerbowdine★

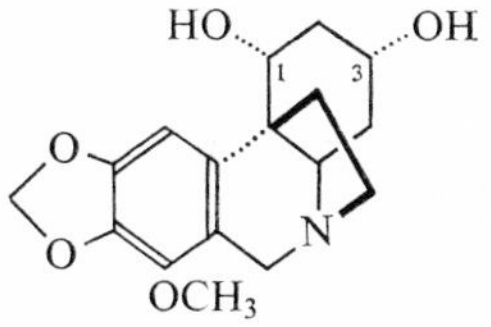

Revised structure

Alkaloid also from *Nerine bowdenii.*
O : O′-*Carbonate*: prisms from AcOEt. M.p. 249–50°. $[\alpha]_D$ −146° ($CHCl_3$).
3-O-*Ac*: alkaloid present in *Buphane disticha* (L.F.) Herb. Needles from Et_2O. M.p. 207–9°. $[\alpha]_D^{21}$ −116° (c, 0·40 in $CHCl_3$), −45° (c, 0·4 in EtOH).

Lloyd *et al.*, *J. Org. Chem.*, 1962, **27**, 373.
Döpke, *Naturwiss.*, 1962, **49**, 469.
Hauth, Stauffacher, *Helv. Chim. Acta*, 1961, **44**, 491; 1963, **46**, 810.

Neuberg Ester. *See* Fructose-6-phosphate.

Neurosporene.★

All *trans-*.
M.p. 115–16°. Light absorption: $\lambda_{max.}$ 416, 440, 470 mμ.

Davis *et al.*, *Proc. Chem. Soc.*, 1961, 261.

Neustab. *See* Thiosemicarbazone *under* *p*-Dietamidobenzaldehyde.

Nicotinamide.★

N-*Oxide*:

Taylor, Crovetti, *Organic Syntheses*, 1957, **37**, 63; Coll. Vol. **4**, 704.

Nitoman. *See* Tetrabenzazine.★

Nitritocobalamin. *See* Vitamin B_{12c}.★

3-Nitrobiphenyl.★

See also:

Kaslow, Summers, *Organic Syntheses*, Coll. Vol. **4**, 718.

2′-Nitrobiphenyl-2-carboxylic Acid.★

See also:

Hey, Leonard, Rees, *J. Chem. Soc.*, 1962, 4579.

4′-Nitrobiphenyl-2-carboxylic Acid.★

See also:

Hey, Leonard, Rees, *J. Chem. Soc.*, 1962, 4579.

2-Nitrobutyric Acid.★

Et ester:★ b.p. 71°/1 mm. n_D^{20} 1·4233.

Kornblum, Blackwood, *Organic Syntheses*, 1957, **37**, 44; Coll. Vol. **4**, 454.

1-Nitrocamphene

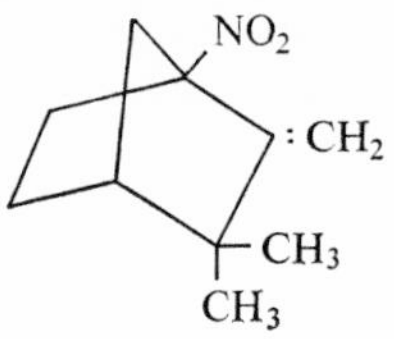

$C_{10}H_{15}ON_2$ MW 179

M.p. 56°. $[\alpha]_D$ +112° (EtOH), 137° (C_6H_6).

Forster, *J. Chem. Soc.*, 1901, **79**, 644.
Brunel, Lemaire, Rassat, *Bull. soc. chim.*, 1964, 1895.

Nitrocobalamin. *See* Vitamin B_{12c}.★

3-*o*-Nitrophenylacrolein.★
See also:

Buckles, Bellis, *Organic Syntheses*, Coll. Vol. **4**, 722.

1-(*p*-Nitrophenyl)-1 : 3-butadiene

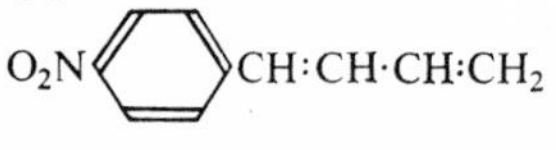

$C_{10}H_9O_2N$ MW 175

Cryst. from light petroleum. M.p. 78·6–79·4°.

Coyner, Ropp, *J. Am. Chem. Soc.*, 1948, **70**, 2283.
Dombrovskiĭ, *Doklady Akad. Nauk. S.S.S.R.*, 1956, **111**, 827 (*Chem. Abstracts*, 1957, **51**, 9507).
Ropp, Coyner, *Organic Syntheses*, 1951, **31**, 80; Coll. Vol. **4**, 727.

3-*o*-Nitrophenyl-2-phenylacrylic Acid.★
Trans-.
See also:

DeTar, *Organic Syntheses*, 1955, **35**, 89; Coll. Vol. **4**, 730.

3-Nitropropionic Acid.★
Biosynthesis:

Birkinshaw, Dryland, *Biochem. J.*, 1964, **93**, 478.

Nitrosocobalamin. *See* Vitamin B_{12c}.★

6-Nitro-*o*-toluidine.★

Howard, *Organic Syntheses*, 1955, **35**, 3; Coll. Vol. **4**, 42.

Nobedon. *See p*-Acetamidophenol.

Nobiletin★ (3′ : 4′ : 5 : 6 : 7 : 8-*Hexamethoxyflavone*).
Constituent of *Citrus delicosa* Tenore. M.p. 132–3°.

Venturella, Bellino, Cusmano, *Ann. Chim.* (Italy), 1961, **51**, 105 (*Chem. Abstracts*, 1961, **55**, 19912).

Nobiline

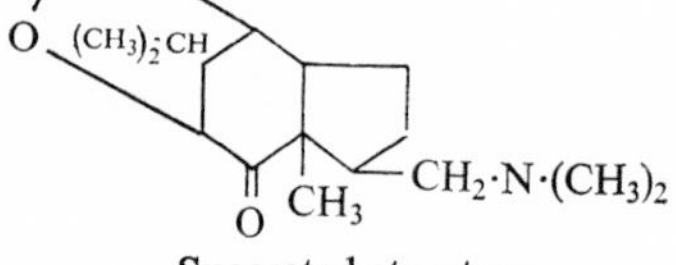

Suggested structure

$C_{17}H_{27}O_3N$ MW 293

Alkaloid from *Dendrobium nobile.* M.p. 87–8°.
B,HCl: m.p. 206–8°.
B,CH$_3$I: m.p. 275–6°.

Yamamura, Hirata, *Tetrahedron Letters*, 1964, 79.

5-Nonadecylresorcinol

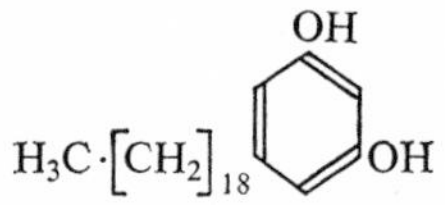

$C_{25}H_{44}O_2$ MW 376

Constituent of wheat bran. Plates from hexane. M.p. 96·5–97·5°.
Di-O-Me: fine needles. M.p. 56·5–57·5°.
Di-Ac: needles from EtOH. M.p. 67·5–68°.

Wenkert *et al.*, *J. Org. Chem.*, 1964, **29**, 435.

Nona-3 : 5-diyne-1 : 2 : 7-triol

CH$_3$·CH$_2$·CH(OH)·C:C·C:C·CH(OH)·CH$_2$OH

$C_9H_{12}O_3$ MW 168

(−)-.
Metabolite of *Clitocybe rhizophora* Velen. Needles from Et$_2$O–hexane. M.p. 71·5–72·5°. $[\alpha]_D^{26}$ −21° (c, 0·53 in EtOH). Ox. → 1 : 2-dihydroxynona-3 : 5-diyne-7-one (*q.v.*).
1 : 2-O-*Isopropylidene deriv.*: oil. $[\alpha]_D^{24}$ −61° (c, 0·23 in EtOH).
(±)-.
Needles. M.p. 68°.

Jones, Lowe, Lowe, *J. Chem. Soc.*, 1964, 1478.

D-*erythro*-L-*gluco*-Nonulose

CH$_2$OH
CO
HO·C·H
H·C·OH
HO·C·H
HO·C·H
H·C·OH
H·C·OH
CH$_2$OH

$C_9H_{18}O_9$ MW 270

Constituent of avocado. Syrup. $[\alpha]_D^{20}$ −40° (c, 0·6 in H$_2$O).
2 : 5-*Dichlorophenylosazone*: m.p. 248–50° decomp.

Sephton, Richtmyer, *J. Org. Chem.*, 1963, **28**, 2388.

Nootkatinol

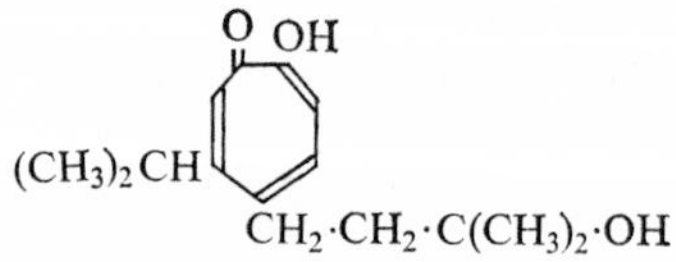

$C_{15}H_{22}O_3$ MW 250

Constituent of *Juniperus rigida* Sieb. et Zucc. Cryst. from light petroleum–C$_6$H$_6$. M.p. 102–3°. Light absorption: $\lambda_{max.}$ 245 (log ε, 4·45), 327 (3·89), 352–5 (3·77), and 372 sh. mμ (3·68).
Cu complex: cryst. from CHCl$_3$. Decomp. *ca.* 265°.

Hirose, *Agric. Biol. Chem.* (Japan), 1963, **27**, 795.

Nootkatone.★

Flavour component of grapefruit and other citrus fruit.

MacLeod, Buigues, *J. Food Sci.*, 1964, **29**, 565.

Norbornane★

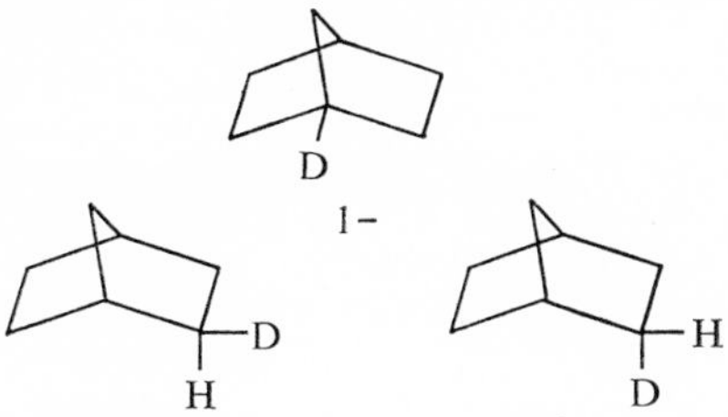

exo- *endo-*

1-^{2}H.
M.p. 84·5–85·5°.
exo-^{2}H.
M.p. 86·5–87°.
endo-^{2}H.
M.p. 85·5–86·5°.

Nickon, Hammons, *J. Am. Chem. Soc.*, 1964, **86**, 3322.

2-Norbornene.★

See also:

Meinwald, Hudak, *Organic Syntheses*, 1957, **37**, 65; Coll. Vol. **4**, 738.

Nor-buxamine (*Buxenine G*)

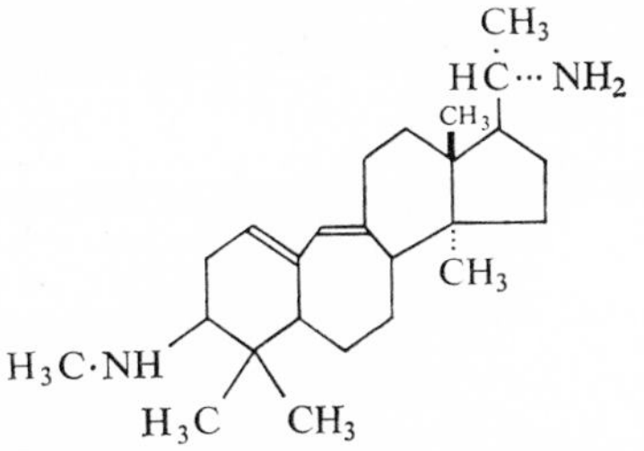

$C_{25}H_{42}N_2$ MW 370

Alkaloid from *Buxus sempervirens* L. Amorph. $[\alpha]_D^{20}$ +20° (c, 0·51 in $CHCl_3$). Light absorption: $\lambda_{max.}$ 238 (log ε, 4·44), 246 (4·47), and 254 mμ (4·26). Bis-*Hydrogen tartrate*: needles from EtOH. M.p. *ca.* 300° decomp. $[\alpha]_D$ +26° (c, 0·52 in 50% EtOH.Aq.).
3-N-*Me*: *see* Buxamine.
N-*Isopropylidene deriv.*: prisms from Me_2CO. M.p. 191–3°. $[\alpha]_D^{20}$ +30° (c, 0·48 in $CHCl_3$) (+51°).

Stauffacher, *Helv. Chim. Acta*, 1964, **47**, 968.
Kupchan, Asbun, *Tetrahedron Letters*, 1964, 3145.

Norgan. *See under* Dihydrocodeinone.

Norisocorydine

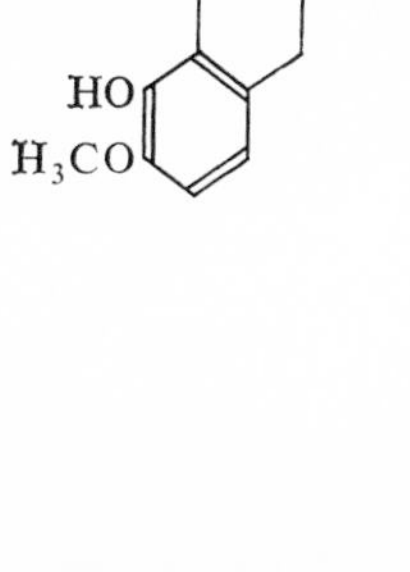

$C_{19}H_{21}O_4N$ MW 327

Constituent of *Peumus boldus* Molina. Free base unstable. $[\alpha]_D$ +158° (EtOH).
B,HBr: m.p. 203–5° decomp.
N-*Me*: *see* Isocorydine.

Ruegger, *Helv. Chim. Acta*, 1959, **42**, 754.

Normicheline A. *See* Norushinsunine.

Norrodiasine

$C_{37}H_{42}O_6N_2$ MW 610

Alkaloid from Greenheart (*Ocotea radiaei*).
B,HCl: $[\alpha]_D$ 74° (c, 1 in H_2O).

Hearst, *J. Org. Chem.*, 1964, **29**, 466.

Norstictic Acid.★

Also present in *Lecidea pantherima* (Ach.) Th. Fr.

Huneck, *Naturwiss.*, 1964, **51**, 536.

Norushinsunine (*Michelalbine, Normicheline A*)

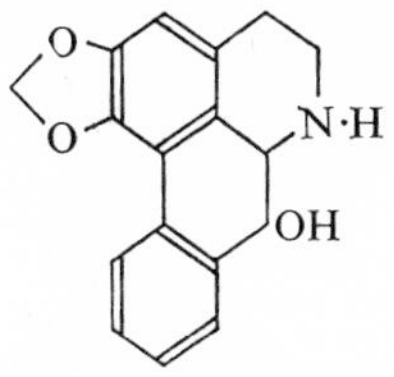

$C_{17}H_{15}O_3N$ MW 281

Alkaloid from *Michelia alba*. M.p. 205–7°. $[\alpha]_D^{15}$ −105·2° ($CHCl_3$).
N-*Me*: *see* Ushinsunine.

Yang, *J. Pharm. Soc. Japan*, 1962, **82**, 811.

Novicodin. *See* Dihydrocodeine.

Noviose.★

3-O-*Carbamoyl*:
Synthesis:

Vaterlaus, Kiss, Spiegelberg, *Helv. Chim. Acta*, 1964, **47**, 381.

See also:

Kiss, Spiegelberg, *Helv. Chim. Acta*, 1964, **47**, 398.

Novobiocin.★

Synthesis:

Vaterlaus *et al.*, *Helv. Chim. Acta*, 1964, **47**, 390.

Nuatigenin

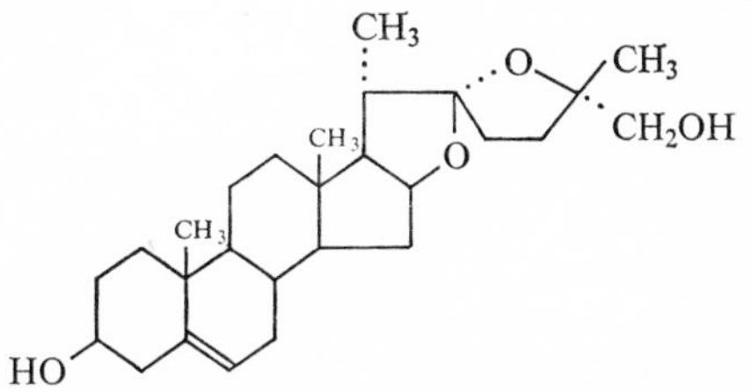

$C_{27}H_{42}O_4$ MW 430

Saponin present in the roots of *Solanum sisymbriifolium*. Plates. M.p. 210–14°. $[\alpha]_D^{23}$ −93° (c, 2 in $CHCl_3$). $H^+ \rightarrow$ isonuatigenin, m.p. 215·8–218·5°. $[\alpha]_D$ −140° (c, 2 in $CHCl_3$).
Di-Ac: cryst. from MeOH–light petroleum. M.p. 156–9°. $[\alpha]_D^{22}$ −95° (c, 2 in $CHCl_3$).

Tschesche, Richert, *Tetrahedron*, 1964, **20**, 387.

Nuciferal

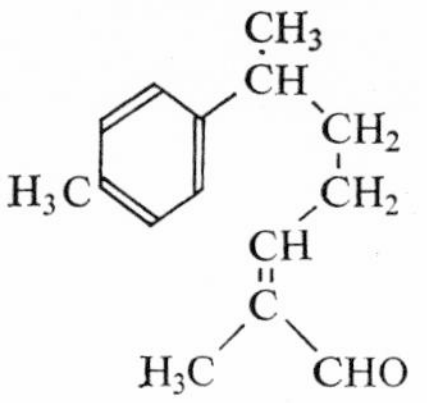

$C_{15}H_{20}O$ MW 216

Constituent of the wood of *Torreya nucifera*. B.p. 107·5–108·5°/0·03 mm. $[\alpha]_D^{20}$ 62·07 (c, 16·5 in $CHCl_3$). Light absorption: $\lambda_{max.}$ 222·5 (ε, 15,700), 229 (14,730), 264·5 (950), 266·5 (880), 273 (800), and 279·5 mμ (370).

2 : 4-*Dinitrophenylhydrazone*: m.p. 138–9°.

Sakai, Nishimura, Hirose, *Tetrahedron Letters*, 1963, 1171.

Nuciferol

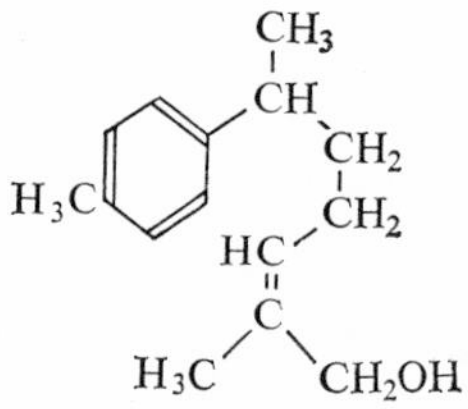

$C_{15}H_{22}O$ MW 218

Constituent of the wood of *Torreya nucifera*. B.p. 131–2°/0·05 mm. $[\alpha]_D^{20}$ 41·06. Light absorption: $\lambda_{max.}$ 252·5 (ε, 374), 259 (478), 264·5 (570), 276·5 (560), 273 mμ (622).

Sakai, Nishimura, Hirose, *Tetrahedron Letters*, 1963, 1171.

Nudiflorine (5-*Cyano*-1-*methyl*-2-*pyridone*)

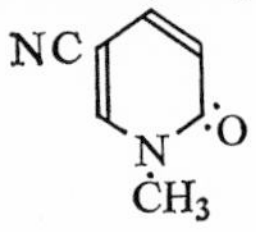

$C_7H_6ON_2$ MW 134

Alkaloid from the leaves of *Trewia nudiflora* L. Needles from $CHCl_3$–light petroleum. M.p. 161°. Isomeric with ricinidine.★

Mukherjee, Chatterjee, *Chemistry and Industry*, 1964, 1524.

Nystatin★

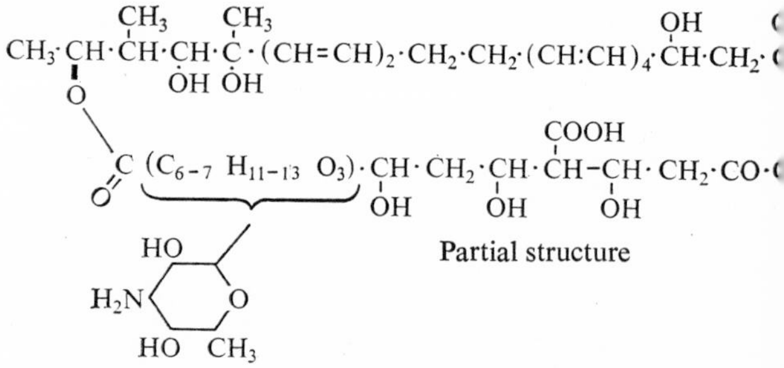

Partial structure

$C_{46-7}H_{73-5}O_{18}N$ MW 927 (941)

Antifungal agent produced by *Streptomyces noursci*.

Birch *et al.*, *Tetrahedron Letters*, 1964, 1485, 1492.

O

Obacunone★

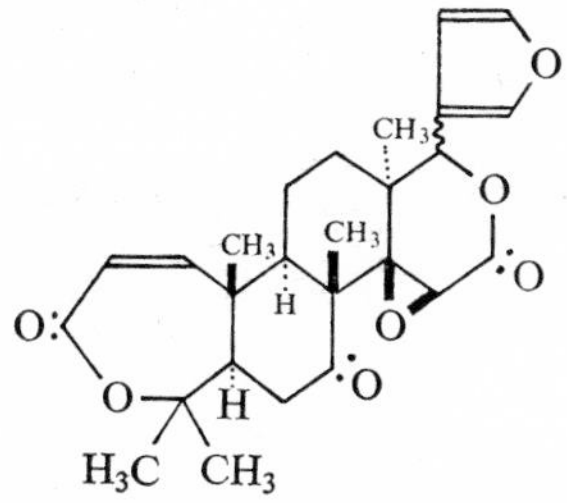

$C_{26}H_{30}O_7$ MW 454

Bitter principle of citrus fruits. Prisms from MeOH. M.p. 229–30°. HCl → hydrochloride. M.p. 230° decomp.

Dean, Geissman, *J. Org. Chem.*, 1958, **23**, 596.
Barton *et al.*, *J. Chem. Soc.*, 1961, 255.
Kubota *et al.*, *Tetrahedron Letters*, 1961, 325.

Obscurinervidine

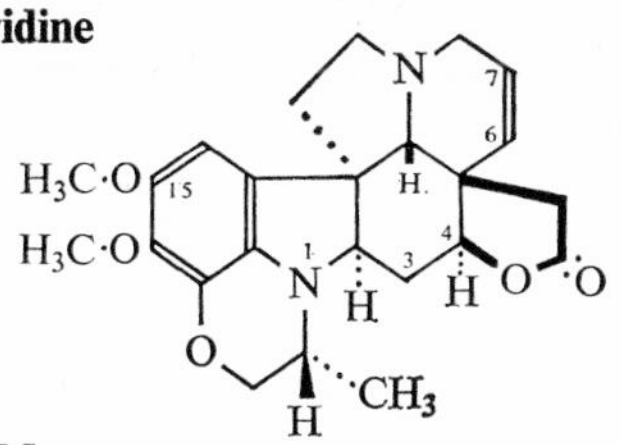

$C_{24}H_{28}O_5N_2$ MW 424

Alkaloid from *Aspidosperma obscurinervium* Azembuja. Cryst. from Me_2CO–hexane. M.p. 206–7° decomp. $[\alpha]_D^{25}$ −39° (c, 0·62 in $CHCl_3$).

Brown, Djerassi, *J. Am. Chem. Soc.*, 1964, **86**, 2451.

Obscurinervine

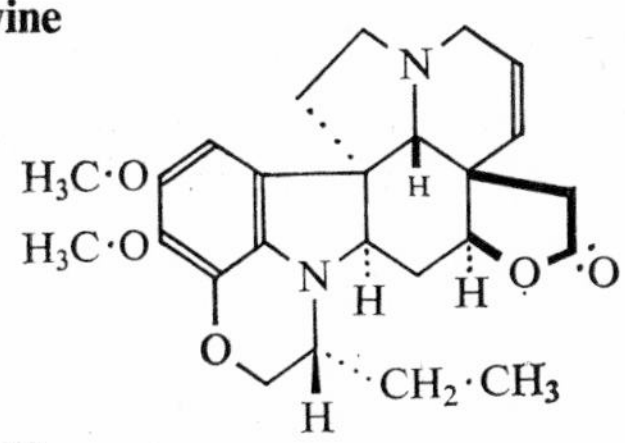

$C_{25}H_{30}O_5N_2$ MW 438

Alkaloid from *Aspidosperma obscurinervium* Azembuja. Cryst. from Me_2CO–hexane. M.p. 203–5° decomp. $[\alpha]_D^{27}$ −54° (c, 0·95 in $CHCl_3$).

Brown, Djerassi, *J. Am. Chem. Soc.*, 1964, **86**, 2451.

Occidentalol

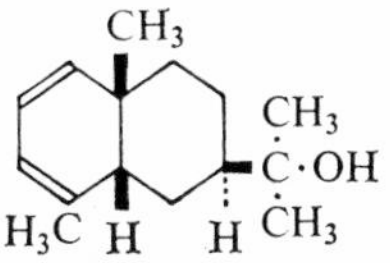

$C_{15}H_{24}O$ MW 220

Constituent of the essential oil from *Thuja occidentalis* L. Cryst. from light petroleum. M.p. 95°. B.p. 115–25°/3 mm., 148–9°/18 mm. $[\alpha]_D^{24}$ +361° (c, 2·44 in $CHCl_3$). Light absorption: $\lambda_{max.}$ 266 mμ (log ε, 3·6). H_2 → dihydro deriv., m.p. 87·5–88·5°. $[\alpha]_D^{24}$ +59·2° (c, 2·99 in $CHCl_3$).

3 : 5-*Dinitrobenzoyl*: cryst. from EtOH. M.p. 137°.

Nakatsuka, Hirose, *Bull. Agric. Chem. Soc. Japan*, 1956, **20**, 215.
von Rudloff, Erdtman, *Tetrahedron*, 1962, **18**, 1315.
Mislow, Moscowitz, *Tetrahedron Letters*, 1963, 699.
von Rudloff, Nair, *Can. J. Chem.*, 1964, **42**, 421.
Ziffer *et al.*, *Tetrahedron*, 1964, **20**, 67.

Occidiol

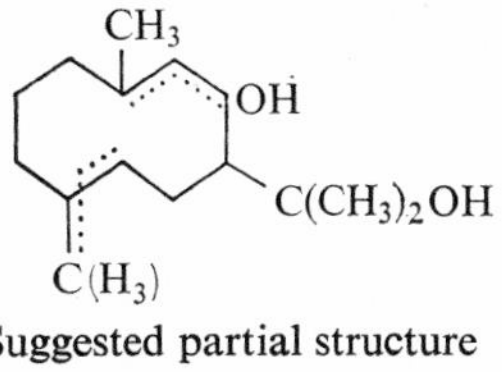

Suggested partial structure

$C_{15}H_{24}O_2$ MW 236

Constituent of the heartwood of the Eastern White Cedar (*Thuja occidentalis* L.). Viscous liquid. B.p. 135–40°/11 mm. n_D^{23} 1·5129. $[\alpha]_D$ −125·5° (c, 2·3 in $CHCl_3$). Pd/C → guaiazulene.

von Rudloff, Nair, *Can. J. Chem.*, 1964, **42**, 421.

Ochropamine

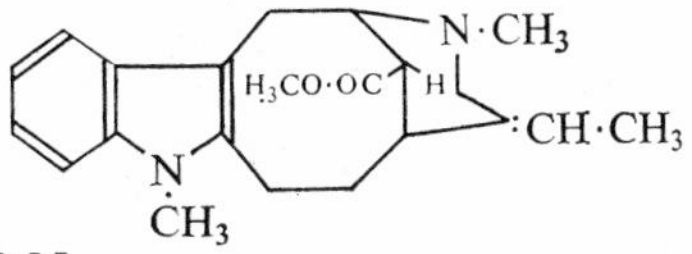

$C_{22}H_{26}O_3N_2$ MW 366

Alkaloid from the stem bark of *Ochrosia poweri* Bailey. Rhombs from MeOH.Aq. M.p. 134°. $[\alpha]_D^{22}$

$-158°$ (c, 1 in Me_2CO). Light absorption: $\lambda_{max.}$ 243 (ε, 18,900) and 315 mμ (17,700).
Picrate: bright yellow plates from Me_2CO–EtOH. M.p. 225° decomp.

Douglas *et al.*, *Austral. J. Chem.*, 1964, **17**, 246.

Ochropine

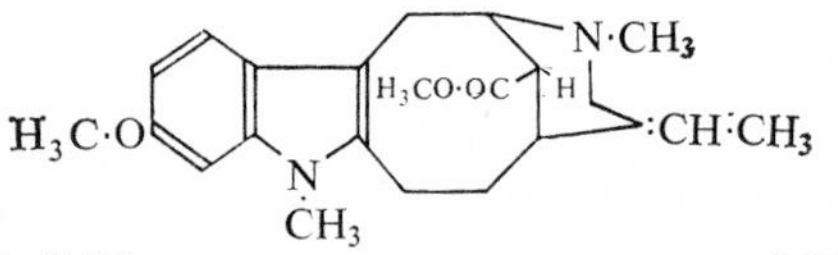

$C_{23}H_{28}O_4N_2$ MW 396

Alkaloid from the stem bark of *Ochrosia poweri* Bailey. Rhombs from MeOH.Aq. M.p. 146°. $[\alpha]_D^{22}$ $-229°$ (c, 1 in Me_2CO). Light absorption: $\lambda_{max.}$ 236 (ε, 14,400), 258 (7950), and 337 mμ (22,600).
Picrate: orange-yellow rhombs. M.p. 235° decomp.

Douglas *et al.*, *Austral. J. Chem.*, 1964, **17**, 246.

Ocodemerine

$C_{37}H_{40}O_6N_2$ MW 608

Alkaloid from Greenheart (*Ocotea rodiaei*).
B,HCl: $[\alpha]_D$ $-170°$ (c, 1 in H_2O).

Hearst, *J. Org. Chem.*, 1964, **29**, 466.

Ocoteamine. *See* Sepeerine.

Ocotine

$C_{35}H_{38}O_6N_2$ MW 582

Alkaloid from Greenheart (*Ocotea rodiaei*). Needles from EtOH. M.p. 162·4°. $[\alpha]_D^{18}$ 32°.
B,HCl: prisms from EtOH–Et_2O. M.p. 240° decomp.
Picrate: yellow prisms. M.p. 178–80° decomp.
N-*Me*, *B,2CH₃I*: prisms. M.p. *ca.* 250° decomp.
O : N-*Di-Ac*: powder. M.p. 159–61°.

Grundon, McGarvey, *J. Chem. Soc.*, 1960, 2739.

9 : 12-Octadecadienoic Acid.

9-*cis* : 12-*cis*-Linoleic Acid.
9 : 10 : 12 : 13-^3H:

Sgoutas, Kummerow, *Biochemistry*, 1964, **3**, 400.

9-Octadecenoic Acid.★

Cis- (*Oleic acid*).
Chloride:

Allen, Byers, Humphlett, *Organic Syntheses*, 1957, **37**, 66; Coll. Vol. **4**, 739.

9-Octadecen-12-ynoic Acid

$CH_3·[CH_2]_4·C:C·CH_2·CH:CH·[CH_2]_7·COOH$

$C_{18}H_{30}O_2$ MW 278

Cis-. (Crepenynic Acid.)
Present in the seed oil of *Crepis foetida* L.
Trans-.
B.p. 120–40°/0·001 mm. n_D^{25} 1·4781.
Benzylisothiouronium salt: m.p. 128°.

Gaudemaris, Arnaud, *Bull. soc. chim.*, 1962, 315.
Mikolajczak *et al.*, *J. Org. Chem.*, 1964, **29**, 318.

9-Octadecynoic Acid★ (*Stearolic acid*).

Present in the seed oil of *Pyrularia pubera* Michx. (Fam. Santalaceae).

Hopkins, Chisholm, *Tetrahedron Letters*, 1964, 3011.

Octahydrocyclopenta[*c*]pyran

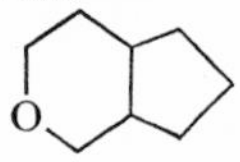

$C_8H_{14}O$ MW 126

Liq. B.p. 167–9°. $n_D^{25·4}$ 1·4680.

Anderson, Harrison, Anderson, *J. Am. Chem. Soc.*, 1963, **85**, 3448.

Octahydrocyclopenta[*c*]thiin (*Octahydrocyclopenta*[c]-*thiapyran*)

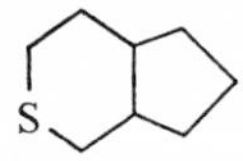

$C_8H_{14}S$ MW 142

Liq. B.p. 107–8°/31 mm. n_D^{25} 1·5210.

Anderson, Harrison, Anderson, *J. Am. Chem. Soc.*, 1963, **85**, 3448.

2*H*-Octahydro-2-pyrindine (*Perhydro-2-pyrindine*)

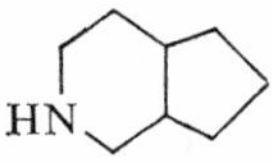

C_8H_{15} MW 111

Liq. B.p. 83–9°/25 mm., 80°/11 mm.
Picrate: cryst. from 95% EtOH. M.p. 143–4°.

Prelog, Metzler, *Helv. Chim. Acta*, 1946, **29**, 1170.
Anderson, Harrison, Anderson, *J. Am. Chem. Soc.*, 1963, **85**, 3448.

Octotillol

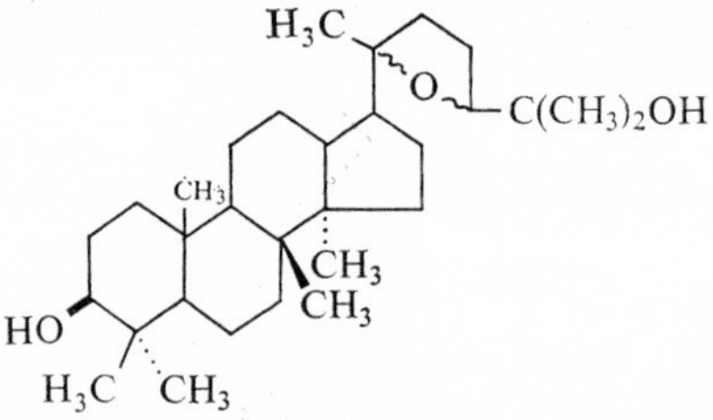

$C_{30}H_{52}O_3$ MW 460

Constituent of the resinous bark of octotillo (*Fouquieria splendens* Engelm.). M.p. 198–200°. $[\alpha]_D$ +28° ($CHCl_3$).
Mono-Ac: m.p. 260–1·5°. $[\alpha]_D$ +41° ($CHCl_3$).

Halls, Warnhoff, *Chemistry and Industry*, 1963, 1986.

17β-Oestradiol.★

3-*Me ether*: m.p. 98°. $[\alpha]_D$ +80° ($CHCl_3$).

Miki, Hiraga, Asako, *Proc. Chem. Soc.*, 1963, 139.

Olivin

$C_{19-21}H_{22-4}O_{9-10}$

Aglycone from olivomycin. Cryst. from AcOEt–C_6H_6. M.p. 189–91°. $[\alpha]_D$ 60·5° (c, 0·5 in EtOH). Light absorption: $\lambda_{max.}$ 230 ($E_{1\,cm.}^{1\%}$ 580), 277 (1000), 324 (160), and 408 mμ (320).
Hexa-Ac: cryst. from $CHCl_3$–AcOEt. M.p. 200–2°. $[\alpha]_D^{22}$ $-7·3°$ (c, 1·3 in $CHCl_3$).

Berlin *et al.*, *Tetrahedron Letters*, 1964, 1323.

Olivomycin

$C_{61-5}H_{90-8}O_{27-9}$

Antibiotic from *Streptomyces olivoreticuli*. Yellow cryst. from AcOEt–hexane. M.p. 160–5°. $[\alpha]_D^{25}$ −35·5° (c, 0·5 in EtOH). Hydrol → olivin. Methanolysis → methyl glycosides of olivomycose, olivomose, and olivose.

Berlin *et al.*, *Tetrahedron Letters*, 1964, 1323.

Olivomose (2 : 6-*Dideoxy*-4-O-*methyl*-D-*lyxo-hexose*)

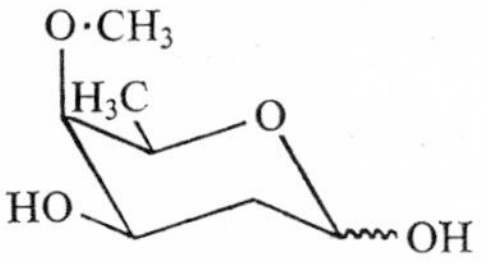

$C_7H_{14}O_4$ MW 162

Degradation product of olivomycin. Cryst. from Me_2CO. M.p. 158–62°. $[\alpha]_D^{23}$ 98·5° (on dissolution) → 89° (1·5 hr.) (c, 0·5 in H_2O).

Methyl glycosides: $C_8H_{16}O_4$. MW 176. Two forms: (A) cryst. from hexane, m.p. 98°, $[\alpha]_D^{26}$ 150° (c, 0·4 in EtOH) and (B) cryst. from hexane, m.p. 152–3°, $[\alpha]_D$ −37·5° (c, 0·4 in EtOH).

Berlin *et al.*, *Tetrahedron Letters*, 1964, 1323, 3513.

Olivomycose (3-C-*Methyl*-2 : 6-*dideoxy*-L-arabo*hexose*)

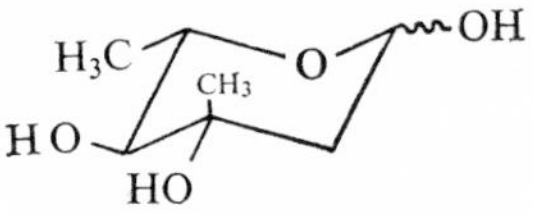

$C_7H_{14}O_4$ MW 162

Degradation product of olivomycin. Cryst. from $Me_2CO–Et_2O$. M.p. 103–6°. $[\alpha]_D^{26}$ −13° (on dissolution) → −22° (20 min., 1·5 hr.) (c, 1·1 in H_2O).

α-*Methyl glycoside*: $C_8H_{16}O_4$. MW 176. Two forms: (A) $[\alpha]_D^{22}$ −147° (c, 1 in EtOH) and (B) cryst. from hexane, m.p. 93–4°. $[\alpha]_D^{23}$ 50° (c, 1 in EtOH).

4-O-*Isobutyrylmethylglycoside*: $C_{12}H_{22}O_5$. MW 246. Two forms: (A) $[\alpha]_D^{25}$ −123° (c, 0·6 in EtOH) and (B) $[\alpha]_D^{25}$ 29° (c, 1·5 in EtOH).

Berlin *et al.*, *Tetrahedron Letters*, 1964, 1323, 3513.

Olivose (2 : 6-*Dideoxy*-D-arabo*hexose*)

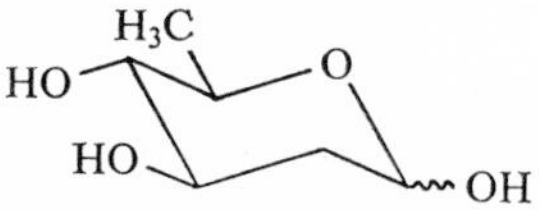

$C_6H_{12}O_4$ MW 148

Degradation product of olivomycin. $[\alpha]_D$ 45° (c, 0·5 in H_2O). Probably identical with Chromosel.

Methyl glycoside: $C_7H_{14}O_4$. MW 162. Two forms: (α) $[\alpha]_D^{25}$ 131° (c, 0·75 in EtOH) and (β). Cryst. from AcOEt–hexane. M.p. 84°. $[\alpha]_D^{22}$ −85° (c, 1 in EtOH).

Berlin *et al.*, *Tetrahedron Letters*, 1964, 1323, 3513.

Onocovin. *See* Vincristine *and* Leurocristine.★

Oospoglycol (*K-I*)

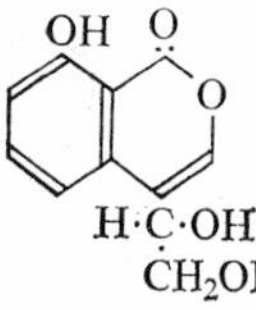

$C_{11}H_{10}O_5$ MW 222

Metabolite of *Oospora astringenes*. M.p. 116°. $[\alpha]_D^{21}$ −71° (Py).

Di-Ac: leaflets from MeOH.Aq. M.p. 119°. $[\alpha]_D$ 62° (c, 1 in Py).

Yamatodani *et al.*, *Nippon Nôgeikagaku Kaish*, 1963, **37**, 240.

Nitta *et al.*, *Agric. Biol. Chem.* (Japan), 1963, **27**, 822.

Oosponol

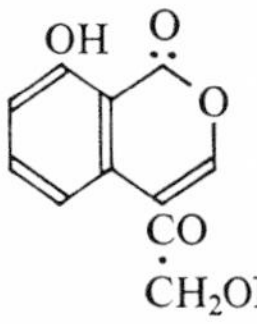

$C_{11}H_8O_5$ MW 220

Metabolic product of *Oospora* sp. Needles from $EtOH–C_6H_6$. M.p. 176°. Light absorption: $\lambda_{max.}$ 335 mμ.

Di-p-*nitrobenzoyl*: pale yellow needles. M.p. 217° decomp.

Di-Ac: prisms from AcOH.Aq. M.p. 146°.

2 : 4-*Dinitrophenylhydrazone*: red prisms from AcOEt. M.p. 243° decomp.

Yamamoto, Nitta, Yamamoto, *Agric. Biol. Chem.* (Japan), 1962, **26**, 486.

Nitta *et al.*, *Agric. Biol. Chem.* (Japan), 1963, **27**, 817.

Orinase. *See* Tolbutamide.★

Ormosajine

$C_{20}H_{33}N_3$ MW 315

Alkaloid from *Ormosia jamaiciensis* Urh. Tetrahydrate: m.p. 38–41°. $[\alpha]_D$ 23°. H_2 → dasycarpine.

B,2HClO₄: m.p. 170–1°.

Hassall, Wilson, *J. Chem. Soc.*, 1964, 2657.

Ormosanine

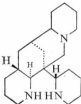

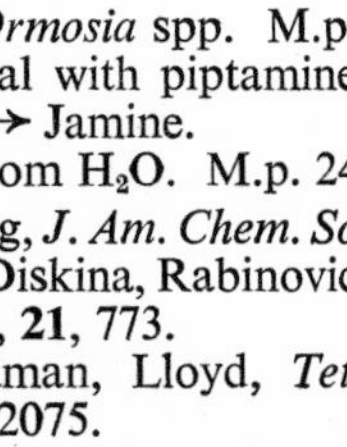

$C_{20}H_{35}N_3$ MW 317

Alkaloid from *Ormosia* spp. M.p. 183–4°. $[\alpha]_D$ 0°. Probably identical with piptamine from *Piptanthus nanus*. H·CHO → Jamine.

B,2HI: prisms from H_2O. M.p. 249° decomp.

Lloyd, Horning, *J. Am. Chem. Soc.*, 1958, **80**, 1506.

Konovalova, Diskina, Rabinovich, *Zhur. Obshcheĭ Khim.*, 1951, **21**, 773.

Naegeli, Wildman, Lloyd, *Tetrahedron Letters*, 1963, 2069, 2075.

Hassall, Wilson, *J. Chem. Soc.*, 1964, 2657.

Ormosinine

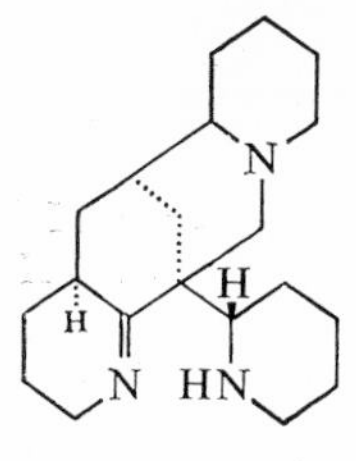

$C_{20}H_{33}N_3$ MW 315

Alkaloid from *Ormosia* spp. M.p. 220–2°. $[\alpha]_{589}$ +9·6°. $[\alpha]_{436}$ +14·9°.
Di-picrate: m.p. 146–8°, which decomposed on attempted recrystallisation.

Lloyd, Horning, *J. Am. Chem. Soc.*, 1958, **80**, 1506.
Naegeli, Wildman, Lloyd, *Tetrahedron Letters*, 1963, 2069, 2075.

Oroboidine. *See* Calpurnine.

Ortho-desaspidin

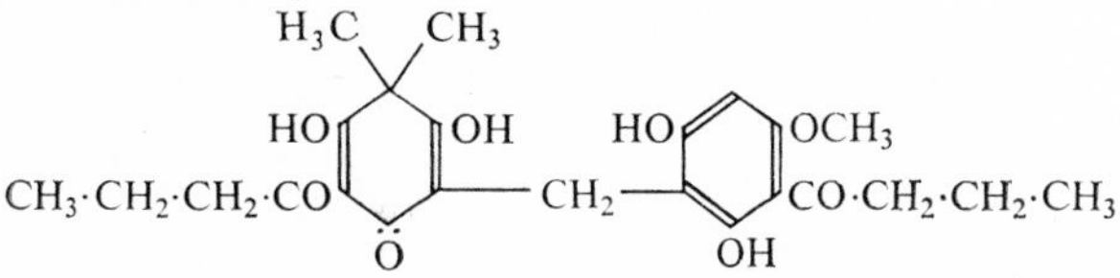

$C_{24}H_{30}O_8$ MW 446

Constituent of the fern *Dryopteris austriaca*. Cryst. from MeOH. M.p. 133–5°. Light absorption: $\lambda_{max.}$ 230 (ε, 24,900) and 293 mμ (23,800).

Penttilä, Sundman, *Acta Chem. Scand.*, 1964, **18**, 1292.

Otocamine

$C_{37}H_{40}O_6N_2$ MW 608

Alkaloid from Greenheart (*Ocotea rodiaei*).
B,HCl: $[\alpha]_D$ 268° (c, 1 in H_2O).

Hearst, *J. Org. Chem.*, 1964, **29**, 466.

9-Oxa-bicyclo-[3,3,1]-nonan-3-one

$C_8H_{12}O_2$ MW 128

M.p. 93–4°.

Bohlmann, Schulz, Riemann, *Tetrahedron Letters*, 1964, 1705.

6-Oxa-estrone

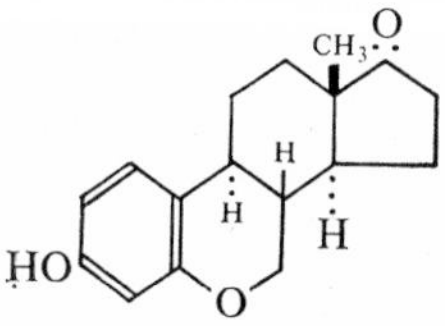

$C_{17}H_{22}O_3$ MW 274

(±)-.
Me ether: $C_{18}H_{24}O_3$. MW 288. M.p. 151–4°. Light absorption: $\lambda_{max.}$ 282 (ε, 3200), 287 mμ (3000).

Smith, Douglas, Walk, *Experientia*, 1964, **20**, 418.

6-Oxa-8α-estrone

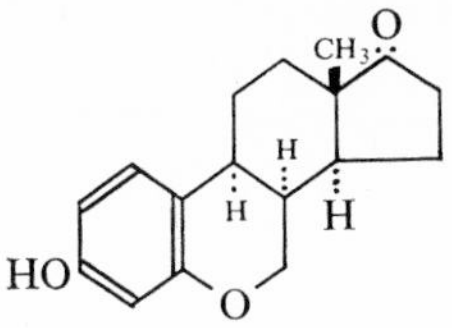

(±)-.
Me ether: m.p. 146–8°. Light absorption: $\lambda_{max.}$ 281 (ε, 3600), 287 mμ (3600).

Smith, Douglas, Walk, *Experientia*, 1964, **20**, 418.

β-*N*-Oxalyl-L-α : β-diaminopropionic Acid

HOOC·CO·NH·CH_2·CH(NH_2)·COOH

$C_5H_8O_5N_2$ MW 176

Neurotoxin present in *Lathyrus sativus*. Cryst. from H_2O. M.p. 206° decomp. $[\alpha]_D^{27}$ −36·9° (c, 0·66 in 4*N*-HCl).

Rao, Adiga, Sarma, *Biochemistry*, 1964, **3**, 432.

1 : 6-Oxido[10]annulene

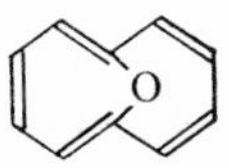

$C_{10}H_8O$ MW 144

Light yellow cryst. M.p. 53–4°. Light absorption: $\lambda_{max.}$ 255 (ε, 72,000), 299 (6900), and *ca.* 392 mμ (240).

Sondheimer, Shani, *J. Am. Chem. Soc.*, 1964, **86**, 3168.

4-Oxodecanoic Acid.★

Cryst. from EtOH.Aq. M.p. 71°.

Lukěs, *Coll. Czech. Chem. Commun.*, 1929, **1**, 119.
Patrick, *J. Org. Chem.*, 1952, **17**, 1009.
Patrick, Erickson, *Organic Syntheses*, 1954, **34**, 51; Coll. Vol. **4**, 430 (*Note*).

9-Oxodec-2-enoic Acid.★

See also:

Van der Plas, Persoons, *Rec. trav. chim.*, 1964, **83**, 701.

2-Oxo-4 : 5-diphenyltricyclo[1,1,1,0^{4,5}]pentane

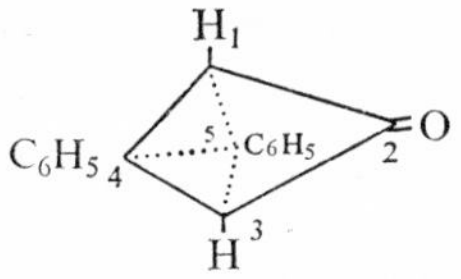

$C_{17}H_{12}O$ MW 232

M.p. 139–40° decomp. H_2 → *cis*-3 : 4-diphenylcyclopentanone.

Masamune, *J. Am. Chem. Soc.*, 1964, **86**, 735.

4-Oxo-1 : 7-heptanedioic Acid.★

Di-Et ester:

Emerson, Langley, *Organic Syntheses*, Coll. Vol. **4**, 302.

6-Oxoheptanoic Acid.★

See also:

Schaeffer, Snoddy, *Organic Syntheses*, 1951, **31**, 3; Coll. Vol. **4**, 19.

2-Oxomanoyl oxide

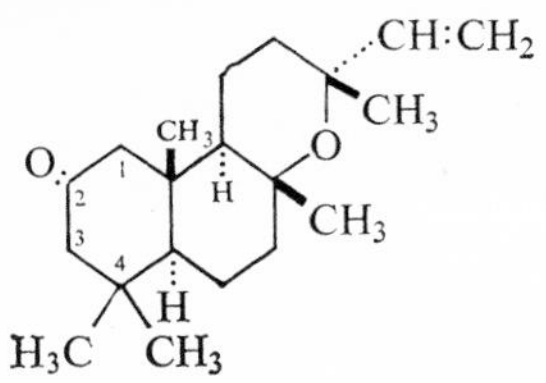

$C_{20}H_{32}O_2$ MW 304

Constituent of *Dacrydium colensoi.* B.p. 170–80°/ 0·4 mm. Cryst. from MeOH.Aq. M.p. 77–8°. $H_2 \rightarrow$ dihydro deriv. M.p. 91–2°.

Oxime: cryst. from MeOH. M.p. 146–7°.

Semicarbazone: cryst. M.p. 135°.

Hoskins, Brandt, *Ber.*, 1934, **67**, 1173; 1935, **68**, 286.

Grant, *J. Chem. Soc.*, 1959, 860.

Grant, Hodges, *Chemistry and Industry*, 1960, 1300.

3-Oxomanoyl oxide

$C_{20}H_{32}O_2$ MW 304

Constituent of the wood of *Xylia dolabriformis* (Pyinkado). Needles from MeOH.Aq. M.p. 99–99·5°. $[\alpha]_D$ 54° (c, 5 in $CHCl_3$).

2 : 4-*Dinitrophenylhydrazone*: m.p. 178·5°.

Laidlaw, Morgan, *J. Chem. Soc.*, 1964, 644.

4-Oxo-norleucine (2-*Amino*-4-*oxohexanoic acid*)

$CH_3 \cdot CH_2 \cdot CO \cdot CH_2 \cdot CH(NH_2) \cdot COOH$

$C_6H_{11}O_3N$ MW 145

Amino acid present in hydrolysates from *Citrobacter freudii* and *Salmonella dablem.* Cryst. from EtOH–Et_2O. M.p. 143–4°.

Barry, Chen, Roark, *J. gen. Microbiol.*, 1963, **33**, 97.

Barry, Roark, *Nature* (Lond.), 1964, **202**, 493; *J. Biol. Chem.*, 1964, **239**, 1541.

γ-Oxoseneciosic Acid. *See* β-Formylcrotonic Acid.

Oxycolchicine

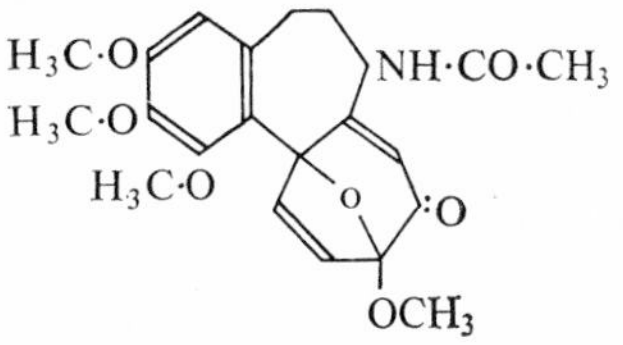

$C_{22}H_{25}O_7N$ MW 415

Oxidation product of colchicine. Cryst. from EtOH.Aq. M.p. 265–6°. Light absorption: $\lambda_{max.}$ 281 mμ (log ε, 2·51).

Semicarbazone: cryst. from MeOH.Aq. M.p. 222–4°. Light absorption: $\lambda_{max.}$ 295 mμ (ε, 19,000).

Windaus, *Ann.*, 1924, **439**, 59.

Buchanan *et al.*, *Chemistry and Industry*, 1958, 418; 1962, 859; *Tetrahedron*, 1964, **20**, 1449.

Oxytocin.★

Isolation:

Schally *et al.*, *Arch. Biochem. Biophys.*, 1964, **107**, 332.

P

Pachysamine A (20α-*Dimethylamino*-3α-*methylamino*-5α-*pregnane*)

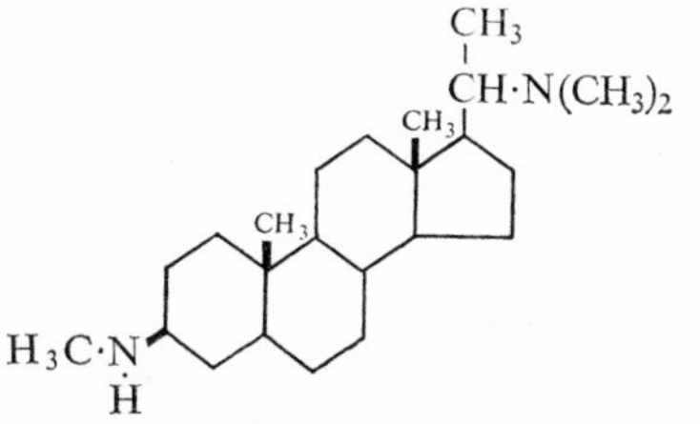

$C_{24}H_{44}N_2$ MW 360

Alkaloid from *Pachysandra terminalis* Sieb. et Zucc. M.p. 167–8°. $[\alpha]_D^{10}$ 20° ($CHCl_3$).

Ac: m.p. 150–2°.

N-*Me*: m.p. 165·5–167°. $[\alpha]_D^{10}$ 16° ($CHCl_3$).

N-ββ-*Dimethylacrylyl*: Pachysamine B. $C_{29}H_{50}ON_2$. MW 442. Alkaloid from *P. terminalis*. M.p. 171–3°. $[\alpha]_D$ 67° ($CHCl_3$). $H_2 \rightarrow$ dihydro deriv. M.p. 138–9°. $[\alpha]_D$ 54° ($CHCl_3$).

Tomita, Uyeo, Kikuchi, *Tetrahedron Letters*, 1964, 1641.

Pachysamine B. *See* *N*-ββ-Dimethylacrylyl *under* Pachysamine A.

Pachysandrine A (4-β-*Acetoxy*-3α-*benzoylmethylamino*-20α-*dimethylamino*-5α-*pregnane*)

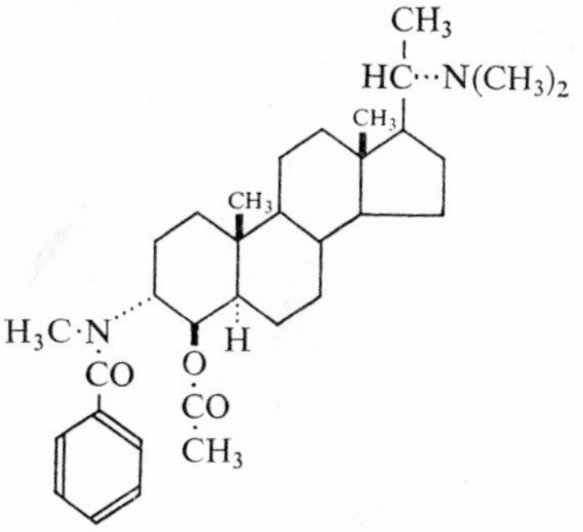

$C_{33}H_{50}O_3N_2$ MW 522

Alkaloid from *Pachysandra terminalis* Sieb. et Zucc. M.p. 235–6°. $[\alpha]_D^{13}$ 80° ($CHCl_3$).

Tomita, Uyeo, Kikuchi, *Tetrahedron Letters*, 1964, 1053.

Pachysandrine B

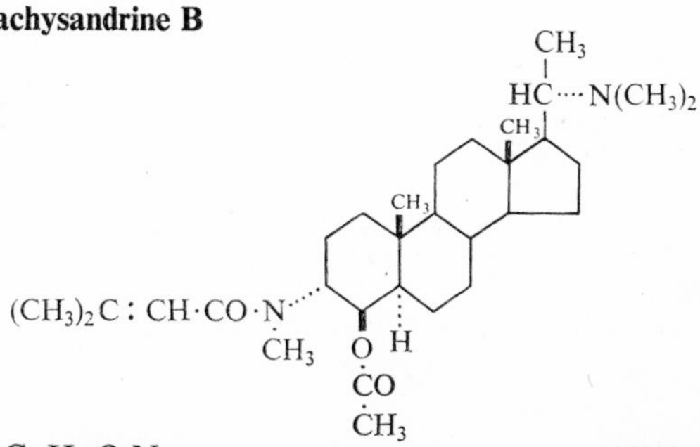

$C_{31}H_{52}O_3N_2$ MW 500

Alkaloid from *Pachysandra terminalis* Sieb. et Zucc. M.p. 187–9°. $[\alpha]_D^{19}$ 93·4° ($CHCl_3$).

Tomita, Uyeo, Kikuchi, *Tetrahedron Letters*, 1964, 1053.

Pachysandrine C

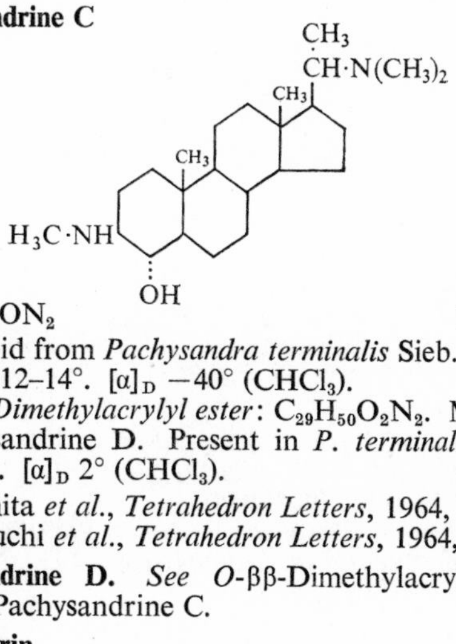

$C_{24}H_{44}ON_2$ MW 376

Alkaloid from *Pachysandra terminalis* Sieb. et Zucc. M.p. 212–14°. $[\alpha]_D$ −40° ($CHCl_3$).

O-ββ-*Dimethylacrylyl ester*: $C_{29}H_{50}O_2N_2$. MW 458. Pachysandrine D. Present in *P. terminalis*. M.p. 184–5°. $[\alpha]_D$ 2° ($CHCl_3$).

Tomita *et al.*, *Tetrahedron Letters*, 1964, 1053.
Kikuchi *et al.*, *Tetrahedron Letters*, 1964, 1817.

Pachysandrine D. *See* *O*-ββ-Dimethylacrylyl ester *under* Pachysandrine C.

Paeoniflorin

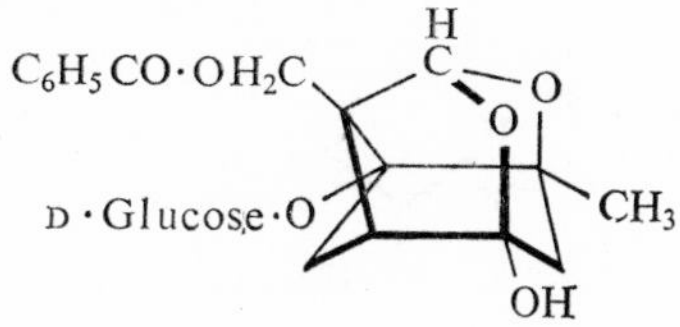

$C_{23}H_{28}O_{11}$ MW 480

Constituent of Chinese Paeony root (*Paeonia albiflora* Pallas). Amorph. $[\alpha]_D^{16}$ −12·8° (c, 4·6 in MeOH).
Tetra-Ac: m.p. 196°. *Me ether*: m.p. 123°.
Penta-Ac: colourless needles. M.p. 158°. $[\alpha]_D^{20}$ +13·5° (c, 4·1 in MeOH).
Shibata, Aimi, Nakahara, *Chem. Pharm. Bull.* (*Tokyo*), 1963, **11**, 372, 379.
Shibata, Aimi, Watanabe, *Tetrahedron Letters*, 1964, 1991.

Palmitenone. *See* Hentriacont-24-en-16-one.

Palustric Acid ($\Delta^{8,13}$-*Abietadienoic acid*)

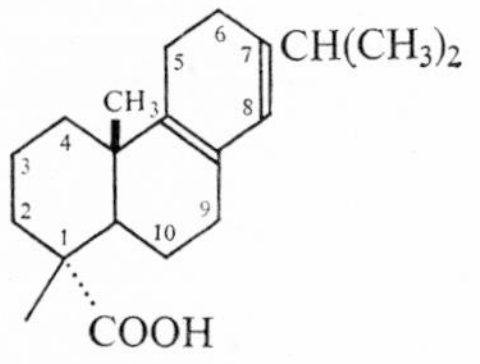

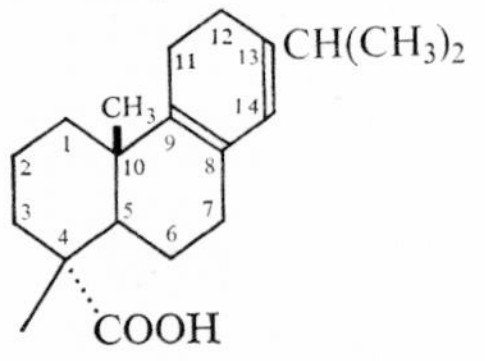

Alternative numbering (Burgstahler, Worden)

$C_{20}H_{30}O_2$ MW 302

Constituent of gum resin. Cryst. from MeOH. M.p. 162–7°. $[\alpha]_D$ 71·6° (EtOH). Light absorption: $\lambda_{max.}$ 265–6 mμ.
Me ester: m.p. 25–7°. $[\alpha]_D$ 67·7° (EtOH).
Loeblich, Baldwin, Lawrence, *J. Am. Chem. Soc.*, 1955, **77**, 2823.
Schuller, Moore, Lawrence, *J. Am. Chem. Soc.*, 1960, **82**, 1734.
Burgstahler, Worden, *J. Am. Chem. Soc.*, 1964, **86**, 96.
Synthesis:
Wenkert *et al.*, *J. Am. Chem. Soc.*, 1964, **86**, 2038.

Palustrol

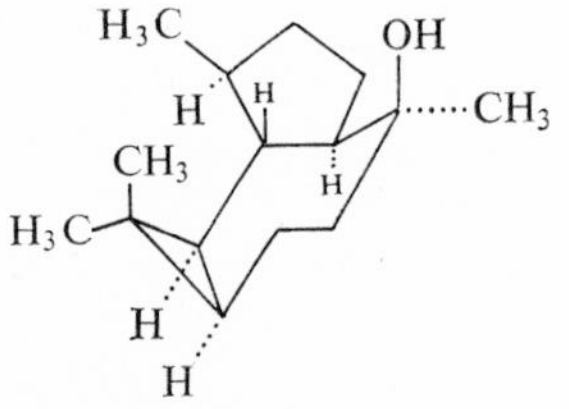

$C_{15}H_{26}O$ MW 222

Constituent of the essential oil of *Ledum palustre*. B.p. 131–3°/3 mm. D_{20}^{20} 0·9654. n_D^{20} 1·4920. $[\alpha]_D^{19}$ −17·6°.
Kir'yalov, *J. Gen. Chem. U.S.S.R.*, 1950, **20**, 777; 1954, **24**, 1257 (*Chem. Abstracts*, 1950, **44**, 7811; 1955, **49**, 13944).
Büchi *et al.*, *Tetrahedron Letters*, 1959, No. 6, 14.
Dolejš, Šorm, *Tetrahedron Letters*, 1959, No. 17, 1.

Panamine

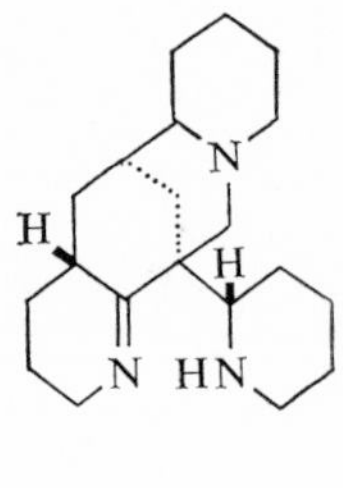

$C_{20}H_{33}N_3$ MW 315

Alkaloid from *Ormosia* spp. Oil. $[\alpha]_{589}$ −11°. $[\alpha]_{436}$ −21·3°.
B,2HClO₄: prisms from MeOH–Et_2O. M.p. 285–7°.
N-*Me*: m.p. 103°. $[\alpha]_{589}$ +5°. $[\alpha]_{436}$ +19°. *B,CH₃I*: m.p. 209–11°.
Di-picrate: needles from Me_2CO–Et_2O. M.p. 237° decomp.
Lloyd, Horning, *J. Am. Chem. Soc.*, 1958, **80**, 1506.
Naegeli, Wildman, Lloyd, *Tetrahedron Letters*, 1963, 2069, 2075.
See also:
Deslongchamps, Wilson, Valenta, *Tetrahedron Letters*, 1964, 3896.

Pandamine

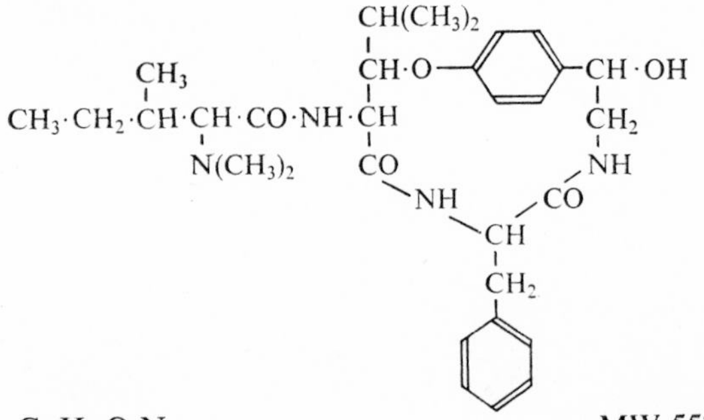

$C_{31}H_{44}O_5N_4$ MW 552

Peptide alkaloid from *Panda oleosa* Pierre. Cryst. from AcOEt. M.p. 256°. $[\alpha]_D$ −103° (c, 0·5 in $CHCl_3$). pK_a' 6·02.
B,HCl: m.p. 235° decomp. $[\alpha]_D$ −77° (c, 1 in MeOH).
O-*Ac*: cryst. from MeOH. M.p. 305–7°. $[\alpha]_D$ −98° (c, 0·5 in Py). *B,HCl*: cryst. from MeOH. M.p. 280° decomp. $[\alpha]_D$ −89° (c, 1 in MeOH).
Païs *et al.*, *Bull. soc. chim.*, 1964, 817.

γ-Pantothenic Acid

$HO{\cdot}CH_2{\cdot}C(CH_3)_2{\cdot}CH(OH){\cdot}CO{\cdot}NH{\cdot}CH_2{\cdot}CH_2{\cdot}CH_2{\cdot}COOH$

$C_{10}H_{19}O_5N$ MW 233

Natural analogue of pantothenic acid with some biological activity. Hydrol. → γ-aminobutyric acid and (−)-α-Hydroxy-ββ-dimethyl-γ-butyrolactone.
Fuerst, Li-chun Li, *Biochim. Biophys. Acta*, 1964, **86**, 26.
DeSha, Fuerst, *Biochim. Biophys. Acta*, 1964, **86**, 33.

Paracodin. *See* Dihydrocodeine.

Paramorphan. *See under* Dihydromorphine.

Parkeol (5α-*Lanosta*-9(11) : 24-*dien*-3β-*ol*)

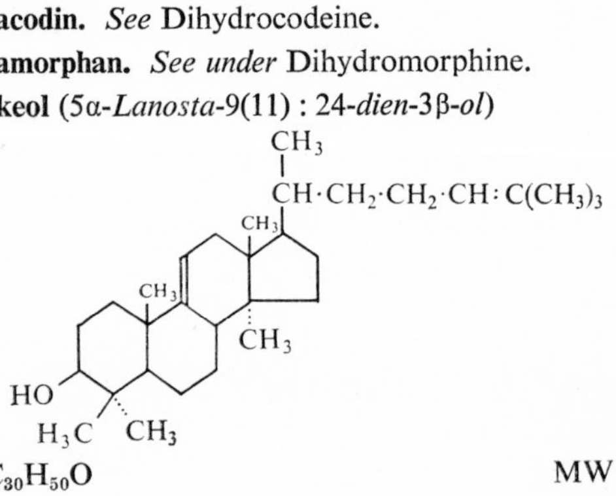

$C_{30}H_{50}O$ MW 426

Constituent of the seeds of *Butyrospermum parkii*. M.p. 162–5°. $[\alpha]_D$ +76·8° (c, 1 in $CHCl_3$).
Ac: m.p. 161–2°. $[\alpha]_D$ +86° (c, 1 in $CHCl_3$).
Benzoyl: m.p. 200·5–201°. $[\alpha]_D$ +95·4° (c, 1 in $CHCl_3$).

Bauer, Mull, *Fette u. Seifen*, 1939, **46**, 560.
Dawson *et al.*, *J. Chem. Soc.*, 1953, 586.
Lawrie, Spring, Watson, *Chemistry and Industry*, 1956, 1458.
Schreiber, Osske, *Tetrahedron*, 1964, **20**, 1803.

Paromose. *See* 2 : 6-Diamino-2 : 6-dideoxy-L-idose.

Parzone. *See* Dihydrocodeine.

α-Pelargone. *See* Furopelargone A.

Penethamate hydrochloride. *See* B,HI *under* 2-Diethylaminoethyl ester *under* Benzylpenicillinic Acid.

Pentadiendioic Acid.★
See also:

Agosta, *J. Am. Chem. Soc.*, 1964, **86**, 2638.

Pentaerythrose (*Trishydroxymethylacetaldehyde*)

$(HO{\cdot}CH_2)_3C{\cdot}CHO$

$C_5H_{10}O_4$ MW 134

Cryst. from butanol. M.p. 132–4°. The cryst. form is most likely dimeric.
2 : 4-*Dinitrophenylhydrazone*: cryst. from H_2O. M.p. 197·5–198°.

Armour *et al.*, *J. Chem. Soc.*, 1964, 301.

3α : 7α : 12α : 26 : 27-Pentahydroxycholestane. *See* Cyprinol.

3 : 3′ : 4 : 4′ : 7-Pentahydroxyflavan.
(−)-. Leucofisetinidin.
See also:

Drewes, Roux, *Biochem. J.*, 1964, **90**, 343.

3 : 5 : 6 : 7 : 8 - Pentamethoxy - 3′ : 4′ - methylenedioxy - flavone. *See* Melibentin.

4 : 8 : 12 : 15 : 15 - Pentamethyltricyclo[9,3,1,0^{3,8}]pentadecane. *See* Taxane.

Pentaphenylarsene

$(C_6H_5)_5As$

$C_{30}H_{25}As$ MW 460

Cryst. from cyclohexane. M.p. 139·5° decomp.

Wittig, Clauss, *Ann.*, 1952, **577**, 33.
Wittig, Hellwinkel, *Chem. Ber.*, 1964, **97**, 769.

Pentaphenylphosphoran

$(C_6H_5)_5P$

$C_{30}H_{25}P$ MW 416

Cryst. from C_6H_6–cyclohexane. M.p. 123–4° decomp.

Wittig, Kochendoerfer, *Chem. Ber.*, 1964, **97**, 741.

Perhydro-2-pyrindine. *See* 2*H*-Octahydro-2-pyrindine.

Perivine

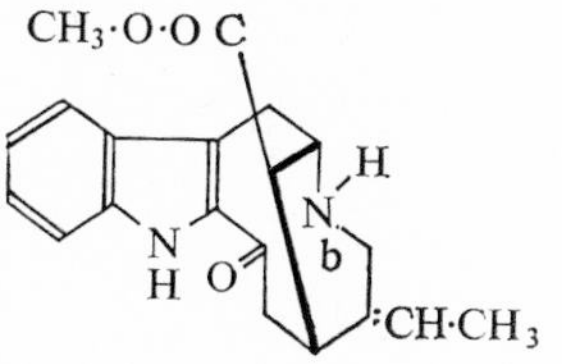

$C_{20}H_{22}O_3N_2$ MW 338

Alkaloid from leaves of *Vinca rosea* L. pK_a' 7·7 (66% $H{\cdot}CONMe_2$).
N_b-*Me*: *see* Vobasine.

Svoboda, *J. Pharm. Sci.*, 1958, **47**, 834.
Gorman, Sweeny, *Tetrahedon Letters*, 1964, 3105.

Perylene
13 : 14-^{14}C:

Pichat, Baret, Bague, *Bull. soc. chim.*, 1964, 1236.

Petidon. *See* 3 : 5 : 5-Trimethyl-2 : 4-oxazolidinedione.★

Phanostenine

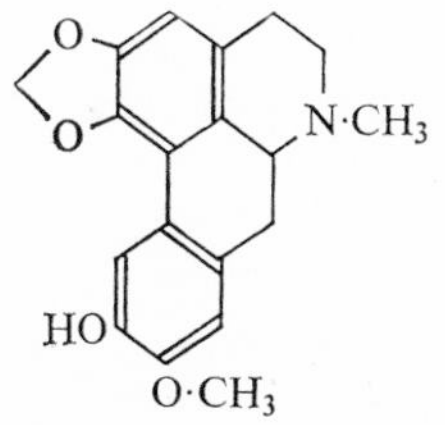

$C_{19}H_{19}O_4N$ MW 325

(−)-.
Alkaloid from *Stephania sasakii*. M.p. 210°. $[\alpha]_D$ −36·7° ($CHCl_3$).
(±)-.
Cryst. from MeOH. M.p. 209–10°.

Tomita, Kikkawa, *J. Pharm. Soc. Japan*, 1957, **77**, 1011, 1015.

Phaseolin.
This name was originally given to phaseollin (*q.v.*), but was withdrawn, as it had earlier been given to a protein present in *Phaseolus vulgaris* L.

Perrin, *Tetrahedron Letters*, 1964, **1**, 438.

Phaseollin (*Phaseolin*)

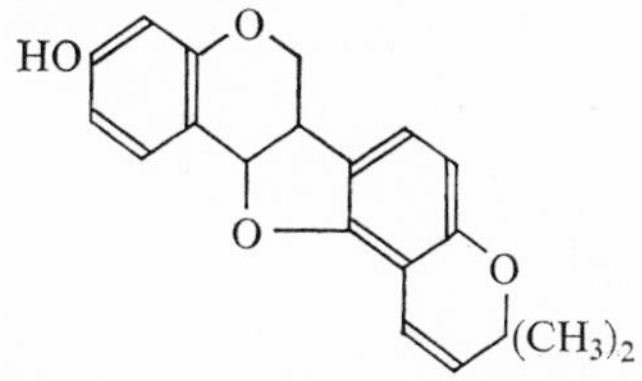

$C_{20}H_{18}O_4$ MW 322

Antifungal, phytoalexin substance from *Phaseolus vulgaris* L. M.p. 177–8°. $[\alpha]_{578}$ −148°. pK_a 9·13.

Perrin, *Tetrahedron Letters*, 1964, **1**, 438.

Phellochryseine (*Methyl 22-feruloyloxydocosanoate*)

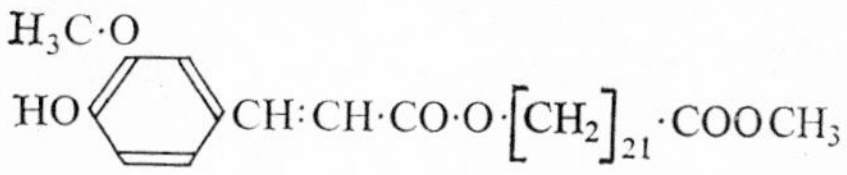

$C_{33}H_{54}O_6$ MW 546

Isolated from cork. Orange-yellow cryst. from hexane. M.p. 69°. Hydrolysis → 22-hydroxydocosanoic (phellonic) + ferulic acids.

Guillemonat, Traynard, *Bull. soc. chim.*, 1963, 142.

Phellogenic Acid. *See* Docosanedioic Acid.

Phenampromid. *See* *N*-(1-Methyl-2-piperidinoethyl)-propionanilide.

Phenanthreno-[9′,10′ : 1,2]-pyrene

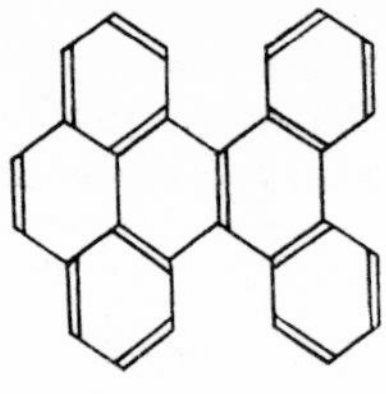

$C_{28}H_{16}$ MW 352

Pale orange prisms from C_6H_6. M.p. 259–61°. H_2SO_4 → yellow-green → brown-red soln. Light absorption: $\lambda_{max.}$ 240 (log ε, 4·65), 248 (4·65), 275 (4·48), 290 (4·42), 301 (4·68), 374 (4·28), and 398 mμ (3·45).

Clar, Guye-Vuillème, Stephen, *Tetrahedron*, 1964, **20**, 2107.

Phencarbamide. *See* Escorpal.

Pheniprazine. *See* α-Methylphenethylhydrazine.

Phenoxadrine. *See* Phenyltoloxamine.

Phenylacetic Acid.★

Amide: m.p. 154–5°.

Wenner, *Organic Syntheses*, 1952, **32**, 92; Coll. Vol. **4**, 760.

γ-Phenylallylsuccinic Acid (*Cinnamoylsuccinic acid*)

$C_6H_5 \cdot CH{:}CH \cdot CH_2 \cdot CH(CH_2 \cdot COOH) \cdot COOH$

$C_{13}H_{14}O_4$ MW 234

Cryst. from MeOH. M.p. 142–3°.

Alder, Pascher, Schmitz, *Chem. Ber.*, 1943, **76**, 27.
Rondestvedt, *Organic Syntheses*, 1951, **31**, 85; Coll. Vol. **4**, 766.

***N*-Phenylbenzamidine**

$C_6H_5 \cdot C({=}NH) \cdot NH \cdot C_6H_5$

$C_{13}H_{12}N_2$ MW 196

Cryst. from C_6H_6. M.p. 114–15·5°.

Bernthsen, *Ann.*, 1877, **184**, 348.
Oxley, Partridge, Short, *J. Chem. Soc.*, 1947, 1112; 1948, 1519.
Cooper, Partridge, *J. Chem. Soc.*, 1952, 5036; 1953, 255; *Organic Syntheses*, 1956, **36**, 64; Coll. Vol. **4**, 769.

Phenylcyanoacetic Acid.

Et ester:★

Horning, Finelli, *Organic Syntheses*, 1950, **30**, 43; Coll. Vol. **4**, 461.

2-Phenylcycloheptanone

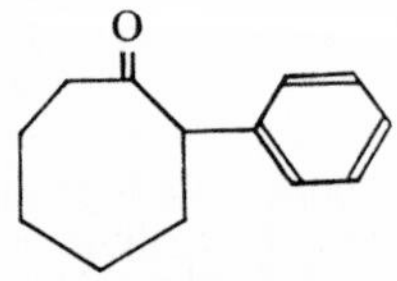

$C_{13}H_{16}O$ MW 188

M.p. 21–3°. B.p. 94–6°/0·4 mm., 124–6°/2 mm., 136–8°/4 mm. n_D^{20} 1·5395–1·5398.

Gutsche, Johnson, *J. Am. Chem. Soc.*, 1949, **71**, 3513; 1955, 77, 109; *Organic Syntheses*, 1955, **35**, 91; Coll. Vol. **4**, 780.
Tiffeneau *et al.*, *Compt. rend.*, 1935, **201**, 277.

4-Phenyl-*m*-dioxane

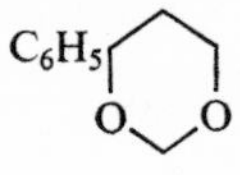

$C_{10}H_{12}O_2$ MW 164

B.p. 94–5°/2 mm. D_4^{20} 1·092. n_D^{20} 1·5300.

Prins, *Chem. Weekblad*, 1917, **14**, 932; 1919, **16**, 1072, 1510.
Fourneau, Benoit, Firmenich, *Bull. soc. chim.*, 1930, **47**, 858.
Shortridge, *J. Am. Chem. Soc.*, 1948, **70**, 873.
Schriner, Ruby, *Organic Syntheses*, Coll. Vol. **4**, 786.

***o*-Phenylene carbonate**

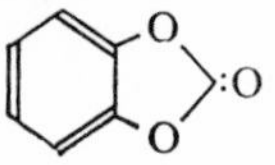

$C_7H_4O_3$ MW 138

Cryst. from toluene. M.p. 119–20°.

Einhorn, Lindenberg, *Ann.*, 1898, **300**, 141.
Hanslick, Bruce, Mascitti, *Organic Syntheses*, 1953, **33**, 74; Coll. Vol. **4**, 788.

1,12-*o*-Phenylene-2,3 : 10,11-dibenzoperylene

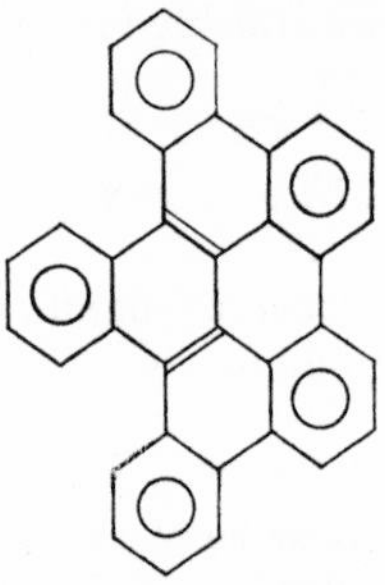

$C_{34}H_{18}$ MW 426

Yellow leaflets from C_6H_6. M.p. 324–324·5°. Light absorption: $\lambda_{max.}$ 426 (log ε, 4·43), 402 (4·37), 382 (4·11), 358 (3·95), 326 (4·87), 313 (4·82), 301 (4·67), and 245 mμ (4·80) in C_6H_6 or C_6H_{12}.

Clar, McCallum, *Tetrahedron*, 1964, **20**, 507.

1-Phenyl-1-penten-4-yn-3-ol

$C_6H_5 \cdot CH{:}CH \cdot CH(OH) \cdot C{:}CH$

$C_{11}H_{10}O$ MW 158

Cryst. from light petroleum. M.p. 67–8°. B.p. *ca.* 90°/1 mm. Light absorption: $\lambda_{max.}$ 251 mμ (log ε, 4·31).

Jones, McCombie, *J. Chem. Soc.*, 1942, 733.
Cymerman, Wilks, *J. Chem. Soc.*, 1950, 1208.
Jones, Skattebøl, Whiting, *J. Chem. Soc.*, 1956, 4765; *Organic Syntheses*, 1959, **39**, 56; Coll. Vol. **4**, 792.

Phenyl-*bis*-phenylenearsene

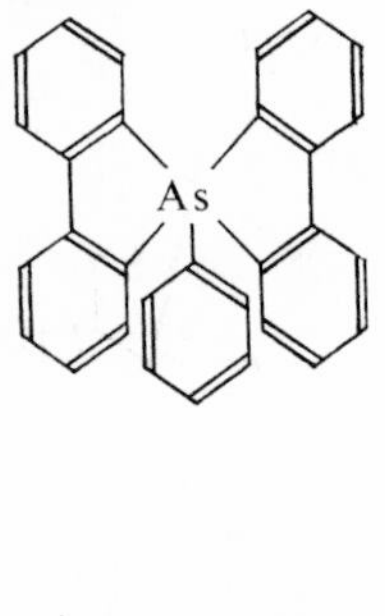

$C_{30}H_{21}As$ MW 456

Cryst. from AcOEt. M.p. 232–4°.

Wittig, Hellwinkel, *Chem. Ber.*, 1964, **97**, 769.

Phenyl-*bis*-phenylenephosphoran

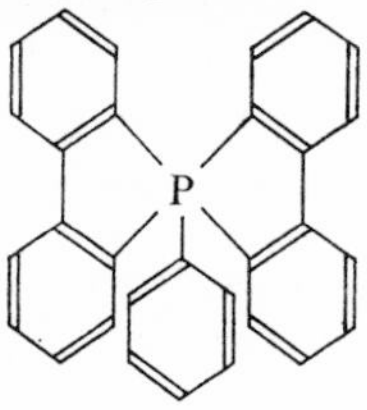

$C_{30}H_{21}P$ MW 412·5

Cryst. from C_6H_6. M.p. 201·5–205·5°.

Wittig, Kochendoerfer, *Chem. Ber.*, 1964, **97**, 741.

1-Phenylpropyne.★

2 : 3-[14]*C*:

Renaud, Leitch, *Can. J. Chem.*, 1964, **42**, 2089.

2-Phenyl-5-propynylthiophene

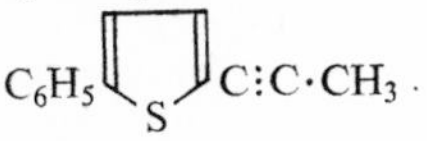

$C_{13}H_{10}S$ MW 198

Constituent of the essential oil of *Coreopsis grandiflora* Hogg ex Sweet. Cryst. from light petroleum. M.p. 42–3°. Light absorption: $\lambda_{max.}$ 310 mμ (log ε, 4·43).

Sorensen, Sorensen, *Acta Chem. Scand.*, 1958, **12**, 765, 771.

Craig, Moyle, *J. Chem. Soc.*, 1963, 3907.

Atkinson, Curtis, Phillips, *Chemistry and Industry*, 1964, 2101.

Phenyltoloxamine (*2-Benzylphenol 2-dimethylaminoethyl ether, Bristamin, Phenoxadrine*)

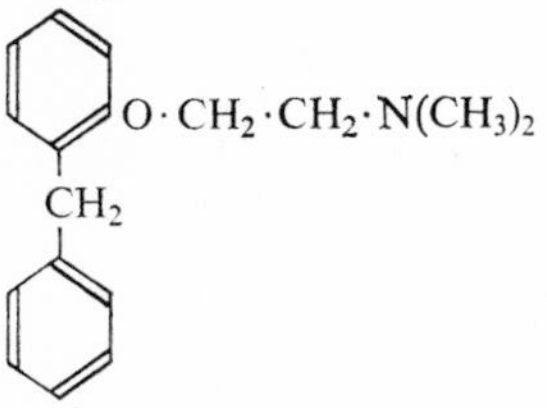

$C_{17}H_{21}ON$ MW 255

Antihistamine. Oil. B.p. 141–4°/0·1 mm.

B,HCl: cryst. from isobutyl methyl ketone. M.p. 119–20°.

Cheney, Smith, Binkley, *J. Am. Chem. Soc.*, 1949, **71**, 60.

Phloraspidinol

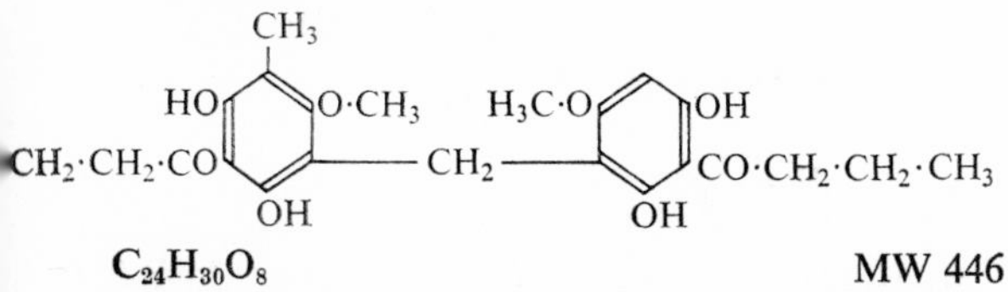

$C_{24}H_{30}O_8$ MW 446

Constituent of the fern *Dryopteris austriaca*. Cryst. from cyclohexane. M.p. 193–4°.

Penttilä, Sundman, *Acta Chem. Scand.*, 1963, **17**, 1886.

Phloraspyron

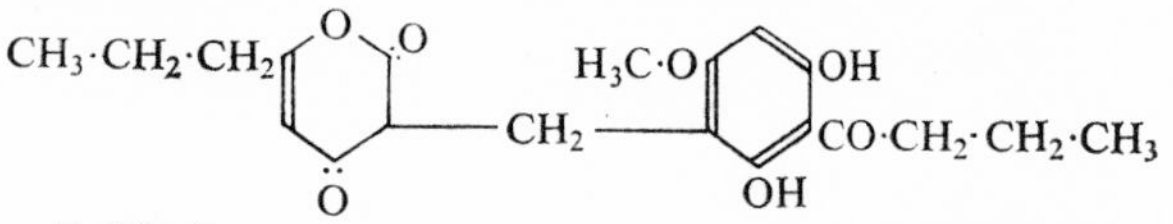

$C_{20}H_{24}O_7$ MW 376

Constituent of the fern *Dryopteris austriaca*. Cryst. from cyclohexane. M.p. 135–6°.

Penttilä, Sundman, *Acta Chem. Scand.*, 1963, **17**, 1886.

Phlorisovalerophenone. *See* 2 : 4 : 6-Trihydroxyisovalerophenone.

Pholcodine. *See* 3-(2-Morpholinoethyl)morphine.

Pholedrine. *See* *p*-(2-Methylaminopropyl)phenol.

Phomazarin

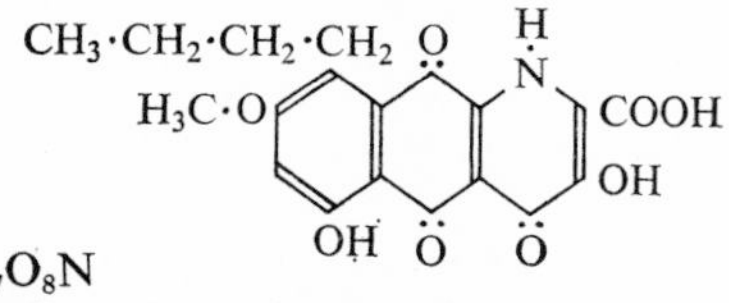

$C_{19}H_{17}O_8N$ MW 387

Metabolite of the fungus *Phoma terrestris* Hansen. Orange needles from Py. M.p. 196° decomp.

Me ester: $C_{20}H_{19}O_8N$. MW 401. Orange-bronze needles. M.p. 213°. *Tri-Ac*: cryst. from light petroleum. M.p. 160–70° decomp.

Tri-Ac: dark orange needles from BuOH. M.p. 184–6° decomp.

Kögl, Sparenburg, *Rec. trav. chim.*, 1940, **59**, 1180.

Kögl, Quackenbush, *Rec. trav. chim.*, 1944, **63**, 251.

Kögl, van Wessen, Elsbach, *Rec. trav. chim.*, 1945, **64**, 23.

Birch, Butler, Rickards, *Tetrahedron Letters*, 1964, 1853.

Phorbic Acid

HOOC·CH₂·CH₂·C(OH)·CH₂·CH(OH)·COOH
COOH

$C_8H_{12}O_8$ MW 236

Water-soluble acid from *Euphorbia* spp. Unstable.

Dilactone: dilactophorbic acid

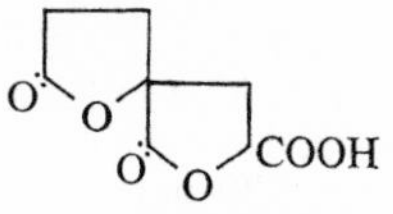

$C_8H_8O_6$ MW 200

Cryst. from EtOH. M.p. 152–4°. *Et ester*: $C_{10}H_{12}O_6$. MW 228. M.p. 91·5–92°. B.p. 175–245°/12 mm.

Bernatek, Nordal, Ogner, *Acta Chem. Scand.*, 1963, **17**, 2375.

Nordal, Ogner, *Acta Chem. Scand.*, 1964, **18**, 830.

Photolevopimaric Acid

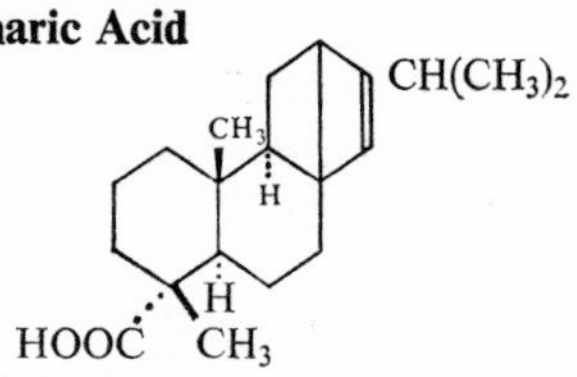

$C_{20}H_{30}O_2$ MW 302

Cryst. from EtOH. M.p. 114–16°. $[\alpha]_D^{16}$ +70° ($CHCl_3$).

Me ester: $C_{21}H_{32}O_2$. MW 316. Liq. $[\alpha]_D^{25}$ 56°. n_D^{25} 1·5037.
2-*Amino*-2-*methylpropan*-1-*ol salt*: cryst. from MeOH. M.p. 178–81°. $[\alpha]_D$ +53° (c, 1·50 in EtOH).

Schuller *et al.*, *J. Org. Chem.*, 1962, **27**, 1178.
Dauben, Coates, *J. Am. Chem. Soc.*, 1964, **86**, 2490.

Phthalimide.★

N(2-*Bromoethyl*):★ cryst. from EtOH.Aq. M.p. 80–2°.

Soine, Buchdahl, *Organic Syntheses*, 1952, **32**, 18; Coll. Vol. **4**, 106.

Phyllalbine (*Vanillyl tropine*)

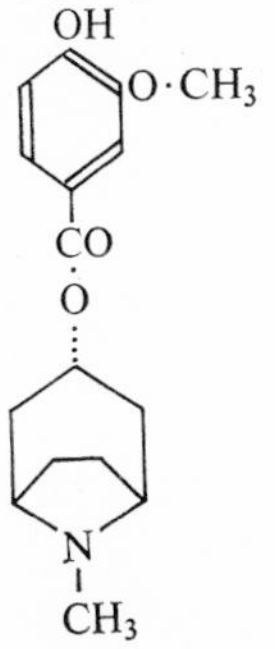

$C_{16}H_{21}O_4N$ MW 291

Constituent of the roots of *Phyllantus discoïdes* Muell. Arg. Cryst. from MeOH. M.p. 209–10°. HCl → vanillic acid + tropine.
B,HCl: cryst. from MeOH. M.p. 254°.
Me ether: *see* Convolamine.

Parello *et al.*, *Bull. soc. chim.*, 1963, 2787.

Phyllanthin

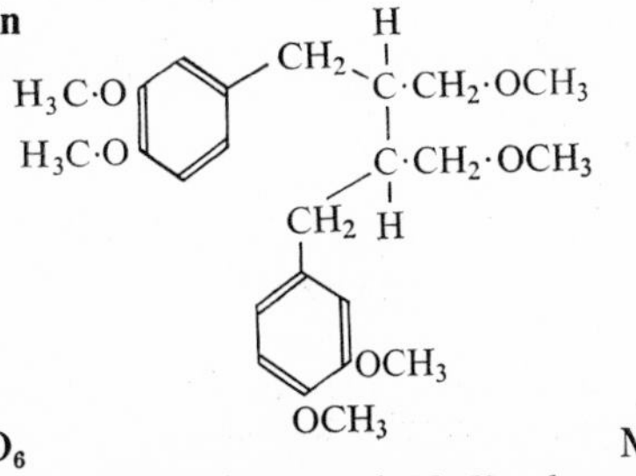

$C_{24}H_{34}O_6$ MW 418

Constituent of the leaves of *Phyllanthus niruri* L. Short needles from MeOH or light petroleum. M.p. 96°. $[\alpha]_D^{30}$ 12·4° (c, 1·45 in $CHCl_3$). Light absorption: $\lambda_{max.}$ 230 and 280 mμ (log ε, 4·33 and 1·89). Br_2 in $CHCl_3$ → dibromo deriv. M.p. 136–7°. $[\alpha]_D^{30}$ 40° (c, 0·5 in $CHCl_3$).

Row *et al.*, *Tetrahedron Letters*, 1964, 1557.

Phyllochrysine. *See* allo *under* Securinine.

Phyllocladene.★

[[14]*C*]-.

Birch, Winter, *J. Chem. Soc.*, 1963, 5547.

Phyllodulcinol (3 : 4-*Dihydro*-8-*hydroxy*-3-(3-*hydroxy*-4-*methoxyphenyl*)*isocoumarin*)

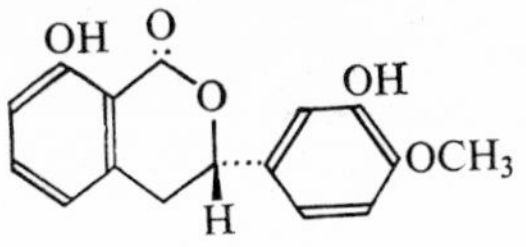

$C_{16}H_{14}O_5$ MW 296

(+) (3R)-.
Sweet principle in the leaves of *Hydrangea macrophylla* Seringe var. *Thunbergii* Makino ("Amacha"). Prisms from EtOH. M.p. 119–21°. $[\alpha]_D$ 70·7–80·8° (c, 1·02 in Me_2CO).
(±)-.
Cryst. M.p. 132°.
3′-*Me ether*: m.p. 115°. *Ac*: needles from EtOH. M.p. 141°.
Di-Me ether: needles from EtOH. M.p. 125°. (From Et_2O a lower melting form, m.p. 105° has been observed.)

Asahina, Asano, *Ber.*, 1929, **62**, 171; 1930, **63**, 429, 2059; 1931, **64**, 1252.
Arakawo, Nakazaki, *Chemistry and Industry*, 1959, 671.
Arakawo, *Bull. Chem. Soc. Japan*, 1960, **33**, 200.

Physalaemin

H·Pyr·Ala·Asp(OH)·Pro·Asp(NH_2)·Lys·Phe·Tyr–
–Gly·Leu·Met·NH_2

$C_{58}H_{84}O_{16}N_{14}S$ MW 1264

Polypeptide which exerts powerful hypotensive action and stimulates extravascular smooth muscle from the skin of South American amphibian *Physalaemus fuscumaculatus*.
B,CF$_3$*·COOH,2H*$_2$*O*: m.p. 180° decomp. $[\alpha]_D^{20}$ −56° (c, 0·2 in EtOH). Light absorption: $\lambda_{max.}$ 278 mμ (ε, 1780).

Erspamer *et al.*, *Experientia*, 1964, **20**, 489.
Bernardi *et al.*, *Experientia*, 1964, **20**, 490.

Physovenine

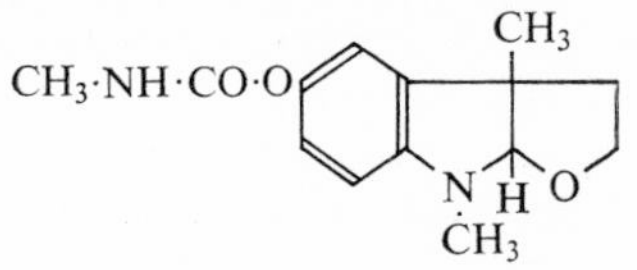

$C_{14}H_{18}O_3N_2$ MW 262

Alkaloid from *Physostigma veneosum* (Calabar beans). M.p. 123°. $[\alpha]_D^{22}$ −92° (EtOH). Light absorption: $\lambda_{max.}$ 252 (ε, 13,200), 310 mμ (3300) in EtOH.

Salway, *J. Chem. Soc.*, 1911, **99**, 2148.
Robinson, *J. Chem. Soc.*, 1964, 1503.

Phytanic Acid. *See* 3 : 7 : 11 : 15-Tetramethylhexadecanoic Acid.

Phytolaccagenin

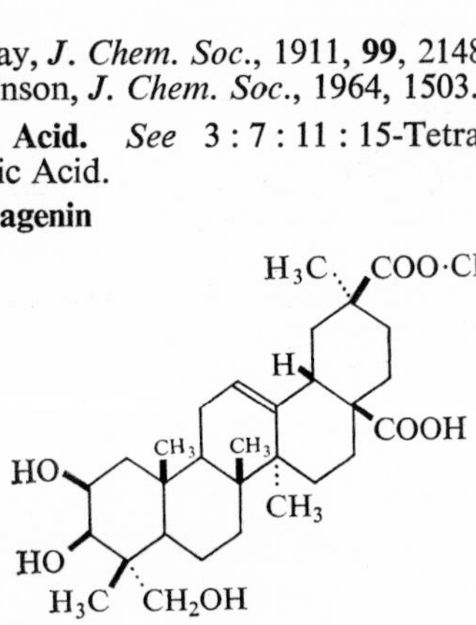

$C_{31}H_{48}O_7$ MW 532

Aglycone from phytolaccatoxin. Cryst. M.p. 317–18° decomp.

Stout, Malofsky, Stout, *J. Am. Chem. Soc.*, 1964, **86**, 957.

Phytolaccatoxin

$C_{55}H_{90}O_{22}$ MW 1102

Toxic principle from pokeroot (*Phytolacca americana* L.). Hydrolysis → glucose, xylose, and phytolaccagenin.

Ahmed, Zufall, Jenkins, *J. Am. Pharm. Assoc.*, 1949, **38**, 443.
Stout, Malofsky, Stout, *J. Am. Chem. Soc.*, 1964, **86**, 957.

Pickrosalvin★

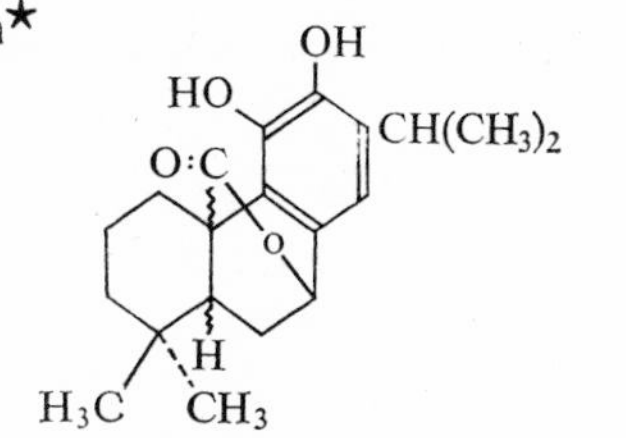

Revised structure

$C_{21}H_{26}O_4$ MW 344

Linde, *Helv. Chim. Acta*, 1964, **47**, 1234.

Picraphylline

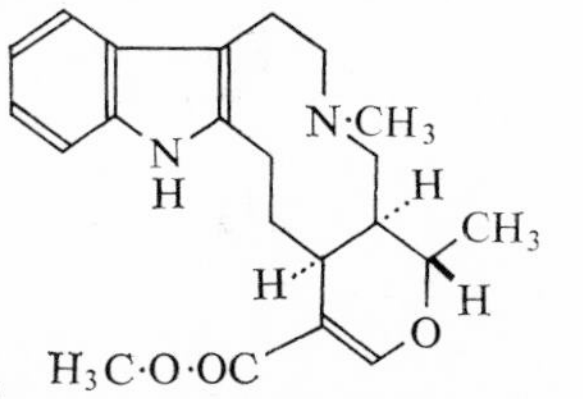

$C_{22}H_{26}O_4N_2$ MW 382

Alkaloid from the flowers of *Picralima nitida* Stapf. M.p. 255°. $[\alpha]_D^{20}$ −37° ($CHCl_3$). Light absorption: $\lambda_{max.}$ 238 (log ε, 4·14) and 313 mμ (3·98).

Ledouble *et al.*, *Ann. pharm. fr.*, 1964, **22**, 463.
Lévy *et al.*, *Bull. soc. chim.*, 1964, 1917.

Piericidin A

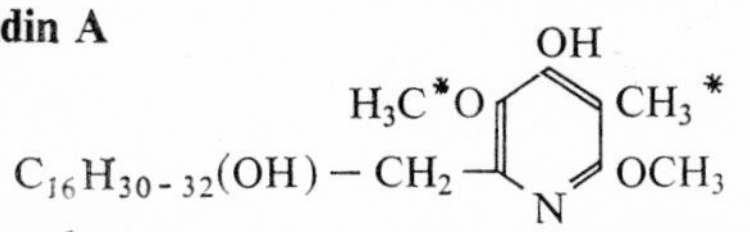

Suggested structure. The groups * may be interchanged

$C_{25}H_{37-9}O_4N$ MW 515 (517)

Metabolite of *Streptomyces* spp. with insecticidal activity. Viscous oil. $n_D^{15\cdot5}$ 1·5429. α_D^{20} −0·9°. Light absorption: $\lambda_{max.}$ 232 (ε, 39,500), 239 (40,500), 267 mμ (ε, 5300).

Di-Ac: oil.

Tamura *et al.*, *Agric. Biol. Chem.* (Japan), 1963, **27**, 576.
Takahashi *et al.*, *Agric. Biol. Chem.* (Japan), 1963, **27**, 583, 798.

Pinusenediol. *See* Serratenediol.

α-Piperonylquinoline. *See* Dubamine.

Piptamine. *See note under* Ormosamine.

Piptanthine

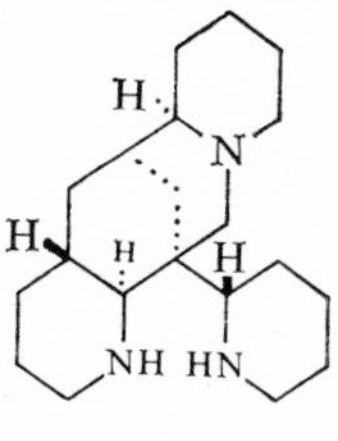

$C_{20}H_{35}N_3$ MW 317

Alkaloid from *Piptanthus nanus*. Cryst. from Me_2CO, AcOEt, or EtOH.Aq. M.p. 142–3°. $[\alpha]_D$ −24·3°.

Di-N-*Ac*: by sublimation. M.p. 218–21°.

N-*Me*: $C_{21}H_{37}N_3$. MW 331. Needles. M.p. 114–15°.

Phenylthiourethane: cryst. from MeOH or C_6H_6–light petroleum. M.p. 154–6°.

2 : 4-*Dinitrophenyl deriv.*: cubes from EtOH. M.p. 161°.

Konovalova, Diskina, Rabinovich, *Zhur. Obshcheĭ Khim.*, 1951, **21**, 773.
Eisner, Šorm, *Coll. Czech. Chem. Commun.*, 1959, **24**, 2348.
Deslongchamps, Wilson, Valenta, *Tetrahedron Letters*, 1964, 3893.

Piptoside

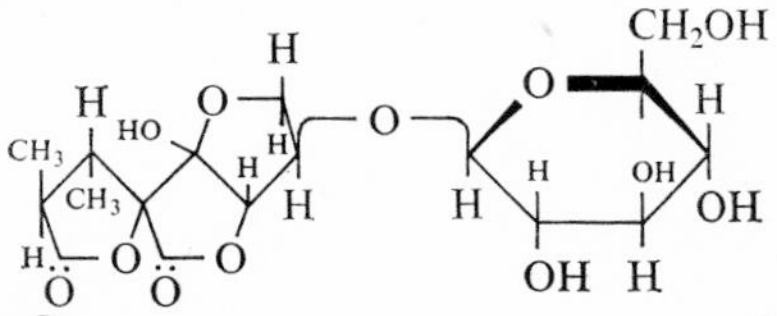

$C_{17}H_{24}O_{12}$ MW 420

Constituent of *Piptocalyx moorei* Oliv. Plates from H_2O. M.p. 228–30°. $[\alpha]_D^{16}$ −28° (c, 2 in H_2O), −23° (c, 1·498 in MeOH).

Penta-Ac: fine needles. M.p. 194–194·5°. $[\alpha]_D^{26}$ −18° (c, 3·162 in $CHCl_3$).

Penta-O-Me deriv.: m.p. 123–4°. $[\alpha]_D^{27}$ −23° (c, 3·3 in EtOH).

Riggs, Stevens, *Austral. J. Chem.*, 1962, **15**, 305; *Tetrahedron Letters*, 1963, 1615.

Pleiocarpamine

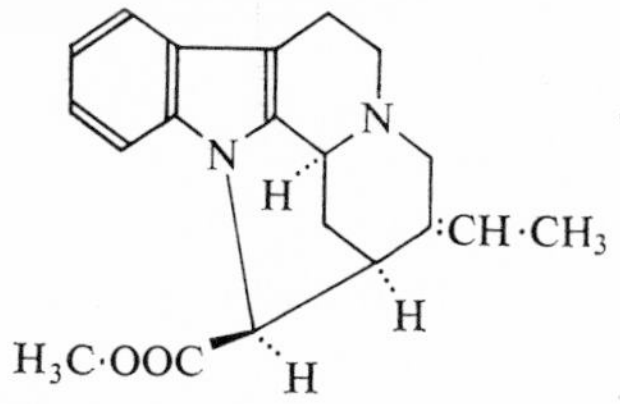

$C_{20}H_{22}O_2N_2$ MW 322

Alkaloid from the root of *Pleiocarpa mutica* Benth. and the bark of *Hunteria eburna* Pichon. M.p. 159°. $[\alpha]_D^{21}$ +136° (c, 0·74 in MeOH). pK_{MCS}* 6·91. Light absorption: $\lambda_{max.}$ 230 (log ε, 4·47) and 285 mμ (3·91).

Kump, Schmid, *Helv. Chim. Acta*, 1961, **44**, 1053.
Bartlett *et al.*, *J. Org. Chem.*, 1963, **28**, 2197.
Hesse *et al.*, *Helv. Chim. Acta*, 1964, **47**, 878.

Pleiocarpinine.★

Also present in leaves of *Pleiocarpa tubicina*.

Bycroft *et al.*, *Helv. Chim. Acta*, 1964, **47**, 1147.

Plumieride.★

Biosynthesis:

Yeowell, Schmid, *Experientia*, 1964, **20**, 250.

Podocarpic Acid.★

Synthesis:

Meyer, Maheshwari, *Tetrahedron Letters*, 1964, 2175.
Wenkert *et al.*, *J. Am. Chem. Soc.*, 1964, **86**, 2038.

Pododacric Acid

$C_{20}H_{28}O_5$ MW 348

Extractive of *Podocarpus daciydioides* A. Rich. and *P. totora*. Needles or prisms from EtOH.Aq. M.p. 213–14°. $[\alpha]_D^{25}$ 118° (c, 0·9 in $CHCl_3$–MeOH [5 : 1]). Light absorption: $\lambda_{max.}$ 225 (log ε, 3·74) and 284 mμ (3·4).

Tri-Ac: granules from 80% MeOH. M.p. 160–160·5°. $[\alpha]_D$ 82° (c, 0·64 in EtOH).

Tribenzoyl: needles from EtOH. M.p. 135–6°. $[\alpha]_D^{22}$ 47° (c, 0·4 in EtOH).

Briggs *et al.*, *Tetrahedron*, 1959, **7**, 270.
Cambie, Mander, *Tetrahedron*, 1962, **18**, 465.

Podospicatin (2′ : 5 : 7-*Trihydroxy-5′ : 6-dimethoxyisoflavone*)

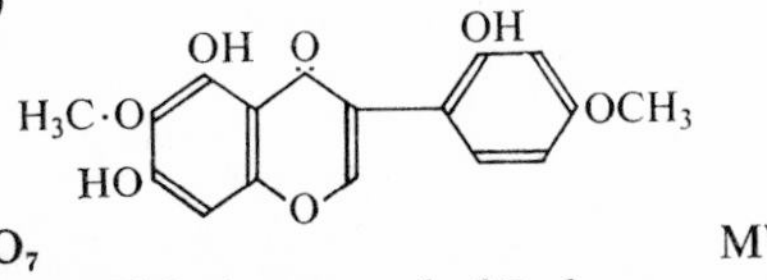

$C_{17}H_{14}O_7$ MW 330

Constituent of the heartwood of *Podocarpus spicatus*. Needles from 60% AcOH. M.p. 211–12°.

2′ : 7-*Di-Me ether*: needles from 60% AcOH. M.p. 148–50°.

Tri-Me ether: prisms from EtOH. M.p. 158–60°.

Briggs, Cain, *Tetrahedron*, 1959, **6**, 143.
Briggs, Cebalo, *Tetrahedron*, 1959, **6**, 145; 1963, **19**, 2301.

Pollinastanol

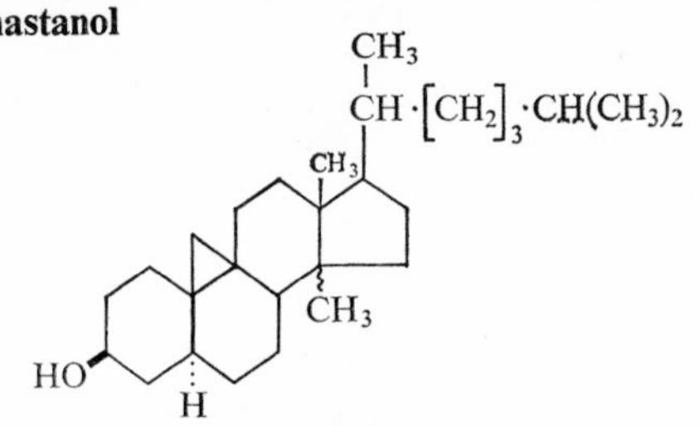

Suggested structure

$C_{28}H_{48}O$ MW 400

Isolated from pollen. Cryst. from MeOH. M.p. 95°. $[\alpha]_D^{20}$ +35° ($CHCl_3$).

Ac: oil. $[\alpha]_D$ +29° ($CHCl_3$).

Hügel, Barbier, Lederer, *Bull. soc. chim.*, 1964, 2012.

Polygalic Acid (*Senegenic acid*)

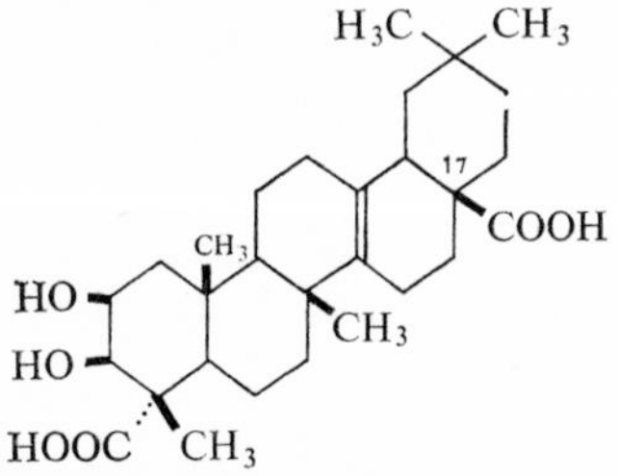

$C_{29}H_{44}O_6$ MW 488

Constituent of *Polygala senega*. Cryst. from EtOH. M.p. 299–301°. $[\alpha]_D^{23}$ +18° (EtOH). Light absorption: $\lambda_{max.}$ 200 mμ (ε, 8100).

Di-Me ester: $C_{31}H_{48}O_6$. MW 516. M.p. 198–200°. $[\alpha]_D$ +20·5°. *Di-Ac*: m.p. 180–2°. $[\alpha]_D$ +31°.

17-*Mono-Et ester*: $C_{31}H_{48}O_6$. MW 516. M.p. 215–18°. $[\alpha]_D^{23}$ +24·5° (EtOH).

Di-Ac: $C_{33}H_{48}O_8$. MW 572. M.p. 276–8° (evacuated capillary). $[\alpha]_D^{23}$ +23° (MeOH) (+34°).

Dugan, de Mayo, Starratt, *Tetrahedron Letters*, 1964, 2567.
Pelletier *et al.*, *Tetrahedron Letters*, 1964, 3065.

Polygonaquinone (2 : 5-*Dihydroxy-3-eicosyl-6-methyl-1 : 4-benzoquinone*)

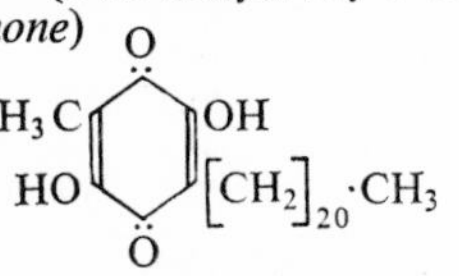

$C_{28}H_{48}O_4$ MW 448

Constituent of the roots of *Polygonatum falcatum* A. Gray. Orange prisms from EtOH. M.p. 133–4°. Light absorption: $\lambda_{max.}$ 295 mμ (log ε, 4·28). Reductive acetylation → Tetra-Ac: m.p. 120–1°.

Di-Ac: yellow needles from EtOH. M.p. 92–3°.

Di-Me ether: $C_{30}H_{52}O_4$. MW 276. Yellow needles from EtOH. M.p. 79–80°.

Nakata *et al.*, *Tetrahedron*, 1964, **20**, 2319.

Polymyxin B$_2$★

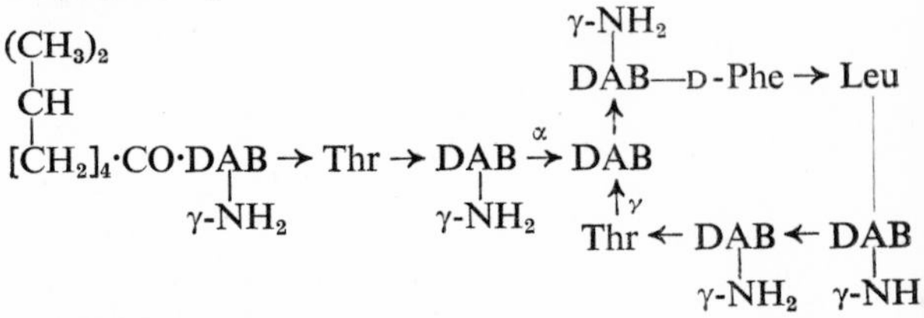

Structure:

Wilkinson, Lowe, *Nature* (Lond.), 1964, **204**, 185, 993.

Polymyxin E$_1$.★

This is identical with Colistin A (*q.v.*).

Wilkinson, Lowe, *Nature* (Lond.), 1964, **204**, 993.

Poweramine

$C_{23}H_{30}O_4N_2$ MW 398

Alkaloid from the leaves of *Ochrosia poweri* Bailey. Colourless prisms from MeOH. M.p. 241–2° decomp.

Picrate: red needles from MeOH. M.p. 156°.

Doy, Moore, *Austral. J. Chem.*, 1962, **15**, 548.

Powerchrine

$C_{22}H_{26}O_3N_2$ MW 366

Alkaloid from the stem bark of *Ochrosia poweri* Bailey. Colourless needles from MeOH. M.p. 213°. $[\alpha]_D^{25}$ −80·8° (c, 1·1 in Me_2CO). Light absorption: $\lambda_{max.}$ 232 (ε, 23,400), 279 (5600), and 297 mμ (ε, 5900).

Douglas *et al.*, *Austral. J. Chem.*, 1964, **17**, 246.

Poweridine

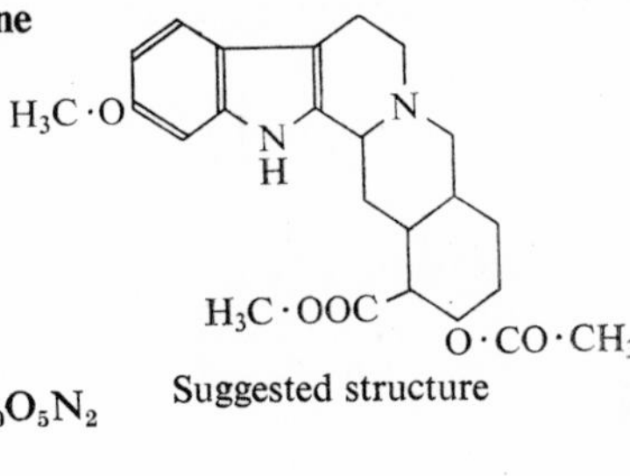

Suggested structure

$C_{24}H_{30}O_5N_2$ MW 426

Alkaloid from *Ochrosia poweri* Bailey. Needles from Me_2CO–MeOH. M.p. 226° decomp. $[\alpha]_D^{22}$ −4·9° (c, 3 in MeOH).
B,CH₃I: colourless rhombs. M.p. 282° decomp.

Doy, Moore, *Austral. J. Chem.*, 1962, **15**, 548.

Powerine

$C_{21}H_{26}O_4N_2$ MW 370

Alkaloid from leaves of *Ochrosia poweri* Bailey. Plates from Me_2CO–MeOH. M.p. 188–9° decomp. $[\alpha]_D^{22}$ −216° (c, 0·33 in Me_2CO).
B,CH_3I: colourless rhombs from Me_2CO. M.p. 230° decomp.

Doy, Moore, *Austral. J. Chem.*, 1962, **15**, 548.

Presinol ((−)-3-[3 : 4-*Dihydroxyphenyl*]-2-*methylalanine*, α-*methyldopa*)

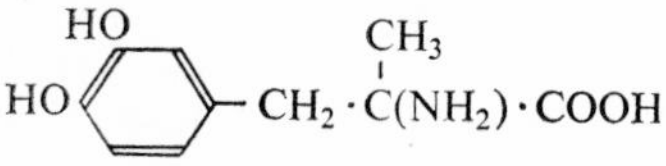

$C_{10}H_{13}O_4N$ MW 211

Hypotensive agent. M.p. 292–3°.

Farbenfabriken Bayer, *Report of Therapy Congress and Pharmaceutical Exhibition*, Karsruhe, 1963 (*Angew. Chem., Int. Ed.*, 1964, **3**, 68).

Primocarcin

$NH\cdot CO\cdot CH_3$
$CH_2{:}C\cdot CO\cdot CH_2\cdot CH_2\cdot CONH_2$

$C_8H_{12}O_3N_2$ MW 184

Antitumour antibiotic from *Nocardia fukayae*. M.p. 130–1°. Light absorption: $\lambda_{max.}$ 253 mμ (ε, 3600).

Nagatsu, Isono, Suzuki, *J. Antibiotics* (*Ser. A*), 1962, **15**, 75, 77, 80.
Bowman, Closier, Islip, *Tetrahedron Letters*, 1964, 1897.

Priscol. *See* 2-Benzylimidazoline.★

Pronuciferine

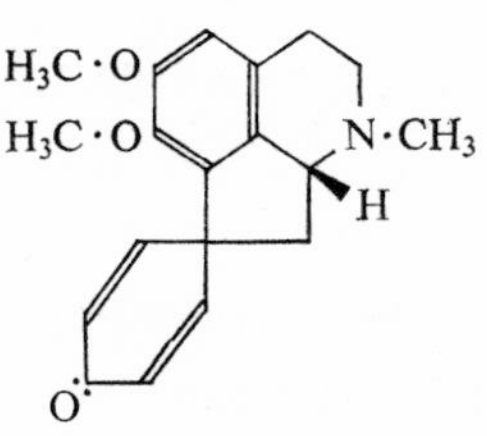

$C_{19}H_{21}O_3N$ MW 311

Alkaloid from Asian lotus (*Nelumbo nucifera* Gaertn.) and *Stephania glabra*. M.p. 127–9°. $[\alpha]_D$ +99° (c, 0·2 in $CHCl_3$), +105·8° (c, 0·41 in EtOH). pK_{MCS} 6·1. Identical with *N-O*-Dimethylcrotonosine. (Haynes, Stuart, *J. Chem. Soc.*, 1963, 1784, 1789.)

Bernauer, *Helv. Chim. Acta*, 1963, **46**, 1783.
Cava *et al.*, *Chemistry and Industry*, 1964, 282.

Synthesis:

Bernauer, *Experientia*, 1964, **20**, 380.

6-[1-Propenyl]-fulvene

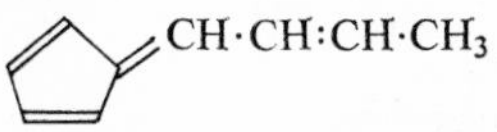

C_9H_{10} MW 118

Cryst. from light petroleum. M.p. −27·4° to −27°. D_4^{18} 0·897. Light absorption: $\lambda_{max.}$ 288 (log ε, 4·42), 296 (4·55), 301 (4·56), 307 (4·57), 317 (4·31), and 392 mμ (2·39).

Neuenschwander, Meuche, Schaltegger, *Helv. Chim. Acta*, 1964, **47**, 1022.

Propiomazine (10-(2-*Dimethylaminopropyl*)-2-*propionylphenothiazine*, *Dorevane*, *Indorm*, *Largon*)

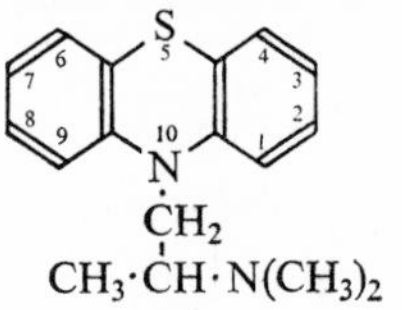

$C_{19}H_{22}O_2NS$ MW 328

Tranquilliser. Oil. B.p. 235–45°/0·5 mm.
Hydrogen maleate: $C_{24}H_{28}O_5N_2S$. MW 456. Cryst. from iso-PrOH. M.p. 160–1°.
Oxime: cryst. from AcOEt. M.p. 173–4°.

Schmitt *et al.*, *Bull. soc. chim.*, 1957, 1474.

Proponesin. *See* B,HCl *under* Tolpronine.★

Propylhexedrine. *See* 1-Cyclohexyl-2-methylaminopropane.

Proscillaridin A

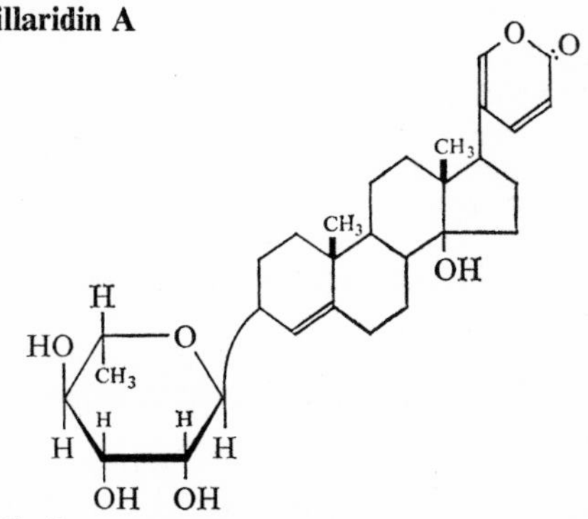

$C_{30}H_{42}O_8$ MW 530

Constituent of white squill (*Scilla maritima* Baker). M.p. 215–18°. $[\alpha]_D^{20}$ −83° (MeOH).

Stoll *et al.*, *Helv. Chim. Acta*, 1933, **16**, 703.
Stoll, Kreis, *Helv. Chim. Acta*, 1951, **34**, 1431.
Stoll, Renz, Brack, *Helv. Chim. Acta*, 1952, **35**, 1934.

Prostaglandin E₂.★

Biosynthesis:

Van Dorp *et al.*, *Biochem. Biophys. Acta*, 1964, **90**, 204.
Bergström, Danielsson, Samuelsson, *Biochem. Biophys. Acta*, 1964, **90**, 207.

Protoaphin-*sl*

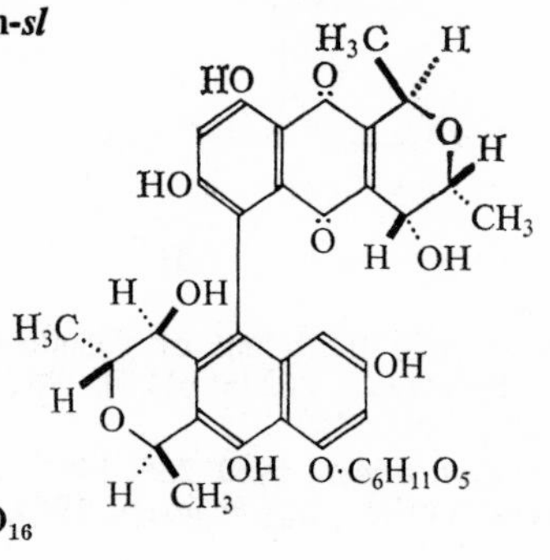

$C_{36}H_{38}O_{16}$ MW 726

Fluorescent colouring matter of the willow aphid, *Tuberolachnus salignus*. Tan cryst. which decomp. on heating. Light absorption: $\lambda_{max.}$ 223 (log ε, 4·73), 274 (4·14), 297 (3·98), 311 (3·91), 343 (3·67), 356 (3·72), and 450 mμ (3·64) in 75% EtOH.

Duewell *et al.*, *J. Chem. Soc.*, 1950, 485.
Cameron *et al.*, *J. Chem. Soc.*, 1964, 51.

Protopanaxadiol★

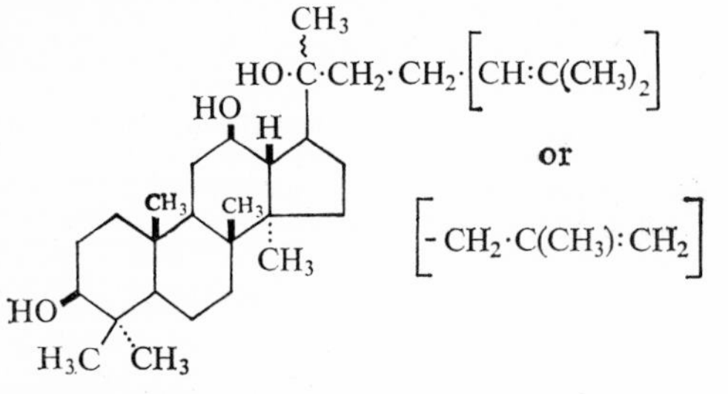

Stereochemistry:

Tanaka, Nagai, Shibata, *Tetrahedron Letters*, 1964, 2291.

Pseudothiobinupharidine

$C_{30}H_{40}O_2N_2S$ MW 492

Alkaloid from the rhizomes of the yellow water-lily (*Nuphar luteum* (L.) Sm.).

B,2HClO₄: prisms. M.p. 173–5°. $[\alpha]_D$ +186·2° (EtOH).

Achmatowicz, Bellen, *Tetrahedron Letters*, 1962, 1121.

Pseudouridine A_F (5-α-D-*Ribopyranosyluracil*)

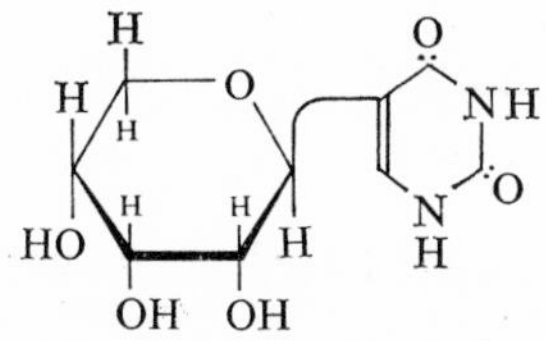

$C_9H_{12}O_6N_2$ MW 244

Produced by acid treatment of Pseudouridine C. Light absorption: $\lambda_{max.}$ 263 (at pH 7), 285 (at pH 12), and 278 mμ (at pH 14)

Cohn, *J. Biol. Chem.*, 1960, **235**, 1488.
Chambers, Kurkov, Shapiro, *Biochemistry*, 1963, **2**, 1192; 1964, **3**, 326.

Pseudouridine A_S (5-β-D-*Ribopyranosyluracil*)

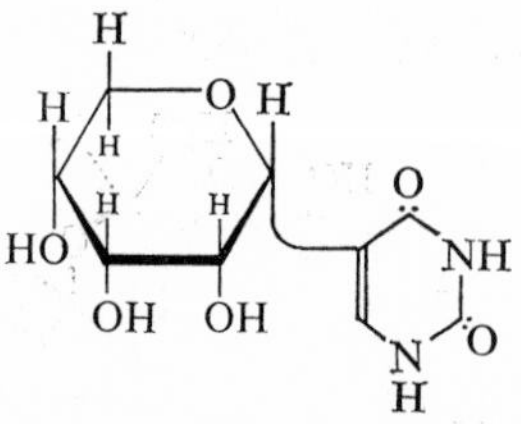

$C_9H_{12}O_6N_2$ MW 244

Produced by acid treatment of Pseudouridine C. Light absorption: $\lambda_{max.}$ 262 (at pH 7), 286 (at pH 12), and 281 mμ (at pH 14).

Cohn, *J. Biol. Chem.*, 1960, **235**, 1488.
Chambers, Kurkov, *Biochemistry*, 1964, **3**, 327.

Pseudouridine B (5-α-D-*Ribofuranosyluracil*)

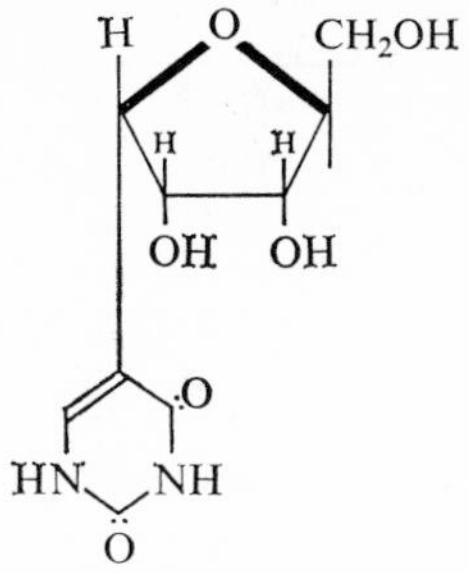

$C_9H_{12}O_6N_2$ MW 244

Produced by acid treatment of Pseudouridine C. Light absorption: $\lambda_{max.}$ 263 (at pH 7), 287 (at pH 12), and 278 mμ (at pH 14).

Cohn, *Biochim. Biophys. Acta*, 1959, **32**, 569; *J. Biol. Chem.*, 1960, **235**, 1488.

Pseudouridine C★ (5-β-D-*Ribofuranosyluracil*)

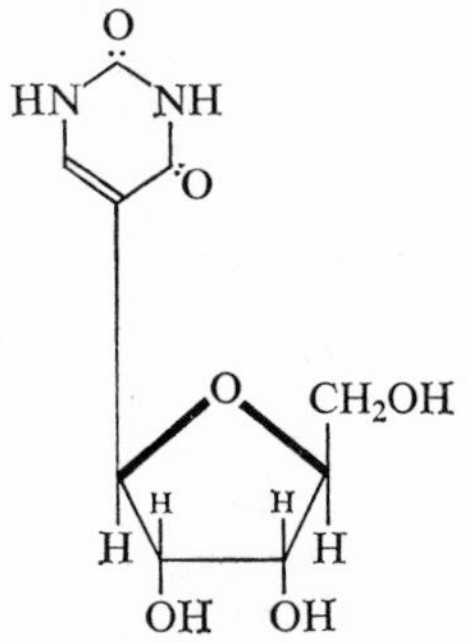

$C_9H_{12}O_6N_2$ MW 244

Nucleoside from yeast ribonucleic acid. Cryst. from EtOH. M.p. 220–1°. Light absorption: $\lambda_{max.}$ 262 (at pH 7), 286 (pH 12), and 278 mμ (pH 14).

Adler, Gutman, *Science*, 1959, **130**, 862.
Cohn, *Biochim. Biophys. Acta*, 1959, **32**, 569; *J. Biol. Chem.*, 1960, **235**, 1488.
Shapiro, Chambers, *J. Am. Chem. Soc.*, 1961, **83**, 3920.
Michelson, Cohn, *Biochemistry*, 1962, **1**, 490.

Pseudouridine C 5′-Diphosphate

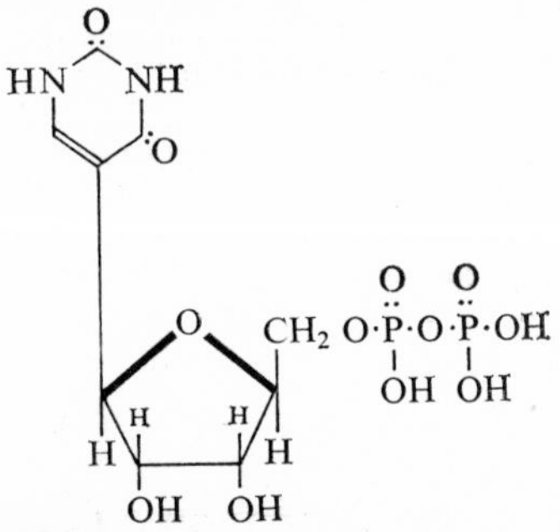

$C_9H_{14}O_{12}N_2P_2$ MW 404

Synthetic nucleotide.

Chambers, Kurkov, Shapiro, *Biochemistry*, 1963, **2**, 1192.

Pterofuran

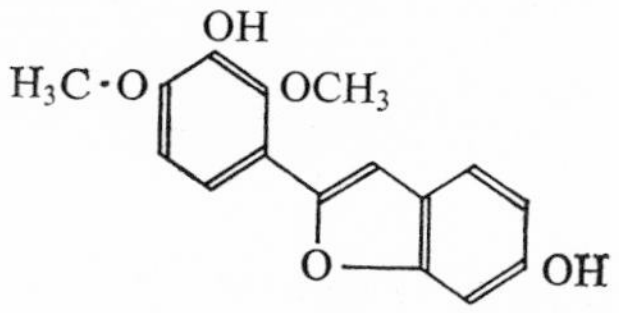

$C_{16}H_{14}O_5$ MW 286

Constituent of the heartwood of *Pterocarpus indicus*. Fine needles from C_6H_6–EtOH. M.p. 208–208·5°. Light absorption: $\lambda_{max.}$ 219·5 (log ε, 4·47), 235·5 (4·22), 285·5 (4·21), 294·5 (4·26), 304·5 (4·39), 317 (4·58), and 332 mμ (4·56).
Ac: needles from EtOH. M.p. 135·5–136·5°.
Di-Me ether: prisms from light petroleum. M.p. 86–7°.

Cooke, Rae, *Austral. J. Chem.*, 1964, **17**, 379.

Ptimal. *See* 3 : 5 : 5-Trimethyl-2 : 4-oxazolidinedione.★

Pulchellin A

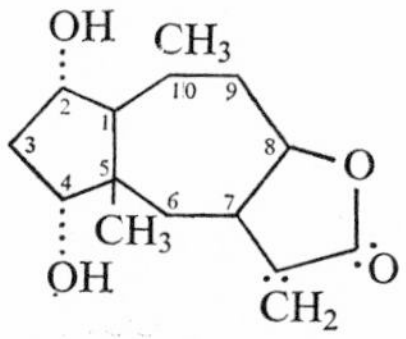

$C_{15}H_{24}O_4$ MW 268

Constituent of *Gaillardia pulchella* Foug. Cryst. from AcOEt, C_6H_6, or H_2O. M.p. 165–8°. $[\alpha]_D^{26}$ $-36{\cdot}2°$ (c, 2·43 in $CHCl_3$).
Di-Ac: cryst. from C_6H_6–light petroleum. M.p. 123–5°. $[\alpha]_D^{25}$ $-28{\cdot}96°$ (c, 1·83 in $CHCl_3$).

Herz, Ueda, Inayama, *Tetrahedron*, 1963, **19**, 483.

Pulchellin B

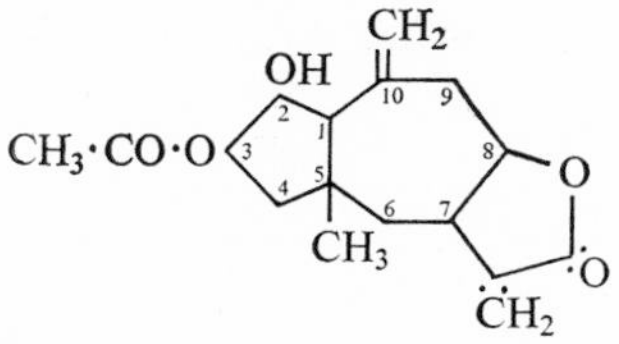

$C_{17}H_{22}O_5$ MW 306

Constituent of *Gaillardia pulchella* Foug. (from New Mexico). M.p. 215–18°. $[\alpha]_D^{27}$ 92·7° (c, 1·54 in 95% EtOH). Light absorption: $\lambda_{max.}$ 210 (ε, 8830) and 325 mμ (53). CH_2N_2 → a pyrazoline: prisms from MeOH. M.p. 164–5° decomp.
Mono-Ac: cryst. from MeOH.Aq. M.p. 190–3°. $[\alpha]_D$ +94·5° (c, 1 in $CHCl_3$).

Herz, Inayama, *Tetrahedron*, 1964, **20**, 341.

Pulchellin C

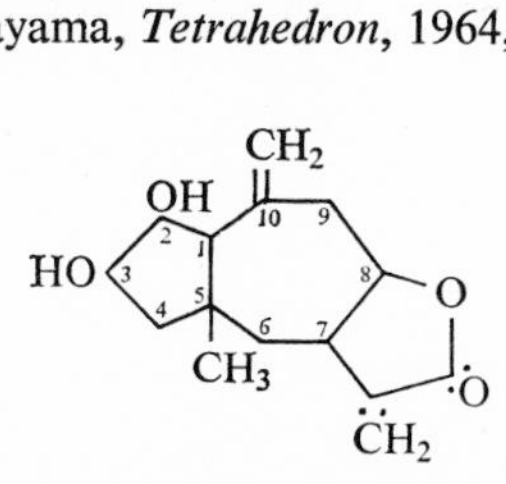

$C_{15}H_{20}O_4$ MW 264

Constituent of *Gaillardia pulchella* Foug. (from New Mexico). M.p. 199–202°. $[\alpha]_D^{27}$ 125° (c, 1·55 in 95% EtOH). Light absorption: $\lambda_{max.}$ 210 mμ (ε, 8960). CH_2N_2 → a pyrazoline from MeOH.Aq. M.p. 165–7° decomp.
3-Mono-Ac: *see* Pulchellin B.
Di-Ac: cryst. from MeOH.Aq. M.p. 190–3°. $[\alpha]_D^{23}$ +94·5° (c, 1 in $CHCl_3$).

Herz, Inayama, *Tetrahedron*, 1964, **20**, 341.

Pulchellin D

$C_{17}H_{24}O_5$ MW 308

Minor constituent of *Gaillardia puchella* Foug. M.p. 182–5°.

Herz, Inayama, *Tetrahedron*, 1964, **20**, 341.

Pulcherrimin.★

Synthesis:

Ohta, *Chem. Pharm. Bull.* (Tokyo), 1964, **12**, 125.

Pulvinic Acid.★

See also:

Agarwal, Seshadri, *Tetrahedron*, 1964, **20**, 17.

Purine.

N.M.R. spectrum:

Schweizer *et al.*, *J. Am. Chem. Soc.*, 1964, **86**, 696.

Pyrazine-2 : 3-dicarboxylic Acid

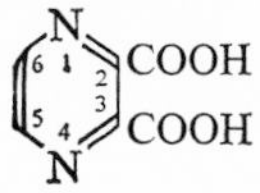

$C_6H_4O_4N_2$ MW 168

M.p. 183–5° decomp.
Di-Me ester: $C_8H_8O_4N_2$. MW 196. M.p. 50°.
Di-Amide: $C_6H_6O_2N_4$. MW 166. Cryst. from H_2O. M.p. 240° decomp.
Di-nitrile: $C_6H_2N_4$. MW 130. M.p. 132·5–133°.

Gabriel, Sonn, *Ber.*, 1907, **40**, 450.
Solomons, Spoerri, *J. Am. Chem. Soc.*, 1953, **75**, 679.
Jones, McLaughlin, *Organic Syntheses*, 1950, **30**, 86; Coll. Vol. **4**, 824.

Pyrazine-2 : 5-dicarboxylic Acid.

Needles + $2H_2O$. M.p. 255–6° (sealed tube) (272°).

Stoehr, *J. prakt. Chem.*, 1893, [2] **47**, 488.

Pyrazine-2 : 6-dicarboxylic Acid.

Needles + $2H_2O$. M.p. 217–18° decomp.

Stoehr, *J. prakt. Chem.*, 1897, [2], **55**, 257.

Pyreno-[1′,2′ : 1,2]-pyrene

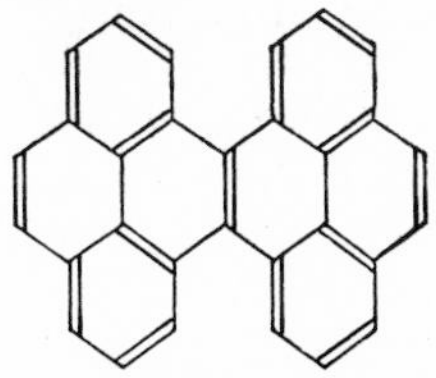

$C_{30}H_{16}$ MW 376

Yellow leaflets from xylene. M.p. 305–7°. H_2SO_4 → dark green soln. Light absorption: $\lambda_{max.}$ 226 (log ε, 4·52), 270 (4·40), 311 (4·75), 326 (5·01), 380 (4·32), 400 mμ (4·34).

Clar, Guye-Vuillème, Stephen, *Tetrahedron*, 1964, **20**, 2107.

Pyrethic Acid

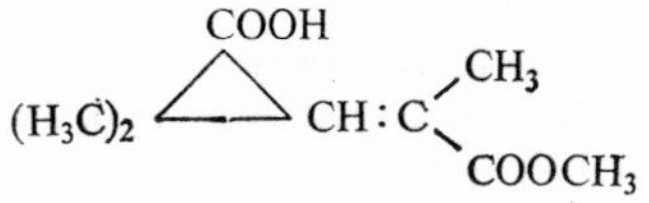

$C_{11}H_{16}O_4$ MW 212

Trans (+)-.

Degradation product of pyrethrins. Oil. $[\alpha]_D^{25}$ 88·7° (c, 0·67 in CCl_4). (The earlier samples, $[\alpha]_D$ 103·9°, were most likely mixtures.)

tert-*Bu ester*: n_D^{28} 1·4710.

Quinine salt: m.p. 171°. $[\alpha]_D^{23}$ −90·3° (c, 1·54 in MeOH).

(±)-.

Cryst. from Et_2O–light petroleum. M.p. 84°. B.p. 135–40°/0·1 mm.

Staudinger, Ruzicka, *Helv. Chim. Acta*, 1924, **7**, 209.
Crombie, Harper, Sleep, *J. Chem. Soc.*, 1957, 2743.
Matsui, Yamada, *Agric. Biol. Chem.* (Japan), 1963, **27**, 373.
Matsui, Meguro, *Agric. Biol. Chem.* (Japan), 1963, **27**, 379.

Pyribenzamine.

This name has been applied to the hydrochloride and the citrate of Tripelennamine★ (*q.v.*).

Pyridine-2-acetic Acid.

Pyridine-3-acetic Acid.

Pyridine-4-acetic Acid.

See also:

Jones, Katritzky, *Austral. J. Chem.*, 1964, **17**, 455.

Pyridine-*N*-oxide

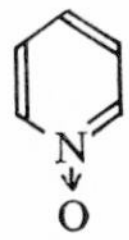

C_5H_5ON MW 95

Colourless solid. M.p. 65–6°. B.p. 100–5°/1 mm., 95–8°/0·5 mm.

B,HCl: cryst. from iso-PrOH. M.p. 179·5–181°.

Meisenheimer, *Ber.*, 1926, **59**, 1848.
Bobranski, Kochanska, Kowalewska, *Ber.*, 1938, **71**, 2385.
Ochiai, *J. Org. Chem.*, 1953, **18**, 534.
Mosher, Turner, Carlsmith, *Organic Syntheses*, 1953, **33**, 79; Coll. Vol. **4**, 828.

5-(2′-Pyridyl)thiazole

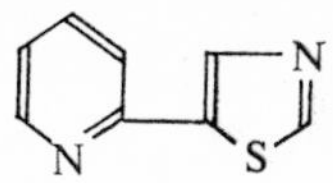

$C_8H_6N_2S$ MW 162

M.p. 63–4°. With Fe^{3+} gives red-violet colour.

Kahmann, Class, Erlenmeyer, *Experientia*, 1964, **20**, 297.

Pyrithioxin (*Pyritinol*, bis-[3-*hydroxy*-4-*hydroxymethyl*-2-*methylpyrid*-5-*ylmethyl*]*disulphide*)

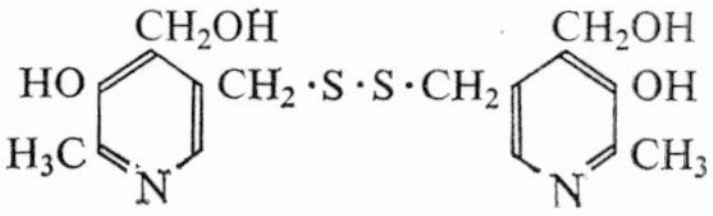

$C_{16}H_{20}O_4N_2S_2$ MW 368

Dynamising neutrotrophic agent.

B,2HCl: cryst. + $1H_2O$.

Merck (Darmstadt), *Report of Therapy Congress and Pharmaceutical Exhibition*, Karlsruhe, 1963 (*Angew. Chem., Int. Ed.*, 1964, 3, 68).

Pyritinol. *See* Pyrithioxin.

Pyrrolidine-2-acetic Acid

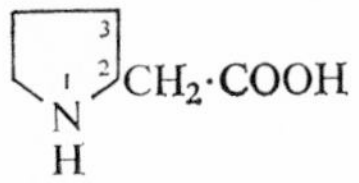

$C_6H_{11}O_2N$ MW 129

Amino acid present in cured tobacco leaves. Needles from propanol. M.p. 166–8°.

B,HCl: m.p. 168–71°.

Baker, Schaub, Williams, *J. Org. Chem.*, 1952, **17**, 116.
Tomita, Mizusaki, Tamaki, *Agric. Biol. Chem.* (Japan), 1964, **28**, 451.

3*H*-Pyrrolizine

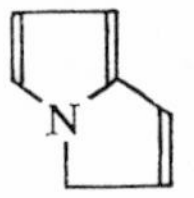

C_7H_7N MW 107

B.p. 65°/7·5 mm. n_D^{27} 1·5751.

Schweizer, Light, *J. Am. Chem. Soc.*, 1964, **86**, 2963.

Pyruvic Acid.★

Et ester:

Cornforth, *Organic Syntheses*, 1951, **31**, 59; Coll. Vol. **4**, 467.

Q

Quadricyclanone. *See* 7-Quadricyclo[2,2,1,$0^{2,6}0^{3,5}$]-heptanone.

Quadricyclene. *See* Quadricyclo[2,2,1,$0^{2,6}0^{3,5}$]heptane.

Quadricyclo[2,2,1,$0^{2,6}$,$0^{3,5}$]heptane (*Quadricyclene*)

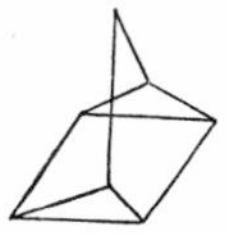

C_7H_8 MW 92

Liquid. B.p. 108°/740 mm. with some decomp. n_D^{20} 1·4804. $n_D^{26·5}$ 1·4830.

Dauben, Cargill, *Tetrahedron*, 1961, **15**, 197.
Hammond, Turro, Fischer, *J. Am. Chem. Soc.*, 1961, **83**, 4674.
Moriarty, *J. Org. Chem.*, 1963, **28**, 2385.

7-Quadricyclo[2,2,1,$0^{2,6}$,$0^{3,5}$]heptanone (*Quadricyclanone*)

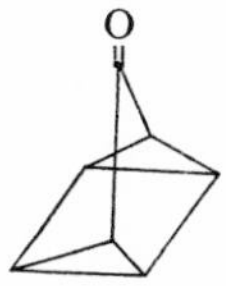

C_7H_6O MW 106

Cryst. from pentane. M.p. 45–7°.
2 : 4-*Dinitrophenylhydrazone*: m.p. 156–9° decomp.

Story, Fahrenholtz, *J. Am. Chem. Soc.*, 1964, **86**, 1270.

Quebrachamine.★

(+)-.
Present in leaves of *Pleiocarpa tubicina*.

Bycroft *et al.*, *Helv. Chim. Acta*, 1964, **47**, 1147.

Quercetagetin.

3 : 3′ : 6-*Tri-Me ether*: *see* Jaceidin.

Quercetagitrin.

3 : 3′ : 6-*Tri-Me ether*: *see* Jacein.

Questin (4 : 7-*Dihydroxy-5-methoxy-2-methylanthraquinone*)

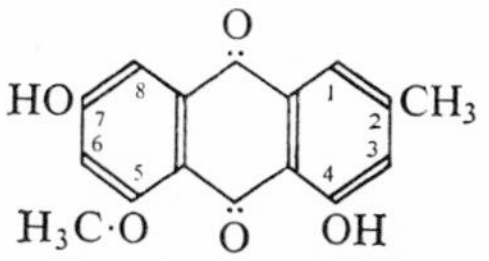

$C_{16}H_{12}O_5$ MW 284

Metabolite of *Penicillium frequentans* Westling. Two forms from AcOEt: either bright yellow or orange-brown needles. M.p. 301–3°. Light absorption: $\lambda_{max.}$ 224 (ε, 39,000), 248 (13,200), 285 (23,400), and 425 mμ (9300).
Di-Ac: cryst. from AcOEt or AcOH. M.p. 160–2°.
7-Me ether: $C_{17}H_{14}O_5$. MW 298. Cryst. from AcOEt. M.p. 208–10°.
Di-Me ether: trimethylemodin. $C_{19}H_{16}O_5$. MW 312. Cryst. from EtOH. M.p. 230–2°.

Mahmoodian, Stickings, *Biochem. J.*, 1964, **92**, 369.

Questinol (4 : 7 - *Dihydroxy* - 2 - *hydroxymethyl* - 5 - *methoxyanthraquinone*)

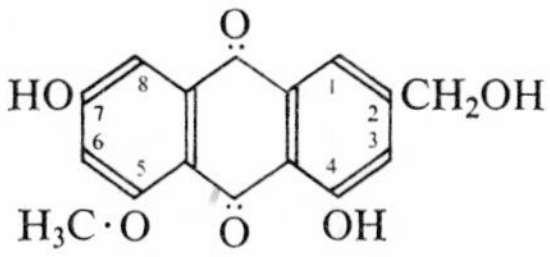

$C_{16}H_{12}O_6$ MW 300

Metabolite of *Penicillium frequentans* Westling. Orange needles from EtOH, MeOH, or AcOH. M.p. 280–2°. Light absorption: $\lambda_{max.}$ 224 (ε, 37,000), 247 (14,300), 286 (21,900), and 432 mμ (9000).
Tri-Ac: yellow plates from AcOEt. M.p. 186–8°.
7-Me ether: $C_{17}H_{14}O_6$. MW 314. Cryst. from AcOH. M.p. 238–40°.
Tri-Me ether: $C_{19}H_{18}O_6$. MW 342. Cryst. from EtOH. M.p. 188–90°.

Mahmoodian, Stickings, *Biochem. J.*, 1964, **92**, 369.

Quinacillin. *See under* 3-Carboxy-2-quinoxalinyl-penicillinic Acid.

Quinoline.★

P.M.R. spectrum:

Block, Heffernan, *Austral. J. Chem.*, 1964, **17**, 558.

Quinovosamine. *See* 2-Amino-2 : 6-dideoxy-D-glucose.

R

Radicicol (*Monorden*)

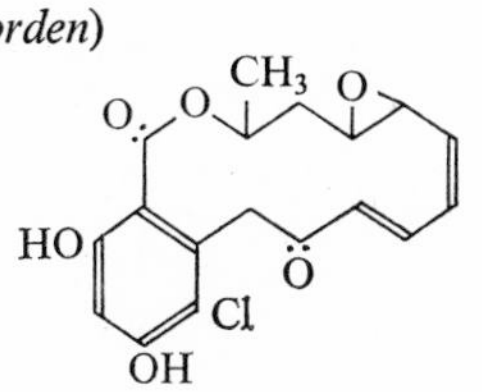

$C_{18}H_{17}O_6Cl$ MW 364·5

Metabolite of *Nectria radicicola* Gerlach et Nilsson (*Cylindrocarpon radicicola* Wr.) and *Monosporium bonorden*. Colourless cryst. M.p. 195°. $[\alpha]_D$ +216° (c, 1 in $CHCl_3$). Light absorption: $\lambda_{max.}$ 265 mμ (ε, 17,700) in neutral EtOH. $\lambda_{max.}$ 254 (ε, 22,600), 274 (22,600), 319 mμ (15,000) in basic EtOH.
Di-Me ether: $C_{20}H_{21}O_6Cl$. MW 392·5. M.p. 186–7°. $[\alpha]_D$ −58° (c, 1 in $CHCl_3$).
Di-Ac: m.p. 189–90°.

Delmotte, Delmotte-Plaquee, *Nature* (Lond.), 1953, **171**, 344.
Mirrington *et al.*, *Tetrahedron Letters*, 1964, 365.
McCapra *et al.*, *Tetrahedron Letters*, 1964, 869.

Ramulosin (3 : 4 : 4a : 5 : 6 : 7-*Hexahydro*-8-*hydroxy*-3-*methyl*-1-*oxo*-1H-2-*benzopyran*)

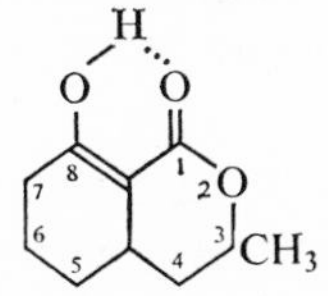

$C_{10}H_{14}O_3$ MW 182

Metabolite of the fungus *Pestalotia ramulosa*. Plates from Me_2CO.Aq. M.p. 120–1°. $[\alpha]_D^{28}$ +18° (c, 2·8 in EtOH). Light absorption: $\lambda_{max.}$ 264 mμ (ε, 10,120) in EtOH. $\lambda_{max.}$ 291 (ε, 16,600) in 0·1*N*-KOH–EtOH. $FeCl_3$ → violet col.
Benzoyl: colourless needles from EtOH.Aq. M.p. 82–3°.
p-*Nitrobenzoyl*: pale yellow needles from Me_2CO.Aq. M.p. 135–6°.
p-*Phenylazobenzoyl*: orange needles. M.p. 137–8°.
4-*Dimethylamino*-3 : 5-*dinitrobenzoyl*: orange-yellow needles. M.p. 180–1°.
Cu chelate: cryst. from C_6H_6–C_6H_{14}. M.p. 219–20°.

Benjamin, Stodola, *Nature* (Lond.), 1960, **188**, 662.
Stodola, Cabot, Benjamin, *Biochem. J.*, 1964, **93**, 92.

Ranol

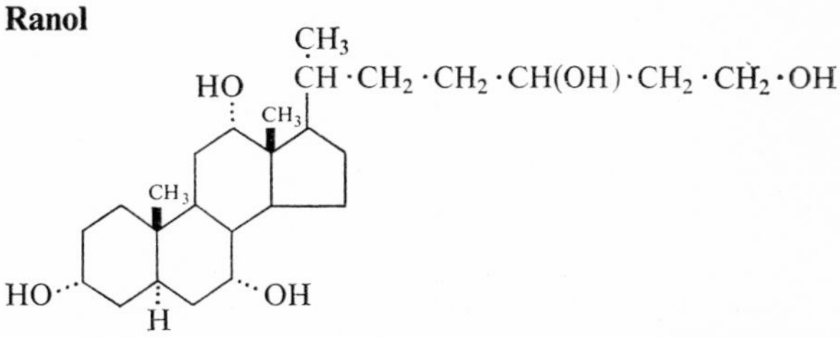

$C_{26}H_{46}O_5$ MW 438

Bile alcohol present in *Rana* (frog) spp. Not obtained cryst. $[\alpha]_D$ 21° (EtOH). Isolated as sodium sulphate salt. M.p. 185° decomp.
Tetra-Ac: cryst. from light petroleum–C_6H_6. M.p. 155–6°. $[\alpha]_D$ −12° ± 4° (c, 1 in $CHCl_3$).

Haslewood, *Biochem. J.*, 1952, **51**, 139; 1963, **90**, 309.
Cross, *Biochem. J.*, 1963, **90**, 314.

Rapacodin. *See* Dihydrocodeine.

Rastinon. *See* Tolbutamide.★

Raujemidine★

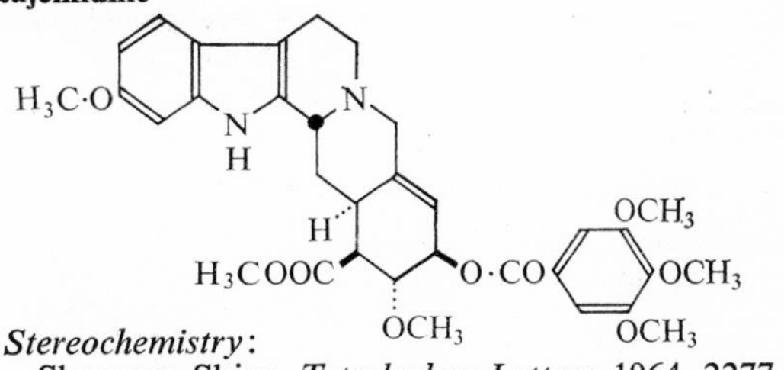

Stereochemistry:
Shamma, Shine, *Tetrahedron Letters*, 1964, 2277.

Raumitorine

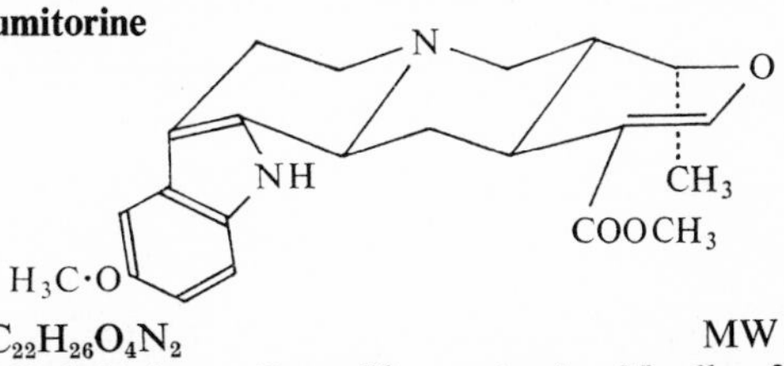

$C_{22}H_{26}O_4N_2$ MW 382

Alkaloid from *Rauwolfia vomitoria*. Needles from MeOH. M.p. 138°. $[\alpha]_D^{20}$ +60° (c, 0·54 in $CHCl_3$). pK_a 6·31.

Poisson *et al.*, *Compt. rend.*, 1954, **239**, 302.
Goutarel *et al.*, *Bull. soc. chim.*, 1954, 1481.
Shamma, Richey, *J. Am. Chem. Soc.*, 1963, **85**, 2507.

Rauniticine

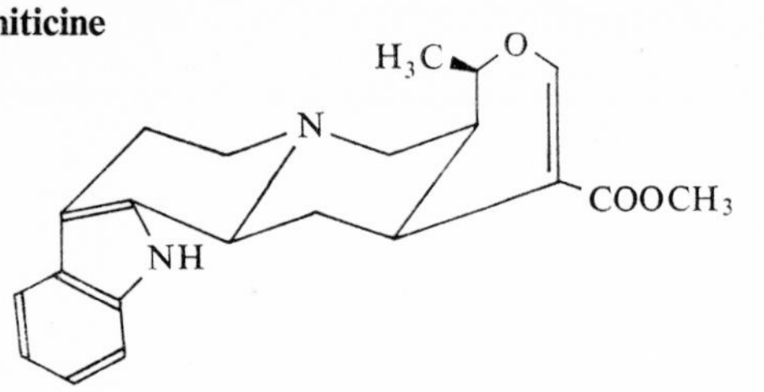

$C_{21}H_{24}O_3N_2$ MW 352

Alkaloid from the leaf of *Rauwolfia nitida*. M.p. 233–5°. Light absorption: $\lambda_{max.}$ 228 (log ε, 4·65), 282 mμ (3·91); $\lambda_{min.}$ 278 mμ (3·86).

Salkin, Hosansky, Jaret, *J. Pharm. Sci.*, 1961, **50**, 1038.
Shamma, Richey, *J. Am. Chem. Soc.*, 1963, **85**, 2507.

Erratum p. 2855

Repandinine.

The second reference should read:

Bick *et al.*, *J. Chem. Soc.*, 1961, 1896.

Repeltin. *See* Trimeprazine.★

Resistab. *See* Thonzylamine.★

Reticulol (6 : 8-*Dihydroxy*-7-*methoxy*-3-*methylisocoumarin*)

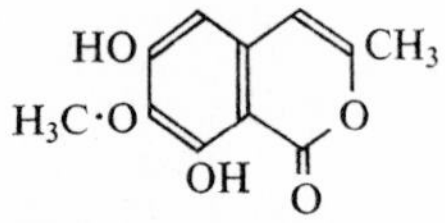

$C_{11}H_{10}O_5$ MW 222

Metabolite of *Streptomyces rubrireticulae*. M.p. 193–193·5°. Light absorption: $\lambda_{max.}$ 245 (log ε, 4·68), 278 (3·86), and 330 mμ (3·76).

Mitscher, Andres, McCrae, *Experientia*, 1964, **20**, 258.

***O*-α-L-Rhamnopyranosyl-(1 → 2)-*O*-[β-D-glucopyranosyl-(1 → 3)-D-galactopyranose.** *See* Solatriose.

L-Rhamnosamine. *See* 2-Amino-2 : 6-dideoxy-L-mannose.

6-(α-L-Rhamnosyl)-D-glucose. *See* Rutinose.★

Rhodinose★ (2 : 3 : 6-*Trideoxy*-threo-*aldohexose*)

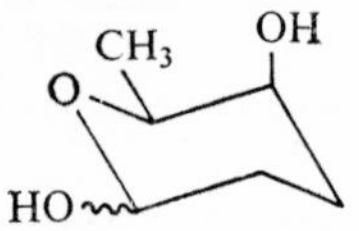

$C_6H_{12}O_3$ MW 132

L-.

Fragment of the structure of rhodomycin and streptolydigin. $[\alpha]_D^{20}$ −11° (Me_2CO).

2 : 4-*Dinitrophenylhydrazone*: m.p. 121–2°. $[\alpha]_D^{25}$ −14·9° (c, 0·5 in Py).

D-.

B.p. 60–5° (bath)/0·1 mm. n_D^{25} 1·4689. $[\alpha]_D^{26}$ −0·2° (c, 0·9 in H_2O), +10·2° (c, 1·1 in Me_2CO).

2 : 4-*Dinitrophenylhydrazone*: m.p. 121–2°. $[\alpha]_D^{25}$ +13·7° (c, 0·9 in Py).

Brockmann, Waehneldt, *Naturwiss.*, 1963, **50**, 43.
Stevens, Blumbergs, Wood, *J. Am. Chem. Soc.*, 1964, **86**, 3592.

Rhodnitin (3-*Hydroxykynurenine*-O-*sulphate*)

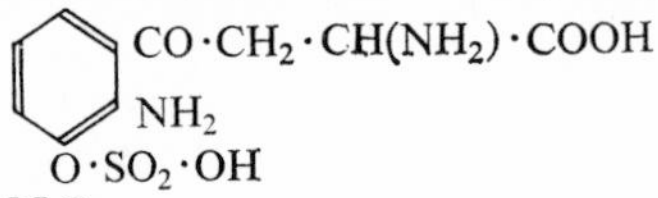

$C_{10}H_{12}O_7N_2S$ MW 304

Fluorescent pigment from *Rhodnius prelixus* Stål.

NH_4 salt: yellow powder. $[\alpha]_D^{25}$ −19·6° (H_2O). Blue fluor. Sol. H_2O, MeOH. Insol. propanol, Me_2CO, Et_2O.

Visconti, Schmid, *Helv. Chim. Acta*, 1963, **46**, 2509.

Rhoifolin.★

Also present in the leaves of *Chorisia* spp. Hexahydrate. Needles which sinter at 200–5°. M.p. 245°. $[\alpha]_D^{29}$ −110° (c, 0·21 in MeOH).

Hattori, Matsuda, *Arch. Biochem. Biophys.*, 1952, **37**, 85.
Coussio, *Experientia*, 1964, **20**, 562.

β-D-Ribofuranosyl-β-D-ribofuranoside

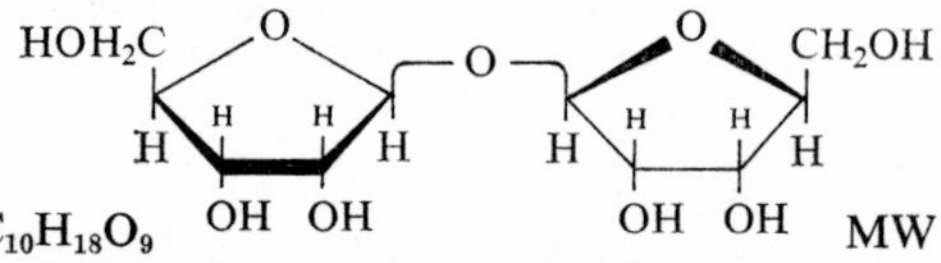

$C_{10}H_{18}O_9$ MW 282

Basic repeating unit of a polyribophosphate, type-specific substance from *Haemophilus influenzae*. Cryst. from EtOH. M.p. 158–60°. $[\alpha]_D$ −102° (c, 0·47 in H_2O).

Hexabenzoyl: cryst. M.p. 143–4°. $[\alpha]_D$ 35·2° (c, 0·475 in $CHCl_3$).

Rosenberg, Zamenhof, *J. Biol. Chem.*, 1961, **236**, 2845; 1962, **237**, 1040.
Zderic, *Experientia*, 1964, **20**, 48.

5-α-D-Ribofuranosyluracil. *See* Pseudouridine B.

5-β-D-Ribofuranosyluracil. *See* Pseudouridine C.

Ribonuclease A

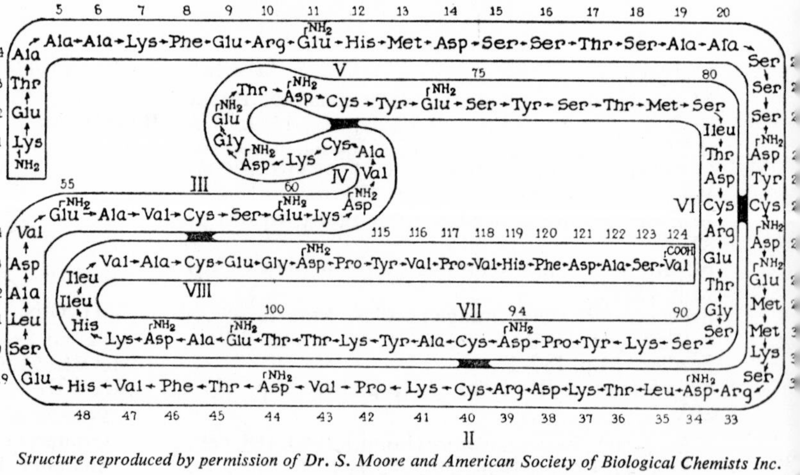

Structure reproduced by permission of Dr. S. Moore and American Society of Biological Chemists Inc.

MW 13,8

Enzyme isolated from bovine pancreas which degrades ribonucleic acid.

Kunitz, *J. Gen. Physiol.*, 1950, **33**, 349.
Hirs, Moore, Stein, *J. Biol. Chem.*, 1953, **200**, 493; 1954, **211**, 941; 1956, **221**, 151; 1960, **235**, 633.
Spackman, Stein, Moore, *J. Biol. Chem.*, 1960, **235**, 648.
Smyth, Stein, Moore, *J. Biol. Chem.*, 1962, **237**, 1845; 1963, **238**, 227.
Scheraga, Rupley, *Adv. in Enzymology*, 1962, **24**, 161 (*Review*).

5-α-D-Ribopyranosyluracil. *See* Pseudouridine A_F.

5-β-D-Ribopyranosyluracil. *See* Pseudouridine A_S.

Ribose.★

p-*Bromophenylhydrazone*: cryst. structure:

Bjåmer, Furberg, Petersen, *Acta Chem. Scand.*, 1964, **18**, 587.

3-Ribosyluric Acid.★

See also:

Lohrmann, Lagowski, Forrest, *J. Chem. Soc.*, 1964, 451.

L-Ribothiafuranose (4-*Thio*-L-*ribose*)

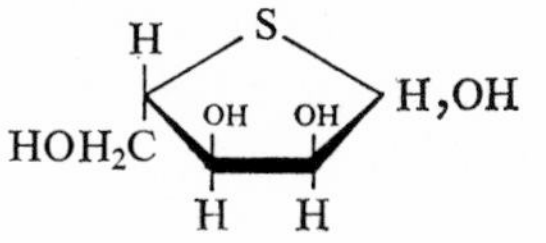

$C_5H_{10}O_4S$ MW 166

Syrup.
Methylglycoside: syrup. *Tri*-p-*nitrobenzoyl*: cryst. + $1H_2O$. M.p. 107–8·5°/195–195·5°. $[\alpha]_D^{24}$ −89° (c, 1 in $CHCl_3$).
Tetra-O-*Ac*: $[\alpha]_D^{25}$ 56° (c, 1·3 in $CHCl_3$).
Tetra-O-p-*Nitrobenzoyl*: m.p. 216–17°. $[\alpha]_D^{25}$ 30° (c, 1·36 in $CHCl_3$).

Reist, Gueffroy, Goodman, *J. Am. Chem. Soc.*, 1963, **85**, 3715.

D-Ribothiapyranose (5-*Thio*-D-*ribopyranose*)

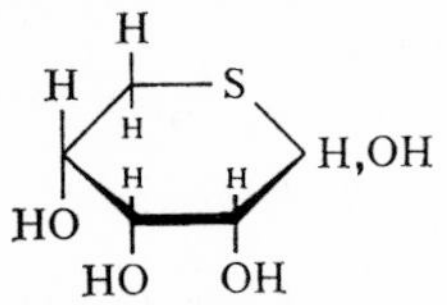

$C_5H_{10}O_4S$ MW 166

Tetra-Ac: (β) m.p. 122–3°. $[\alpha]_D^{20}$ −61° (c, 1 in MeOH).
Me glycoside: $C_6H_{12}O_4S$. MW 178. Two forms: (α) Syrup. *Tri-Ac*: m.p. 64–5°. $[\alpha]_D^{20}$ +227° (c, 0·8 in MeOH); (β) m.p. 122–3°. $[\alpha]_D^{20}$ −246° (c, 1·1 in MeOH).

Clayton, Hughes, *Chemistry and Industry*, 1962, 1795.

Rifacin. *See* Rifamycin SV.

Rifamycin (*Rifomycin*).

A group of antibiotics produced by *Streptomyces mediterranei*. The following rifamycins have been described.

Rifamycin B

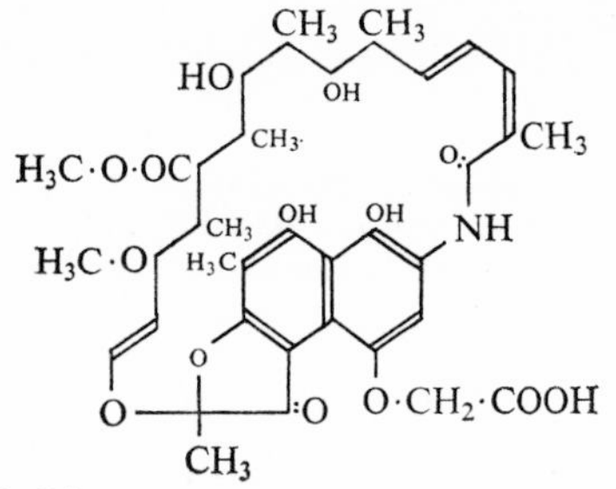

$C_{39}H_{49}O_{14}N$ MW 755

Pale yellow. pK^{*}_{MCS} 2·6, 7·76. Ox. → rifamycin O.

Rifamycin O

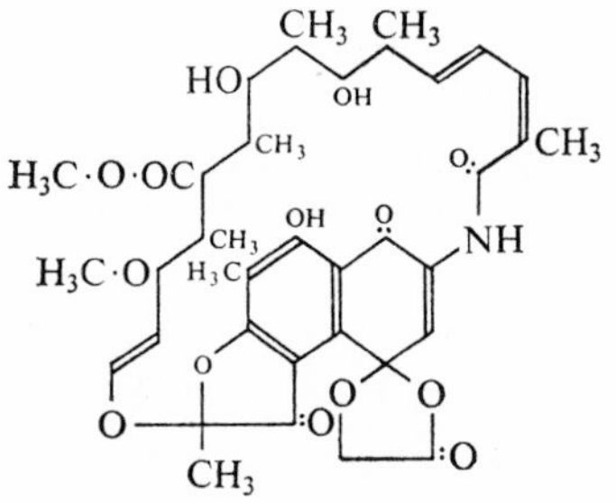

$C_{39}H_{47}O_{14}N$ MW 753

Red. → ribamycin B. Acid → rifamycin S.

Rifamycin S

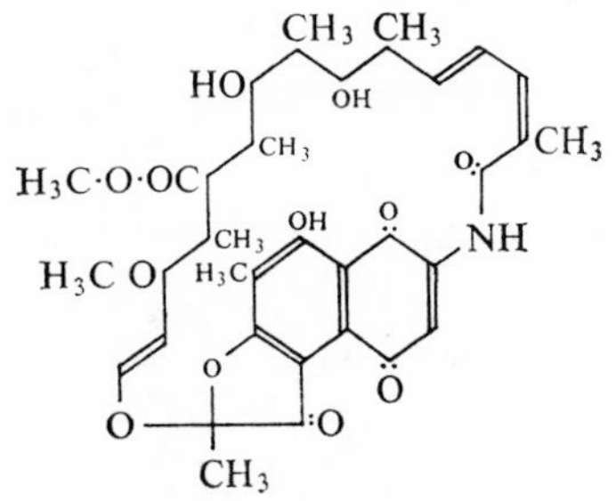

$C_{37}H_{45}O_{12}N$ MW 718

Red. → rifamycin SV.

Rifamycin SV (*Rifacin*)

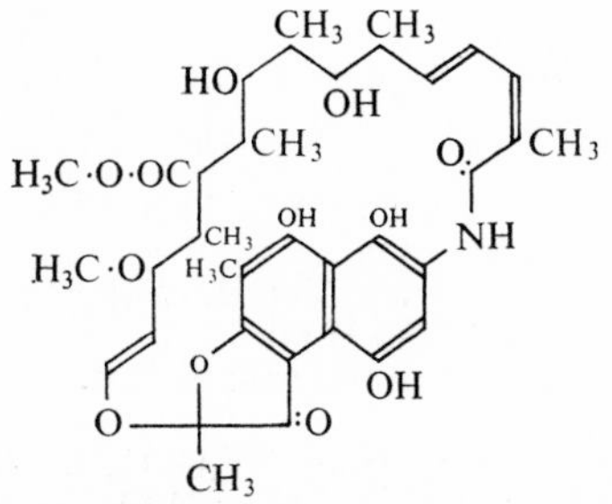

$C_{37}H_{47}O_{12}N$ MW 720

Ox. → rifamycin S.

Sensi, Greco, Ballotta, *Antibiotics Annual*, 1959–60, p. 262.
Sensi, Ballotta, Greco, *Farmaco* (*Pavia*) *Ed. Sci.*, 1960, **15**, 228; 1961, **16**, 165.

Gallo, Pasqualucci, Radaelli, *Farmaco (Pavia) Ed. prat.*, 1963, **18**, 78.
Prelog, *Symposium on Chemistry and Biochemistry of Fungi and Yeasts*, Dublin, 1963, p. 551 (*Review*).
Oppolzer, Prelog, Sensi, *Experientia*, 1964, **20**, 336.
Brufani *et al.*, *Experientia*, 1964, **20**, 339.
Leitich, Oppolzer, Prelog, *Experientia*, 1964, **20**, 343.

Rimuene★

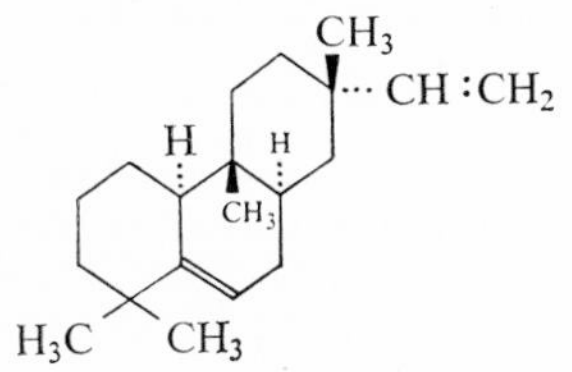

Structure:
Corbett, Wyllie, *Tetrahedron Letters*, 1964, 1903.
Connolly *et al.*, *Tetrahedron Letters*, 1964, 1983.

(±)-.
M.p. 85–8°.
Synthesis:
Ireland, Mander, *Tetrahedron Letters*, 1964, 3453.

Robison Ester. *See* Glucose-6-phosphate.

Robustic Acid

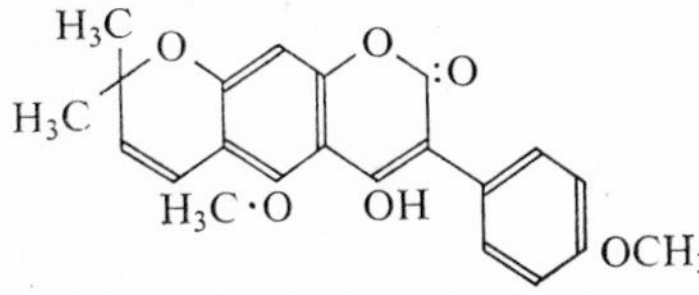

$C_{20}H_{20}O_6$ MW 380
Constituent of the roots of *Derris robusta*. M.p. 208–10°. Light absorption: $\lambda_{max.}$ 233 (log ε, 4·26), 255 (4·29), 264 (infl., 4·30), and 342·5 mμ (4·27).
H_2 → dihydro deriv. M.p. 198–200°.

Harper, *J. Chem. Soc.*, 1942, 181.
Murti, Subba Rao, Seshadri, *Proc. Ind. Acad. Sci.*, 1946, **24A**, 465; 1948, **26A**, 41.
Johnson, Pelter, Barber, *Tetrahedron Letters*, 1964, 1267.

Rodiasine

$C_{36}H_{40(44)}O_6N_2$ MW 596 (600)
Alkaloid from Greenheart (*Ocotea rodiaei*). Cubes from EtOH. M.p. 195°. $[\alpha]_D^{18}$ 134° (c, 0·63 in $CHCl_3$).
B,HCl: cubes from EtOH. M.p. 255–9° decomp. $[\alpha]_D$ 74° (c, 1 in H_2O).
B,2CH₃I: cryst. from MeOH. M.p. 321° decomp. $[\alpha]_D^{20}$ 68° (c, 0·147 in H_2O).
B,dimethopicrate: two forms: (i) m.p. 180°, (ii) m.p. 253°.
B,2CH₃Cl: cryst. from Pr^i_2O–H_2O. M.p. 286° decomp. $[\alpha]_D$ 81·5° (c, 0·98 in H_2O).
O-Me: cryst. from Et_2O. M.p. 172–3°. $[\alpha]_D$ 85° (c, 0·57 in $CHCl_3$). *B,HCl*: cryst. from MeOH–Et_2O. M.p. 232–6° decomp. *B,2CH₃I*: plates from MeOH. M.p. 294–8° decomp. $[\alpha]_D$ 47°.

McKennis *et al.*, *J. Am. Chem. Soc.*, 1956, **78**, 245.
Grundon, McGarvey, *J. Chem. Soc.*, 1960, 2739.
Hearst, *J. Org. Chem.*, 1964, **29**, 466.

Rogersine

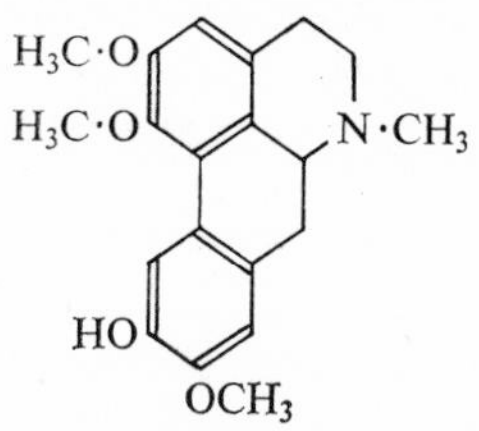

$C_{20}H_{23}O_4N$ MW 341
Alkaloid from *Phylica rogersii* Pillans. Cryst. with 0·5CH_3OH. M.p. 100–5°. $[\alpha]_D$ 111° (c, 0·86 in EtOH). Light absorption: $\lambda_{max.}$ 219 (ε, 65,080), 282 (25,630), and 304 mμ (25,630).
B,HI: m.p. 245°.
B,CH₃I: cryst. from Me_2CO–EtOH. M.p. 199–200°.
O-Et-(−)-tartrate: cryst. from MeOH. M.p. 206–7° decomp. $[\alpha]_D$ 53° (c, 0·4 in EtOH).

Manske, Charlesworth, Ashford, *J. Am. Chem. Soc.*, 1951, **73**, 3751.
Arndt, Baarschers, *J. Chem. Soc.*, 1964, 2244.

Roridin C. *See* Trichodermol.

Rosellinic Acid (*6-Carboxy-8-hydroxy-2-methylchromanone*)

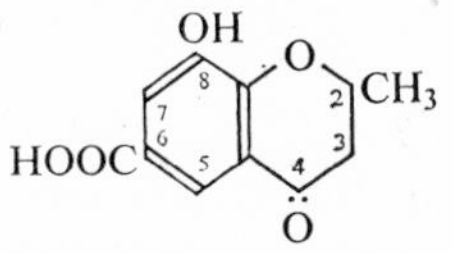

$C_{11}H_{10}O_5$ MW 222
Plant growth inhibitor from culture filtrate of *Rosellinia necatrix Berlese*. M.p. 206–8°.
Ac: white plates from AcOEt–light petroleum. M.p. 174–5°.
Mono-Me ether: $C_{12}H_{12}O_5$. MW 236. Needles from EtOH. M.p. 137–8°.
Me ester, Me ether: $C_{13}H_{14}O_5$. MW 250. Needles. M.p. 137–8°.
2 : 4-*Dinitrophenylhydrazone*: red plates from EtOH. M.p. 138° decomp.

Chen, *Agric. Biol. Chem.* (Japan), 1960, **24**, 372; 1964, **28**, 431.

Rugulosin.★

Major metabolite of *Penicillium brunneum* Udagawa.
Shibata, Udagawa, *Chem. Pharm. Bull* (Tokyo), 1963, **11**, 402.
Biosynthesis:
Shibata, Ikekawa, *Chem. Pharm. Bull.* (Tokyo), 1963, **11**, 368.

S

Salidroside (2-(4-*Hydroxyphenyl*)*ethyl*-1β-D-*glucopyranoside*)

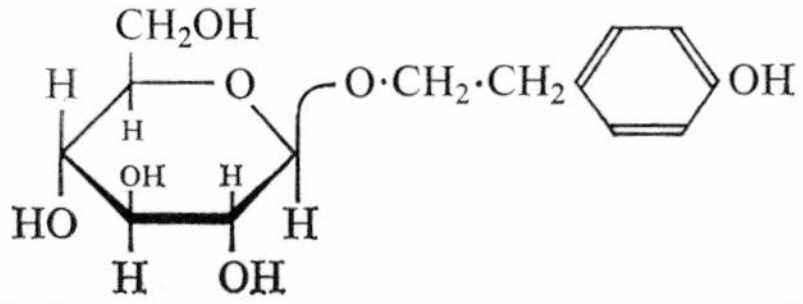

$C_{14}H_{20}O_7$ MW 300

Constituent of almond bark (*Salix trianda* L.). Plates from AcOEt and light petroleum. M.p. 159–60°. $[\alpha]_D^{20}$ −32·1° (c, 1·26 in H_2O).

Bridel, Béguin, *Compt. rend.*, 1926, **183**, 231.
Thieme, *Naturwiss.*, 1964, **51**, 360.

Samaderacine A. *See* Samaderol.

Samaderine A

$C_{18}H_{18}O_6$ MW 330

Constituent of *Samadera indica* nuts. Yellow needles from AcOEt. M.p. 255–8°. $[\alpha]_D$ −18·6° (Py). Light absorption: $\lambda_{max.}$ 290 mμ (log ε, 4·26).

Polonsky, Zylber, *Bull. soc. chim.*, 1962, 1715.

Samaderine B

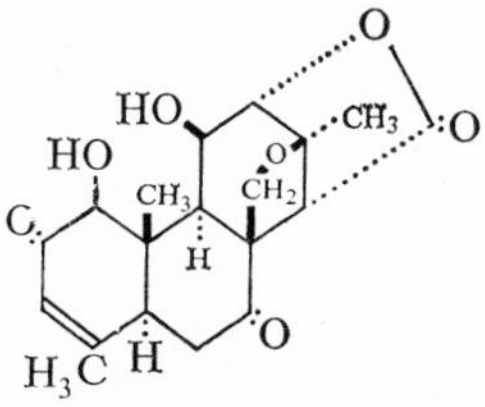

$C_{19}H_{22}O_7$ MW 362

Constituent of *Samadera indica.* Prisms from AcOEt. M.p. 235–40°. $[\alpha]_D$ +67·5° (Py). Light absorption: $\lambda_{max.}$ 240 mμ (log ε, 3·98). H_2SO_4 → red-violet col.

Polonsky, Zylber, *Bull. soc. chim.*, 1963, 1715.
Zylber, Polonsky, *Bull. soc. chim.*, 1964, 2016.

Samaderine C (*Samaderoside A*)

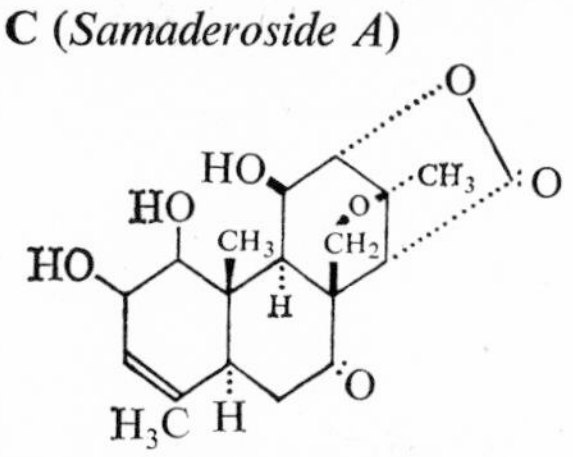

$C_{19}H_{24}O_7$ MW 364

Constituent of *Samadera indica* nuts. Plates from AcOEt. M.p. 265–8° (275–6° decomp.). $[\alpha]_D$ +58·5° (Py), +97·4° (c, 1 in EtOH). Light absorption: $\lambda_{max.}$ 295 mμ (log ε, 3·63).

Di-Ac: m.p. 217–20°. $[\alpha]_D$ +83·2°.

Polonsky, Zylber, *Bull. soc. chim.*, 1962, 1715.
Mitra, Garg, *Naturwiss.*, 1962, **49**, 327.
Zylber, Polonsky, Mitra, *Bull. soc. chim.*, 1963, 1322.
Zylber, Polonsky, *Bull. soc. chim.*, 1964, 2016.

Samaderol (*Samaderacine A*)

$C_{19}H_{20}O_5$ MW 328

Dehydration product of Samaderine C. M.p. 115–20°/230–40°. $[\alpha]_D$ 140·5°.

Mono-Ac: m.p. 185–90°. $[\alpha]_D$ −3·8° ($CHCl_3$).
Di-Ac: m.p. 145–8°. $[\alpha]_D$ −3·2° ($CHCl_3$).

Polonsky, Zylber, *Bull. soc. chim.*, 1962, 1715.
Zylber, Polonsky, Mitra, *Bull. soc. chim.*, 1963, 1322.

Samaderoside A. *See* Samaderine C.

Samaderoside B

$C_{26}H_{32}O_{10}$ MW 456

Glycoside in *Samadera indica* nuts. M.p. 301–3° decomp. $[\alpha]_D$ ±0° (c, 1 in EtOH).

Mitra, Garg, *Naturwiss.*, 1962, **49**, 327.

Sandaracopimaradiene

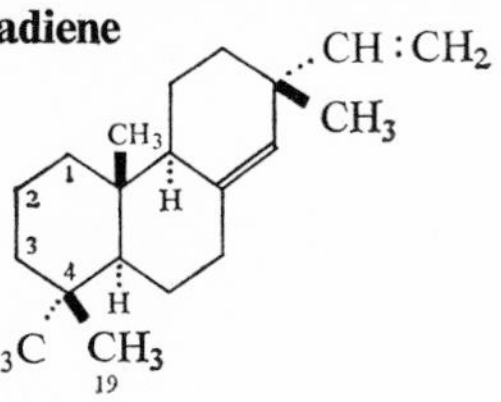

$C_{20}H_{32}$ MW 272

(−)-.

Constituent of the wood of *Xylia dolabriformis* (Pyinkado). M.p. 40·5–41°. $[\alpha]_D$ −12·4° (c, 5 in $CHCl_3$).

Ireland, Schiess, *Tetrahedron Letters*, 1960, No. 25, 37.
Laidlaw, Morgan, *J. Chem. Soc.*, 1963, 644.

Sandaracopimaradiene-3β : 18-diol

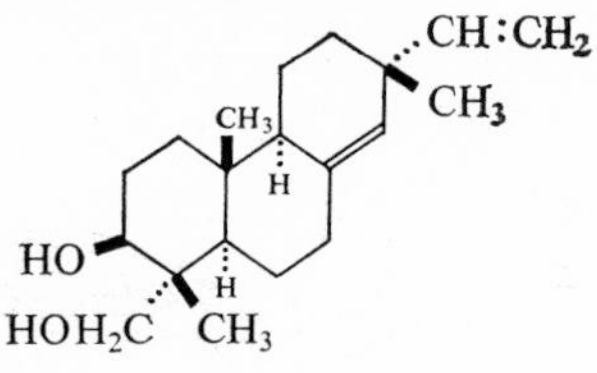

$C_{20}H_{22}O_2$ MW 290

Constituent of the wood of *Xylia dolabriformis* (Pyinkado). Cryst. from light petroleum. M.p. 152–3°. $[\alpha]_D$ −18·5° (c, 4 in $CHCl_3$).
Di-Ac: m.p. 131·5°. $[\alpha]_D$ 13·5° (c, 2 in $CHCl_3$).
Laidlow, Morgan, *J. Chem. Soc.*, 1963, 644.

Sandaracopimaradien-3β-ol

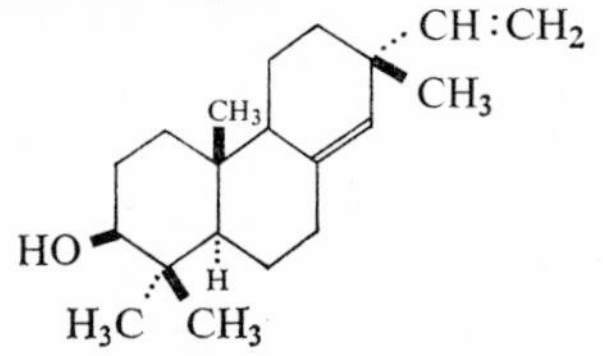

$C_{20}H_{32}O$ MW 274
Constituent of the wood of *Xylia dolabriformis* (Pyinkado). Needles from MeOH. M.p. 126·5–127·5°. $[\alpha]_D$ −19·5° (c, 5 in $CHCl_3$).
Laidlaw, Morgan, *J. Chem. Soc.*, 1963, 644.

Sandaracopimaradien-3-one

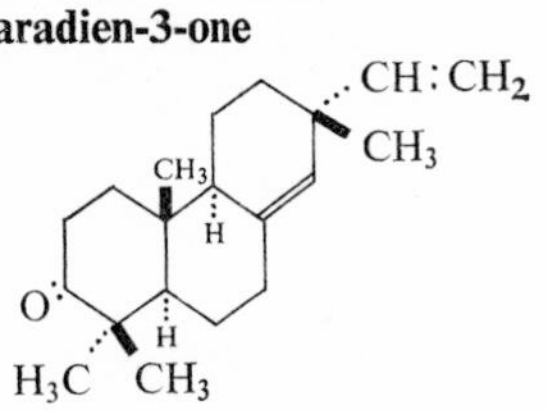

$C_{20}H_{30}O$ MW 286
Constituent of the wood of *Xylia dolabriformis* (Pyinkado). Leaflets from MeOH. M.p. 59–60°. $[\alpha]_D$ −56° (c, 2 in $CHCl_3$).
2 : 4-*Dinitrophenylhydrazone*: m.p. 176·5–177°.
Laidlaw, Morgan, *J. Chem. Soc.*, 1963, 644.

Erratum p. 2884
Sandaracopimaric Acid.
Line 3 should read: (Sandarac resin).

α-Santonin.★
Conversion to β-santonin:
Nakazaki, Naemura, *Chemistry and Industry*, 1964, 1708.

Saramycetin (*X*-5079*C*) MW 14000 ± 200
Polypeptide antibiotic from *Streptomyces saraceticus*. Amorph. M.p. *ca.* 220° decomp. $[\alpha]_D$ −28·4° (c, 2 in H_2O), −32° (c, 2 in 8*M*-urea). Light absorption: $\lambda_{max.}$ 227 ($E^{1\%}_{1\,cm.}$ 440), 270 ($E^{1\%}_{1\,cm.}$ 275), and 305 sh. mμ ($E^{1\%}_{1\,cm.}$ 205). Hydrol. → Asp (8·5 residues), Gly (8·18), Thr (7·30), Pro (8·33), and Cys (23·09) and other products.
Berger *et al.*, *Antimicr. Agents Chemotherapy*, 1961, 436.
Baudet, Cherbuliez, *Helv. Chim. Acta*, 1964, **47**, 611.

Saussurea Lactone

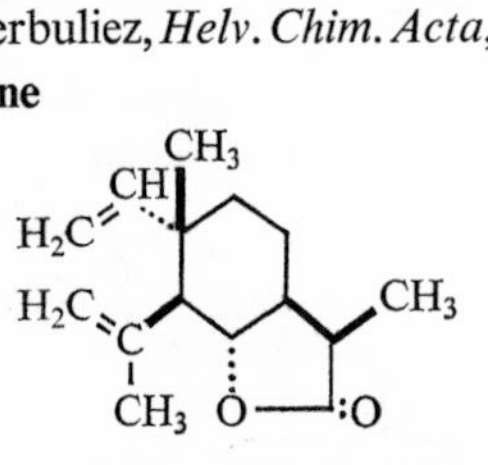

$C_{15}H_{22}O_2$ MW 234
From Costus root oil (*Saussurea lappa* C. B. Clarke). Cryst. from MeOH. M.p. 148–9°. $[\alpha]_D$ +66° ($CHCl_3$). Most likely formed by pyrolysis of dihydrocostunolide.
Rao, Varma, *J. Sci. Ind. Res.*, 1951, **10B**, 166.
Rao *et al.*, *J. Sci. Ind. Res.*, 1958, **17B**, 228; *Tetrahedron*, 1961, **13**, 319.

Scandenin

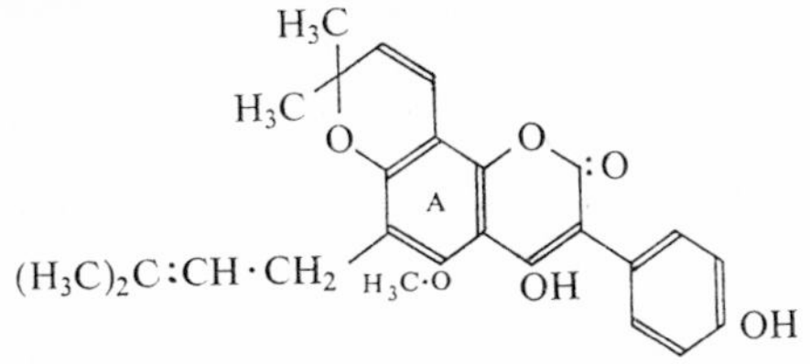

$C_{26}H_{26}O_6$ MW 434
Constituent of *Derris scandens*. M.p. 231°.
Ac: m.p. 150°.
Di-Me ether: m.p. 129°.
Clarke, *J. Org. Chem.*, 1943, **8**, 489.
Subba Rao, Seshadri, *Proc. Ind. Acad. Sci.*, 1946, **24A**, 465.
Pelter, Stainton, *Tetrahedron Letters*, 1964, 1209.
Pelter, Johnson, *Tetrahedron Letters*, 1964, 2817.

Sciadopic Acid. *See under* Methyl Sciadopate.

Scillaren F. *See* Scilliglaucoside.

Scillarenin

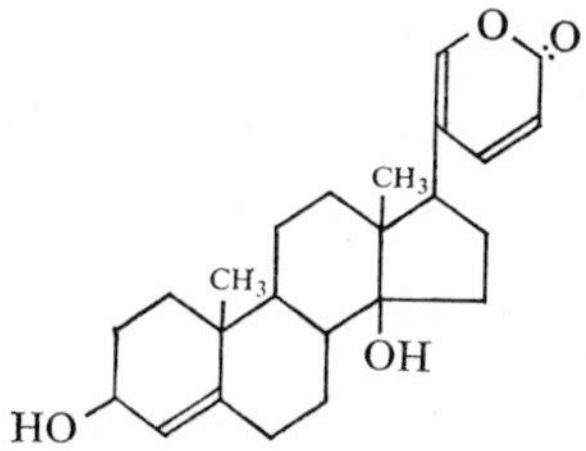

$C_{24}H_{32}O_4$ MW 384
Cryst. from Me_2CO. M.p. 214–34°. $[\alpha]_D^{20}$ −20·3° (c, 0·517 in MeOH), +13·5° ($CHCl_3$). Dehydration → bufa-3 : 5 : 20 : 22-tetraenolide.★
Ac: m.p. 240–3°. $[\alpha]_D$ −23·4° ($CHCl_3$).
Rhamnosyl: *see* Proscillaridin A.
Scillabiosyl: *see* Scillacen A.★
Stoll, Renz, Brack, *Helv. Chim. Acta*, 1951, **34**, 2301; 1952, **35**, 1934.
von Wartburg, *Helv. Chim. Acta*, 1964, **47**, 1228.
See also Glucoscillaren.★

Scillarenin β-D-glucoside

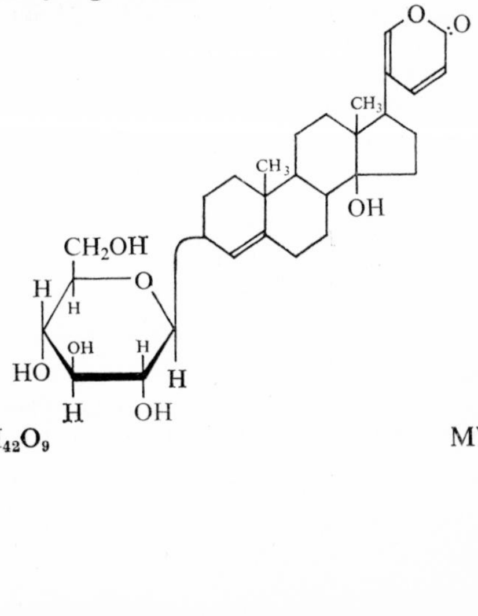

$C_{30}H_{42}O_9$ MW 546

Constituent of the red variety of squill (*Scilla maritima* (Baker) L.). Colourless prisms from EtOH. M.p. 208–12°. $[\alpha]_D^{20}$ $-54{\cdot}2°$ (c, 0·508 in MeOH).
Tetra-Ac: needles from Me_2CO–Et_2O. M.p. 176–8°. $[\alpha]_D^{20}$ $-22{\cdot}7°$ (c, 0·507 in $CHCl_3$).

von Wartburg, *Helv. Chim. Acta*, 1964, **47**, 1228.

Scilliglaucoside (*Scillaren F*)

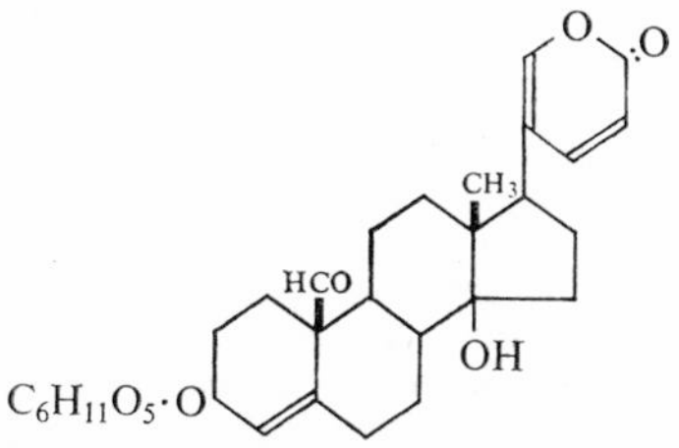

$C_{30}H_{40}O_{10}$ MW 560
Constituent of squill (*Scilla maritima* Baker). Cryst. from Me_2CO–Et_2O. M.p. 245–8°. $[\alpha]_D^{20}$ $+49{\cdot}5°$ (MeOH), $+78°$ (c, 0·685 in $CHCl_3$: MeOH (98 : 2)).
Ac: cryst. from MeOH. M.p. 224–7°. $[\alpha]_D^{21}$ $+40{\cdot}7°$ ($CHCl_3$).
19-*Oxime*: needles from MeOH.Aq. M.p. 249–52°.
19-*Semicarbazone*: cryst. from MeOH.Aq. Did not melt. Decomp. 210–45°. $[\alpha]_D^{20}$ $+57{\cdot}1°$ (c, 0·645 in MeOH).

Stoll, Renz, *Helv. Chim. Acta*, 1942, **25**, 43.
Stoll, von Wartburg, Renz, *Helv. Chim. Acta*, 1953, **36**, 1531.

Scillirosidine

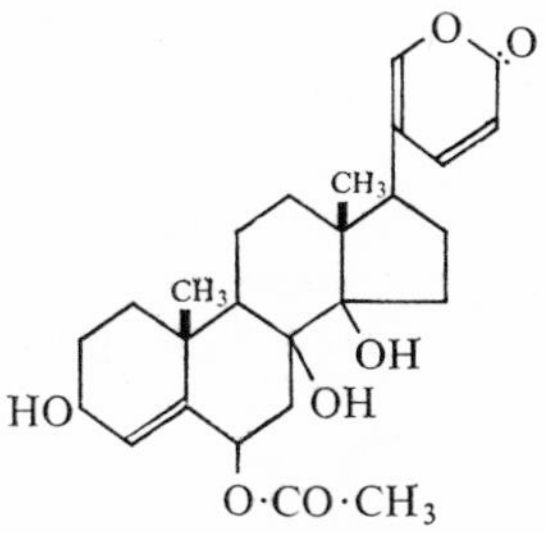

$C_{26}H_{34}O_7$ MW 458
Aglycone obtained by enzymatic hydrolysis of Scilliroside. Prisms from MeOH.Aq. Double m.p. (i) 177–8°, (ii) 200–5°. $[\alpha]_D^{20}$ $-23°$ (c, 0·841 in MeOH), $-4{\cdot}6°$ (c, 0·546 in $CHCl_3$). Hydrol. → deacetyl deriv. M.p. 250–65°.
3-O-*Ac*: plates. M.p. 259–61°. $[\alpha]_D^{20}$ $-61°$ (c, 0·50 in MeOH), $-46{\cdot}1°$ (c, 0·68 in $CHCl_3$).

von Wartburg, Renz, *Helv. Chim. Acta*, 1959, **42**, 1620.

Sclerotiorin.★

(−)-.
Metabolite of *Penicillium hirayamae* Udagawa. Yellow needles. M.p. 203–4°. $[\alpha]_D^{26}$ $-482°$ (c, 0·11 in EtOH).
(±)-.
M.p. 170–4°.

Udagawa, *Chem. Pharm. Bull.* (Tokyo), 1963, **11**, 366.

Erratum p. 2892

Scoparin.

The first reference should read:

Stenhouse, *Ann. Chem. Pharm.*, 1851, **78**, 15.

Sebacoin. *See* 2-Hydroxycyclodecanone.

Securinine.★

Allo-.
Minor constituent of *Phyllanthus discoides*. M.p. 126°. $[\alpha]_D^{26}$ $-1230°$ (c, 2 in $CHCl_3$).
Picrolonate: m.p. 229° decomp.

Bevan *et al.*, *Chemistry and Industry*, 1964, 838.
Bevan, Patel, Rees, *Chemistry and Industry*, 1964, 2054.

Cryst. structure:

Imado, Shiro, Horri, *Chemistry and Industry*, 1964, 1691.

Sedanolide.★

Is a mixture of Neocnidilide and butyl phthalide (*q.v.*).

Barton, de Vries, *J. Chem. Soc.*, 1963, 1916.
Mitsuhashi, Muramatsu, *Tetrahedron*, 1964, **20**, 1971.

Senegenic Acid. *See* Polygalic Acid.

Senegenin

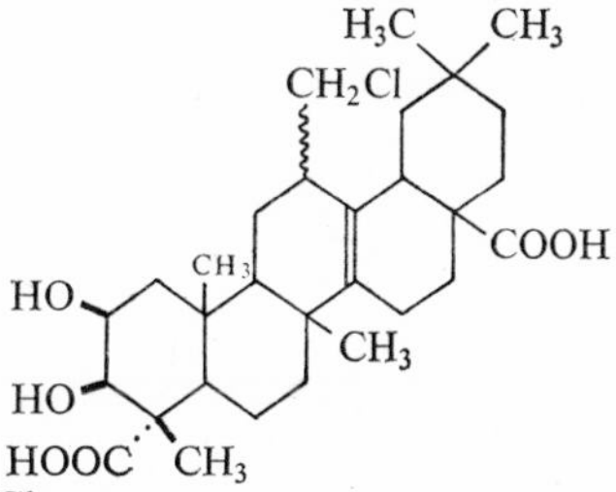

$C_{30}H_{45}O_6Cl$ MW 536·5
Sapogenin from *Polygala senega*. Cryst. from EtOH.Aq. or Me_2CO.Aq. M.p. 281–3° (290–2°). $[\alpha]_D$ 19° (c, 0·74 in EtOH).
Mono-Ac: cryst. from MeOH–$CHCl_3$. M.p. 209–11°. $[\alpha]_D$ 23° (c, 1·32 in $CHCl_3$).
Di-Ac: m.p. 257–63° decomp. $[\alpha]_D$ 29° (c, 1·09 in MeOH).
Acetonide: m.p. 282–4°. $[\alpha]_D$ 28° (c, 0·93 in MeOH).

Wedekind, Krecke, *Ber.*, 1924, **57**, 1118.
Jacobs, Isler, *J. Biol. Chem.*, 1937, **119**, 155.
Shamma, Reiff, *Chemistry and Industry*, 1960, 1272.
Dugan, de Mayo, Sharratt, *Can. J. Chem.*, 1964, **42**, 491; *Proc. Chem. Soc.*, 1964, 264.

Sepeerine (*Ocoteamine*)

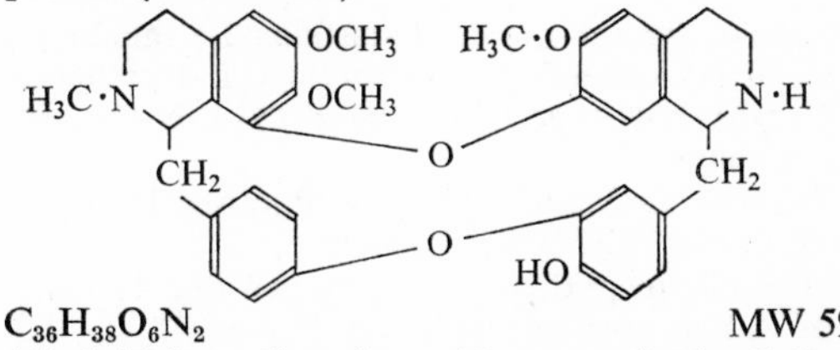

$C_{36}H_{38}O_6N_2$ MW 594
Alkaloid from Greenheart (*Ocotea rodiaei*). Colourless rods from MeOH. M.p. 197–9°. Prisms from EtOH. M.p. 194–6°. Plates from C_6H_6. M.p. 164–6°.

B,2HCl: prisms from MeOH–Et_2O. M.p. 254–6° decomp. $[\alpha]_D$ 250° (c, 1 in H_2O).
B,$(HSO_4)_2$: from EtOH. M.p. >300°.
B,H_2SO_4: prisms. M.p. >300°.
Picrate: yellow powder. M.p. 178–80° decomp.
O : N-*Di-Ac*: cubes from Et_2O. M.p. 156–8°.
B,2CH_3I: prisms. M.p. 249–55° decomp.
N-*Ac*: cryst. from Et_2O. M.p. 174–6°.
N-*Me*, *B,2CH_3I*: cryst. from H_2O. M.p. 253–8° decomp.
O-*Me*, *B,2HCl*: prisms from EtOH. M.p. 230–5° decomp.

Grundon, McGarvey, *J. Chem. Soc.*, 1960, 2739; 1962, 2077.
Hearst, *J. Org. Chem.*, 1964, **29**, 466.

Seredine

$C_{23}H_{30}O_5N$ MW 400

Alkaloid from the roots of *Rauwolfia vomitoria* Afz. Small white prisms from MeOH. M.p. 291°. $[\alpha]_D^{20}$ $-1° \pm 1°$ (c, 0·43 in $CHCl_3$). Isomeric with *Me ester* of Reserpic Acid.

Poisson *et al.*, *Compt. rend.*, 1954, **239**, 302.
Goutarel *et al.*, *Bull. soc. chim.*, 1954, 1481.

Seroden. *See* Thiosemicarbazone *under* p-Acetamidobenzaldehyde.

Serratenediol (*Pinusenediol*)

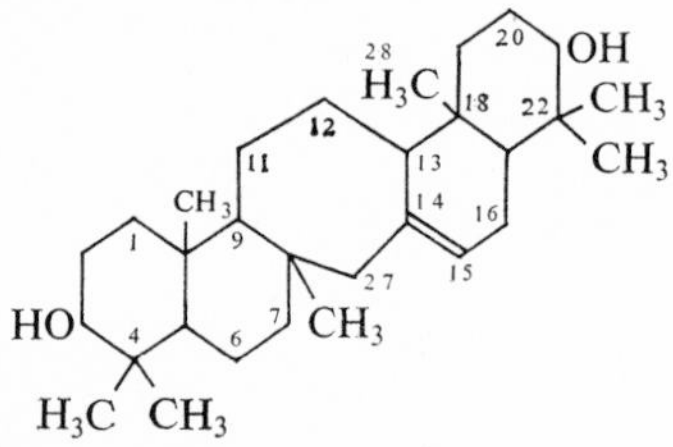

$C_{30}H_{50}O_2$ MW 442

Constituent of the club moss, *Lycopodium serrata* Thunb. var. *Thunbergii* Makino and the barks of various pines. M.p. 302·5–304·5°. $[\alpha]_D^{22}$ −19° (c, 0·9 in $CHCl_3$).
Di-Ac: m.p. 350·5–352·5°. $[\alpha]_D^{21}$ 22° (c, 0·9 in $CHCl_3$).
Di-3 : 5-dinitrobenzoyl: m.p. 284·5–285°. $[\alpha]_D^{21}$ 53° (c, 0·4 in $CHCl_3$).

Inubushi, Sano, Tsuda, *Tetrahedra Letters*, 1964, 1303.
Tsuda *et al.*, *Tetrahedron Letters*, 1964, 1279.
Rowe, *Tetrahedron Letters*, 1964, 2347.

Seryl β-MSH. *See* Bovine *under* β-Melanotropin.

L-Seryl-L-tyrosyl-L-seryl-L-methionyl-L-glutamyl-L-histidyl-L-phenylalanyl-L-arginyl-L-tryptophenyl-glycyl-L-lysyl-L-prolyl-L-valyl-glycyl-L-lysyl-L-lysyl-L-arginine

Ser·Tyr·Ser·Met·Glu(OH)·His·Phe·Arg·Try·Gly–
–Lys·Pro·Val·Gly·Lys·Lys·Arg

Heptadecapeptide with sequence of first 17 residues of Adrenocorticotropin. $[\alpha]_D^{25}$ −97·1° (c, 0·5 in 0·1*N*-AcOH).

Li *et al.*, *J. Am. Chem. Soc.*, 1964, **86**, 2703.

Sesquigoyol. *See* (+)-δ-Cadinol.

***o*-Sexiphenyl**

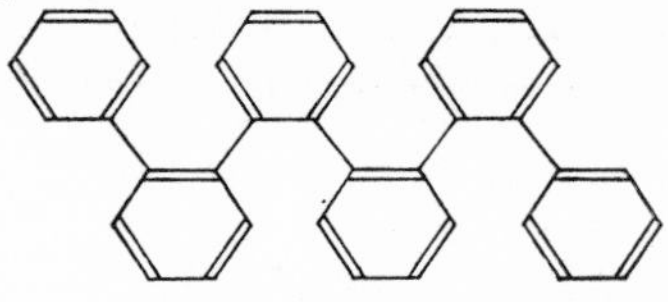

$C_{36}H_{26}$ MW 458

Cryst. from EtOH and C_6H_{12}. M.p. 216–17°. Light absorption: $\lambda_{max.}$ 235 mμ (ε, 39,800).

Cade, Pilbeam, *J. Chem. Soc.*, 1964, 114.

***m*-Sexiphenyl**

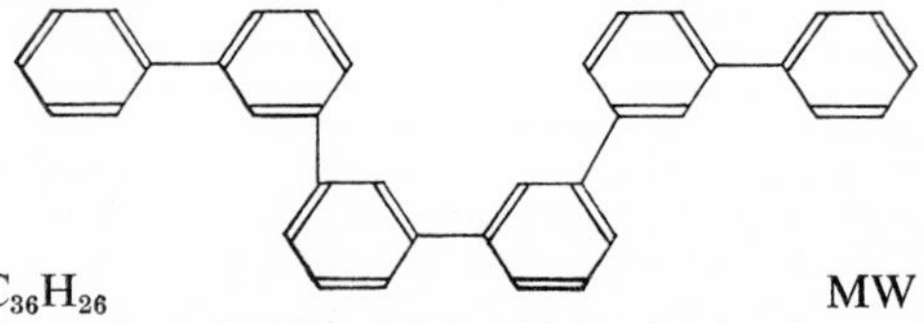

$C_{36}H_{26}$ MW 458

Cryst. from EtOH. M.p. 146–7°. Light absorption: $\lambda_{max.}$ 249 mμ (ε, 102,000).

Alexander, *J. Org. Chem.*, 1956, **21**, 1464.
Cade, Pilbeam, *J. Chem. Soc.*, 1964, 114.

***p*-Sexiphenyl.★**

M.p. 465°. Light absorption: $\lambda_{max.}$ 308 mμ (ε, 60,000). *See also*:

Cade, Pilbeam, *J. Chem. Soc.*, 1964, 114.
Kovacic, Lange, *J. Org. Chem.*, 1964, **29**, 2416.

$1^1,1^2:4^2,1^3:2^3,1^4:2^4,1^5:4^5,1^6$-Sexiphenyl

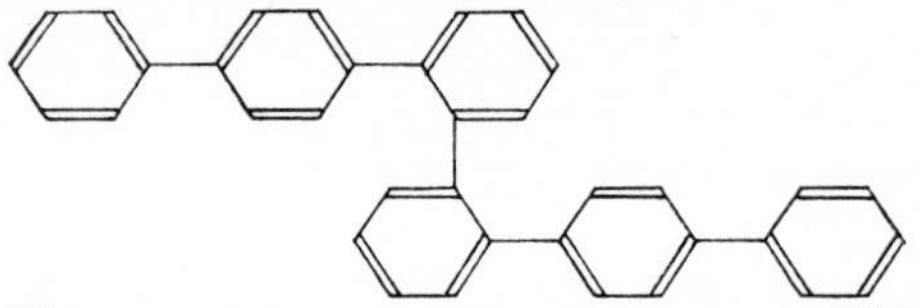

$C_{36}H_{26}$ MW 458

Cryst. from light petroleum. M.p. 189–90°. Light absorption: $\lambda_{max.}$ 273 mμ (ε, 47,300).

Cade, Pilbeam, *J. Chem. Soc.*, 1964, 114.

$1^1,1^2:4^2,1^3:3^3,1^4:3^4,1^5:4^5,1^6$-Sexiphenyl

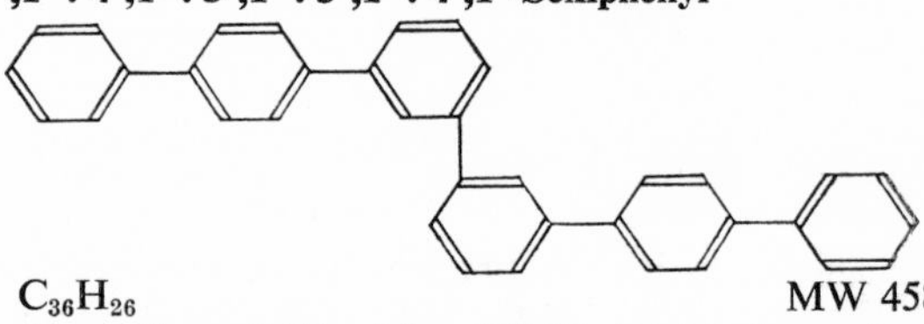

$C_{36}H_{26}$ MW 458

Cryst. from C_6H_6. M.p. 247·5°. Light absorption: $\lambda_{max.}$ 274 mμ (ε, 72,500).

Cade, Pilbeam, *J. Chem. Soc.*, 1964, 114.

$1^1,1^2:4^2,1^3:4^3,1^4:3^4,1^5:4^5,1^6$-Sexiphenyl

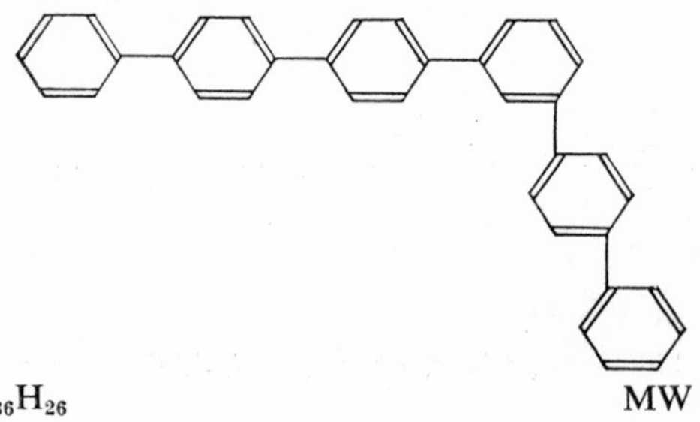

$C_{36}H_{26}$ MW 458

Cryst. from C_6H_6. M.p. 312–14°. Light absorption: $\lambda_{max.}$ 291 mμ (ε, 62,500).

Cade, Pilbeam, *J. Chem. Soc.*, 1964, 114.

Shionone

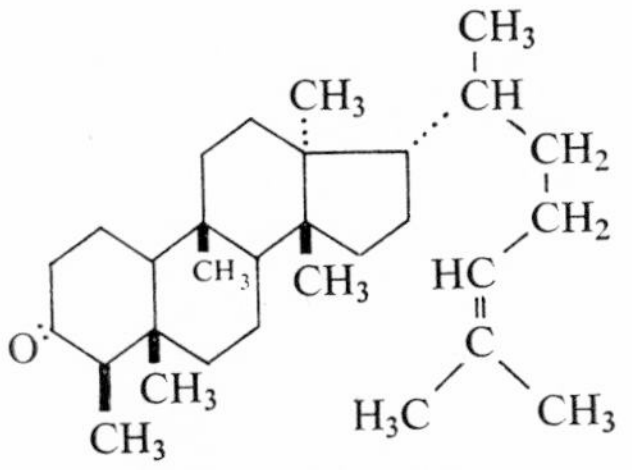

Suggested structure

$C_{30}H_{50}O$ MW 426

Constituent of the root of *Aster tataricus* L. M.p. 161–2°. $[\alpha]_D$ −56° (c, 1·1 in $CHCl_3$).

Takahashi *et al.*, *J. Pharm. Soc. Japan*, 1959, **79**, 1281; 1960, **80**, 592.
Tanahashi *et al.*, *Bull. soc. chim.*, 1964, 584.
Patil *et al.*, *Bull. soc. chim.*, 1964, 1422.

Simarolide

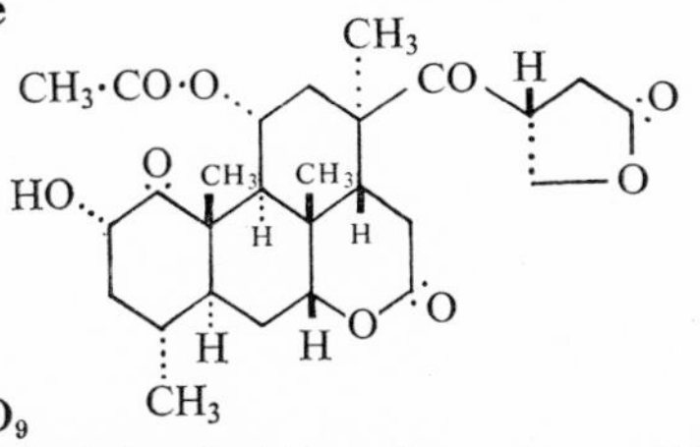

$C_{27}H_{36}O_9$ MW 504

Bitter principle of *Simarouba amara*. Cryst. from AcOEt or MeOH. M.p. 264–70°. $[\alpha]_D$ +73·6° (c, 0·788 in $CHCl_3$).

Ac: m.p. 290–4°. $[\alpha]_D$ −28·9° (c, 0·86 in $CHCl_3$).

Polonsky, *Bull. soc. chim.*, 1959, 1546; *Proc. Chem. Soc.*, 1964, 292.
Brown, Sim, *Proc. Chem. Soc.*, 1964, 293.

Sisaustricin. *See* 4-Ethyloxazolidine-2-thione.

Sitsirikine

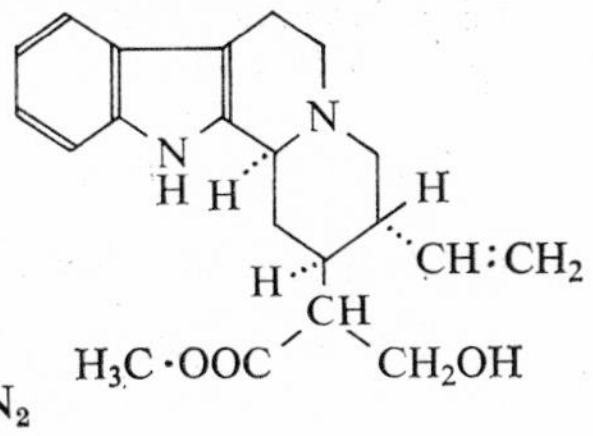

$C_{21}H_{26}O_3N_2$ MW 354

Alkaloid from *Vinca rosea* L. Cryst. from MeOH. M.p. 206–8°. $[\alpha]_D^{26}$ −58° (MeOH). Solvated cryst. from Me_2CO. M.p. 181°. Light absorption: $\lambda_{max.}$ 226 (ε, 36,000), 282 (8000), 290 mμ (6500). H_2 → dihydrositsirikine.

Mono-Ac: m.p. 198°. $[\alpha]_D^{26}$ −26° (MeOH).

B,½H₂SO₄: m.p. 239–41° decomp.

Picrate: m.p. 226–8° decomp.

Svoboda *et al.*, *J. Pharm. Sci.*, 1961, **50**, 409.
Kutney, Brown, *Tetrahedron Letters*, 1963, 1815.

α-Smegma-mycolic Acid

$CH_3{\cdot}[CH_2]_{17}{\cdot}CH{:}CH{\cdot}[CH_2]_{13}{\cdot}CH{:}CH{\cdot}CH(CH_3)-$
$-[CH_2]_{17}{\cdot}CH(OH){\cdot}CH(C_{22}H_{45}){\cdot}COOH$

$C_{79}H_{154}O_3$ MW 1150

Constituent of the lipids of *Mycobacterium smegmatis*. M.p. 56–61·5°.

Me ester: m.p. 47–51°. $[\alpha]_D$ 1·4° ($CHCl_3$). *Ac*: m.p. 34–8°. $[\alpha]_D$ 3° ($CHCl_3$).

Etemadi, Okuda, Lederer, *Bull. soc. chim.*, 1964, 868.

Sodium ethylmercurisalicylate. *See* Thiomersal.★

Solabiose (3-O-β-D-*Glucopyranosyl*-D-*galactopyranose*)

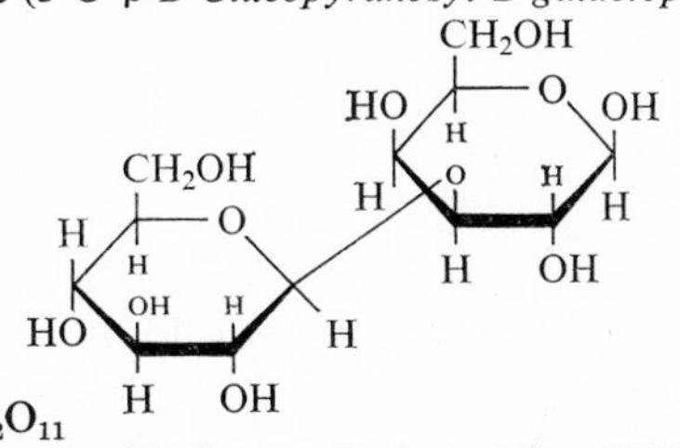

$C_{12}H_{12}O_{11}$ MW 342

Oligosaccharide from solanine. M.p. 200° decomp. after sintering at 175°. $[\alpha]_D^{22}$ +40·7° (c, 1·376 in H_2O).

Osazone: yellow needles from MeOH. M.p. 225° (216–18°).

Kühn, Löw, Trischmann, *Chem. Ber.*, 1955, **88**, 1492.
Briggs, Cambie, Hoare, *J. Chem. Soc.*, 1963, 2848.

α-Solamarine

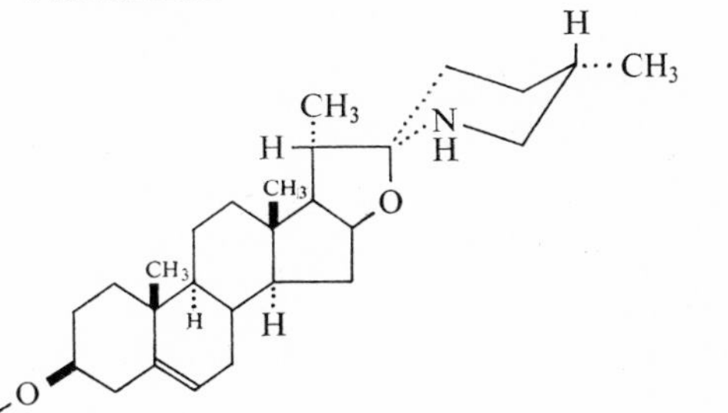

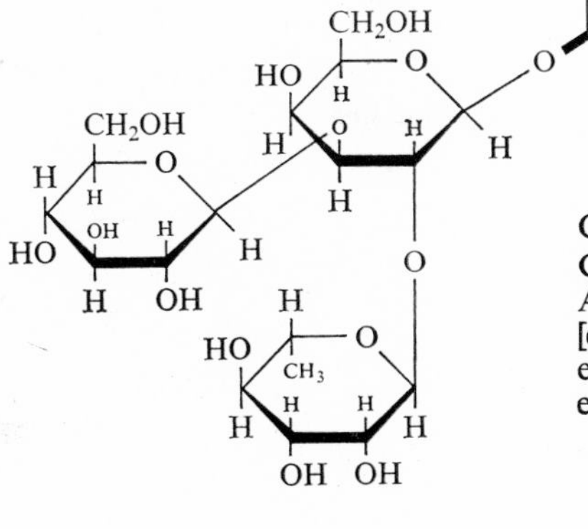

$C_{45}H_{73}O_{16}N$ MW 883

Glycoside from *Solanum dulcamara* L. (Lyngby Aamose). M.p. 278–81° decomp. (sinters at 236°). $[\alpha]_D^{20}$ −45° (c, 0·05 in Py). Hydrolysis → tomatid-5-en-3β-ol + galactose + glucose + rhamnose (1 mole each). Under mild conditions → solatriose.

Boll, *Acta Chem. Scand.*, 1962, **16**, 1819; 1963, **17**, 2126.

β-Solamarine

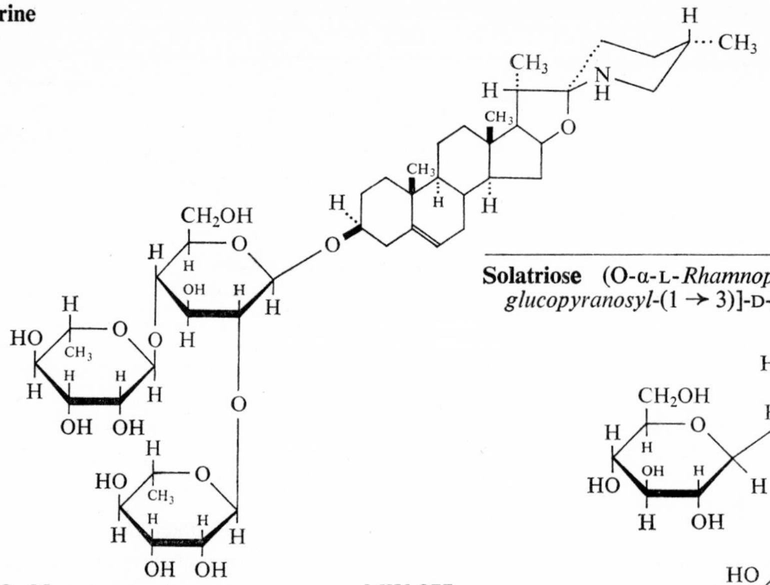

$C_{45}H_{73}O_{15}N$ MW 877

Glycoside from *Solanum dulcamara* L. M.p. 275–7° decomp. (sinters at 270°). $[\alpha]_D^{20}$ −85·6° (c, 0·4 in Py). Hydrolysis → tomatid-5-en-3β-ol + 2 mols. rhamnose + 1 mole glucose.

Picrate: rectangular plates. M.p. 193–5° decomp.

Boll, *Acta Chem. Scand.*, 1962, **16**, 1819; 1963, **17**, 1852.

γ-Solamarine

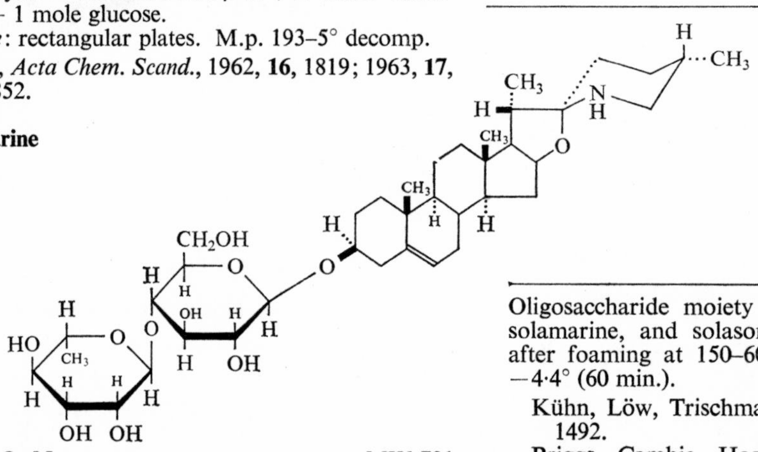

$C_{39}H_{63}O_{11}N$ MW 721

Glycoside from *Solanum dulcamara* L. M.p. 243–8° decomp. (sinters at 195°). $[\alpha]_D^{20}$ −86·1° (c, 0·36 in Py). Hydrolysis → tomatid-5-en-3β-ol + 1 mole glucose + 1 mole rhamnose.

Boll, *Acta Chem. Scand.*, 1962, **16**, 1819; 1963, **17**, 1852.

Solanidine.★

Mass spectrum:

Budzikiewicz, *Tetrahedron*, 1964, **20**, 2267.

Solanocapsin.★

Mass spectrum:

Budzikiewicz, *Tetrahedron*, 1964, **20**, 2267.

Solasodine.★

Synthesis:

Schreiber, Walther, Rönsch, *Tetrahedron*, 1964, **20**, 1939.

Solatriose (O-α-L-*Rhamnopyranosyl*-(1 → 2)-O-[β-D-*glucopyranosyl*-(1 → 3)]-D-*galactopyranose*)

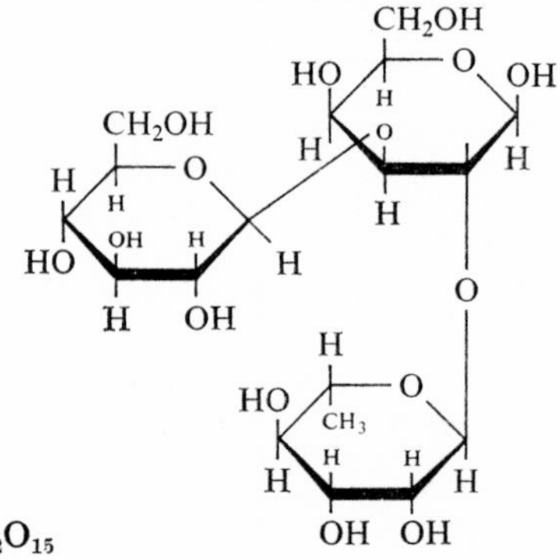

$C_{18}H_{32}O_{15}$ MW 488

Oligosaccharide moiety present in α-solanine, α-solamarine, and solasonine. M.p. 200° decomp. after foaming at 150–60°. $[\alpha]_D^{27}$ −7·5° (5 min.), −4·4° (60 min.).

Kühn, Löw, Trischmann, *Chem. Ber.*, 1955, **88**, 1492.

Briggs, Cambie, Hoare, *J. Chem. Soc.*, 1963, 2848.

Boll, *Acta Chem. Scand.*, 1963, **17**, 2126.

α-Sorigenin.★

See also:

Horii, Katagi, Tumura, *Chem. Pharm. Bull.* (Tokyo), 1963, **11**, 312, 317.

Speciofoline

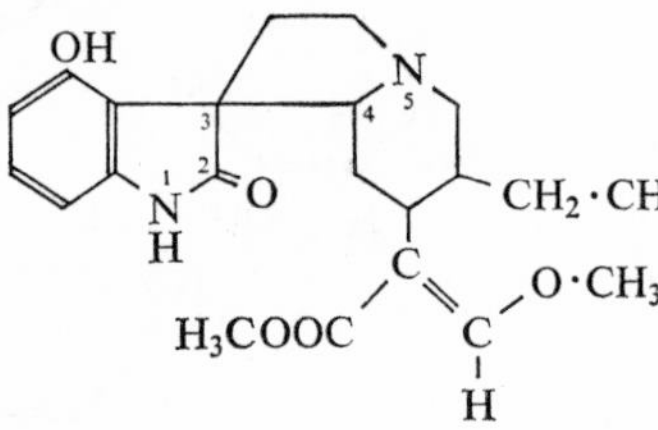

$C_{22}H_{28}O_5N_2$ MW 400

Alkaloid from the leaves of *Mitragyna speciosa*. Stereoisomer of rotundifoline. Colourless needles. M.p. 202–4°. $[\alpha]_D^{22}$ −103° (c, 2 in $CHCl_3$). pK_a 6·3 (H_2O). Light absorption: $\lambda_{max.}$ 223 (log ε, 4·47), 242 (4·27), 290 mμ (3·49).

Beckett, Lee, Tackie, *Tetrahedron Letters*, 1963, 1709.

Spermatheridine (*Liriodenine*)

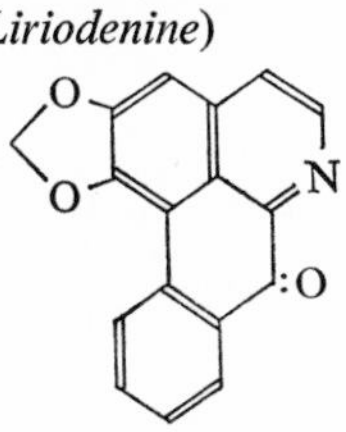

$C_{17}H_9O_3N$ MW 275

Alkaloid from *Atherosperma moschatum* Labill. M.p. 275–6° decomp. Identical with liriodenine (*q.v.*).

Bick, Clezy, Crow, *Austral. J. Chem.*, 1956, **9**, 111.
Bick, Douglas, *Tetrahedron Letters*, 1964, 1629.

Spinaceamine (4 : 5 : 6 : 7-*Tetrahydroimidazo*[5,4-c]*pyridine*)

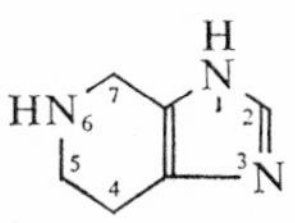

$C_6H_9N_3$ MW 123

Present in the skin of *Leptodactylus* spp.
B,2HCl: prism + H_2O. M.p. 277–9°.
Dipicrate: m.p. 224–5°.
6-*Me deriv.*: $C_7H_{11}N_3$. MW 137. Present in skin of *Leptodactylus* spp. *B,2HCl*: m.p. 272–4°. *Dipicrate*: m.p. 230–1 °.

Vitali, Bertaccini, *Gazzetta*, 1964, **94**, 296.
Erspamer *et al.*, *Arch. Biochem. Biophys.*, 1964, **105**, 620.

Spinacine (4 : 5 : 6 : 7-*Tetrahydroimidazo*[5,4-c]*pyridine*-5-*carboxylic acid*)

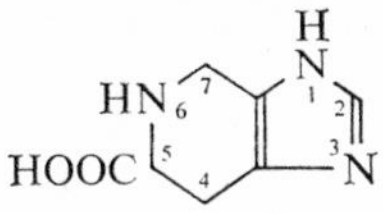

$C_7H_9O_2N_3$ MW 167

(−)-.
Present in the liver of the shark *Acanthias vulgaris* and in the crab *Crango vulgaris*. M.p. 265°. $[\alpha]_D^{20}$ −174·6°.
DL(±)-.
M.p. 265°.

Ackermann, Muller, *Z. physiol. Chem.*, 1941, **268**, 277; 1962, **328**, 275.
Ackermann, Skraup, *Z. physiol. Chem.*, 1949, **284**, 129.

Spinochrome A★ (*Spinochrome M*)

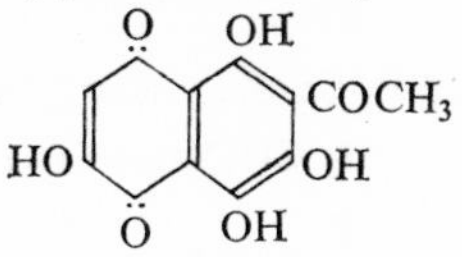

Revised structure

$C_{12}H_8O_7$ MW 264

Major pigment in spines of the sea urchins *Echinometra oblonga* Blainville, *Colobocentrotus atratus* L., and *Strongylocentratus purpuratus*. Purple needles from MeOH. M.p. 192–3° or as MeOH solvate, m.p. 182–3°. Light absorption: $\lambda_{max.}$ 251 (log ε, 4·16), 270 sh. (4·14), 317 (4·10), and 514 mμ (3·67). Identical with Spinochrome M.

Tyler, *Proc. Nat. Acad. Sci.*, U.S.A., 1939, **25**, 523.
Chang, Moore, Scheuer, *J. Am. Chem. Soc.*, 1964, **86**, 2959.

Spinochrome B (*Spinochrome* B_1, M_2, *N, and* P_1, 2 : 3 : 5 : 7-*tetrahydroxy*-1 : 4-*naphthoquinone*)

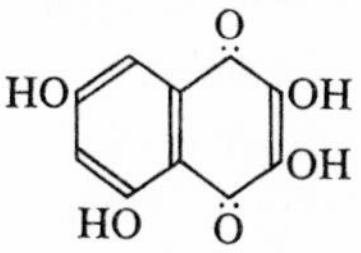

$C_{10}H_6O_6$ MW 222

Constituent of the spines of many echinoids (*e.g.*, *Paracentrotus lividus*, *Strongylocentrotus pulcherrimus*, *Anthocidaris* (*Heliocidaris*) *crassispina*, and *Salmacis sphaeroides*). Forms solvated cryst. from MeOH. M.p. 325–30° decomp. From dioxan. M.p. 350–5°. Light absorption: $\lambda_{max.}$ 271, 322, 388, and 477 mμ.
Tetra-Ac: m.p. 157°.
Leuco-Ac: 1 : 2 : 3 : 4 : 5 : 7-Hexa-acetoxynaphthalene. M.p. 242° decomp.
Tri-Me ether: orange cryst., m.p. 102° → red cryst., m.p. 112°.
Tetra-Me ether: thin yellow needles. M.p. 131°.

Kuroda, Iwakura, *Proc. Imp. Acad. Tokyo*, 1942, **18**, 24.
Musajo, Minchilli, *Chem. Zentr.*, 1943, **1**, 1275.
Kuroda, Koyasu, *Proc. Imp. Acad. Tokyo*, 1944, **20**, 23.
Goodwin, Srisukh, *Biochem. J.*, 1950, **47**, 69.
Kuroda, Okajima, *Proc. Japan. Acad.*, 1950, **26**, 33.
Goodwin, Lederer, Musajo, *Experientia*, 1951, **7**, 375.
Lederer, *Biochim. Biophys. Acta*, 1952, **9**, 92.
Okajima, *Sci. Papers Inst. Phys. Chem. Res. Tokyo*, 1959, **53**, 356.
Smith, Thomson, *J. Chem. Soc.*, 1961, 1008.
Gough, Sutherland, *Tetrahedron Letters*, 1964, 269.

Spinochrome B_1 (Kuroda *et al.*). *See* Spinochrome B.

Spinochrome C (*Spinochrome F, Spinone A, Isoerhinochrome*)

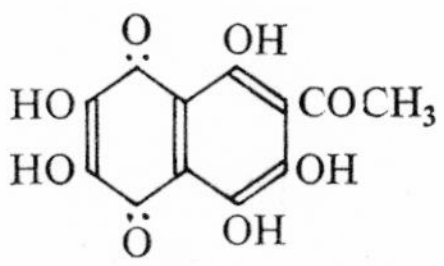

$C_{12}H_8O_8$ MW 280

Constituent of sea urchins *Paracentrotus* (*Strongylocentrotus*) *lividus*, *Echinometra oblonga* Blainville, *Hemicentrotus*, and *Acbacia* spp. Red-orange needles from MeOH. M.p. 246–8°. Light absorption: $\lambda_{max.}$ 238·5 (log ε, 4·13), 293 (4·15), 348 (3·98), and 460 mμ (3·77).
Tri-Me ether: $C_{15}H_{14}O_8$. MW 322. M.p. 116–17°.

Glaser, Lederer, *Compt. rend.*, 1939, **208**, 1939.

Kuhn, Wallenfels, *Ber.*, 1939, **72**, 1407; 1941, **74**, 1594.

Kuroda, Okshima, *Proc. Imp. Acad.* (Tokyo), 1940, **16**, 214.

Lederer, *Biochim. Biophys. Acta*, 1952, **9**, 92.

Kuroda, Okajima, *Proc. Japan Acad.*, 1960, **36**, 424.

Chang, Moore, Scheuer, *Tetrahedron Letters*, 1964, 3557.

Spinochrome F. *See* Spinochrome C.

Spinochrome M. *See* Spinochrome A.

Spinochrome M₂ (Kuroda *et al.*). *See* Spinochrome B.

Spinochrome N (Smith and Thomson). *See* Spinochrome B.

Spinochrome P₁ (Musajo and Minchilli). *See* Spinochrome B.

Spinone A. *See* Spinochrome C.

Spinulosin.★

Biosynthesis:

Pettersson, *Acta Chem. Scand.*, 1964, **18**, 335.

Sporidesmolide I★ (*Cyclo-*(L-α-*hydroxyisovaleryl*-L-*valyl*-N-*methyl*-L-*leucyl*-L-α-*hydroxyisovaleryl*-D-*valyl*-D-*leucyl*)).

Sporidesmolide II (*Cyclo-*(L-α-*hydroxyisovaleryl*-L-*valyl*-N-*methyl*-L-*leucyl*-L-α-*hydroxyisovaleryl*-D-allo-*iso-leucyl*-D-*leucyl*))

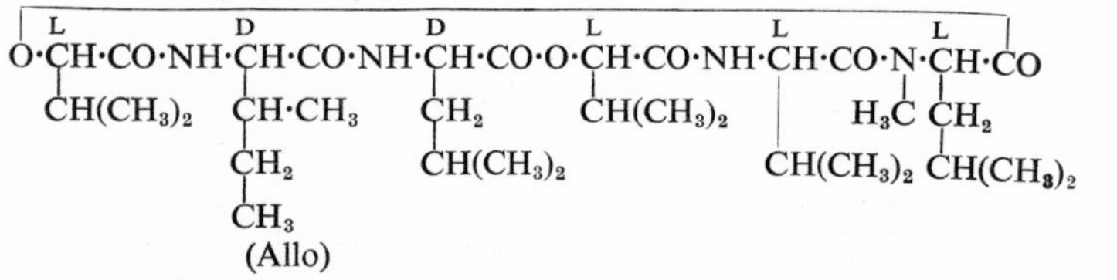

$$O \cdot \overset{\text{L}}{\text{CH}} \cdot CO \cdot NH \cdot \overset{\text{D}}{\text{CH}} \cdot CO \cdot NH \cdot \overset{\text{D}}{\text{CH}} \cdot CO \cdot O \cdot \overset{\text{L}}{\text{CH}} \cdot CO \cdot NH \cdot \overset{\text{L}}{\text{CH}} \cdot CO \cdot N \cdot \overset{\text{L}}{\text{CH}} \cdot CO$$

CH(CH₃)₂   CH·CH₃   CH₂   CH(CH₃)₂   H₃C CH₂

CH₂   CH(CH₃)₂   CH(CH₃)₂ CH(CH₃)₂

CH₃

(Allo)

C₃₄H₆₀O₈N₄   MW 648

Metabolic product of *Pithomyces chartorum* (Burk and Curt.) M. B. Ellis. M.p. 228–3°. [α]$_D^{20}$ −195° (c, 0·6 in CHCl₃).

Russell, *Biochim. Biophys. Acta*, 1960, **45**, 411; *J. Chem. Soc.*, 1962, 753.

Shemyakin *et al.*, *Tetrahedron Letters*, 1963, 1927.

Macdonald, Shannon, Taylor, *Tetrahedron Letters*, 1964, 2087.

Sporidesmolide III (*Demethylsporidesmolide I, cyclo-*(L-α-*hydroxyisovaleryl*-L-*valyl*-L-*leucyl*-L-α-*hydroxy-isovaleryl*-D-*valyl*-D-*leucyl*))

$$O \cdot \overset{\text{L}}{\text{CH}} \cdot CO \cdot NH \cdot \overset{\text{D}}{\text{CH}} \cdot CO \cdot NH \cdot \overset{\text{D}}{\text{CH}} \cdot CO \cdot O \cdot \overset{\text{L}}{\text{CH}} \cdot CO \cdot NH \cdot \overset{\text{L}}{\text{CH}} \cdot CO \cdot NH \cdot \overset{\text{L}}{\text{CH}} \cdot CO$$

CH(CH₃)₂   CH(CH₃)₂   CH₂   CH(CH₃)₂   CH(CH₃)₂   CH₂

CH(CH₃)₂   CH(CH₃)₂

C₃₂H₅₆O₈N₄   MW 620

Minor metabolite of *Pithomyces chartarum*. Cryst. from CHCl₃. M.p. 277–8°. [α]$_D$ −80° (c, 1·6 in AcOH).

Russell, *J. Chem. Soc.*, 1962, 753.

Russell, Macdonald, Shannon, *Tetrahedron Letters*, 1964, 2759.

Sporidesmolide IV (*Cyclo-*(L-α-*hydroxylisohexanoyl*-L-*valyl*-N-*methyl*-L-*leucyl*-L-α-*hydroxyisovaleryl*-D-*valyl*-D-*leucyl*))

$$O \cdot \overset{\text{L}}{\text{CH}} \cdot CO \cdot NH \cdot \overset{\text{D}}{\text{CH}} \cdot CO \cdot NH \cdot \overset{\text{D}}{\text{CH}} \cdot CO \cdot O \cdot \overset{\text{L}}{\text{CH}} \cdot CO \cdot NH \cdot \overset{\text{L}}{\text{CH}} \cdot CO \cdot NH \cdot \overset{\text{L}}{\text{CH}} \cdot CO$$

CH(CH₃)₂   CH(CH₃)₂   CH₂   CH₂   H₃C CH₂

CH(CH₃)₂ CH₂   CH(CH₃)₂   CH(CH₃

CH(CH₃)₂

C₃₄H₆₀O₈N₄   MW 648

Depsipeptide from *Pithomyces maydicus*. M.p. 227–8°. [α]$_D$ −195° (c, 1 in CHCl₃).

Bishop, Russell, *Biochem. J.*, 1964, **92**, 19P.

Stachene.

This is (+)-Hibaene.

Murray, McCrindle, *Chemistry and Industry*, 1964, 500.

Kapadi, Dev, *Tetrahedron Letters*, 1964, 2751.

Wenkert, Jeffs, Mahajan, *J. Am. Chem. Soc.*, 1964, **86**, 2218.

Stelabid. An anticholergenic and neuroleptic drug containing trifluoperazine and isopropamide.

Stephanine

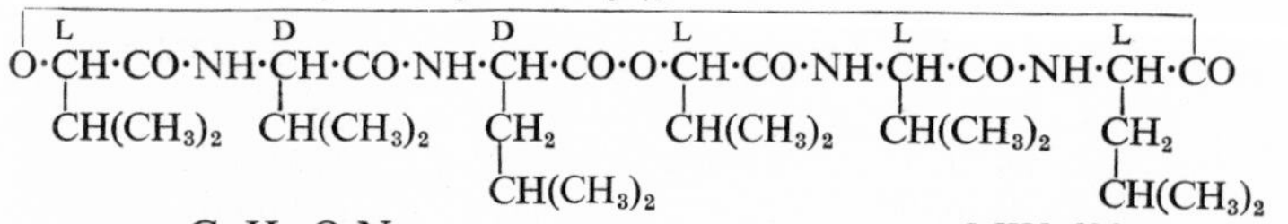

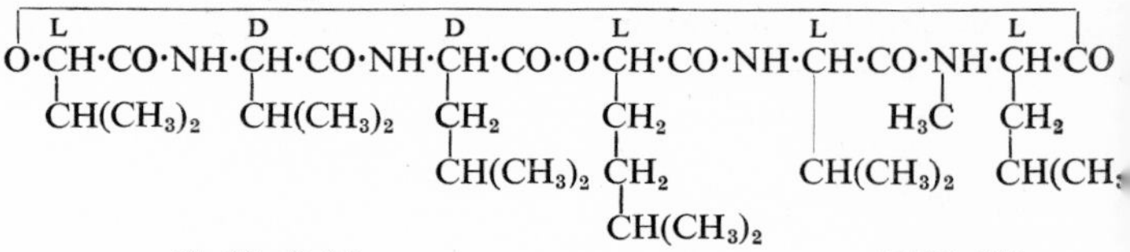

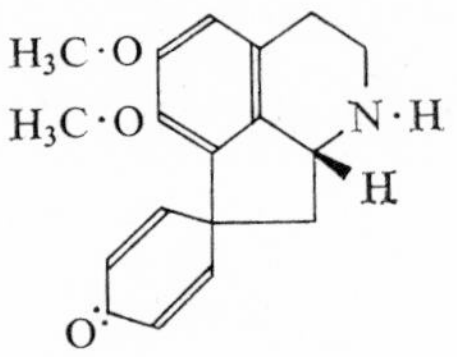

C₁₈H₁₉O₃N   MW 297

D (or R)-.

Alkaloid from *Stephania glabra* (*Menispermaceae*). M.p. 179–81°. [α]$_D^{26}$ +143° (c, 1·88 in CHCl₃). N-*Ac*: m.p. 234–5°. [α]$_D^{24}$ −80° (c, 1·57 in CHCl₃). N-*Me*: *see* Pronuciferine.

Cava *et al.*, *Chemistry and Industry*, 1964, 282.

Stipatonic Acid

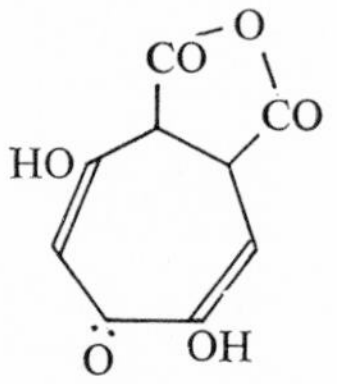

C₉H₄O₆   MW 208

Metabolite of *Penicillium stipitatum* Thom. Yellow cryst. M.p. 237° decomp.

Segal, *Chemistry and Industry*, 1957, 1040; 1958, 1726.

Doi, Kitahara, *Bull. Chem. Soc. Japan*, 1958, **31**, 788.

Andrew, Segal, *J. Chem. Soc.*, 1964, 607.

Stizolobic Acid (β-(6-*Carboxy-*α′-*pyron-4-yl*)*alanine*)

C₉H₉O₆N   MW 227

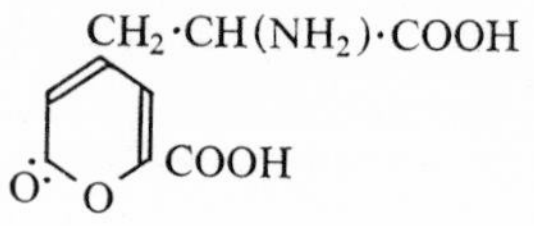

Amino acid from *Stizolobium hassjoo*. M.p. 231–3°. Light absorption: $\lambda_{max.}$ 303 mμ (log ε, 3·89) at pH 5.

DL-.

Decomp. above 270°.

Hattori, Komamine, *Nature* (Lond.), 1959, **183**, 1116.

Senoh *et al.*, *Tetrahedron Letters*, 1964, 3431, 3439.

Stizolobinic Acid (β-(6-*Carboxy-α′-pyron-3-yl*)*alanine*)

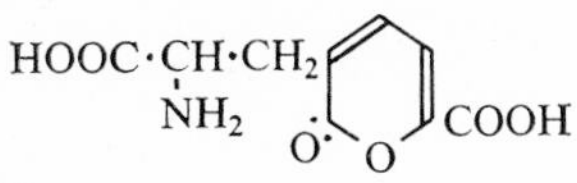

$C_9H_9O_6N$ MW 227

Amino acid from *Stizolobium hassjoo*. Does not decompose under 300°. Light absorption: $\lambda_{max.}$ 233 (log ε, 3·41) and 306 mμ (4·00) at pH 5.

Hattori, Komamine *Nature* (Lond.), 1959, **183**, 1116.

Senoh *et al.*, *Tetrahedron Letters*, 1964, 3431, 3439.

Streptidine★

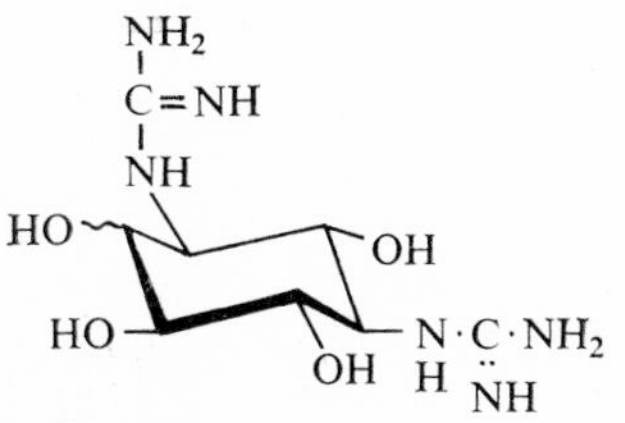

Absolute configuration:

Dyer, Todd, *J. Am. Chem. Soc.*, 1963, **85**, 3896.

Streptolic Acid

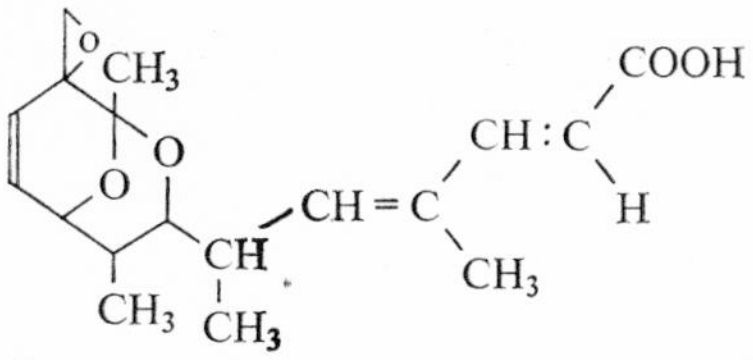

$C_{18}H_{24}O_5$ MW 320

Degradation product of Streptolydigin. M.p. 168–70°. $[\alpha]_D^{26}$ +147° (c, 1·22 in 95% EtOH).

Rinehart *et al.*, *J. Am. Chem. Soc.*, 1963, **85**, 4035.

Streptolydigin

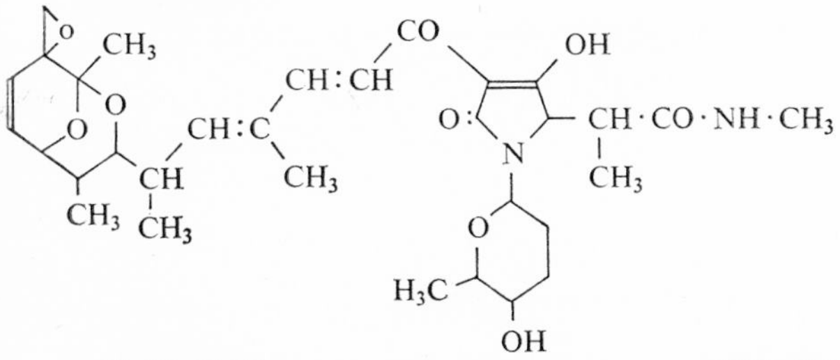

$C_{32}H_{44}O_9N_2$ MW 600

Antibiotic from *Streptomyces lydicus*. Cryst. from AcOEt which lose birefringence at 110° and have m.p. 144–50°. $[\alpha]_D$ −65·7° (c, 2·28 in 0·005*N*-NaOH), −93° (c, 1·6 in $CHCl_3$). pK_a 5·3 (65% MeOH). Light absorption: $\lambda_{max.}$ 357 ($E^{1\%}_{1\,cm.}$ 591), 370 mμ (560) in 0·01*N*-H_2SO_4. $\lambda_{max.}$ 262 ($E^{1\%}_{1\,cm.}$ 227), 291 (273), 335 mμ (333) in 0·01*N*-NaOH. Hyd. → Rhodinose.

Na salt: m.p. 225°. $[\alpha]_D^{25}$ +153° (c, 1·35 in $CHCl_3$).

Eble *et al.*, *Antibiotics Ann.*, 1955–56, 893.

Rinehart *et al.*, *J. Am. Chem. Soc.*, 1963, **85**, 4035, 4037, 4038.

Stevens, Blumbergs, Wood, *J. Am. Chem. Soc.*, 1964, **86**, 3592.

Streptomycin★

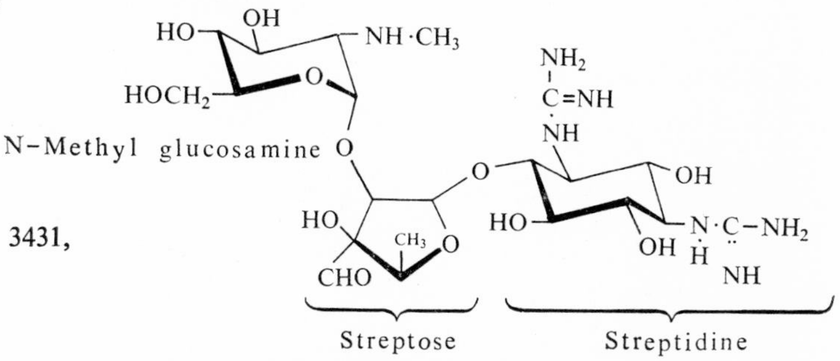

Absolute configuration:

Dyer, Todd, *J. Am. Chem. Soc.*, 1963, **85**, 3896.

Strigosine

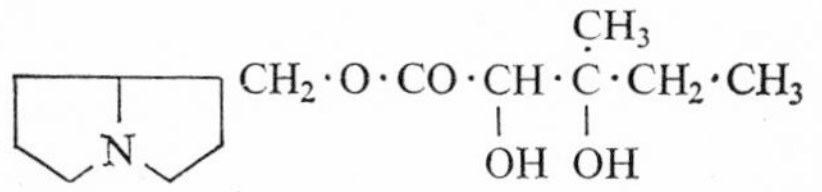

$C_{14}H_{25}O_4N$ MW 271

Major alkaloid from *Heliotropium strigosum*. Colourless gum. $[\alpha]_D^{20}$ −19·3° (c, 6·56 in EtOH). Hydrol. → trachelanthamidine and (−)-2 : 3-dihydroxy-3-methylvaleric acid.

B,HCl: needles from EtOH–Et_2O. M.p. 137·5°.

B,CH_3I: leaflets from EtOH–Et_2O. M.p. 135–6°. [α] −15·5° (c, 2·84 in EtOH).

Picrate: yellow leaflets from C_6H_6–light petroleum. M.p. 141°.

Mattocks, *J. Chem. Soc.*, 1964, 1974.

Sulochrin.★

Also found as a metabolite of *Penicillium frequentans*.

Mahmoodian, Stickings, *Biochem. J.*, 1964, **92**, 369.

Sulphurenic Acid (15α-*Hydroxyeburicoic acid*)

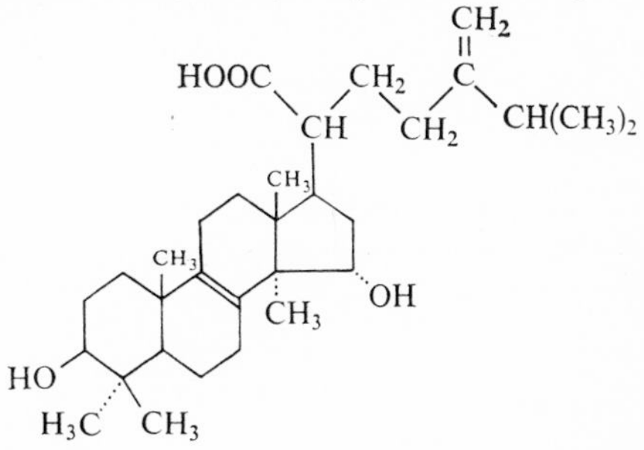

$C_{31}H_{50}O_4$ MW 486

Metabolite of *Polyporus sulphureus*. Cryst. from Me_2CO. M.p. 252–4°. $[\alpha]_D^{23}$ +42° (c, 0·51 in Py).
Me ester: $C_{32}H_{52}O_4$. MW 500. Cryst. from MeOH–$CHCl_3$. M.p. 190–2°. $[\alpha]_D^{23}$ +66° (c, 0·42 in $CHCl_3$). *Di-Ac*: cryst. from MeOH. M.p. 138–40°. $[\alpha]_D^{23}$ +67° (c, 0·41 in $CHCl_3$).
Di-Ac: cryst. from MeOH. M.p. 234–5°. $[\alpha]_D^{23}$ +58° (c, 1 in $CHCl_3$).

Fried *et al.*, *Tetrahedron*, 1964, **20**, 2297.

Swerchirin (1 : 8-*Dihydroxy*-3 : 5-*dimethoxyxanthone*)

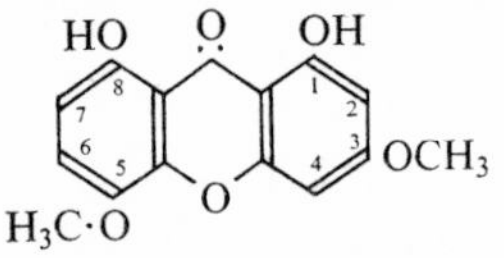

Suggested structure

$C_{15}H_{12}O_6$ MW 288

Xanthone pigment from *Swertia decussata* (*S. chirata*). Yellow needles. M.p. 185–6°. Probably identical with methyl bellidifolium.
Di-Me ether: $C_{17}H_{16}O_6$. MW 316. M.p. 210–11°.

Dalal, Shah, *Chemistry and Industry*, 1956, 664; 1957, 140.
Markham, *Tetrahedron*, 1964, **20**, 991.

Swertinin (7 : 8-*Dihydroxy*-1 : 3-*dimethoxyxanthone*)

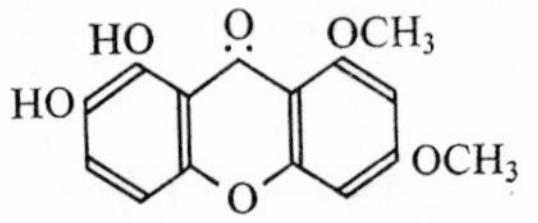

$C_{15}H_{12}O_6$ MW 288

Constituent of the flowers of *Swertia decussata*. Yellow needles from EtOH–$CHCl_3$. M.p. 217°. Sol. $CHCl_3$, EtOH, Me_2CO, and C_6H_6.
Ac: white needles from EtOH. M.p. 157°.
Di-Me ether: *see* Tetra-Me ether *under* 1 : 3 : 7 : 8-Tetrahydroxyxanthone.

Dalal, Sethna, Shah, *J. Indian Chem. Soc.*, 1953, **30**, 457, 463.
Dalal, Shah, *Chemistry and Industry*, 1957, 140.

Swietenine

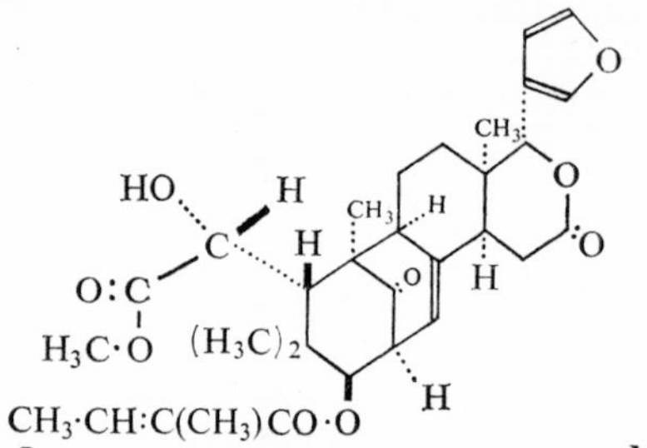

$C_{32}H_{40}O_9$ MW 568

Constituent of *Swietenia macrophylla*. Cryst. from AcOH. M.p. 256–8° decomp. $[\alpha]_D^{30}$ −133·5° (c, 4·25 in $CHCl_3$), −183·5° (c, 2·5 in C_6H_6). Hydrol. → tiglic acid.

Sircar, Chakrabarthy, *J. Ind. Chem. Soc.*, 1951, **28**, 207.
Chakrabarthy, Chatterjee, *J. Ind. Chem. Soc.*, 1955, **32**, 179.
Connolly *et al.*, *Tetrahedron Letters*, 1964, 2593.
McPhail, Sim, *Tetrahedron Letters*, 1964, 2599.

Sympathol.★

(−)-.

Present in citrus leaves and fruit. Plates from Me_2CO.Aq. or H_2O. M.p. 162–4° decomp. $[\alpha]_D^{25}$ −55·6° (0·5*N*-HCl).
$2B,(COOH)_2$: cryst. from MeOH.Aq. M.p. 221–2° decomp.

Stewart, Newhall, Edwards, *J. Biol. Chem.*, 1964, **239**, 930.

Synkay. *See* 2-Methyl-1 : 4-naphthoquinone.

Synkonin. *See under* Dihydrocodeinone.

T

Tanginol

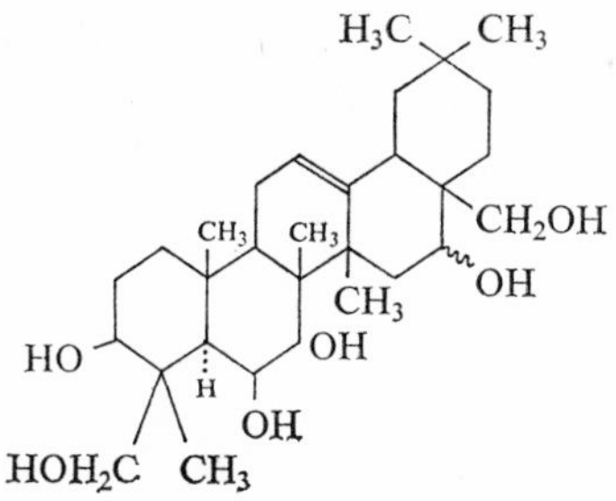

$C_{30}H_{50}O_6$ MW 506

Constituent of the heartwood of *Barringtonia acutangula*. M.p. 283–4°. $[\alpha]_D^{30}$ 9°.
Penta-benzoyl: m.p. 306–8°. $[\alpha]_D^{30}$ 43°.
Hexa-Ac: (with $HClO_4$). M.p. 150–3°. $[\alpha]_D^{30}$ −63°.

Ramachandra Tow, Sastry, *Indian J. Chem.*, 1963, **1**, 322.

Tauranin

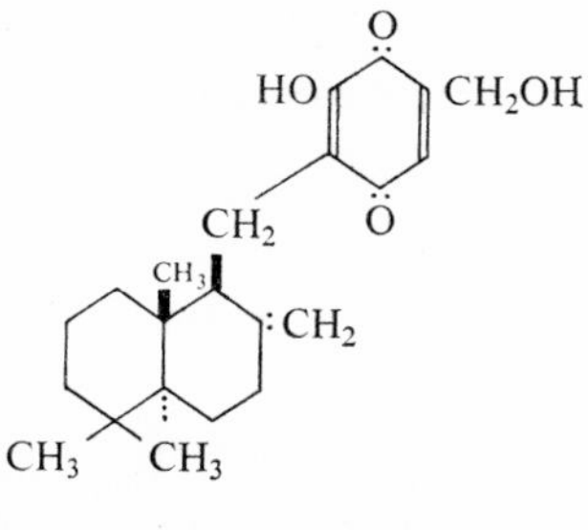

$C_{22}H_{30}O_4$ MW 358

Metabolite of *Oospora aurantia* (Cooke) Sacc. et Vogl. M.p. 155° decomp. Light absorption: $\lambda_{max.}$ 266 (log ε, 4·07) and 415 mμ (3·07).

Kawashima *et al.*, *Tetrahedron Letters*, 1964, 1227.

Taxane (4 : 8 : 12 : 15 : 15 - *Pentamethyltricyclo* - [9,3,1,$0^{3,8}$]*pentadecane*)

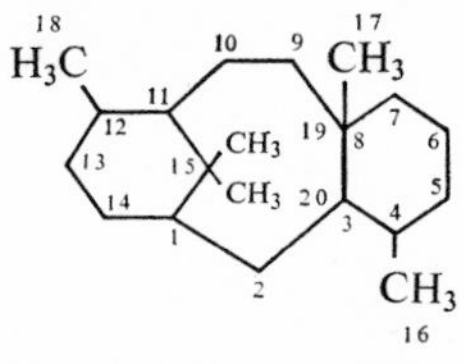

$C_{20}H_{36}$ MW 276

Diterpenoid skeleton of constituents of *Taxus* spp.

Lythgoe, Nakanishi, Uyeo, *Proc. Chem. Soc.*, 1964, 301.

Taxicin.

Degradation product of Taxine (*q.v.*).
See O-Cinnamoyltaxicin I and II.

Taxine.

Amorph. mixture of alkaloids present in the yew (*Taxus baccata* L.) which consist of nitrogen-free polyhydroxylic compounds partially esterified with 3-dimethylamino-3-phenylpropionic and acetic acid. Elimination of dimethylamine followed by acetylation leads to crystalline acetylated *O*-cinnamoyltaxicins (*see O*-Cinnamoyltaxicin).

Baxter *et al.*, *J. Chem. Soc.*, 1962, 2964.

Taxinine.

As well as the alkaloid from *Taxus canadensis* (*see* main work), this name has been given to the nitrogen-free compound from the leaves of *T. baccata* L. sub-spp. *cuspidata*.
See Tri-Ac *under O*-Cinnamoyltaxicin II.

Taxiphyllin (β-D-*Glucopyranosyloxy*-D-p-*hydroxymandelonitrile*)

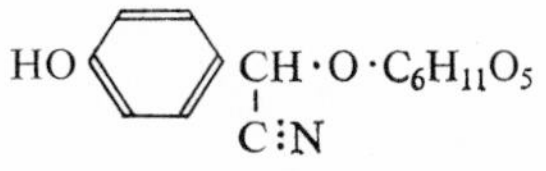

$C_{14}H_{13}O_7N$ MW 311

Present in the leaves of *Taxus* spp. Cryst. from EtOH–C_6H_6. M.p. 168–9° decomp. $[\alpha]_D^{20}$ −66·7° (c, 0·372 in EtOH).
Penta-Ac: cryst. from AcOEt–light petroleum. M.p. 144–144·8°. $[\alpha]_D^{20}$ −22·1° (c, 0·320 in EtOH).

Towers, McInnes, Neish, *Tetrahedron*, 1964, **20**, 71.

See also Dhurrin.

Tecostanine

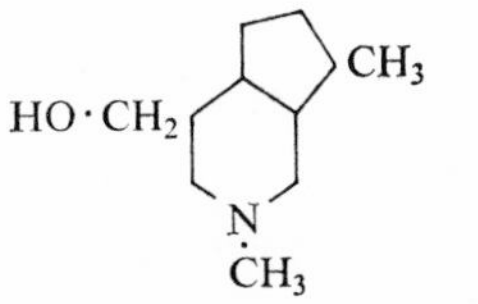

$C_{11}H_{21}ON$ MW 183

Alkaloid present in the leaves of *Tecoma stans*. M.p. 85°. $[\alpha]_D^{20}$ 0° ± 2° (MeOH).

Hammouda, Plat, Le Men, *Bull. soc. chim.*, 1963, 2802.

Tecostidine (11-*Hydroxy-(−)-actinidine*)

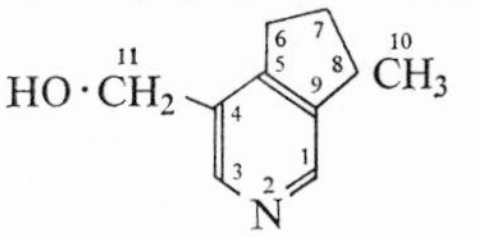

$C_{10}H_{13}ON$ MW 163

Constituent of the leaves of *Tecoma stans* Jugs. Colourless liq. $[\alpha]_D^{22}$ −4° (c, 1·22 in $CHCl_3$). Light absorption: $\lambda_{max.}$ 262 (log ε, 3·27), 270 mμ (3·21).

Ac: liq. $[\alpha]_D$ −4·5° (c, 1·55 in $CHCl_3$). *Picrate*: m.p. 111–13°.

Picrate: cryst. from EtOH–Et_2O. M.p. 152–3°.

Hammouda, Le Men, *Bull. soc. chim.*, 1963, 2901.

Tectol

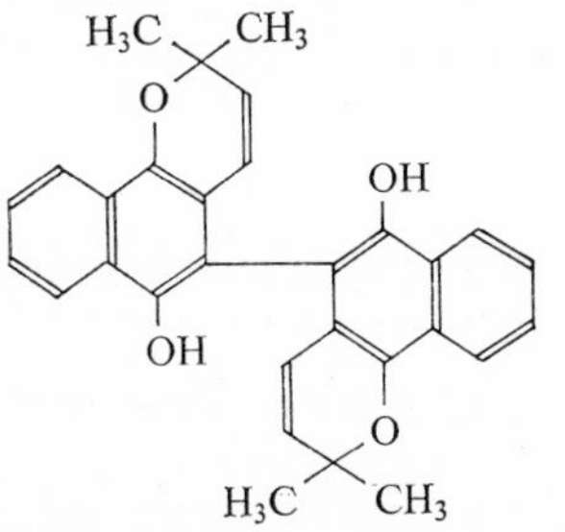

$C_{30}H_{26}O_4$ MW 450

Extractive of teak wood (*Tecona grandis* L.f.). M.p. 216–18°. Dichloranil → dehydrotectol.

Di-Ac: m.p. 198–204°.

Di-Me ether: m.p. 215–20°.

Sandermann, Dietrichs, *Holzforschung*, 1959, **13**, 137 (*Chem. Abstracts*, 1960, **54**, 7142).

Sandermann, Simatupang, *Tetrahedron Letters*, 1963, 1269; *Chem. Ber.*, 1964, **97**, 588.

Tectorigenin.★

7-*Me ether*: *see* 4′ : 5′-Dihydroxy-6 : 7-dimethoxy-isoflavone.

Tembetarine

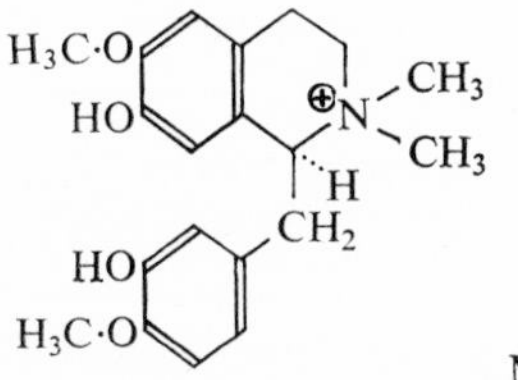

$C_{20}H_{26}O_4N$ MW 344 (ion)

(+)-.

Chloride (X = Cl): $C_{20}H_{26}O_4NCl$. MW 379·5. Alkaloid from the bark of *Fagara naranjillo* (Griseb.) Engl. (Rutaceae). M.p. 236–7°. $[\alpha]_D^{29}$ +123·3° (c, 0·9 in EtOH). Light absorption: $\lambda_{max.}$ 284 mμ (log ε, 3·83).

Di-Me ether: *see N*-Methyl *under* Laudanosine.

Di-Et ether iodide: m.p. 91–2°. $[\alpha]_D^{18}$ +96·2° (c, 0·85 in $CHCl_3$).

Albonico, Kuck, Deulofeu, *Chemistry and Industry*, 1964, 1580.

α-Terthienyl.★

Present in the roots of *Tagetes patula*, *T. erecta*, and *T. minuta* L.

Atkinson, Curtis, Phillips, *Tetrahedron Letters*, 1964, 3159.

1,12 : 2,3 : 6,7 : 8,9-Tetrabenzanthanthrene

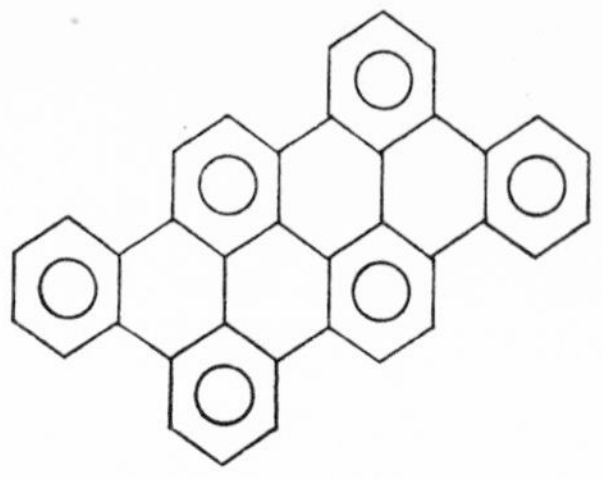

$C_{36}H_{18}$ MW 450

Yellow plates. M.p. 530°. Insol. conc. H_2SO_4. Light absorption: $\lambda_{max.}$ 404 (log ε, 4·86), 380 (4·69), 362 (4·35), 324 (4·89), and 309 mμ (4·88) in trichlorobenzene.

Clar, McCallum, *Tetrahedron*, 1964, **20**, 507.

Tetrabenzo[*b,fg,k,op*][1,4]diazocyclo-octadecine

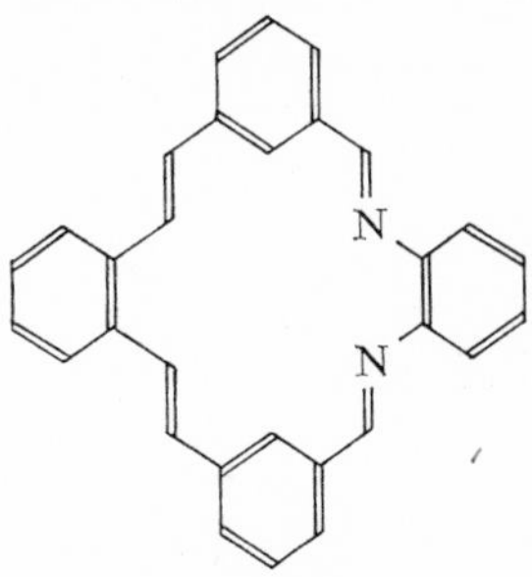

$C_{30}H_{22}N_2$ MW 410

Yellow needles from chlorobenzene. M.p. >360°. Light absorption: $\lambda_{max.}$ 284 (ε, 51,500), 322 (infl.) mμ (27,900).

Houghton, *J. Chem. Soc.*, 1963, 6075.

Tetracyclo[3,3,0,0^{4,6},0^{2,8}]octan-3-one

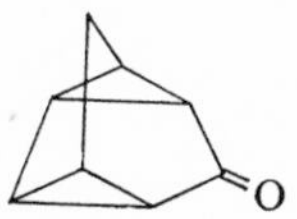

C_8H_8O MW 120

M.p. 69·5–70·5°. Light absorption: $\lambda_{max.}$ 205 (ε, 5360) and 281 mμ (50).

2 : 4-*Dinitrophenylhydrazone*: m.p. 225–6° decomp.

Le Bel, Phillips, Liesemer, *J. Am. Chem. Soc.*, 1964, **86**, 1877.

Tetra-(ββ-diphenylvinyl)ethylene ("*Tetraphenylpentatetraene*")

$(C_6H_5)_2\cdot C{:}CH\cdot C\cdot CH{:}C(C_6H_5)_2$

$\qquad\qquad\quad \|$

$(C_6H_5)_2\cdot C{:}CH\cdot C\cdot CH{:}C(C_6H_5)_2$

$C_{58}H_{44}$ MW 740

M.p. 329° (276°). Light absorption: $\lambda_{max.}$ 254, 327·5, and 407 mμ.

Bohlmann, Kieslich, *Abh. braunschweig. wiss Ges.*, 1957, IX, 147.

Cadiot, Chodkiewicz, Rauss-Godineau, *Bull. soc. chim.*, 1961, 2176.

Kuhn, Schulz, *Angew. Chem.*, 1963, **75**, 452; *Int. Ed.*, 1963, **2**, 395.

Δ^1-3 : 4-*trans*-Tetrahydrocannabinol

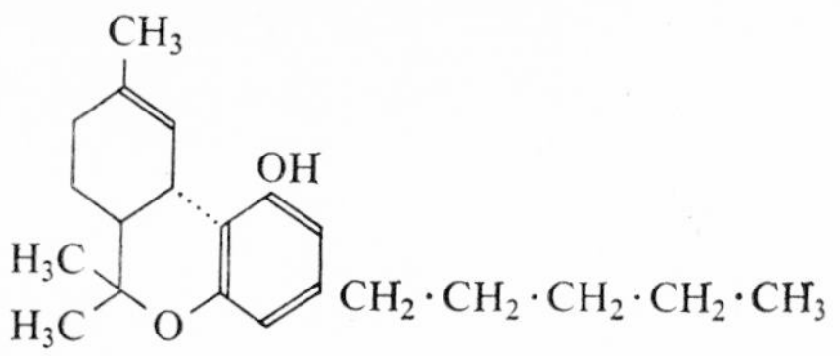

$C_{21}H_{30}O_2$ MW 314

Active constituent of hashish (*Cannabis sativa*). B.p. 155–7°/0·05 mm. $[\alpha]_D$ −150° ($CHCl_3$). Light absorption: $\lambda_{max.}$ 278 (ε, 2040), 282 (2075), and 300 sh. mμ (840).

3 : 5-*Dinitrophenylurethane*: m.p. 115–16°. $[\alpha]_D$ −140° ($CHCl_3$).

Gaoni, Mechoulam, *J. Am. Chem. Soc.*, 1964, **86**, 1646.

Tetrahydrocorticosterone (3α : 11β : 21-*Trihydroxy*-5β-*pregnan*-20-*one*)

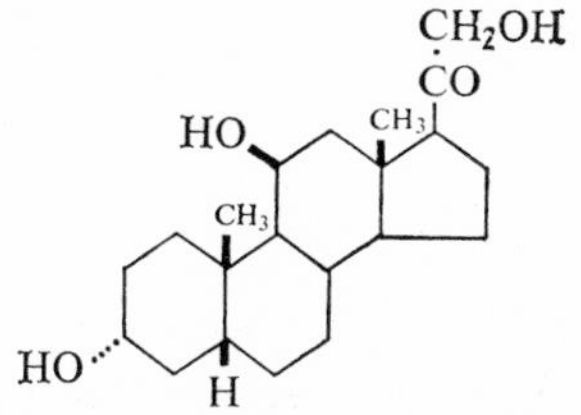

$C_{21}H_{34}O_4$ MW 350

Present in urine in various pathological conditions. Amorph. from Et_2O–light petroleum. M.p. 70–90° loosing solvent to give fine tetragonal prisms. M.p. 156–8°.

Dohan *et al.*, *J. Clin. Invest.*, 1955, **34**, 485; *Arch. Biochem. Biophys.*, 1959, **81**, 5.
Danilewicz, Klyne, *J. Chem. Soc.*, 1964, 537.

1 : 2 : 1′ : 2′-Tetrahydro-1 : 1′-dihydroxylycopene

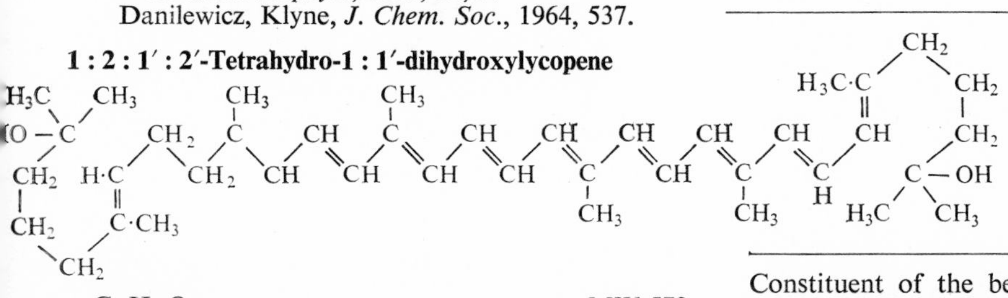

$C_{40}H_{60}O_2$ MW 572

Carotenoid present in *Rhodomicrobium vannielii* Duchow. Cryst. from Py. M.p. 193°. Light absorption: $\lambda_{max.}$ 446, 472·5, and 504·5 mμ in light petroleum. 475, 503, and 541 mμ in CS_2.

Di-hexadecanoate: $C_{72}H_{120}O_4$. MW 1048. Cryst. from Me_2O. M.p. 118°.

Surmatis, Ofner, *J. Org. Chem.*, 1963, **28**, 2737.
Ryvarden, Liaaen, Jensen, *Acta Chem. Scand.*, 1964, **18**, 643.

Tetrahydroharmine

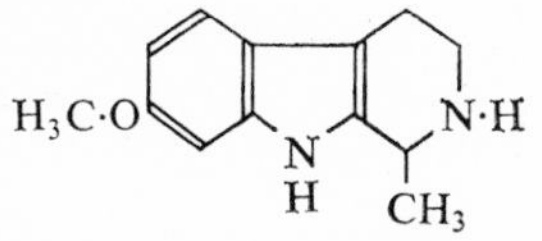

$C_{13}H_{16}ON_2$ MW 216

(+)-.

Constituent of *Banisteria caapi* and snuff used by South American Indians. M.p. 198·4–199·8°. $[\alpha]_D^{25}$ +32° ($CHCl_3$).

Hochstein, Paradies, *J. Am. Chem. Soc.*, 1957, **79**, 5735.
Bernauer, *Helv. Chim. Acta*, 1960, **47**, 1075.

1 : 2 : 3 : 4-Tetrahydro-3-hydroxyfuran

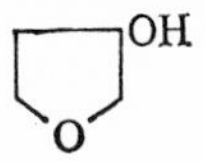

C_4H_8O MW 72

B.p. 93–5°/26 mm., 75–7°/16 mm., 50°/1 mm. n_D^{25} 1·4497. D_4^{20} 1·095.

Pariselle, *Ann. chim.* (Paris), 1911 [8], **24**, 315.
Reppe, *Ann.*, 1955, **596**, 1.
Wynberg, Bantjes, *Organic Syntheses*, 1958, **38**, 37; Coll. Vol. **4**, 534.

1 : 2 : 3 : 4-Tetrahydro-7-hydroxy-1-isobutyl-6-methoxy-2-methylisoquinoline. *See* Lophocerine.

4 : 5 : 6 : 7-Tetrahydroimidazo[5,4-*c*]pyridine. *See* Spinaceamine.

4 : 5 : 6 : 7-Tetrahydroimidazo[5,4-*c*]pyridine-5-carboxylic Acid. *See* Spinacine.

1 : 2 : 3 : 4-Tetrahydro-6-methoxy-1-methyl-2-carboline (*Adrenoglomerulotropin*)

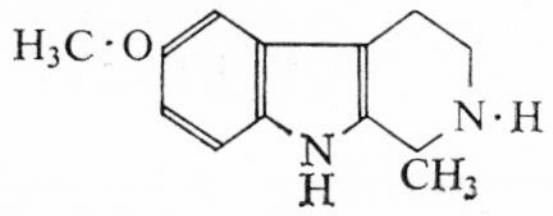

$C_{13}H_{16}ON_2$ MW 216

Constituent of the beef pineal gland. M.p. 152–152·5°. Light absorption: $\lambda_{max.}$ 225 (log ε, 4·34), 280 (3·86), 294 sh. (3·80), 307 sh. mμ (3·56) in EtOH. 220 (4·40), 273 (3·86), 293 sh. (3·69), 304 sh. mμ (3·52) in 0·1*N*-HCl.

Picrate: m.p. 226–33° decomp.

Farrell, McIsaac, *Arch. Biochem. Biophys.*, 1961, **94**, 543.
McIsaac, *Biochim. Biophys. Acta*, 1961, **52**, 607.
Meek, Szinai, Wallis, *Chemistry and Industry*, 1964, 622.

Tetrahydro-2-methylfuran-3-one

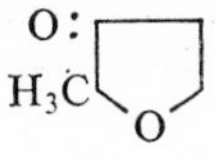

$C_5H_8O_2$ MW 84

Volatile constituent of coffee. B.p. 139°. n_D^{20} 1·4291.
2 : 4-*Dinitrophenylhydrazone*: m.p. 179–81°.

Gianturco, Friedel, Giammarino, *Tetrahedron*, 1964, **20**, 1763.

4 : 4′ : 6 : 6′-Tetrahydroxybiphenyl 2 : 2′-dicarboxylic Acid Dilactone. *See* Nasutin A.

4 : 4′ : 5 : 5′ -Tetrahydroxy -3 : 3′ -diazadipheno -2 : 2′ - quinone

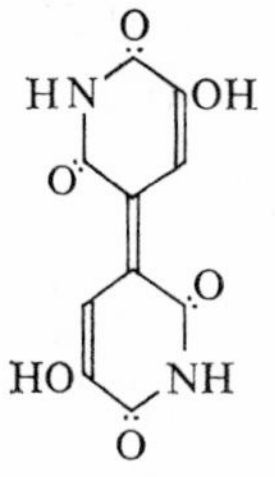

$C_{18}H_6O_6N_2$ MW 250

Bronze-green pigment from *Arthrobacter crystallopoietes*. Reductive acetylation → hexa-leuco-Ac: m.p. 160–2°.
Di-Ac: gold-yellow plates from nitrobenzene. Light absorption: $\lambda_{max.}$ 596 mμ (log ε, 4·26).

Ensign, Rittenberg, *Arch. Mikrobiol.*, 1963, **47**, 137.
Kuhn *et al.*, *Naturwiss.*, 1964, **51**, 409.

2 : 3 : 5 : 7 - Tetrahydroxy - 1 : 4 - naphthoquinone. *See* Spinochrome B.

3 : 3′ : 5 : 7 - Tetrahydroxy - 4′ : 6 : 8 - trimethoxyflavone. *See* Isolimocitrol.

3 : 4′ : 5 : 7 - Tetrahydroxy - 3′ : 6 : 8 - trimethoxyflavone. *See* Limocitrol.

1 : 3 : 5 : 8-Tetrahydroxyxanthone

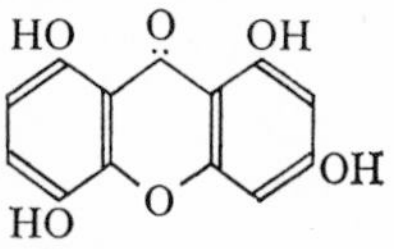

$C_{13}H_8O_6$ MW 260

Constituent of *Gentiana bellidifolia*. M.p. 315–20°.
Tetra-Ac: m.p. 244°.
3-*Me ether*: *see* Bellidifolium.
5-*Me ether*: $C_{14}H_{10}O_6$. MW 274. M.p. 271°. *Tri-Ac*: m.p. 222°.
Di-Me ether: *see under* Bellidifolium and Swerchirin.
Tri-Me ether: *see under* Bellidifolium.
Tetra-Me ether: $C_{17}H_{16}O_6$. MW 316. M.p. 209–10°.

Tanase, *J. Pharm. Soc. Japan*, 1941, **61**, 341.
Dalal, Shah, *Chemistry and Industry*, 1957, 140.
Markham, *Tetrahedron*, 1964, **20**, 991.

1 : 3 : 7 : 8-Tetrahydroxyxanthone.

M.p. 335°.
Tetra-Ac: m.p. 208°.
7-*Me ether*: m.p. >300°.
1 : 3-*Di-Me ether*: *see* Swertinin.
1 : 3 : 7-*Tri-Me ether*: *see* Decussatin.★
Tetra-Me ether: m.p. 166–7°.

Kulkarni, Merchant, *J. Sci. Ind. Res. India*, 1955, **14B**, 153.
Dalal, Shah, *Chemistry and Industry*, 1957, 140.

2 : 2 : 4 : 4-Tetramethylbicyclo[1,1,0]butyl propionate

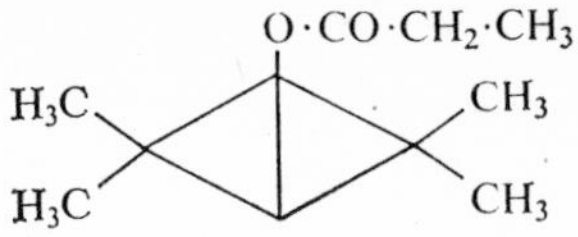

$C_{11}H_{18}O_2$ MW 182

Proposed structure for sex attractant of American cockroach.

Day, Whiting, *Proc. Chem. Soc.*, 1964, 368.

Tetramethylenephosphorochloridite. *See* 2 - Chloro - 1 : 3 : 2-dioxaphosphepan.

3 : 7 : 11 : 15-Tetramethylhexadecanoic Acid (*Phytanic acid*)

$(CH_3)_2CH{\cdot}[CH_2]_3$ $CH(CH_3){\cdot}[CH_2]_3$ COOH
$CH(CH_3){\cdot}[CH_2]_3$ $CH(CH_3){\cdot}CH_2$

$C_{20}H_{40}O_2$ MW 312

Oxidation of product of phytol present in ox-plasma lipids. B.p. 221°/7·5 mm. D_4^0 0·8879. D_4^{20} 0·8761. $[\alpha]_{500}^{20}$ −3·80° (c, 4 in MeOH : $CHCl_3$ 2 : 1).
Amide: cryst. from light petroleum and MeOH. M.p. 53–53·5°.

Willstätter, Mayer, Huni, *Ann.*, 1910, **378**, 73.
Lough, *Biochem. J.*, 1964, **91**, 584.

2 : 6 : 10 : 14-Tetramethylpentadecanoic Acid

$(CH_3)_2CH{\cdot}[CH_2]_3$ $CH(CH_3){\cdot}[CH_2]_3$
$CH(CH_3){\cdot}[CH_2]_3$ $CH(CH_3){\cdot}COOH$

$C_{19}H_{38}O_2$ MW 298

Component of butterfat.
Me ester: $C_{20}H_{40}O_2$. MW 312. M.p. below −70°.

Hansen, *Nature* (Lond.), 1964, **201**, 192.
Hansen, Morrison, *Biochem. J.*, 1964, **93**, 225.

2 : 2 : 4 : 4 : -Tetramethyl-3-pentanone.★

See also:

Dubois *et al.*, *Bull. soc. chim.*, 1964, 2024.

Tetrapheno-[6′,5′ : 5,6]-tetraphene

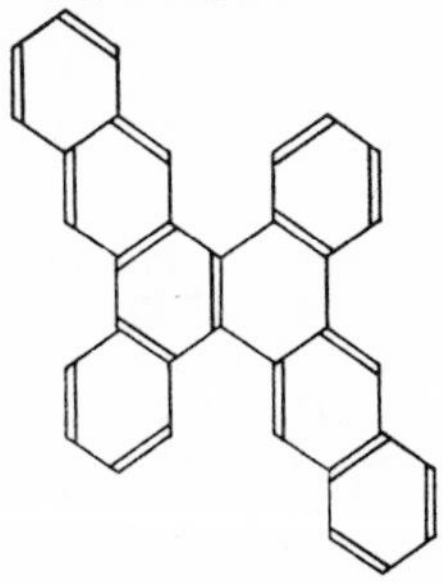

$C_{34}H_{20}$ MW 428

Yellow needles from xylene. M.p. 339–40°. H_2SO_4 → yellow-brown soln. Light absorption: $\lambda_{max.}$ 240 (log ε, 4·80), 272 (4·65), 304 (4·81), 322 (4·84), 336 (4·54), 400 (4·14), and 420 mμ (4·14).

Clar, Guye-Vuillème, Stephen, *Tetrahedron*, 1964, **20**, 2107.

"Tetraphenylpentatetraene." *See* Tetra-(ββ-diphenylvinyl)ethylene.

Tetrodotoxin.★
See also:
Woodward, *Pure Appl. Chem.*, 1964, **9**, 49.

Thalicarpine★

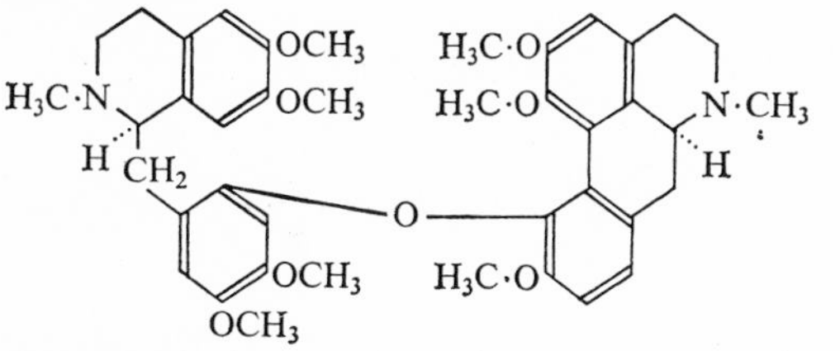

$C_{41}H_{48}O_8N_2$ MW 696
Hypotensive alkaloid from *Thalictrum dasycarpum* Fisch. and Lall. M.p. 151–3°. $[\alpha]_D^{21}$ +131° (c, 1·30 in MeOH).

Kupchan, Chakravarti, Yokoyama, *J. Pharm. Sci.*, 1963, **52**, 985.
Kupchan, Yokoyama, *J. Am. Chem. Soc.*, 1964, **86**, 2177.

Thalicthuberine. *See* (±)-Nantenine.

Thalictrine. *See* Magnoflorine.

Thalmelatine

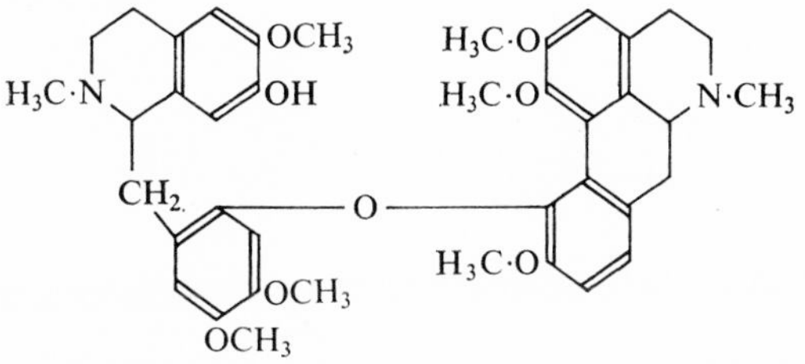

$C_{40}H_{46}O_8N_2$ MW 682
Alkaloid of *Thalictrum minus* var. *elatum* Jacq. Cryst. from EtOH. M.p. 131–5°. $[\alpha]_D^{21}$ 110° (c, 1 in EtOH).
Me ether: *see* Thalicarpine.
Et ether: cryst. from EtOH. M.p. 133–5°.

Mollov, Dutschewska, *Tetrahedron Letters*, 1964, 2219.

2-Thia-3-selenaspiro-[4,5]decane

$C_8H_{14}SSe$ MW 221
B.p. 109–12°/0·1 mm. Orange-red needles. M.p. 29–30°. Light absorption: $\lambda_{max.}$ 405 mμ.

Biezais, Bergson, *Acta Chem. Scand.*, 1964, **18**, 815.

1 : 4-Thiazane-3-carboxylic Acid

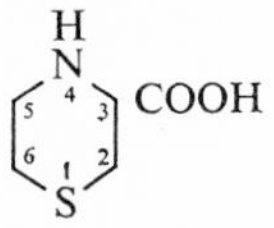

$C_5H_9O_2NS$ MW 147
Cryst. from H_2O–EtOH. M.p. 263–5° (sealed tube). Ninhydrin → violet col. H_2O_2 → *S*-oxide.

S-*Oxide*: Chondrine. Occurs in *Chondria crassicaulis* and *Undaria pinnatifida*. Cryst. from H_2O–EtOH. M.p. 248–50° decomp. (sealed tube). Ninhydrin → cobalt-blue col.

Kuriyama, Takagi, *Murata*, *Bull. Fac. Fisheries, Hokkaido Univ.*, 1960, **11**, 58.
Tominaga, Oka, *J. Biochem.* (Japan), 1963, **54**, 222.

Thiazolo[3,2-*a*]pyridinium

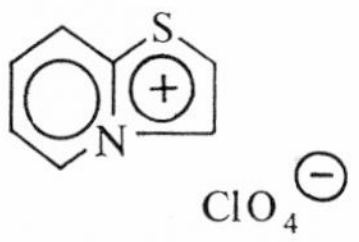

Perchlorate: $C_7H_6O_4NSCl$. MW 235·5. M.p. 281–3°. Light absorption: $\lambda_{max.}$ 208 (log ε, 4·00), 224 (4·08), 228 sh. (4·02), 295 (4·11), and 306 mμ (4·24).

Bradsher, Lohr, *Chemistry and Industry*, 1964, 1801.

7-[(2-Thienyl)acetamido]-3-(1-pyridylmethyl)-3-cephem-4-carboxylic Acid. *See* Cephaloridine.

6-(2-Thienyl)-2 : 4-hexadienoic Acid

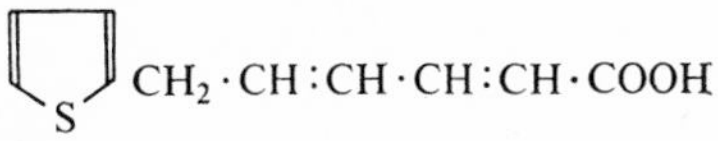

$C_{10}H_{10}O_2S$ MW 194
Free acid not known.
Me ester: b.p. 155°/0·01 mm.
Isobutylamide: $C_{11}H_{19}ONS$. MW 249. Constituent of the root of *Chrysanthemum frutescens*. Cryst. from Et_2O. M.p. 105°. Light absorption: $\lambda_{max.}$ 252 mμ (ε, 30,000). With alkali → conjugated isomer, m.p. 115°. Light absorption: $\lambda_{max.}$ 306 mμ (ε, 29,000).

Winterfeldt, *Chem. Ber.*, 1963, **96**, 3349.

9-(2-Thienyl)-non-6-en-8-yn-3-one

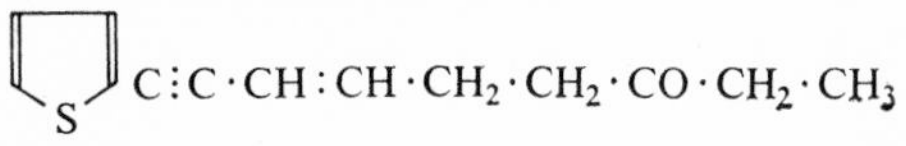

$C_{13}H_{14}OS$ MW 218
6-*Trans*-.
Constituent of the root of *Matricaria inodora* L. B.p. 79–82°/0·02 mm. Light absorption: $\lambda_{max.}$ 290 mμ (ε, 16,200).

Sörensen, *Proc. Chem. Soc.*, 1961, 98.
Bohlmann, *Chem. Ber.*, 1964, **97**, 801.

2-(2′-Thienyl)pyridine

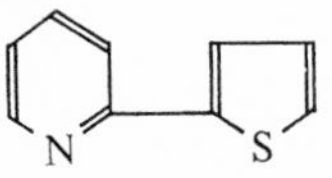

C_9H_7NS MW 161
M.p. 90–1°.

Kahmann, Class, Erlenmeyer, *Experientia*, 1964, **20**, 297.

Thiobidesoxynupharidine
$C_{30}H_{40}ON_2S$ MW 476
Alkaloid from the rhizomes of the yellow water-lily (*Nuphar luteum* (L.) Sm.).

B,2HClO$_4$: prisms. M.p. 225–6°. $[\alpha]_D$ +26·6° (EtOH).

Achmatowicz, Bellen, *Tetrahedron Letters*, 1962, 1121.

Thiobinupharidine

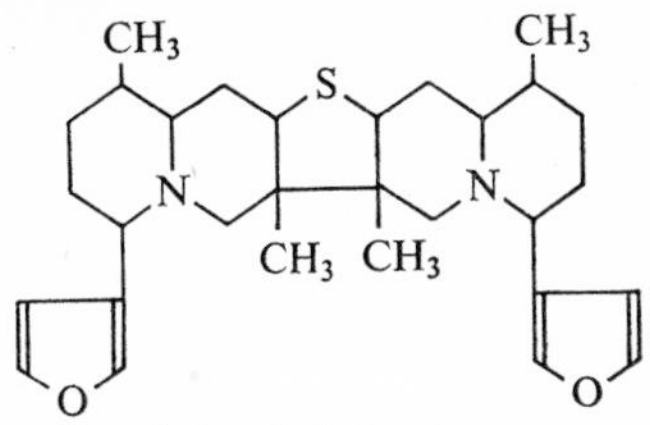

Suggested structure

$C_{30}H_{42}O_2N_2S$ MW 494

Alkaloid from the rhizome of the yellow water-lily (*Nuphar luteum* L.) Sm.). Prismatic needles. M.p. 129–30°.

B,2HClO$_4$: prisms. M.p. 282–4°. $[\alpha]_D$ +49·8° (H_2O). Light absorption: $\lambda_{max.}$ 298 mμ (ε, 1115).

Achmatowicz, Bellen, *Tetrahedron Letters*, 1962, 1121.

Achmatowicz, Wróbel, *Tetrahedron Letters*, 1964, 129, 927.

1-Thioisocoumarin

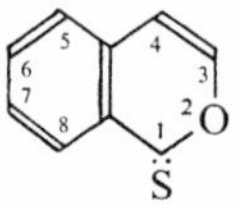

C_9H_6OS MW 162

M.p. 106°.

Legrand, Lozac'h, *Bull. soc. chim.*, 1964, 1787.

5-Thio-D-ribopyranose. *See* D-Ribothiapyranose.

4-Thio-L-ribose. *See* L-Ribothiapyranose.

Thiostreptine

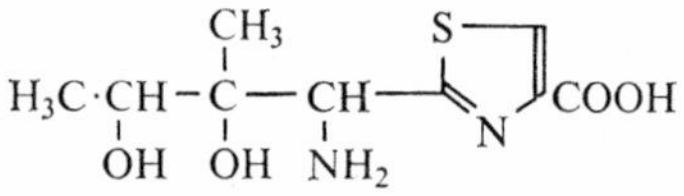

$C_9H_{14}O_4N_2S$ MW 246

Produced by acid hydrolysis of Thiostrepton. White solid. $[\alpha]_D^{20}$ −4° (c, 1 in *N*-AcOH).

Bodanszky *et al., J. Am. Chem. Soc.*, 1964, **86**, 2478.

Thiostreptoic Acid

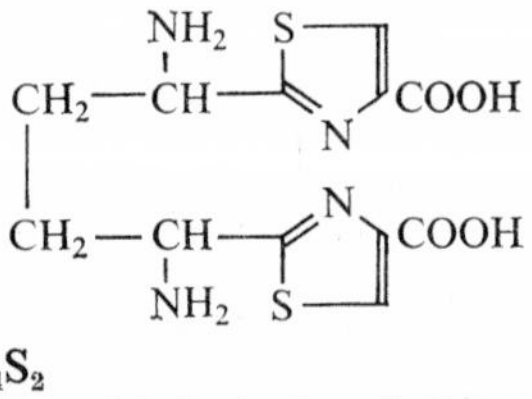

$C_{12}H_{14}O_4N_4S_2$ MW 454

Produced by acid hydrol. of thiostrepton. Two forms: (i) m.p. 225° decomp., (ii) m.p. 308° decomp.

B,4H$_2$SO$_4$: cryst. M.p. 270° decomp.

Di-Ac: m.p. 275–7° decomp.

Di-Me ester, Di-Ac: platelets. M.p. 295–8° decomp.

Bodanszky *et al., J. Am. Chem. Soc.*, 1964, **86**, 2478.

Thiostrepton

MW *ca.* 1650

Antibiotic from *Streptomyces azureus*. Cryst. from $CHCl_3$–EtOH. Hydrol. → L-threonine, L-alanine (2 moles), L-isoleucine, D-cystine, thiostreptoic acid, and thiostreptine.

Bodanszky *et al., J. Am. Chem. Soc.*, 1964, **86**, 2478.

5-Thio-D-xylopyranose. *See* D-Xylothiapyranose.

Thomosamine. *See* 4-Amino-4 : 6-dideoxy-D-galactose.

Threitol★

1-^{14}C:

Kent, Wood, *J. Chem. Soc.*, 1964, 2812.

Threoflavin (6 : 7-*Dimethyl*-9-[1' : -D-*threityl*]*isoalloxazine*)

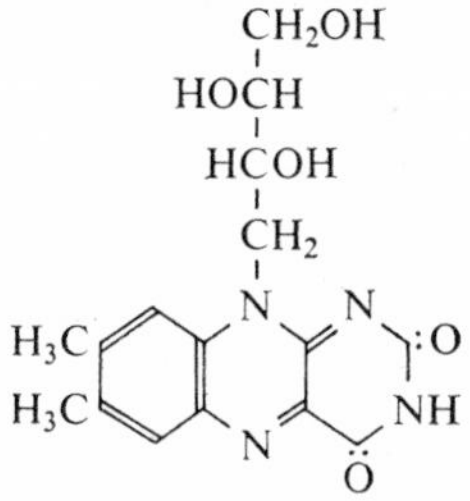

$C_{16}H_{18}O_5N_4$ MW 346

Brick-red needles from 6*N*-HCl. M.p. 282° decomp. $[\alpha]_D^{15}$ 30°.

4'-*Phosphate*: m.p. 202° decomp. $[\alpha]_D^{15}$ 64°.

Uehara, Sugeno, Mizoguchi, *J. Biochem.* (Japan), 1963, **54**, 267.

Thujopsene.★

(±)-.

Synthesis:

Büchi, White, *J. Am. Chem. Soc.*, 1964, **86**, 2884.

Thyloquinone. *See* 2-Methyl-1 : 4-naphthoquinone.

α-Tocopherylhydroquinone

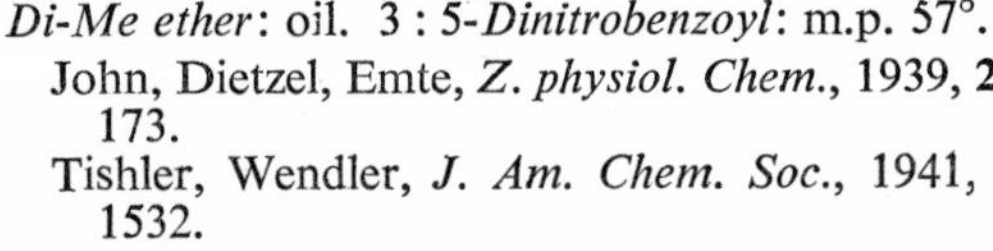

$C_{29}H_{52}O_3$ MW 448

Oil.

Di-Ac: needles from EtOH. M.p. 65°.

Tri-Ac: m.p. 75°.

Di-p-bromobenzoyl: m.p. 114°.

Di-Me ether: oil. 3 : 5-*Dinitrobenzoyl*: m.p. 57°.

John, Dietzel, Emte, *Z. physiol. Chem.*, 1939, **257**, 173.

Tishler, Wendler, *J. Am. Chem. Soc.*, 1941, **63**, 1532.

α-Tocopherylquinone

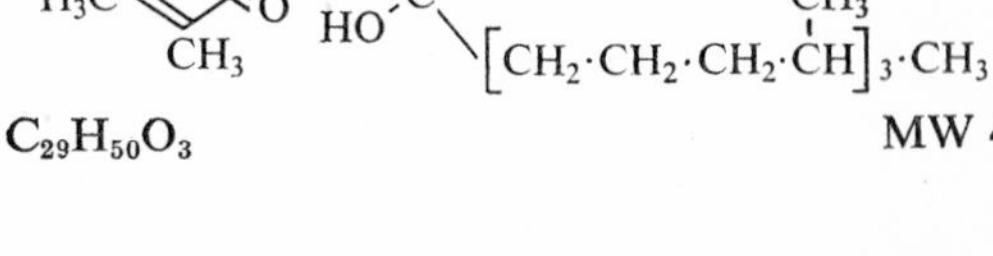

$C_{29}H_{50}O_3$ MW 446

Present in maize and barley seedlings, holly leaves, etc. B.p. 120°/0·002 mm. Has no vitamin E activity. Red. → α-tocopherylhydroquinone.

Karrer *et al.*, *Helv. Chim. Acta*, 1938, **21**, 951; 1940, **23**, 455.
John, Dietzel, Emte, *Z. physiol. chem.*, 1939, **257**, 173.
Tischler, Wendler, *J. Am. Chem. Soc.*, 1941, **63**, 1532.
Griffiths, Threlfall, Goodwin, *Biochem. J.*, 1964, **90**, 40P.
Bucke, Hallaway, Morton, *Biochem. J.*, 1964, **90**, 41P.

Tonoquil. Psychotherapeutic drug containing chlorphencycloin and thiopropazate.

Tordan. *See* 4-Amino-3 : 5 : 6-trichloropicolinic Acid.

Torreyal

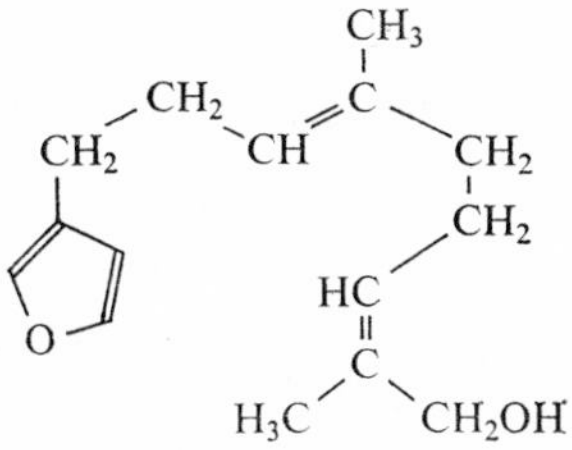

$C_{15}H_{20}O_2$ MW 232

Constituent of the wood of *Torreya nucifera*. B.p. 124–6°/0·05 mm. $[\alpha]_D^{20}$ 1·90°. Light absorption: $\lambda_{max.}$ 224 mμ (ε, 15,940).
2 : 4-*Dinitrophenylhydrazone*: m.p. 111–12°.

Sakai, Nishimura, Hirose, *Tetrahedron Letters*, 1963, 1171.

Torreyol.

The substance from *Torreya nucifera* originally designated Torreyol was shown to be (+)-δ-cadinol (*q.v.*), and the name was then applied to another compound isolated from the same source.

Torreyol

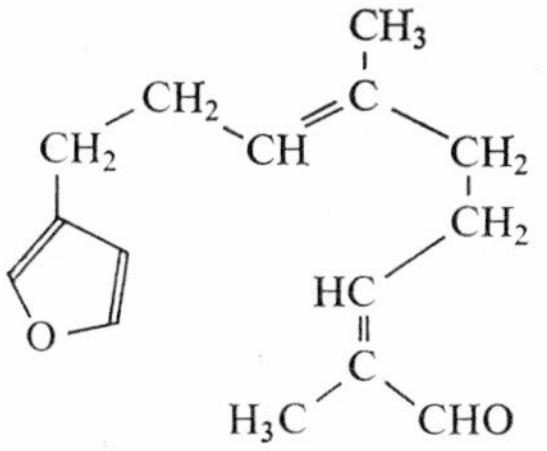

$C_{15}H_{22}O_2$ MW 234

Constituent of the wood oil of *Torreya nucifera*. B.p. 117–19°/0·03 mm. $[\alpha]_D^{20}$ 0°.
Note. This compound is not identical with δ-cadinol.

Sakai, Nishimura, Hirose, *Tetrahedron Letters*, 1963, 1171.

Torularhodin

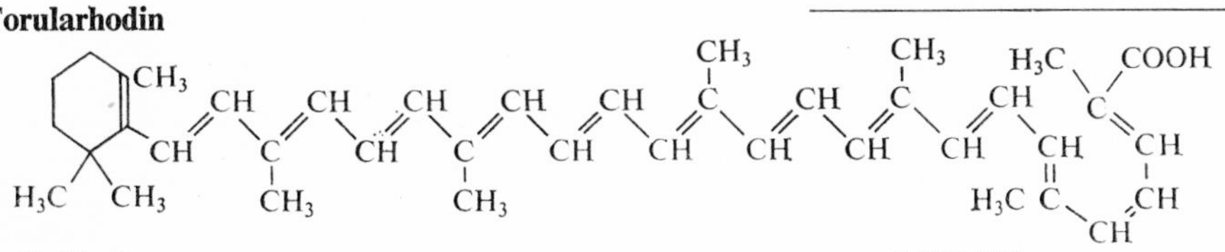

$C_{40}H_{52}O_2$ MW 564

Metabolite of *Rhodotorula rubra* and *R. sanniei.* Red needles. M.p. 202° (*in vacuo*). Light absorption: $\lambda_{max.}$ 483, 515, and 554 mμ in $CHCl_3$. $\lambda_{max.}$ 502, 541, and 582 mμ in CS_2.
Me ester: $C_{41}H_{54}O_2$. MW 578. Dark red needles from C_6H_6–MeOH. M.p. 172–3°. Light absorption: $\lambda_{max.}$ 502, 541, and 581 mμ in CS_2.

Lederer, *Bull. soc. chim. biol.*, 1938, **20**, 611.
Fromageot, Tchang, *Arch. Mikrobiol.*, 1938, **9**, 424.
Karrer, Rutschmann, *Helv. Chim. Acta*, 1946, **29**, 355.
Entschel, Karrer, *Helv. Chim. Acta*, 1959, **42**, 466.
Ruegg *et al.*, *Chimica*, 1958, **12**, 327.

Biosynthesis:

Simpson, Nakayama, Chichester, *Biochem. J.*, 1964, **92**, 508.

Torulosal

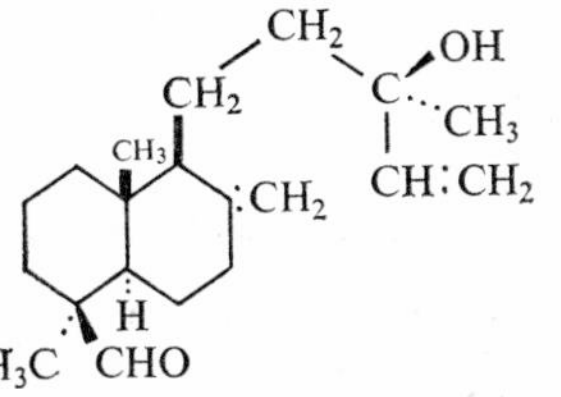

$C_{20}H_{32}O_2$ MW 304

Constituent of the heartwood of *Cupressus torulosa* Don. Unstable oil. n_D^{25} 1·521. $[\alpha]_D$ +29° (c, 1·8 in $CHCl_3$). With CCl_4 gives "inclusion compound": m.p. 80–5°. $[\alpha]_D$ +24° (c, 2 in $CHCl_3$).
Semicarbazone: m.p. 195–7° decomp. $[\alpha]_D$ −9° (c, 1 in Py).

Enzell, *Acta. Chem. Scand.*, 1961, **15**, 1303.
Barreto, Enzell, *Acta Chem. Scand.*, 1961, **15**, 1315.

Torulosic Acid

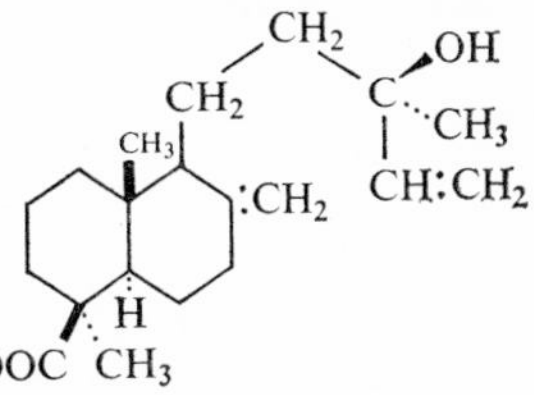

$C_{20}H_{32}O_3$ MW 320

Minor constituent of the resin of *Tetraclinis articulata* (N. African sandarac).

Gough, *Chemistry and Industry*, 1964, 2059.

Torulosol

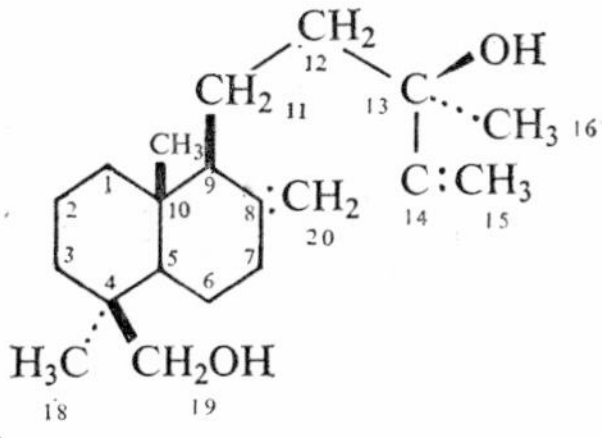

$C_{20}H_{34}O_2$ MW 306

Heartwood constituent of *Cupressus torulosa* Don. Cryst. from di-isopropyl ether. M.p. 110–11°. $[\alpha]_D$ +31° (c, 2 in $CHCl_3$). $H_2 \rightarrow$ tetrahydro deriv. M.p. 119–24°. $[\alpha]_D$ +16° (c, 2 in $CHCl_3$).
18-*Ac*: constituent of *Tetraclinis articulata.*

Enzell, *Acta Chem. Scand.*, 1961, **15**, 1303.
Barreto, Enzell, *Acta Chem. Scand.*, 1961, **15**, 1313.
Gough, *Chemistry and Industry*, 1964, 2059.

Toxiferine I.★

17 : 17′-^2H-.

Grdinic, Nelson, Boekelheide, *J. Am. Chem. Soc.*, 1964, **86**, 3357.

Toxol★

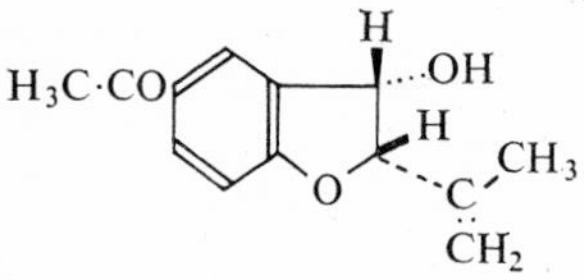

(R) (−)-.
Absolute configuration:

Bonner *et al.*, *Tetrahedron*, 1964, **20**, 1419.

Toyocamycin

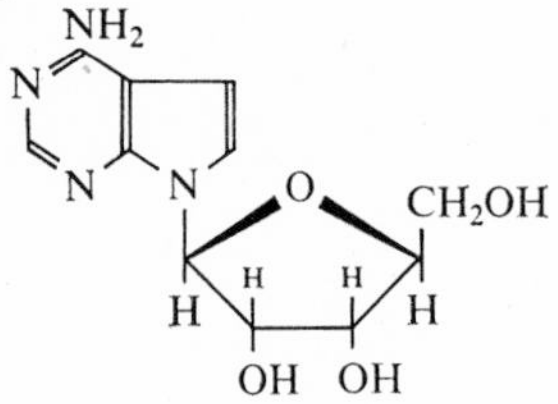

$C_{12}H_{13}O_4N_5$ MW 291

Antibiotic from *Streptomyces toyocaensis.* Colourless needles or prisms of monohydrate. M.p. 243°. Hydrol. → 4-amino-5-cyanopyrrolo[2,3-*d*]pyrimidine (*q.v.*).

Kikuchi, *J. Antibiotics* (Japan), 1955, **9A**, 145.
Nishimura *et al.*, *J. Antibiotics* (Japan), 1956, **9A**, 60.

Trehalose-6-phosphate

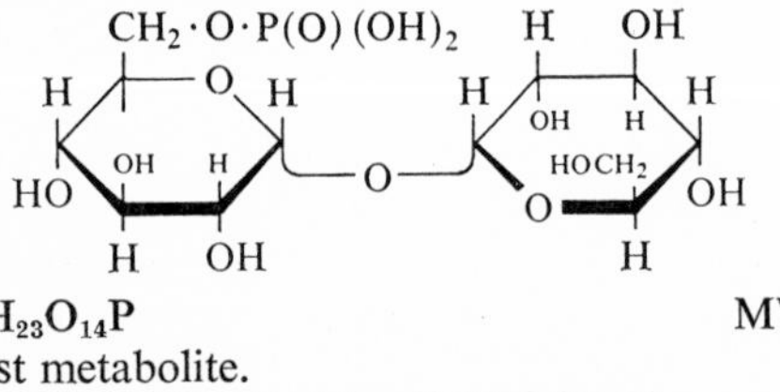

$C_{12}H_{23}O_{14}P$ MW 422

Yeast metabolite.
Ba salt: $[\alpha]_D^{20}$ 118°. $[\alpha]_{5461}^{20}$ 138° (H_2O).

Robison, Morgan, *Biochem. J.*, 1928, **22**, 1277; 1930, **24**, 119.
Helferich *et al.*, *Z. physiol. Chem.*, 1923, **128**, 141.

Cabib, Leloir, *J. Biol. Chem.*, 1958, **231**, 259.
MacDonald, Wong, *Biochim. Biophys. Acta*, 1964, **86**, 390.

Tremetone★

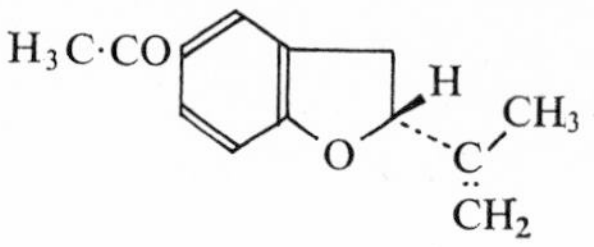

(R) (−)-.
Absolute configuration:

Bonner *et al.*, *Tetrahedron*, 1964, **20**, 1419.

1 : 2 : 3 : -Triacetylbenzene

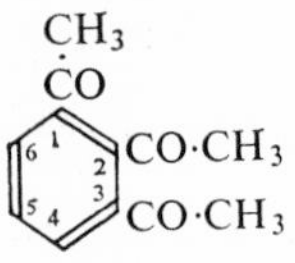

$C_{12}H_{12}O_3$ MW 204

Cryst. M.p. 149°. Gives intense colours with amino acids.

Riemschneider, Diedrich, *Ann.*, 1961, **646**, 18.

1 : 2 : 4-Triacetylbenzene

$C_{12}H_{12}O_3$ MW 204

Pale pink needles from Et_2O. M.p. 75°. Gives deeply coloured solutions with low concentrations of amino acids.

Hopff, Grasshoff, *Helv. Chim. Acta*, 1964, **47**, 1333.

Triaspidin

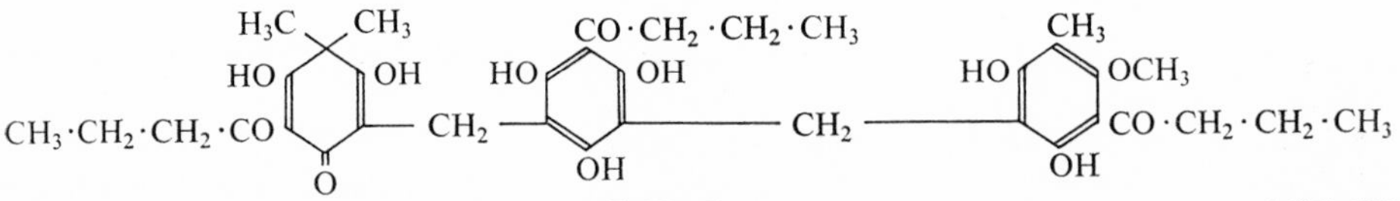

$C_{36}H_{44}O_{12}$ MW 620

Constituent of the fern *Dryopteris austriaca.* Cryst. from Me_2CO. M.p. 156–9°.

Penttilä, Sundman, *Acta Chem. Scand.*, 1963, **17**, 2361.

1,2 : 3,4 : 5,6-Tribenzocoronene

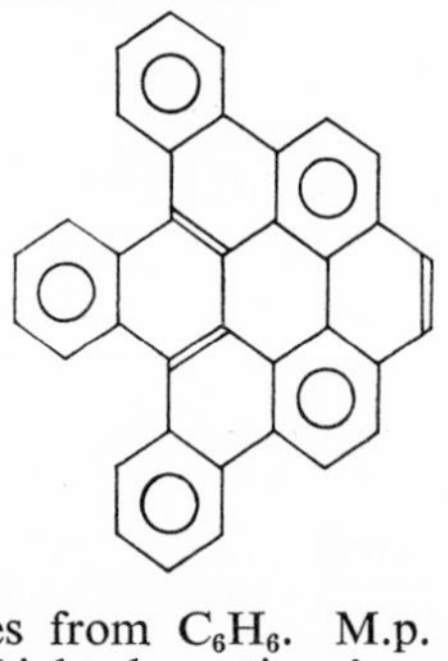

$C_{36}H_{18}$ MW 450

Yellow needles from C_6H_6. M.p. 350–1°. Insol. conc. H_2SO_4. Light absorption: $\lambda_{max.}$ 464 (log ε, 2·62), 436 (2·98), 407 (4·25), 384 (4·34), 354 (5·00), 340 (4·78), 293 (4·62), and 272 mμ (4·60) in C_6H_6. $\lambda_{max.}$ 236 mμ (4·81) in C_6H_{12}.

Clar, McCallum, *Tetrahedron*, 1964, **20**, 507.

1 : 3 : 5-Tri-*tert.*-butylbenzene

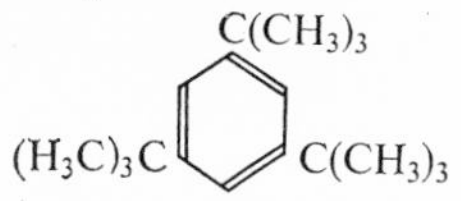

$C_{18}H_{30}$ MW 246

White cryst. M.p. 74°. B.p. 248°. Light absorption: $\lambda_{max.}$ 262 mμ (ε, 182).

McCaulay, Lien, *J. Am. Chem. Soc.*, 1953, **75**, 2411.

2 : 4 : 6-Tri-*tert.*-butyltoluene

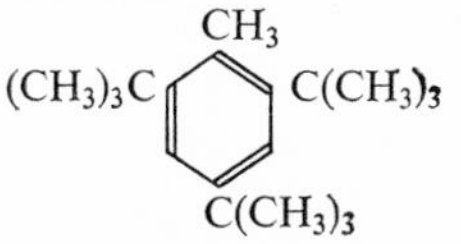

$C_{19}H_{32}$ MW 260

White cryst. M.p. 149°. Light absorption: $\lambda_{max.}$ 259 mμ (ε, 220) in methylcyclohexane.

Gibbons, Fischer, *Tetrahedron Letters*, 1964, 43.

3 : 5 : 6-Trichloro-1 : 2 : 4-triazine

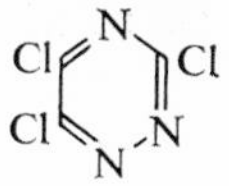

$C_3H_3Cl_3$ MW 184·5

M.p. 57–8°.

Piskala, Gut, Šorm, *Chemistry and Industry*, 1964, 1752.

Trichocarpin (2β-D-*Glucopyranosyl-5-hydroxybenzoic acid benzyl ester*)

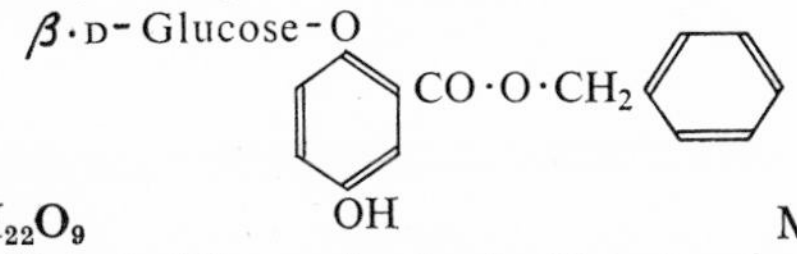

$C_{20}H_{22}O_9$ MW 406

Constituent of the poplar bark. Rosettes from H_2O. M.p. 134–6°. $[\alpha]_D^{20}$ −46·3° (c, 5 in MeOH). Hydrol. → D-glucose + benzyl 2 : 5-dihydroxybenzoate (Trichocarpinin).

Loeschcke, Francksen, *Naturwiss.*, 1964, **51**, 140.

Trichodermin

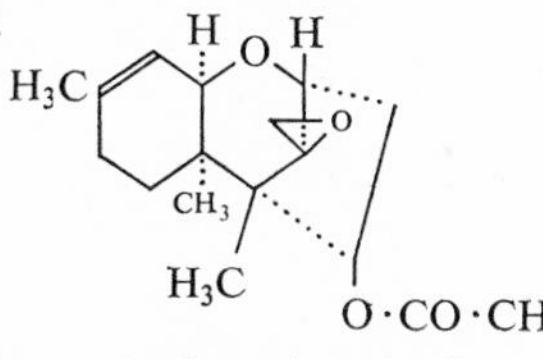

$C_{17}H_{24}O_4$ MW 292

Antifungal metabolite of a strain of *Trichoderma*. M.p. 45–6°. $[\alpha]_D^{20}$ −11°. Hydrol. → trichodermol + AcOH.

Abrahamsson, Nilsson, *Proc. Chem. Soc.*, 1964, 188.

Godtfredsen, Vangedal, *Proc. Chem. Soc.*, 1964, 188.

Trichodermol (*Roridin C*)

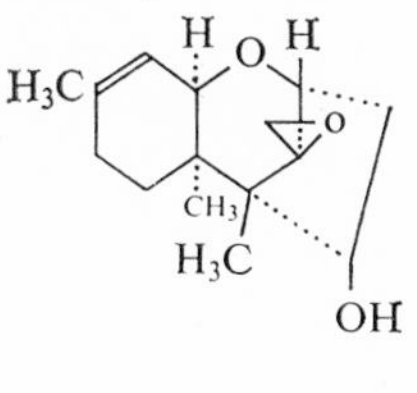

$C_{15}H_{22}O_3$ MW 250

Metabolite of *Myrothecium roridum*. M.p. 118°. $[\alpha]_D^{20}$ −34°.

Ac: *see* Trichodermin.

p-*Bromobenzoyl*: m.p. 161–3°.

Härri *et al.*, *Helv. Chim. Acta*, 1962, **45**, 839.

Abrahamsson, Nilsson, *Proc. Chem. Soc.*, 1964, 188.

Godlfredsen, Vangedul, *Proc. Chem. Soc.*, 1964, 188.

Tricyclo[3,3,1,1^{3,7}]decane. *See* Adamantane.

Tricyclo[2,2,1,0^{2,6}]heptane★ (*Nortricyclene*).

See also:

Nickon, Hammons, *J. Am. Chem. Soc.*, 1964, **86**, 3322.

Tricyclo[2,2,0,0^{2,6}]hexane

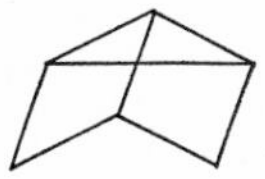

C_6H_8 MW 80

Liquid separated by preparative gas chromatography.

Lemal, Shim, *J. Am. Chem. Soc.*, 1964, **86**, 1550.

Tricyclo[5,1,0,0^{3,5}]octane

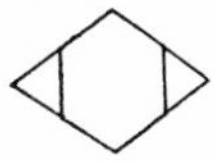

C_8H_{12} MW 108

Trans-.

Colourless liquid. B.p. 140·6°/749·6 mm. n_D^{25} 1·4760.

Neale, Whipple, *J. Am. Chem. Soc.*, 1964, **86**, 3126.

2 : 3 : 6-Trideoxy-D-*erythro*-aldohexose. *See* Amicetose.

2 : 3 : 6-Trideoxy-L-*threo*-aldohexose. *See* Rhodinose.

1 : 3 : 5-Triethynylbenzene

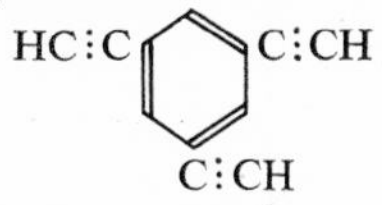

$C_{12}H_6$ MW 150

Colourless needles or prisms. M.p. 105–7° (77–8°).

Hubel, Merényi, *Chem. Ber.*, 1963, **96**, 930; *Angew. Chem., Int. Ed.*, 1963, **2**, 42.

Trifoliol

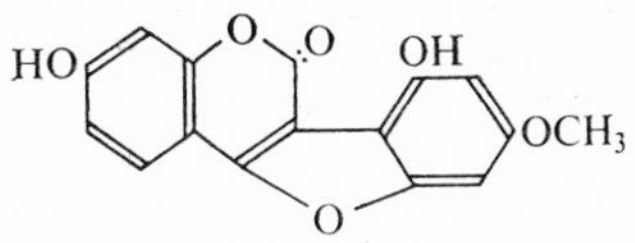

$C_{16}H_{10}O_6$ MW 298

Constituent of ladino clover. Rods from H·CONMe$_2$. M.p. 332° decomp. Light absorption: $\lambda_{max.}$ 270, 303, 349 mμ.

Di-Ac: white needles from Me$_2$CO. M.p. 243°.

Mono-Me ether: $C_{17}H_{12}O_6$. MW 312. Cryst. from MeOH. M.p. 209–12°.

Di-Me ether: $C_{18}H_{14}O_6$. MW 326. Cryst. from H·CONMe$_2$. M.p. 255–8°.

Livingston *et al.*, *Tetrahedron*, 1964, **20**, 1963.

2′ : 4 : 4′-Trihydroxybiphenyl-2-carboxylic Acid (2 : 2′)-lactone (*Castoreum pigment I, Urolithin A*)

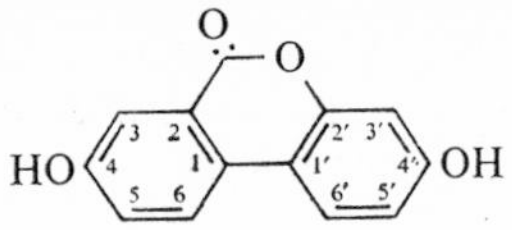

$C_{13}H_8O_4$ MW 228

Constituent of castoreum (the dried scent glands of the Canadian beaver, *Castor fiber*) and of "clover stone" a type of renal calculus found in sheep. Yellow needles. M.p. 340–5° decomp. (>360° decomp.).

Di-Ac: needles from AcOEt. M.p. 210°.

4-*Me ether*: $C_{14}H_{10}O_4$. MW 242. Needles. M.p. 275–8°.

Di-Me ether: $C_{15}H_{12}O_4$. MW 256. Needles. M.p. 153–4·5°.

Lederer, *Trav. Soc. chim. biol.*, 1942, **24**, 1155; *J. Chem. Soc.*, 1949, 2115.
Lederer, Polonsky, *Bull. soc. chim.*, 1948, 831.
Pope, *Biochem. J.*, 1964, **93**, 474.

2′ : 5 : 7-Trihydroxy-5′ : 6-dimethoxyisoflavone. *See* Podospicatin.

4′ : 6 : 7-Trihydroxyisoflavone.★

Present in fermented soybeans (Tempeh).

György, Murata, Ikehata, *Nature* (Lond.), 1964, **203**, 870.

2 : 4 : 6-Trihydroxyisovalerophenone (*Phlorisovalerophenone*)

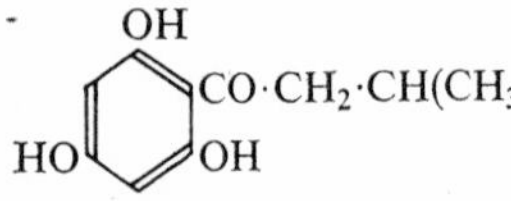

$C_{11}H_{14}O_4$ MW 210

Anhydrous. M.p. 145° (176–8°). Monohydrate 95°.

2 : 4-*Dinitrophenylhydrazone*: m.p. 196°.

2-*Me ether*: m.p. 132°. *Bis*(3 : 5-*dinitrobenzoyl*): m.p. 198–200°.

4-*Me ether*: m.p. 96–7°. *Dibenzoyl*: m.p. 104°. *Bis*(3 : 5-*dinitrobenzoyl*): m.p. 175–6°.

Karrer, Rosenfeld, *Helv. Chim. Acta*, 1921, **4**, 712.
Rosenmund, Lohfert, *Ber.*, 1928, **61**, 2607.
Kenny, Robertson, George, *J. Chem. Soc.*, 1939, 1601.
Orth, Riedl, *Ann.*, 1963, **663**, 74.

1 : 5 : 8-Trihydroxy-3-methoxyxanthone. *See* Bellidifolium.

1 : 3 : 8-Trihydroxy-6-methylanthraquinone.★

1-*Me ether*: *see* Questin.
1 : 8-*Di-Me*: m.p. 280–5°.
3β-*Rhamnosyl*: *see* Frangulin A.
See also Frangulin B.

3β : 16β : 28-Trihydroxy-18β-olean-12-ene. *See* Longispinogenin.

3 : 16 : 21 - Trihydroxyolean - 12 - en - 28 - oic Acid. *See* Acacic Acid.

3β : 11α : 14-Trihydroxy-12-oxo-5β-bufa-20 : 22-dienolide. *See* Arenobufagin.

3 : 4 : 5-Trihydroxyphthalicaldehyde. *See* Fomecin B.

3α : 11β : 21-Trihydroxy-5β-pregnan-20-one. *See* Tetrahydrocorticosterone.

3′ : 5 : 5′-Trihydroxy-3 : 4′ : 6 : 7-tetramethoxyflavone

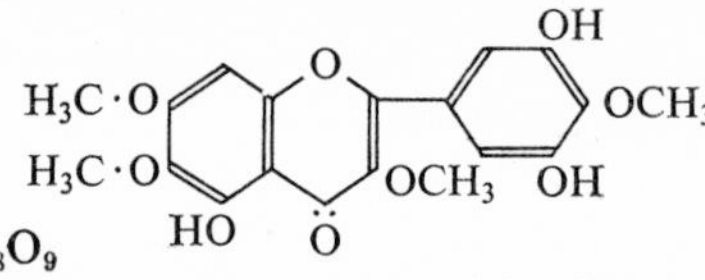

$C_{19}H_{18}O_9$ MW 390

Pigment present in *Eremophila fraseri* F. Muell. Plates from C_6H_6–EtOH. M.p. 172–3° and 211–12°. Light absorption: $\lambda_{max.}$ 218 (log ε, 4·59), 273 (4·20), 341 mμ (4·37).

Tri-Ac: needles from C_6H_6–light petroleum. M.p. 156–7°.

3′ : 5′-*Di-Me ether*: pale yellow needles from C_6H_6–light petroleum. M.p. 176–8°.

Tri-Me ether: needles from C_6H_6–light petroleum. M.p. 155–6°.

Tri-Et ether: prisms from C_6H_6–light petroleum. M.p. 120–1°.

Jefferies, Knox, Middleton, *Austral. J. Chem.*, 1962, **15**, 532.

3′ : 5 : 5′-Trihydroxy-3 : 4′ : 7-trimethoxyflavone

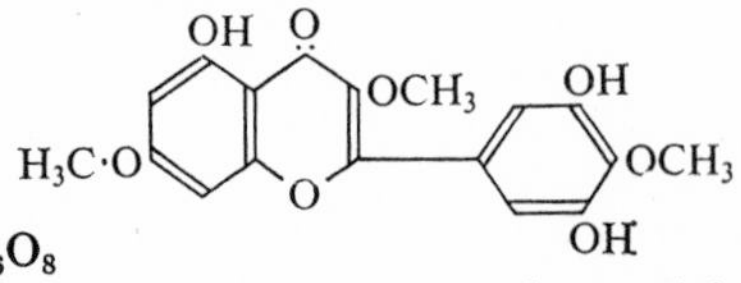

$C_{18}H_{16}O_8$ MW 360

Constituent of *Ricinocarpus stylosus* Diels. Yellow spike needles from MeOH. M.p. 208–10°. Light absorption: $\lambda_{max.}$ 264 (log ε, 4·27) and 350 mμ (4·24).

Tri-Ac: needles from C_6H_6–light petroleum. M.p. 203–5°.

3′ : 5′-*Di-Me ether*: *see under* Myricetin.

3 : 5 : 5′-*Tri-Me ether*: *see under* Myricetin.

Henrick, Jefferies, *Austral. J. Chem.*, 1964, **17**, 934.

4′ : 5 : 7-Trihydroxy-3 : 3′ : 6-trimethoxyflavone. *See* Jaceidin.

Trimethidium methosulphate. *See under* 3-(3-Dimethylaminopropyl)-1 : 8 : 8-trimethyl-3-azabicyclo-[3,2,1]octane.

4′ : 5 : 7-Trimethoxyflavan

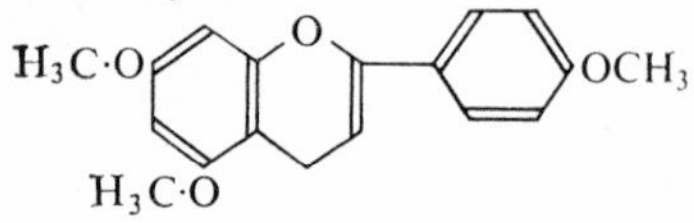

$C_{18}H_{20}O_4$ MW 300

From the resin of *Xanthorrhoea preissii*. M.p. 109–11°. Light absorption: $\lambda_{max.}$ 235 sh. (log ε, 4·42), 274 (3·36), and 280 sh. mμ (3·26).

Birch, Salahuddin, *Tetrahedron Letters*, 1964, 2211.

3 : 4 : 5 - Trimethoxy - 1 - propenylbenzene. *See* Isoelemicin.

3 : 7 : 11 - Trimethyl - 1 : 3 : 6 : 10 - dodecatetraene★ (*Farnesene*).

Present in natural coating of apples.

Murray, Huelin, Davenport, *Nature*, 1964, **204**, 80.

Trimethylsilanol

$(CH_3)_3{\cdot}Si{\cdot}OH$

$C_3H_{10}Si$ MW 74

B.p. 31–4°/26 mm. n_D^{20} 1·3880.

Sauer, *J. Am. Chem. Soc.*, 1944, **66**, 1707.
Birkofer, Ritter, Dickopp, *Chem. Ber.*, 1963, **96**, 1473.

Triphenyl-biphenylenearsene

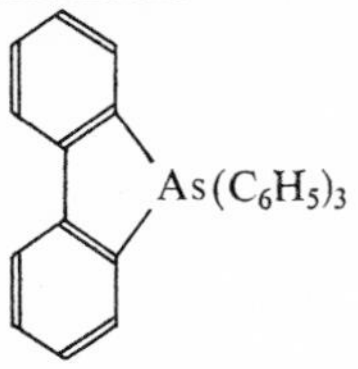

$C_{30}H_{23}As$ MW 458

Cryst. from C_6H_6. M.p. 191–2°.
Wittig, Hellwinkel, *Chem. Ber.*, 1964, **97**, 769.

Triphenylbiphenylenephosphoran

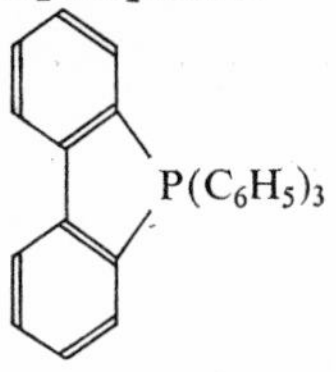

$C_{30}H_{23}P$ MW 414·5

Cryst. from cyclohexane or toluene. M.p. 155·5–156·5°.
Wittig, Kochendoerfer, *Chem. Ber.*, 1964, **97**, 741.

Triptycene (9 : 10-*Dihydro*-9 : 10-o-*benzenoanthracene*, *Tryptycene*)

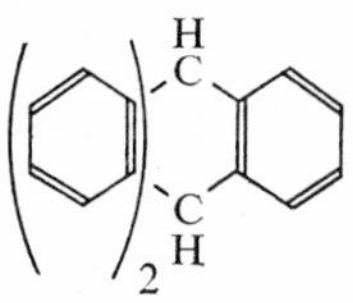

$C_{20}H_{14}$ MW 254

M.p. 256°.
Bartlett, Ryan, Cohen, *J. Am. Chem. Soc.*, 1942, **64**, 2649.
Bartlett, Lewis, *J. Am. Chem. Soc.*, 1950, **72**, 1005.
Wittig, Ludwig, *Angew. Chem.*, 1956, **68**, 40.
Wittig, *Organic Syntheses*, 1959, **39**, 75; Coll. Vol. **4**, 964.

Triquinacene (*Tricyclo*[5,2,1,$0^{4,10}$]*deca*-2 : 5 : 8-*triene*)

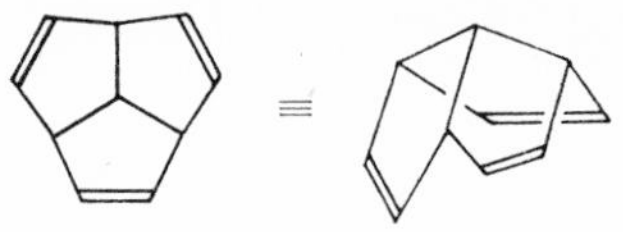

$C_{10}H_{10}$ MW 130

M.p. 18·1–19·1°. Light absorption: $\lambda_{max.}$ 187 mμ (ε, 13,000).
Woodward, Fukunaga, Kelly, *J. Am. Chem. Soc.*, 1964, **86**, 3162.

Trisdesaspidin

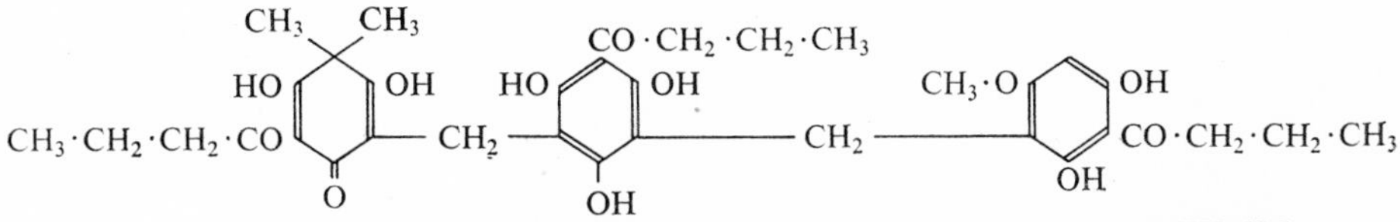

$C_{35}H_{42}O_{12}$ MW 606

Constituent of the fern *Dryopteris austriaca*. Cryst. from cyclohexane–hexane. M.p. 148–52° decomp.
Penttilä, Sundman, *Acta Chem. Scand.*, 1963, **17**, 2361.

Trisflavaspidic Acid

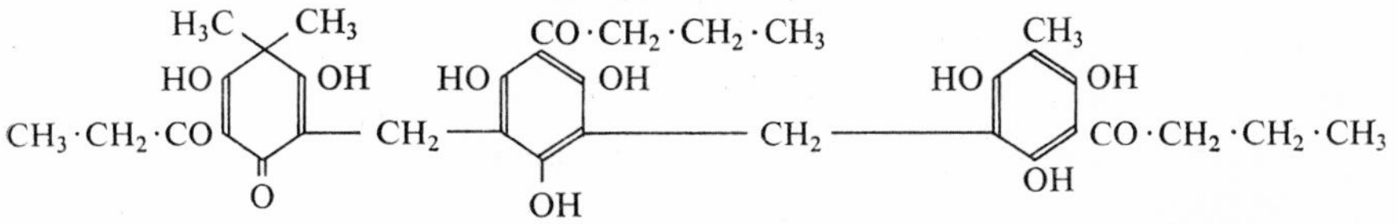

$C_{35}H_{42}O_{12}$ MW 606

Constituent of the fern *Dryopteris austriaca*. Cryst. from cyclohexane–hexane (1 : 1). M.p. 169–74° decomp.
Penttilä, Sundman, *Acta Chem. Scand.*, 1963, **17**, 2361.

Trishydroxymethylacetaldehyde. *See* Pentaerythrose.

Tropane-3α : 6β-diol.
(−)-3*S* : 6*S*.
Revised stereochemistry:
Fodor, Sóti, *Tetrahedron Letters*, 1964, 1917.

Tropan-2-one

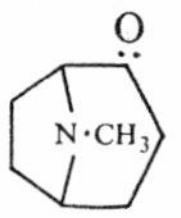

$C_8H_{13}ON$ MW 139

(+)-.
Obtained by degradation of (−)-cocaine. B.p. 101°/13·5 mm. M.p. 27–8°. $[\alpha]_D^{20}$ +23·8° (c, 1·81 in H_2O).
(−)-.
B.p. 103–4°/13 mm. $[\alpha]_D$ −23·3° (c, 1·93 in H_2O).
(±)-.
B.p. 99–99·5°/11 mm.
Picrate: prisms from C_6H_6–EtOH. M.p. 235° decomp.
B,CH₃I: parallelepipeds from H_2O. M.p. 307–8° decomp.
Bell, Archer, *J. Am. Chem. Soc.*, 1958, **80**, 6147; 1960, **82**, 4642.
Davies, Pinder, Morris, *Tetrahedron*, 1962, **18**, 405.

Trypacidin
$C_{18}H_{16}O_7$ MW 344
Antiprotozoal antibiotic from *Aspergillus fumigatus*. M.p. 228–31°. $[\alpha]_D^{20}$ −102·9°.

Balan, Ebringer, Nemec, *Naturwiss.*, 1964, **51**, 227.

Tryptophane.★
DL-5^{14}*C*:

Mathur, Ng, Henderson, *J. Biol. Chem.*, 1964, **239**, 2184.

Carboxy ^{14}*C*:

Slater, *Can. J. Chem.*, 1964, **42**, 1768.

Tryptycene. *See* Triptycene.

Tubercidin

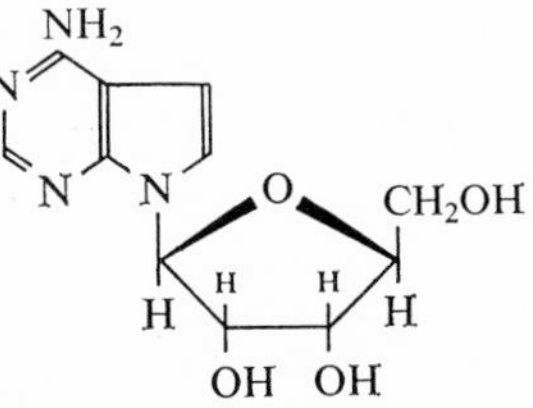

$C_{11}H_{14}O_4N_4$ MW 266
Antibiotic from a *Streptomycete*. Cryst. M.p. 247° decomp. Hydrol. → 4-Aminopyrrolo[2,3-*d*]pyrimidine (*q.v.*).

Anzai, Nakamura, Suzuki, *J. Antibiotics* (Japan), 1957, **10A**, 201.
Suzuki, Marumo, *J. Antibiotics* (Japan), 1960, **12A**, 360; 1961, **14A**, 34.
Mizuno *et al.*, *J. Org. Chem.*, 1963, **28**, 3329.

Tuboxenin

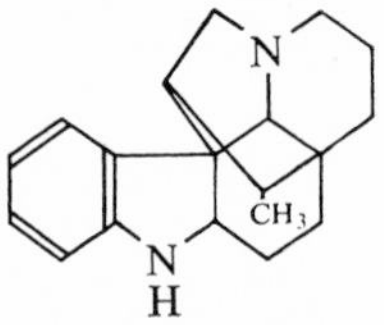

$C_{19}H_{24}N_2$ MW 280
Alkaloid from *Pleiocarpa tubicina*. Sublimes. M.p. 139–40°. $[\alpha]_D^{20}$ +5·4° (c, 0·168 in $CHCl_3$). Light absorption: $\lambda_{max.}$ 206 (log ε, 4·39), 244 (3·81), and 295 mμ (3·44).
Formyl: b.p. 120°/0·001 mm.
Ac: b.p. 140°/0·005 mm.
Picrate: m.p. 163–6°.

Kump, Seibl, Schmid, *Helv. Chim. Acta*, 1964, **47**, 358.

Tubulosine

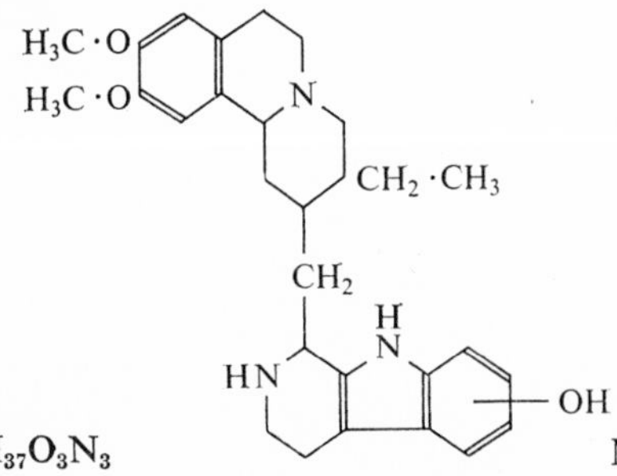

$C_{29}H_{37}O_3N_3$ MW 475

Constituent of the bark of *Pogonopus tubulosus* (DC.) Schumann. M.p. 259–61°. $[\alpha]_D^{24}$ −65·9° (c, 2 in Py). pK_{MCS} 6·3 and 8. Light absorption: $\lambda_{max.}$ 225 sh. (log ε, 4·55) and 281 mμ (4·16).
Mono-Ac: m.p. 184–6°.
Di-Ac: m.p. 149–51°.

Brauchli *et al.*, *J. Am. Chem. Soc.*, 1964, **86**, 1895.

Turumiquirensine
$C_{42}H_{54}O_{11}N_2$ MW 762
Quaternary alkaloid from *Croton turumiquirensis* Stayerm. Light absorption: $\lambda_{max.}$ 220 (ε, 63,700), 265 (18,700), and 300 mμ (15,600).
Iodide: $C_{42}H_{52}O_9N_2I_2$. MW 982. M.p. 235°.
Nitrate: m.p. 240–1° decomp.

Burnell, Casa, *Nature*, 1964, **203**, 297.

Tylosin

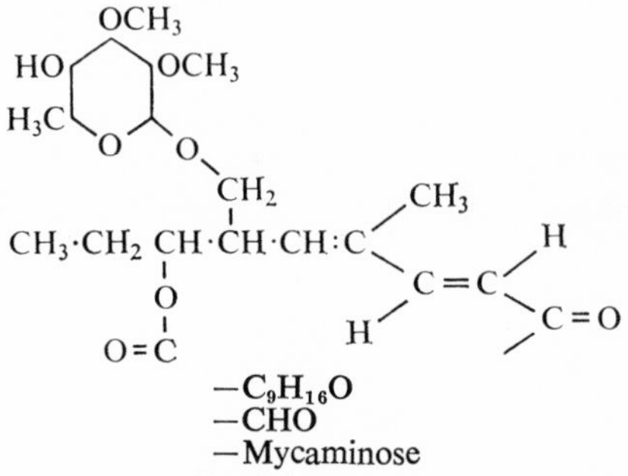

Partial structure

$C_{45}H_{79}O_{17}N$ MW 905
Macrolide antibiotic from *Streptomyces fradiae*. Colourless cryst. M.p. 128–32°. $[\alpha]_D^{25}$ −46° (c, 2 in MeOH).

Hamill *et al.*, *Antibiotics and Chemotherapy*, 1961, **11**, 328.
Woodward, *Angew. Chem.*, 1957, **69**, 50.
Morin, Gorman, *Tetrahedron Letters*, 1964, 2339.

Tyrimide. *See* Isopropamide.

Tyrosine-*O*-phosphate

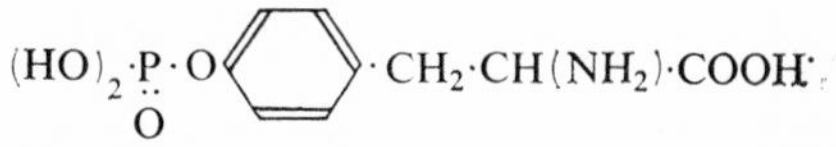

$C_9H_{12}O_6NP$ MW 261
Constituent of *Drosophila* spp. Cryst. from EtOH–Et_2O. M.p. 246–7°.

Levene, Schormüller, *J. Biol. Chem.*, 1933, **100**, 583.
Plimmer, *Biochem. J.*, 1941, **35**, 461.
Pasternak, Grafl, *Helv. Chim. Acta*, 1945, **28**, 1258.
Mitchell, Lunan, *Arch. Biochem. Biophys.*, 1964, **106**, 219.

U

Uleine.★

Mass spectrometry:
Joule, Djerassi, *J. Chem. Soc.*, 1964, 2777.

1-Undecene★

$$CH_3 \cdot [CH_2]_8 \cdot CH \! : \! CH_2$$

$C_{11}H_{22}$ MW 154
B.p. 192·7°/760 mm., 73°/10 mm. M.p. −49·1°.
D_4^{20} 0·7509. D_4^{25} 0·7472. n_D^{20} 1·4261. n_D^{25} 1·4241.
Asinger Fell, Steffan, *Chem. Ber.*, 1964, **97**, 1555.

2-Undecene★

$$CH_3 \cdot [CH_2]_7 \cdot CH \! : \! CH \cdot CH_3$$

Trans-.
B.p. 195·2°/760 mm., 75·5°/10 mm. M.p. −48·3°.
D_4^{20} 0·7528. D_4^{25} 0·7491. n_D^{20} 1·4292. n_D^{25} 1·4272.
Cis-.
B.p. 196·1°/760 mm., 75·8°/10 mm. M.p. −66·5°.
D_4^{20} 0·7576. D_4^{25} 0·7538. n_D^{20} 1·4312. n_D^{25} 1·4290.
Asinger, Fell, Steffan, *Chem. Ber.*, 1964, **97**, 1555.

3-Undecene

$$CH_3 \cdot [CH_2]_6 \cdot CH \! : \! CH \cdot CH_2 \cdot CH_3$$

Trans-.
B.p. 193·5°/760 mm., 73·9°/10 mm. M.p. −62·1°.
D_4^{20} 0·7516. D_4^{25} 0·7478. n_D^{20} 1·4290. n_D^{25} 1·4270.
Cis-.
B.p. 193·4°/760 mm., 73·1°/10 mm. M.p. −69·6°.
D_4^{20} 0·7540. D_4^{25} 0·7503. n_D^{20} 1·4301. n_D^{25} 1·4279.
Asinger, Fell, Steffan, *Chem. Ber.*, 1964, **97**, 1555.

4-Undecene

$$CH_3 \cdot [CH_2]_5 \cdot CH \! : \! CH \cdot [CH_2]_2 \cdot CH_3$$

Trans-.
B.p. 193°/760 mm., 73·3°/10 mm. M.p. −63·7°.
D_4^{20} 0·7508. D_4^{25} 0·7471. n_D^{20} 1·4285. n_D^{25} 1·4264.
Cis-.
B.p. 192·6°/760 mm., 72·3°/10 mm. M.p. −97°.
D_4^{20} 0·7541. D_4^{25} 0·7504. n_D^{20} 1·4302. n_D^{25} 1·4281.
Asinger, Fell, Steffan, *Chem. Ber.*, 1964, **97**, 1555.

5-Undecene★

$$CH_3 \cdot [CH_2]_4 \cdot CH \! : \! CH \cdot [CH_2]_3 \cdot CH_3$$

Trans-.
B.p. 193°/760 mm., 73·2°/10 mm. M.p. −61·1°.
D_4^{20} 0·7497. D_4^{25} 0·7460. n_D^{20} 1·4285. n_D^{25} 1·4264.

Cis-.
B.p. 192·3°/760 mm., 72°/10 mm. M.p. −106·5°.
D_4^{20} 0·7537. D_4^{25} 0·7500. n_D^{20} 1·4302. n_D^{25} 1·4281.
Asinger, Fell, Steffan, *Chem. Ber.*, 1964, **97**, 1555.

1-Undecyne★

$$CH_3 \cdot [CH_2]_8 \cdot C \! : \! CH$$

$C_{11}H_{20}$ MW 152
B.p. 194·9°/760 mm., 76·4°/10 mm. M.p. −17·7°.
D_4^{20} 0·7730. D_4^{25} 0·7692. n_D^{20} 1·4310. n_D^{25} 1·4288.
Asinger Fell, Steffan, *Chem. Ber.*, 1964, **97**, 1555.

2-Undecyne★

$$CH_3 \cdot [CH_2]_7 \cdot C \! : \! C \cdot CH_3$$

B.p. 204·2°/760 mm., 84·2°/10 mm. M.p. −30·1°.
D_4^{20} 0·7827. D_4^{25} 0·7789. n_D^{20} 1·4394. n_D^{25} 1·4374.
Asinger, Fell, Steffan, *Chem. Ber.*, 1964, **97**, 1555.

3-Undecyne

$$CH_3 \cdot [CH_2]_6 \cdot C \! : \! C \cdot CH_2 \cdot CH_3$$

B.p. 199·9°/760 mm., 80·1°/10 mm. M.p. −58·2°.
D_4^{20} 0·7759. D_4^{25} 0·7721. n_D^{20} 1·4375. n_D^{25} 1·4353.
Asinger, Fell, Steffan, *Chem. Ber.*, 1964, **97**, 1555.

4-Undecyne

$$CH_3 \cdot [CH_2]_5 \cdot C \! : \! C \cdot CH_2 \cdot CH_2 \cdot CH_3$$

B.p. 198·5°/760 mm., 78·8°/10 mm. M.p. −74·7°.
D_4^{20} 0·7752. D_4^{25} 0·7714. n_D^{20} 1·4369. n_D^{25} 1·4347.
Asinger Fell, Steffan, *Chem. Ber.*, 1964, **97**, 1555.

5-Undecyne★

$$CH_3 \cdot [CH_2]_4 \cdot C \! : \! C \cdot [CH_2]_3 \cdot CH_3$$

B.p. 198·1°/760 mm., 78·3°/10 mm. M.p. −74·1°.
D_4^{20} 0·7753. D_4^{25} 0·7715. n_D^{20} 1·4369. n_D^{25} 1·4346.
Asinger, Fell, Steffan, *Chem. Ber.*, 1964, **97**, 1555.

Urea.★

Tetra-Me: b.p. 174·5°/740 mm., 63–4°/12 mm. M.p. −1·2°. D_4^{20} 0·9687. n_D^{23} 1·4496.
Lüttringhaus, Dirksen, *Angew. Chem.*, 1963, **75**, 1059; *Int. Ed.*, 1964, **3**, 260.

Ureidoglutaric Acid. *See* Carbamoyl *under* Glutamic Acid.

Ureidosuccinic Acid. *See* Carbamoyl *under* Aspartic Acid.

Uridine.

2′-O-*Me*: present in the ribonucleic acid from various plant, animal, and bacterial sources.

Smith, Dunn, *Biochim. Biophys. Acta*, 1959, **31**, 573.

Hall, *Biochim. Biophys. Acta*, 1963, **68**, 278; *Biochem. Biophys. Research Commun.*, 1963, **12**, 429.

Urolithin A.★

Has been shown to be 2′:4:4′-Trihydroxybiphenyl-2-carboxylic Acid (2:2′)-lactone (*q.v.*).

Urolithin B.★

Has been shown to be 2′:4′-Dihydroxybiphenyl-2-carboxylic Acid (2:2′)-lactone (*q.v.*).

Ushinsunine (*Micheline A*)

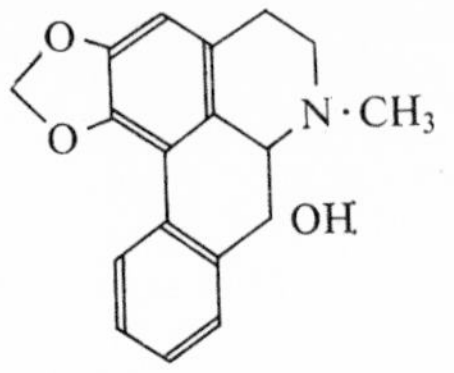

$C_{18}H_{17}O_3N$ MW 295

Alkaloid from *Michelia alba*, *M. champaca*, and *M. compressa*. M.p. 180–1°. $[\alpha]_D^{18}$ −117° ($CHCl_3$).

Tomita, Furukawa, *J. Pharm. Soc. Japan*, 1962, **82**, 925.

Yang *et al.*, *J. Pharm. Soc. Japan*, 1962, **82**, 794, 798, 804, 811; 1963, **83**, 216.

V

Vakerin. *See* Bergenin.

Valeranone★

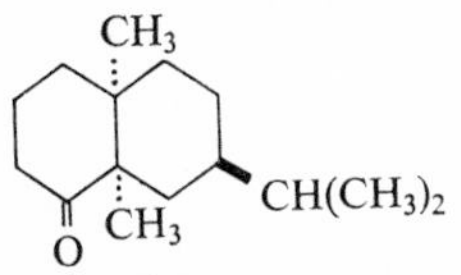

Absolute stereochemistry:

Klyne *et al.*, *Tetrahedron Letters*, 1964, 1443.

Valeroidine.★

Revised stereochemistry:

3*S* : 6*S*.

Fodor, Sóti, *Tetrahedron Letters*, 1964, 1917.

Valium (*7-Chloro*-1 : 3-*dihydro*-1-*methyl*-5-*phenyl*-2H-1 : 4-*benzodiazepin*-2-*one*)

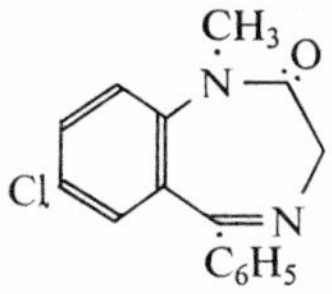

$C_{15}H_{13}ON_2Cl$ MW 292·5

Tranquilliser.

Hoffmann-la-Roche, *Report of Therapy Congress and Pharmaceutical Exhibition*, Karlsruhe, 1963 (*Angew. Chem., Int. Ed.*, 1964, **63**, 68).

Vanillyltropine. *See* Phyllalbine.

Variotin

$$\underset{[CH_2]_3\cdot CO\cdot CH}{CH_3} = \underset{CH\cdot CH{:}CH}{C(CH_3)\cdot CH} \quad \underset{COOCH_3}{CO\cdot NH\cdot [CH_2]_3}$$

$C_{18}H_{27}O_4N$ MW 321

Antibiotic from *Paecilomyces varioti* Bainier var. *antibioticus*. Yellow oil. Light absorption: $\lambda_{max.}$ 320 mμ (ε, 39,500). Hydrol. → 4-aminobutyric acid.

Takeuchi, Yonehara, *J. Antibiotics* (Japan), 1961, **14A**, 44.

Veatchine.★

Synthesis:

Valenta, Wiesner, Wong, *Tetrahedron Letters*, 1964, 2437.

Velban. *See* Vinblastine.

Velbe. *See* B,H_2SO_4 *under* Vinblastine.

Venenatine

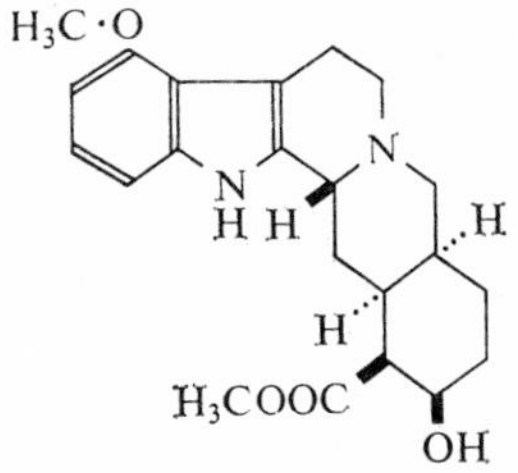

$C_{22}H_{28}O_4N_2$ MW 384

Alkaloid from the bark of *Alstonia venenata* R. Br. M.p. 123–6° decomp. $[\alpha]_D^{24}$ −76·07°. pK_a 7·2.

O-*Ac*: m.p. 98–101° decomp.

B,HI: m.p. 255–7° decomp.

B,CH_3I: m.p. 285–90° decomp.

Picrate: m.p. 243° decomp.

Govindachari *et al.*, *Tetrahedron Letters*, 1964, 901.

Veratramine.★

Mass spectrum:

Budzikiewicz, *Tetrahedron*, 1964, **20**, 2267.

Veritain. *See p*-(2-Methylaminopropyl)phenol.

Veritol. *See p*-(2-Methylaminopropyl)phenol.

Verrucarin A★

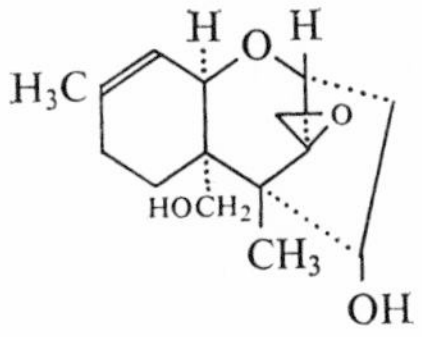

Alternative structure:

Godtfredsen, Vangedal, *Proc. Chem. Soc.*, 1964, 188.

Verticillol

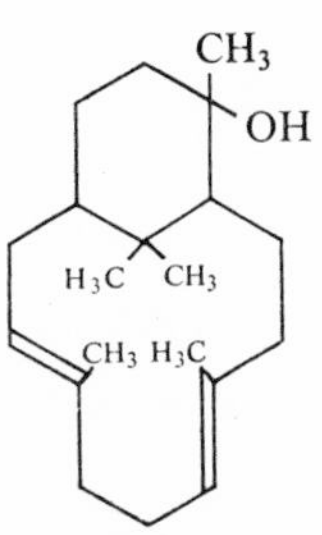

Suggested structure

$C_{20}H_{34}O$ MW 290

Constituent of the wood of *Sciadopitys verticillata* Sieb. et Zucc. M.p. 104–5°. $[\alpha]_D$ +168° (c, 1·5 in $CHCl_3$). Monoperphthalic acid (2 moles) → diepoxide. M.p. 160°. $[\alpha]_D$ +68·7° (c, 1·8 in $CHCl_3$).

Erdtman *et al.*, *Tetrahedron Letters*, 1964, 3879.

Vimalin. *See* 1-β-Glucopyranoside *under* *p*-Methoxycinnamyl Alcohol.

Vinblastine (*Vincaleukoblastine*, *Velban*)

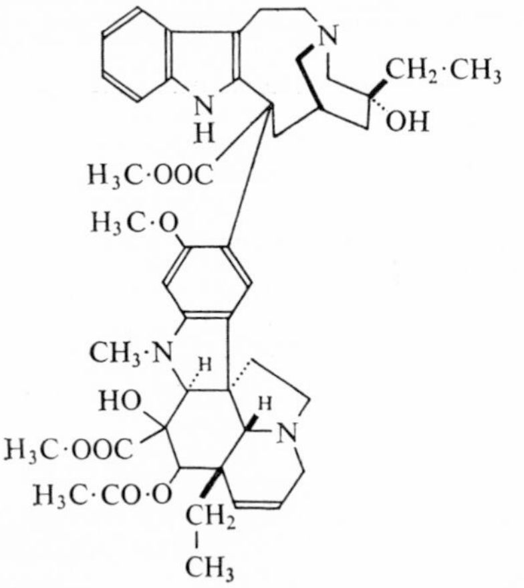

$C_{46}H_{58}O_9N_4$ MW 810

Constituent of *Vinca rosea* L. with antitumour activity. Cryst. from Et_2O with solvent. M.p. 180–2° (loss of solvent). M.p. 201–11°. $[\alpha]_D$ +42° ($CHCl_3$). Cryst. from MeOH. M.p. 211–16°. pK_a' 5·4, 7·4 (H_2O).

B,H₂SO₄: Velbe. M.p. 284–5°. $[\alpha]_D^{26}$ −28° (MeOH).

B,2HCl,2H₂O: m.p. 244–6° decomp.

Di-Ac: m.p. 168–70°. $[\alpha]_D$ −26·4° ($CHCl_3$).

Noble, Beer, Cutts, *Biochemical Pharmacology*, 1958, **1**, 347.

Neuss *et al.*, *J. Am. Chem. Soc.*, 1959, **81**, 4754; 1962, **84**, 1509; 1964, **86**, 1440.

Bommer, McMurray, Biemann, *J. Am. Chem. Soc.*, 1964, **86**, 1439.

Vincadine★

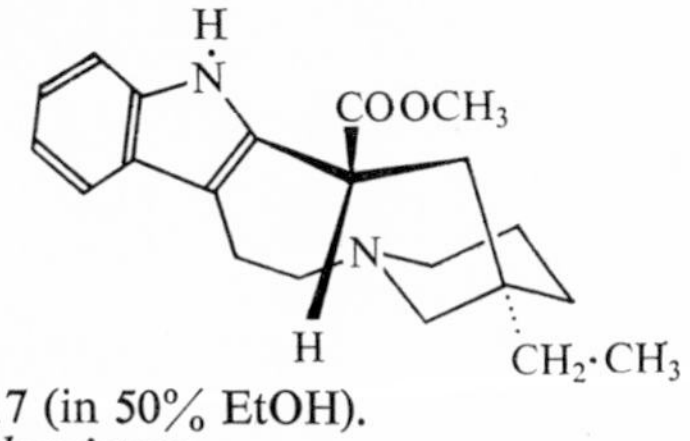

pK_a 7·17 (in 50% EtOH).

Stereochemistry:

Mokřy *et al.*, *Chemistry and Industry*, 1964, 1988.

Vincaleukoblastine. *See* Vinblastine.

Vincamicine.

Minor alkaloid from *Vinca rosea* L. M.p. 224–8° decomp. $[\alpha]_D$ +418°. pK_a' 4·80, 5·85. Light absorption: $\lambda_{max.}$ 214, 264, 315, 341 mμ.

Svoboda *et al.*, *J. Pharm. Sci.*, 1961, **50**, 409.

Vincamine.★

Total synthesis:

Kuehne, *J. Am. Chem. Soc.*, 1964, **86**, 2946.

14-*epi*-Vincamine

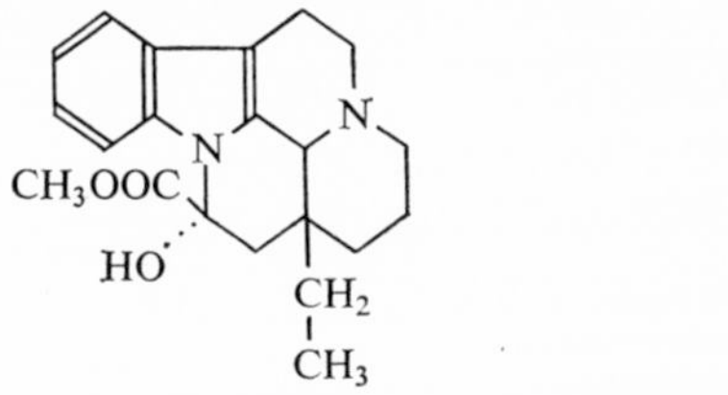

$C_{21}H_{26}O_3N_2$ MW 354

Alkaloid from *Vinca minor* L. M.p. 181–5°. $[\alpha]_D^{22}$ −36·4° (c, 1·04 in $CHCl_3$). Light absorption: $\lambda_{max.}$ 226 (log ε, 4·51) 276 mμ (3·93).

Mokrý, Kompiš, *Tetrahedron Letters*, 1963, 1917.

Vincaminoreine★

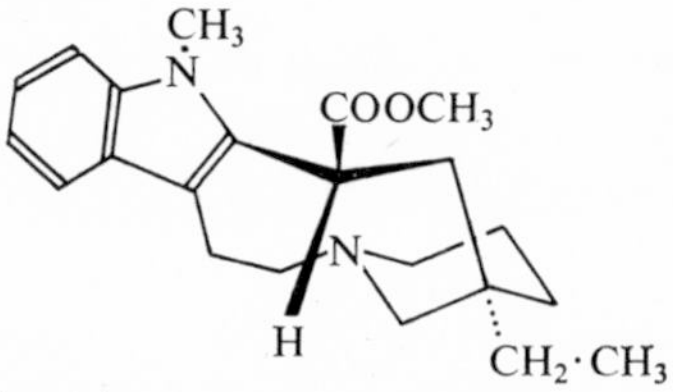

Stereochemistry:

Mokřy *et al.*, *Chemistry and Industry*, 1964, 1988.

Vincaminorine★

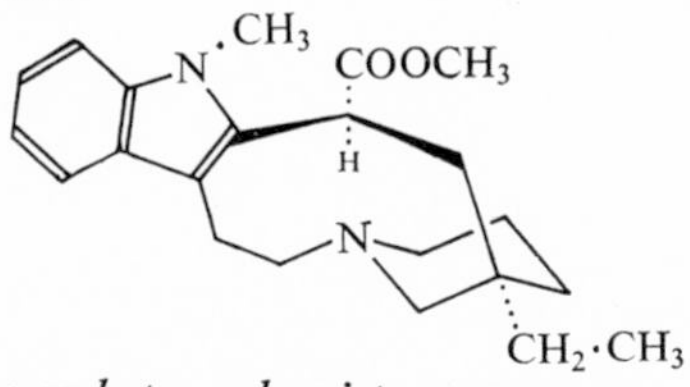

Structure and stereochemistry:

Mokřy *et al.*, *Chemistry and Industry*, 1964, 1988.

Vincristine (*Leurocristine*, *Oncovin*)

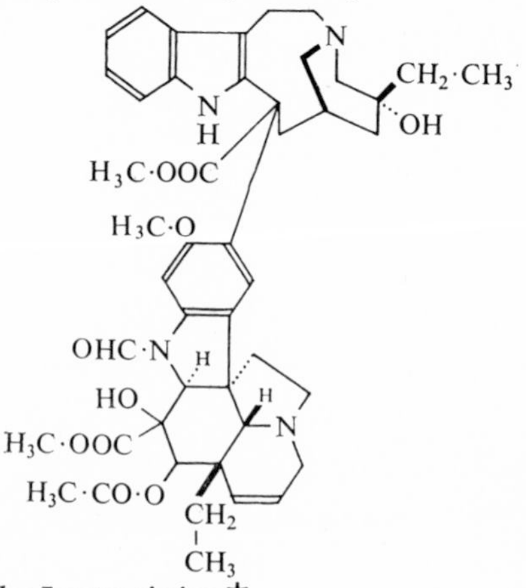

See also Leurocristine.★

$C_{46}H_{56}O_{10}N_4$ MW 824

Vincristine is the name approved by the American Medical Association for the alkaloid previously called leurocristine,★ which has antitumour activity.
Revised structure:

Neuss *et al.*, *J. Am. Chem. Soc.*, 1964, **86**, 1440.

Vindolicine

$C_{25}H_{32}O_6N_2$ MW 456

Minor alkaloid of *Vinca rosea* L. Double m.p. (i) 248–51°. (ii) 265–7° decomp. $[\alpha]_D^{26}$ −48·4°. pK_a' 5·4 (66% H·CONMe$_2$). Light absorption: $\lambda_{max.}$ 212, 257, 308 mμ.

Svoboda *et al.*, *J. Pharm. Sci.*, 1961, **50**, 409.

***S*-Vinyl-*O-tert.*-butyl thiolcarbonate**

$CH_2{:}CH{\cdot}S{\cdot}COOC(CH_3)_3$

$C_7H_{12}O_2S$ MW 160

Oil. B.p. 60·5–61°/15 mm. n_D^{25} 1·4642.

Overberger, Daly, *J. Org. Chem.*, 1964, **29**, 757; *J. Am. Chem. Soc.*, 1964, **86**, 3402.

8-Vinylheptafulvene

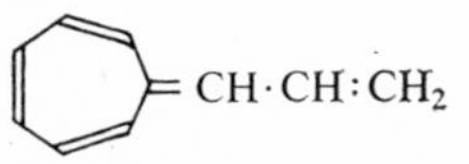

$C_{10}H_{10}$ MW 130

Unstable. Only obtained in solution. Light absorption: 326 (ε, 47,900) and 443 mμ (500).

Bertelli, Golino, Dreyer, *J. Am. Chem. Soc.*, 1964, **86**, 3329.

Vinylphosphoric Acid (*Ethylenephosphoric acid*)

$CH_2{:}CH{\cdot}O{\cdot}P(OH)_2{:}O$

$C_2H_5O_4P$ MW 124

Very unstable, isolated as di-Li salt.

Baer, Ciplijauskas, Visser, *J. Biol. Chem.*, 1959, **234**, 1.

Viosamine. *See* 4-Amino-4 : 6-dideoxy-D-glucose.

Viridicatol (2 : 3-*Dihydroxy*-4(3′-*hydroxyphenyl*)*quinoline*)

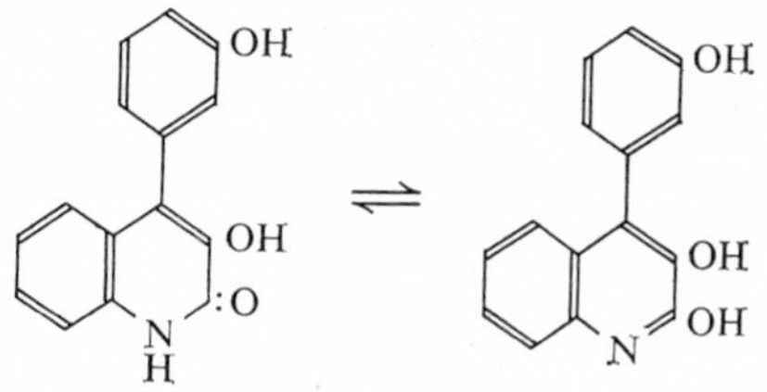

$C_{15}H_{11}O_3N$ MW 253

Metabolite of *Penicillium viridicatum* Westling. Hydrolysis product of cyclopenol. Cryst. from AcOEt. M.p. 280°. Light absorption: $\lambda_{max.}$ 226 (log ε, 4·45), 284 (3·95), 304 sh. (3·96), 316 (4·04), 329 sh. mμ (3·88). $FeCl_3$ → green col.
Di-Ac: needles from AcOEt–light petroleum. M.p. 195–6°.
3′-O-*Me*: cryst. from EtOH. M.p. 257°. *Ac*: needles from AcOEt–light petroleum. M.p. 174°.
3′-O-N-*Di-Me*: m.p. 235°.

Birkinshaw *et al.*, *Biochem. J.*, 1963, **89**, 196.
Luckner, Mohammed, *Tetrahedron Letters*, 1964, 1987.

Vitamin K_1★

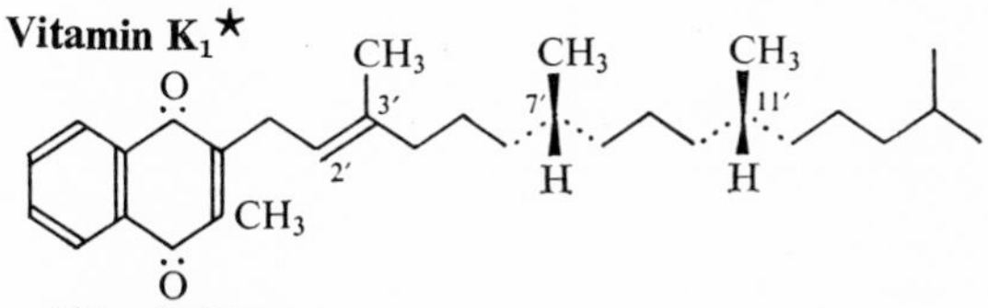

7′R : 11′R-.
Absolute configuration:

Mayer *et al.*, *Helv. Chim. Acta*, 1964, **47**, 221.

Vitamin K_3. *See* 2-Methyl-1 : 4-naphthoquinone.

Vitamin K_9 (*H*).

$C_{56}H_{82}O_2$ MW 786

Isolated from *Mycobacterium phlei.* Orange oil. Light absorption: $\lambda_{max.}$ 242·5 ($E^{1\%}_{1\,cm.}$ 192), 247·5 (200), 260 (198), 270 (196), and 325 mμ (37). The structure is that of Vitamin $K_{2(45)}$, in which one of the non-terminal sidechain double bonds has been reduced.

Gale *et al.*, *Biochemistry*, 1963, **2**, 200.

W

Warfarin. *See* 3-(2-Acetyl-1-phenylethyl)-4-hydroxycoumarin.

X

Xanthoaphin-*fb*★

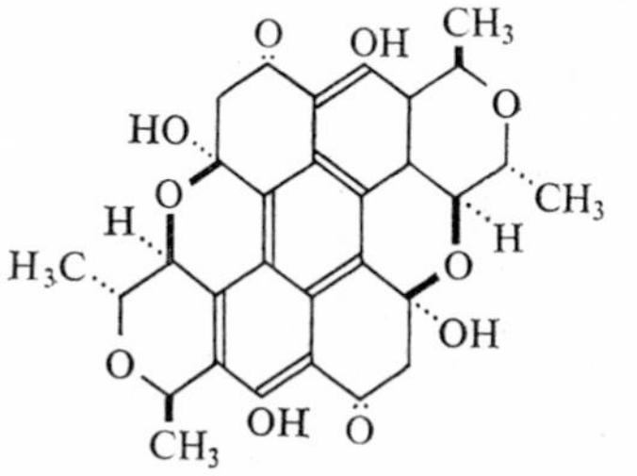

$C_{30}H_{26}O_{10}$ MW 546

Structure:

Calderbank *et al.*, *J. Chem. Soc.*, 1964, 80.

Xanthoaphin-*sl*★

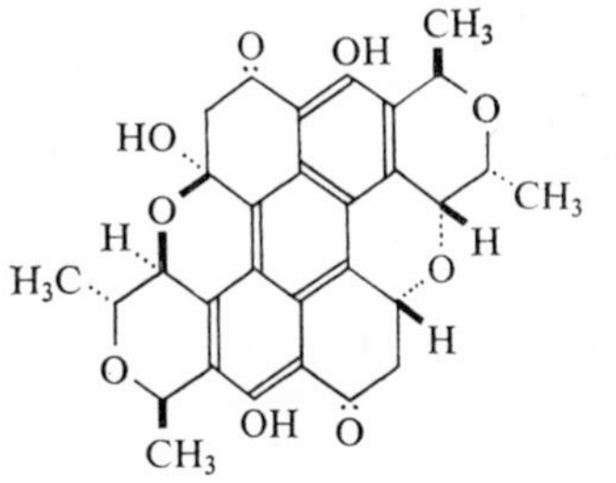

$C_{30}H_{26}O_{10}$ MW 546

Structure:

Calderbank *et al.*, *J. Chem. Soc.*, 1964, 80.

Xanthophanic Acid

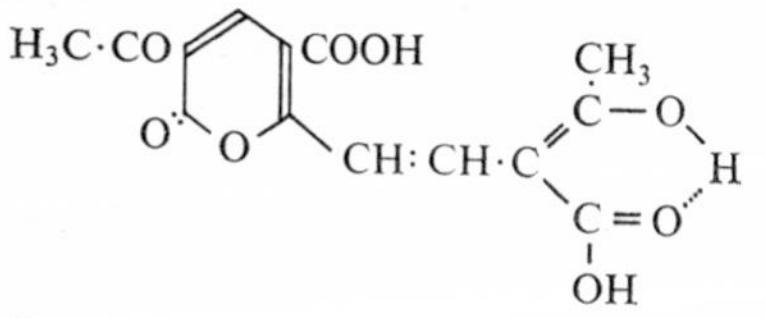

$C_{14}H_{12}O_8$ MW 308

Di-Me ester: $C_{16}H_{16}O_8$. MW 336. Red needles from C_6H_6. M.p. 179°.
Di-Et ester: $C_{18}H_{20}O_8$. MW 364. Orange-yellow needles from EtOH. M.p. 143–5°. Light absorption: $\lambda_{max.}$ 298 (ε, 13,250), 440 (22,600), and 526 mμ (3950).
p-*Bromophenylhydrazone*: red needles from C_6H_6. M.p. 180–1°.

Claisen, *Ann.*, 1897, **297**, 1.

Liebermann, Truchsass, *Ber.*, 1906, **39**, 2071; 1907, **40**, 3584; 1909, **42**, 1405.

Crombie, Games, Knight, *Tetrahedron Letters*, 1964, 2313.

Xanthoplanine

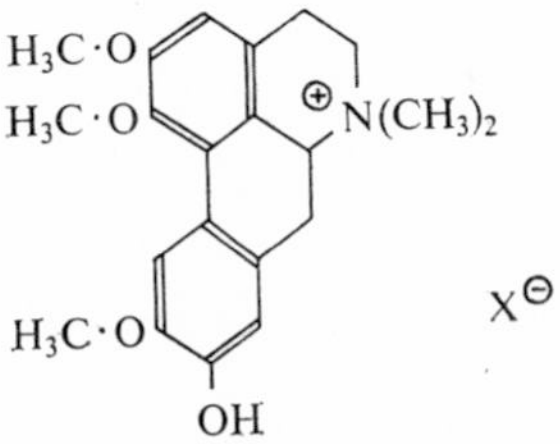

Quaternary alkaloid from *Xanthoxylum planispium*.
B,I (X = I): $C_{21}H_{26}O_4NI$. MW 483. *Hemihydrate*: m.p. 148–9° decomp. $[\alpha]_D^{21}$ +71° (EtOH).
O-*Me*, *B,I*: m.p. 225–7° decomp. $[\alpha]_D^{26}$ +80° (EtOH).

Ishii, Harada, *J. Pharm. Soc. Japan*, 1961, **81**, 243.

Xanthorrhoein

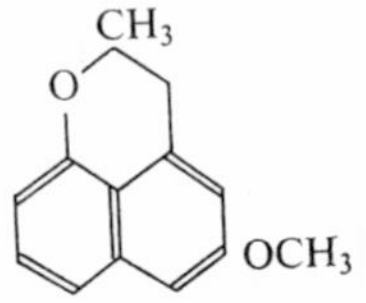

$C_{14}H_{14}O_2$ MW 214

Constituent of *Xanthorrhoea preissi* and *X. reflexa*. M.p. 68–9°. $[\alpha]_D^{13}$ 55·6° (c, 10 in C_6H_6). Light absorption: $\lambda_{max.}$ 225 (log ε, 4·70), 244 (4·44), 287 (3·67), 298 (3·64), 323 (3·40), and 338 mμ (3·49).

Rennie, Cooke, Findlayson, *J. Chem. Soc.*, 1920, **117**, 338.

Findlayson, *J. Chem. Soc.*, 1926, 2763.

Birch, Salahud-Din, Smith, *Tetrahedron Letters*, 1964, 1623.

Xylose.★

o-*Nitrophenyl-β-*D*-xylopyranoside*: $C_{11}H_{13}O_7N$. MW 271. Cryst. from EtOH. M.p. 170–3°. $[\alpha]_D^{24}$ −78·6° (c, 1 in MeOH). 2 : 3 : 4-*Tri-Ac*: cryst. from isoPrOH–EtOH. M.p. 112–14°. $[\alpha]_D^{22}$ −52·6° (c, 2 in $CHCl_3$).
p-*Nitrophenyl-β-*D*-xylopyranoside*: needles from EtOH. Two forms: (*a*) m.p. 159–61°, (*b*) m.p. 143°. $[\alpha]_D^{24}$ −56° (c, 0·5 in H_2O). 2 : 3 : 4-*Tri-Ac*: cryst. from isoPrOH–EtOH. M.p. 149–51°. $[\alpha]_D^{24}$ −73·5° (c, 2 in $CHCl_3$).

Loontiens, de Bruyne, *Naturwiss.*, 1964, **51**, 359.

Y

Ydiginic Acid

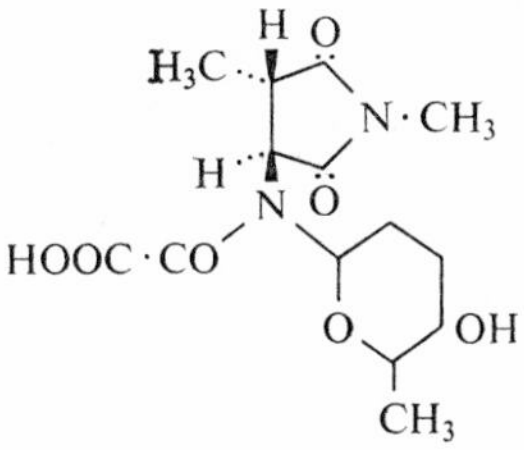

$C_{14}H_{20}O_7N$ MW 314

Oxidation product of streptolydigin. M.p. 97–103°. $[\alpha]^{25}$ $-37°$ (c, 1·01 in 95% EtOH).
Me ester: *O-Ac*: m.p. 276–9°. $[\alpha]_D^{31}$ $-25°$ (c, 1·13 in MeOH).

Rinehart, Borders, *J. Am. Chem. Soc.*, 1963, **85**, 4037.

Z

Zeatin

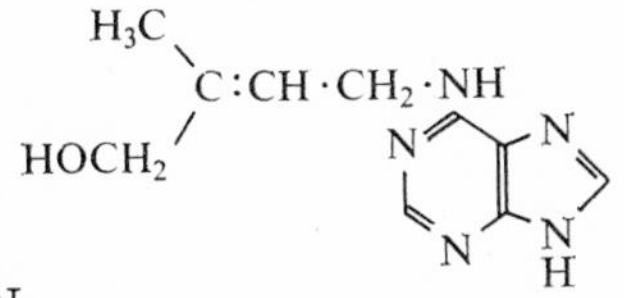

$C_{10}H_{13}ON_5$ MW 219

A factor, present in maize, inducing cell division. M.p. 207–8°. pK_a 4·4, 9·8 (H_2O).

Picrate: m.p. 180–90°.

Letham, Shannon, McDonald, *Proc. Chem. Soc.*, 1964, 230.
Shaw, Wilson, *Proc. Chem. Soc.*, 1964, 231.

Zoxazolamine. *See* 2-Amino-5-chlorobenzoxazole.

Zygacine.★

Mass spectrum:

Budzikiewicz, *Tetrahedron*, 1964, **20**, 2267.